Aphids – Aphidinae
(Macrosiphini)

Roger L. Blackman

ROGER L. BLACKMAN

Published for the Royal Entomological Society
The Mansion House
Bonehill
Chiswell Green Lane
Chiswell Green
St Albans
AL2 3NS
www.royensoc.co.uk

By the   Field Studies Council
The Annexe
Preston Montford Lane
Shrewsbury
SY4 1DU
www.field-studies-council.org

BRINGING
ENVIRONMENTAL
UNDERSTANDING TO ALL

ISBN: 978 0 901546 91 3

Contents

Abstract

The Macrosiphini are the predominant group of aphids on herbaceous plants in Britain, comprising about half of the British aphid fauna. This handbook aims to provide an introduction and guide to the identification and biology of the Macrosiphini that can be used by non-specialists. It includes sections on the general classification of aphids, the recognition of the subfamilies of Aphididae and the tribes of Aphidinae, a host-plant list for Aphidinae, a checklist of Macrosiphini, and keys to the genera of Macrosiphini for apterous parthenogenetic females, alate parthenogenetic females and alate males. There then follows a systematic treatment of the 305 species on the British list with keys to apterous and alate females and alate males of each genus, and information on appearance in life, host plants, distribution, and what is known of their biology.

Acknowledgements

First and foremost I give heartfelt thanks to Victor Eastop, who generously gave me full access to the 'green files' in which he has accumulated literally thousands of pages of morphometric data on the world's aphids, and these have proved to be a great help in compiling the keys in this handbook. His comments and friendly advice in the course of compiling this work, and his critical reading of the manuscript, have also been invaluable. Yet another reason to be grateful to Dr Eastop is for the refinements he has introduced over many years to the system of curation used for the national aphid collection, including tab cards which make it a quick and easy task to find specimens of any species according to country, host plant, or time of year.

Compilation of this handbook would not have been possible without full access to the national aphid collection and facilities at the Natural History Museum, and I am grateful to the Museum's trustees for granting me the ongoing status of a Research Associate and all the associated benefits. For the two years in which much of the work was done I was in receipt of an Emeritus Fellowship from the Leverhulme Trust, and this was a great help not only in covering expenses but also keeping my mind focussed on the project.

I am grateful to Mark Taylor at Rothamsted Research and Kim Davie at SASA (Science and Advice for Scottish Agriculture) for providing suction trap data to complement my records of the distribution of various aphid species in Britain.

In the 160+ years since Francis Walker collected and described aphids at Southgate - at that time a small village to the north of London - a remarkably small number of British entomologists have taken much notice of aphids. The task of putting together the information in this handbook brings home to one just how much of our knowledge of British aphids is due to the efforts of very few people. In the 19th century Walker was followed many years later by G. B. Buckton, and in the first part of the 20th century by F.V. Theobald, whose three-volume work (1926-9) can still be a valuable source of information, except that frequently one cannot be certain of the identity of the species being discussed. After that it was not until after World War II that British aphids received any more attention. Since then by far the greatest contribution to knowledge of the British aphid fauna has been made by Henry Stroyan, working at the Plant Pathology Laboratory at Harpenden. His series of papers and handbooks from 1950 to1991 brought Britain into line with the significant advances in aphid biosystematics made in the 1940s and early 1950s by Carl Börner in Germany and by D. Hille Ris Lambers in the Netherlands. Stroyan's work and publications not only almost doubled the number of species on the British list but provided much additional information on life cycles and host-plant relationships. The large collection of slide-mounted aphids donated to the Natural History Museum on Stroyan's retirement is also a lasting testimony to his achievement, and includes much valuable reared material. Many of the photographs in this handbook are of his specimens, or those of R.N.B. Prior who assisted him for many years.

Another significant contribution to our knowledge of British aphids has been that of Jon Martin, on the staff of the Natural History Museum, whose collecting activities over more than 30 years in Britain (mostly in south London, Nottinghamshire and the Isle of Man) as well as overseas have greatly enhanced the national collection. Photographs of his specimens also provided many of the illustrations in this handbook. Several other past and present British entomologists have done valuable regional collecting; H.C. Dale and C.S. Wood-Baker in south-east England (the latter also in the south of Ireland), V.F. Eastop at Cambridge and Kew, I. Thomas and F.H. Jacob in North Wales, and most recently E. A. Baker in South Wales.

I should also acknowledge the contribution made to the taxonomy of British aphids by the late J.P. Doncaster, notably his (1961) work on Francis Walker's aphids, and his immaculate curation of Theobald's British aphid collection.

Regrettably, thousands of slides of aphids mounted in gum chloral in the 1950s to 1970s are gradually deteriorating, and need remounting in a more permanent medium such as Canada balsam. Natural History Museum staff, notably Paul Brown, have rescued much type and other unique material, but this is an uphill struggle and at least some of the specimens photographed for this book will unfortunately soon be lost to science.

Finally, I should like to thank Sharon Reid for meticulously reading the manuscript, and making some important corrections, additions and suggestions for improvement.

Introduction

The Macrosiphini are the predominant group of aphids on herbaceous plants in Britain, and the world. There are 305 British species and subspecies, comprising 49% of the 620 Aphididae on the British list. They include many important pest species, some of which are highly polyphagous, but there are also very many more species feeding more-or-less specifically on indigenous and naturalised plants and playing a significant role in natural food chains. The last systematic treatment of this group was by Theobald (1926-9) in his three-volume work on British aphids. A handbook of the British Macrosiphini, to complement Stroyan's (1984) account of its sister group the Aphidini, is therefore clearly long overdue.

Aphids are generally looked upon by entomologists as a difficult group, requiring specialist attention, and they consequently tend to be overlooked and under-recorded. At first glance the keys in this handbook may reinforce this view, as many of the characters needed for identification of aphid species *away from their host plants* depend on examination and measurement of slide-mounted specimens under the microscope. There is also the problem of polymorphism, requiring separate keys for alate and apterous morphs, as well as the need to take into account the effects of the environment on morphology, so that for example aphids developing at different temperatures may differ markedly in the morphometric ratios that are often needed to distinguish between closely-related species.

These problems are inevitable – aphid taxonomists have not gone out of their way to make life difficult for themselves and others! – but it is a pity if they are allowed to deter anyone from studying such an interesting, rewarding and important group of insects. The main point to emphasise here is that most aphids have very specific plant associations, so that if you can identify the plant that the aphid is feeding on then you can greatly reduce the number of possible options. There are some polyphagous aphids – most of them are well-known to applied entomologists as crop pests - but they are relatively few in number, and anyone studying aphids for a short time will become familiar with these.

To take an example almost at random, if you find colonies of an ant-attended aphid on the bases of the lower leaves of cow parsley (*Anthriscus sylvestris*), reference to the host plant list (p. 19) will show that 12 species are recorded from this plant, but further investigation of the relevant passages of text in this book, and in that of Stroyan's (1984) handbook for the *Aphis* species, will show that your aphid is most likely to be either *Aphis brohmeri* or one of three species of *Dysaphis*, and the colour of the living aphids will enable a choice between these two alternatives. Separation of the three *Dysaphis* species recorded from *Anthriscus* may look difficult by use of the key and would require slide preparation, but examination of the photographs of each species (*anthrisci, crataegi, hirsutissima*) will provide distinguishing characters visible without slide preparation, such as the differences in the lengths of the antennal hairs. Morphological features of all species can be examined in greater detail on the accompanying CD.

So, why bother with keys at all, or why not have separate keys for the aphids on each host plant? With Victor Eastop I published a series of books in which aphids of the world were keyed according to their host plants. This approach greatly simplified the problems of aphid identification but does have certain limitations. In particular it relies heavily on past records, and may obscure the presence of new host-aphid associations or hitherto unrecognised aphid species. In the present handbook I have reverted to keys to genera and species based entirely on morphology, thus providing a pathway to identification that is independent of the host plant and appearance in life, information which if available can then be used (together with the photographs) for the confirmation of identity. Separate keys also enable alate aphids trapped away from their host plants to be identified.

All the illustrations in this book and in the accompanying CD are based on photomicrographs, which have the advantage of resembling the images one sees through a microscope more than can any line drawings. Digital enhancement has been used to overcome depth-of-field problems and to clean up the images, but certain features cannot be illustrated; for example, it is not possible to show all the hairs on the last rostral or first tarsal segments, as they are positioned on opposite sides. Of course, single illustrations of an aphid or of a morphological feature are always liable to mislead as they cannot show the range of variation, and this is a particular problem with dorsal body pigmentation which in some species can vary considerably. Readers comparing their own specimens with those illustrated here need always to bear this in mind.

So this identification handbook can work at two levels. It should be possible to identify many if not most aphids found on their host plants without having to prepare slides and work through the keys, but that option is available when the host or appearance in life are unknown, or where the identity is unclear, or where very similar species can only be distinguished by details of micromorphology, or by taking careful measurements. I hope that it will also prove useful to anyone who wishes to take their studies of aphids a stage further, and perhaps tackle some of the many questions that still need to be answered about the taxonomy and biology of the British aphid fauna.

Much useful information on aphids, their life cycles, host-plant relationships and natural enemies can be obtained by field observation and simple experiments. In several genera of Macrosiphini there are groups of closely-related species which still await taxonomic clarification, and where observations of the differential colonisation of plant species can provide clues about specific aphid-host associations. A classic example is provided by Hille Ris Lambers (1939a), who noted that aphids identified as *Uroleucon* (then called *Dactynotus*) *cichorii* were abundant in the Netherlands on various composite plants at different times and in different locations, suggesting that the name was being applied to a complex of very similar species. In this book you can find many other examples of species groups that are 'taxonomically difficult', perhaps because they are rapidly evolving and developing new host plant associations. In such cases field studies can greatly increase our understanding, and provide the basis for further work such as molecular analysis.

There may also be life cycle differences within a group of species, where a host-alternating species has a close relative that remains on the primary or the secondary host (see below), and in many of these cases the nature of the relationship between host-alternating and non-host-alternating populations remains obscure. Autumn populations of native aphid species have generally been little studied, and for many species the males and/or sexual, egg-laying females (oviparae) are still unrecorded in Britain, or in some cases unknown to science. There is therefore considerable scope for uncovering new information, particularly if cultures are kept alive for a few weeks in a cool glasshouse or insectary (see p.396).

General characteristics of Aphididae

Stroyan (1977, 1984) provided an excellent description of the general characteristics of aphids in the two previous handbooks in this series, and rather than repeat his account I shall restrict this section to what I consider to be the most important points. For more detailed information on aphid anatomy and morphology consult Heie (1980) or Minks & Harrewijn (1987).

The Aphididae belong to the superfamily Aphidoidea within the suborder Sternorrhyncha of the order Hemiptera. In Sternorrhyncha the rostrum is not articulated to the sclerotic part of the head but appears to arise from beneath the body between the fore coxae. This character is shared with scale insects and mealy bugs (Coccoidea), jumping plant-lice (Psylloidea) and white-flies (Aleyrodoidea). True aphids, as opposed to the phylloxerids and adelgids which make up the rest of the Aphidoidea, have two outstanding attributes that distinguish them from all other insects.

First, they possess a pair of siphunculi (or cornicles), unique organs on the fifth or sixth abdominal segment, usually present as tubular or conical structures but sometimes secondarily reduced to pores or absent. See Fig. 1 below:

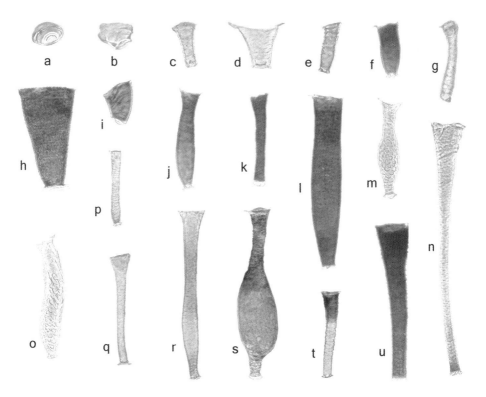

Figure 1. A selection of Macrosiphine siphunculi (all apterous viviparae). (a) *Brachycolus cerastii*; (b) *Diuraphis holci*; (c) *Hyalopteroides humilis*; (d) *Longicaudus trirhodus*; (e) *Hayhurstia atriplicis*; (f) *Brevicoryne brassicae*; (g) *Jacksonia papillata*; (h) *Anuraphis farfarae*; (i) *Semiaphis pimpinellae*; (j) *Hyadaphis foeniculi*; (k) *Metopeurum fuscoviride*; (l) *Megoura viciae*; (m) *Decorosiphon corynothrix*; (n) *Acyrthosiphon pisum*; (o) *Vesiculaphis theobaldi*; (p) *Coloradoa artemisiae*; (q) *Cryptaphis poae*; (r) *Illinoia azaleae*; (s) *Rhopalosiphoninus latysiphon*; (t) *Idiopterus nephrelepidis*; (u) *Uroleucon campanulae*.

ROGER L. BLACKMAN

For organs that are so characteristic of aphids and have persisted at least since the beginning of the Tertiary, and probably since the Cretaceous, the precise function of siphunculi is still remarkably unclear. We know that when an aphid is molested a waxy secretion may emerge from the terminal pore of each siphunculus, and that this secretion contains an alarm pheromone (E-farnesene). The wax solidifies rapidly and sometimes clogs the mouthparts of an attacking predator, providing a direct means of defence, but more often it will be daubed onto the body of the attacker, which then becomes a walking alarm signal as it moves around the colony (Mondor & Roitberg, 2004). This may be why siphunculi are so important to aphids, but is still a long way from explaining their great variety of size and form, from simple pores to long tubes or swollen vase-like structures in Macrosiphini (Fig.1), long and densely hairy in the East Asian group Greenideini, or as the broad dark hairy cones typical of Lachininae.

The other notable attribute of true aphids, and the one which has probably contributed most to their remarkable success in exploiting the flowering plants of the northern hemisphere, is their way of combining viviparity with parthenogenesis. Cyclical parthenogenesis, the regular alternation of parthenogenesis and sexual reproduction, is found in the closest relatives of aphids, the phylloxerids and adelgids, but in those groups the parthenogenetic females lay eggs. Some time early in the lineage that gave rise to Aphididae, parthenogenetic oocytes began to develop in the ovarioles soon after ovulation, and the reproductive system became modified for viviparity leading to generations being telescoped into one another, and consequently to a remarkable increase in reproductive potential. It seems likely that the ability thus gained to produce large numbers of migrant alatae during the spring flush of tree growth pre-equipped aphids for the colonisation of flowering plants when these became widespread in the mid-Tertiary.

There are certain other consistent features of aphids as a group that make them easily recognisable (Figs 2-6):

• The antennae have two short basal segments and a thinner distal part, the *flagellum*, which in adults is usually either three- or four-segmented, making a total of five or six segments in most aphids. The last segment of the flagellum has a bipartite structure with the terminal part more-or-less produced as a *processus terminalis* (PT), which may vary in length from peg-like to very long and filamentous. The last two antennal segments each bear a single chemosensory organ or *primary rhinarium*, in consistent positions; that on the penultimate segment is subapical, and that on the last segment is situated at the point where the PT arises from the basal part (Fig. 2).

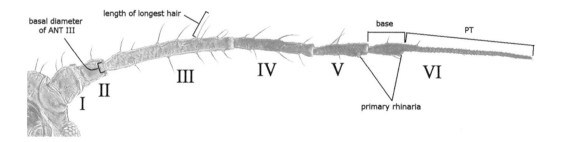

Figure 2. Antenna (of aptera of *Dysaphis chaerophylli*) showing labelling of segments and principal features referred to in keys.

4

- When compound eyes are present these usually bear a posterior tubercle with three facets representing the primary larval eye or triommatidium (see Fig. 6a).

- The rostrum has five segments, with the last two usually more-or-less combined, and here termed R IV+V (Fig. 3). On R IV+V there are three constant pairs of subapical hairs, and a very small and inconspicuous pair at the base. Accessory hairs are also usually present in adults; these can vary greatly in number and be an important taxonomic character.

- The legs typically have two-segmented tarsi, the second segment considerably longer than the first and bearing two claws (Fig. 4). The number of hairs on the first segment of the hind tarsus (HT I) can be a useful discriminant character, particularly at the generic level (in Macrosiphini it ranges from two to six). The ratio of the length of R IV+V to that of HT II is one of the most important discriminants in aphid taxonomy at the species level.

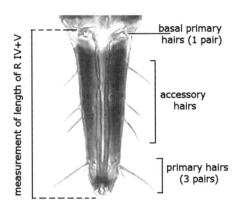

Figure 3. Combined last two segments of rostrum (R IV+V) showing labelling of hairs and measurement of length.

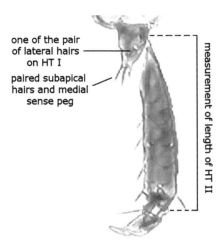

Figure 4. Hind tarsus (HT) showing hairs on HT I (in this case there is a lateral pair, making a total of 5) and measurement of length of HT II.

- The wing venation of alate aphids is also highly characteristic. The fore-wings have the anterior margin strengthened by a thick subcostal band terminating in a well-developed, variably pigmented pterostigma. From this band arise three oblique veins, two unbranched veins derived from the cubitus (Cu_{1a} and Cu_{1b}), and a media (M) which usually has one or two branches. From the pterostigma a curved radial sector (Rs) usually arises that terminates near the tip of the wing (Fig. 5). The hind wings are much smaller and have reduced venation with a maximum of two oblique veins.

- The abdomen has eight visible segments, the first seven having pairs of spiracles, and in adults it usually ends in an elongate, triangular or rounded, hair-bearing cauda (Fig. 6b).

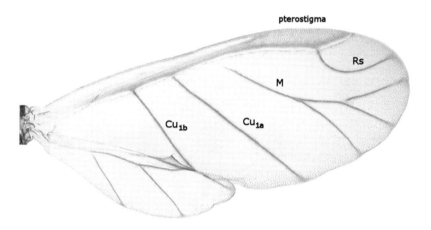

Figure 5. Typical wing of a Macrosiphine aphid, in this case with twice-branched media.

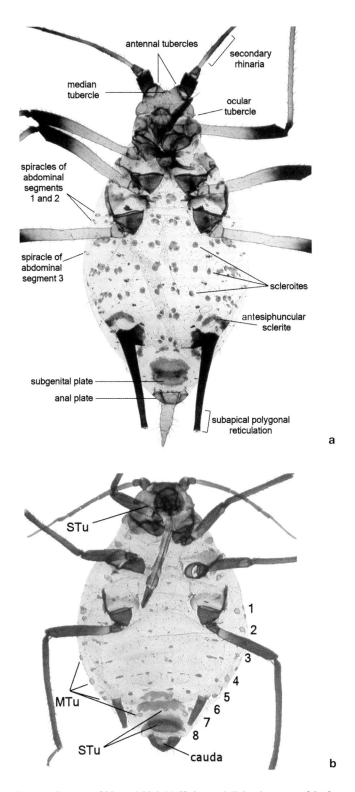

Figure 6. Morphological features of apterae of Macrosiphini. (a) *Uroleucon cirsii* showing many of the features used in keys; (b) *Dysaphis apiifolia* showing abdominal segmentation and positions of marginal (MTu) and spinal (STu) tubercles.

Classification

Since Stroyan's previous two aphid handbooks in this series (1977, 1984), there have been some significant developments in the field of aphid classification and taxonomy. Remaudière & Remaudière (1997) published a catalogue of the world's Aphididae in which the groups treated as families of Aphidoidea in the scheme adopted by Stroyan are reduced to the rank of subfamilies. As the Remaudière catalogue is widely used and is likely to be the main work consulted for matters of aphid nomenclature for many years to come, it seems wise to adopt this classification in the present monograph. A comparison of the two classification schemes (including only those categories represented in the British aphid fauna) is as follows:

Stroyan 1977, 1984 (also used with minor differences by Heie, 1980-1995)	This monograph (mostly following Remaudière & Remaudière, 1997, as do Blackman & Eastop, 2000 and 2006)
APHIDOIDEA	**APHIDIDAE**
Mindaridae	Mindarinae
Hormaphididae	Hormaphidinae
Pemphigidae	Eriosomatinae[1]
Phloeomyzidae	Phloeomyzinae
Thelaxidae	Thelaxinae
Anoeciidae	Anoeciinae
Lachnidae	Lachninae
Callaphididae[2]	Calaphidinae[1] + Drepanosiphinae + Phyllaphidinae + Saltusaphidinae
Chaitophoridae[2]	Chaitophorinae
Aphididae: Pterocommatinae[3] Aphididae: Aphidinae: Aphidini[3] Aphididae: Aphidinae: Macrosiphini	Aphidinae: Aphidini Aphidinae: Macrosiphini, incl. genera formerly in Pterocommatinae (*Plocamaphis*, *Pterocomma*)

[1] Revision of subfamily names as proposed by Nieto-Nafría et al. (1998)
[2] British species reviewed by Stroyan, 1977
[3] British species reviewed by Stroyan, 1984

At the bottom right of the above table it will be seen that I have placed *Pterocomma* and the related genus *Plocamaphis* within Macrosiphini. This group of robust hairy ant-attended aphids, living without host alternation on twigs of Salicaceae, has until recently been regarded by all aphid taxonomists as a separate subfamily and sister group to the Aphidinae. Molecular studies have now shown beyond reasonable doubt that, despite the great differences in their morphology there is a close relationship between *Pterocomma* and *Cavariella*, both genera being firmly nested within the Macrosiphini. *Cavariella* have *Salix* as their primary host, forming colonies on the shoots and leaves, unattended by ants, before migrating for the summer to Umbelliferae. Apparently the differences in feeding position and biology have led to a quite remarkable divergence in morphology between related genera.

Key to subfamilies of Aphididae

Although it is usually easy to recognise an insect as an aphid, it is much harder to find clear diagnostic characters by which to recognise several of the subfamilies and tribes within the Aphididae, and the keys for these groups therefore tend to be rather complicated. Here I have tried to provide a key to the subfamilies of Aphididae for species occurring in Britain that is as simple to use as possible, and does not necessarily require slide-mounted preparations. It is based to some extent on those of Shaposhnikov (1964), Stroyan (1977) and Heie (1980).

1. Apterous viviparous females 2

- Alate viviparous females 13

2. Head capsule and pronotum fused, so that the eyes, composed of only three facets (triommatidia), appear to be situated near the middle of the "head" 3

- Head capsule separated from pronotum at least laterally behind the eyes, which may be three-facetted or multi-facetted 6

3. Cauda tongue-shaped, triangular with blunt apex. On conifers in the genera *Abies* and *Picea* .... **Mindarinae**

- Cauda knobbed or broadly rounded 4

4. Legs very short, concealed or almost concealed beneath the body, and often without tarsi. Cauda knobbed, anal plate bilobed. (In blister galls on birch leaves, or on orchids where they are aleyrodiform, flat and almost circular with a fringe of wax) ...... **Hormaphidinae**

- Legs not concealed beneath body, and always with tarsi. Cauda knobbed or broadly rounded, anal plate rounded 5

5. Wax pore plates present on ABD TERG 7, in two large groups. Cauda broadly rounded. Antennae with spinules forming a reticulate pattern. (On poplar bark) .... **Phloeomyzinae**

- Wax pore plates absent. Cauda either knobbed or broadly rounded. Antennae with spinules in transverse rows. (On oaks, birch or alder) .... **Thelaxinae**

6. ANT PT shorter than half of length of base of last antennal segment. Eyes often reduced, if large and multifacetted then body is densely hairy 7

- ANT PT more than half of length of base of last antennal segment, or if shorter then body is sparsely hairy. Eyes always large and multifacetted 9

7. Dorsal body and appendages usually with short sparse hairs, or if densely hairy then siphunculi absent *and* hind tarsi not elongate. Wax pore plates often evident. (In galls on trees or on roots or basal parts of various plants) .... **Eriosomatinae**

- Densely hairy aphids with siphuncular pores typically placed on low hairy cones, or if siphunculi are absent then hind tarsi are much elongated. Wax pore plates absent 8

8. Rounded, flattish marginal tubercles present on prothorax and most abdominal tergites. (On leaves of *Cornus* and roots of grasses) .... **Anoeciinae**

- Marginal tubercles absent. (On woody plants, mostly conifers, Fagaceae and Rosaceae, or on roots of Compositae) .... **Lachninae**

9. Ocular tubercle absent, being absorbed into compound eye. Body elongate, or if oval then with distinctive black dorsal markings and fore and mid-femora much enlarged for jumping. Siphunculi stump-shaped or raised pores. Cauda knobbed and anal plate strongly bilobed. (On sedges and rushes) .... **Saltusaphidinae** (see Stroyan, 1977)

- Ocular tubercle usually forming a distinct projection to rear of compound eye, or if not then other characters do not fully apply 10

10. Dorsal body hairs numerous, long and bristle-like (except in three species with very elongate body and poriform siphunculi). Siphunculi are usually stump-shaped or truncate conical, sometimes with flared apices, and if antennae are 6-segmented they have reticulate sculpture on distal part. (On *Acer, Aesculus, Salix,* or *Populus* (Chaitophorini), or on grasses, sedges or rushes (Siphini) .... **Chaitophorinae** (see Stroyan, 1977, Chaitophoridae)

- Dorsal body hairs varying in length and form but if long and/or numerous then not bristle-like. Siphunculi very variable but if stump-shaped or truncate conical they are usually without reticulate sculpture 11

11. PT very short and peg-like, less than one quarter of length of base of last segment. Dorsum with extensive pleuro-spinal and marginal variably pigmented areas with numerous wax pores. (In curled leaves of beech, clothed in life with flocculent wax) .... **Phyllaphidinae** (see Stroyan, 1977, *Phyllaphis*)

- PT at least one half of length of base of last segment. Dorsum without extensive areas with wax pores 12

12. Anal plate bilobed or at least slightly emarginate posteriorly in midline, or if without any trace of emargination then ANT III has 20-30 transversely oval secondary rhinaria on ANT III. Cauda knobbed, bluntly triangular or broadly rounded. Siphunculi short, truncate or stump-shaped or poriform, situated on ABD TERG 6. (On birch or alder, or on Leguminosae) ... **Calaphidinae** (see Stroyan, 1977, Callaphidinae and Therioaphidinae)

-   Anal plate not bilobed or emarginate, and rhinaria if present on ANT III are not transversely oval. Cauda variable in shape but not knobbed. Siphunculi also very variable, but often tubular and usually situated on ABD TERG 5. On many plant families .... **Aphidinae** (p. 14)

13. Pterostigma curved around margin of wing and ending in a fine point close to where the R_S meets the wing apex .... **Mindarinae**

-   Pterostigma not curved around to wing apex, ending on anterior margin of wing at some distance from end of R_S 14

14. ANT PT less than half of length of base of last segment. Cauda broadly rounded or knobbed, but if knobbed then antennae are 5-segmented 15

-   ANT PT almost always more than half of length of base of last segment, less in a few species but these have the cauda knobbed *and* the antennae 6-segmented 20

15. Dorsal body (except where heavily sclerotised) and appendages densely hairy. Siphunculi placed on hairy cones or poriform, or absent, but if absent then hind tarsi are much elongated 16

-   Dorsal body and appendages usually sparsely hairy, if densely hairy then siphunculi are absent *and* hind tarsi are not elongate. Siphunculi poriform or absent 17

16. Pterostigma very dark, short and wide forming a conspicuous spot on anterior margin of wing. Dorsal abdomen usually (and in autumn populations always) with an extensive solid black patch. Rounded, flattish marginal tubercles present .... **Anoeciinae**

-   Pterostigma not very dark and much longer than wide. Dorsal abdomen without an extensive solid black patch. Marginal tubercles absent .... **Lachninae**

17. Antennae without secondary rhinaria .... **Phloeomyzinae**

-   Antennae always with some secondary rhinaria 18

18. Anal plate bilobed, cauda knobbed. Antennae with narrow, ring-like secondary rhinaria .... **Hormaphidinae**

-   Anal plate not bilobed, cauda knobbed or rounded. Secondary rhinaria may be ring-like, transversely oval or circular 19

19. Antennae 5-segmented, ornamented with transverse rows of fine spinules, and with a few almost circular rhinaria on ANT III only. Hind wing with only one oblique vein. R IV and R V separately discernible, with RV beak-like or needle-shaped ...... **Thelaxinae**

- Antennae 5- or 6-segmented, usually with transversely oval, ring-like or circular rhinaria, not confined to ANT III. Hind wing with one or two oblique veins. R IV+V not separately discernible .... **Eriosomatinae**

20. Antennae 5- or 6-segmented, but if 6-segmented they have stump-shaped or truncate conical siphunculi (sometimes flared at apices) with reticulate sculpturing on distal part. Cauda is short, broadly rounded or knobbed ....
.... **Chaitophorinae** (see Stroyan, 1977, Chaitophoridae)

- Antennae are usually 6-segmented; if they are 5-segmented, or if there is reticulate sculpturing on the siphunculi, then the cauda is not broadly rounded or knobbed 21

21. Ocular tubercle absent, being absorbed into compound eye. Body elongate, or if oval then with distinctive black markings on dorsal abdomen and wings. Siphunculi stump-shaped or raised pores. Cauda knobbed and anal plate strongly bilobed. (On sedges and rushes) .... **Saltusaphidinae** (see Stroyan, 1977)

- Ocular tubercle usually forming a distinct projection to rear of compound eye, or if not then other characters do not fully apply 22

22. PT very short and peg-like, less than one quarter of length of base of last segment, and siphunculi poriform .... **Phyllaphidinae** (see Stroyan,1977, *Phyllaphis*)

- PT usually at least half of length of base of last segment, and usually longer; if less than half then siphunculi stump-shaped or truncate conical 23

23. Siphunculi tubular, much longer than wide, narrowing towards apices. Cauda knobbed. Secondary rhinaria in a row on basal part of ANT III transversely oval, most of them occupying more than half of width of segment ....
.... **Drepanosiphinae** (see Stroyan, 1977, *Drepanosiphum*)

- If siphunculi are long and tubular then cauda is not knobbed and secondary rhinaria are not transversely oval 24

24. Anal plate bilobed or at least slightly emarginate posteriorly in midline, or if without any trace of emargination then ANT III has 20-50 transversely oval secondary rhinaria on ANT III. Cauda knobbed, bluntly triangular or broadly rounded. Siphunculi short, truncate conical or stump-shaped or poriform, and situated on ABD TERG 6 ....
.... **Calaphidinae** (see Stroyan, 1977, Callaphidinae and Therioaphidinae)

- Anal plate not bilobed or emarginate, and the rhinaria on ANT III are not transversely oval. Cauda variable in shape but not knobbed. Siphunculi also very variable, but often tubular and usually situated on ABD TERG 5 .... **Aphidinae** (p. 14)

The life-cycle in the Aphidinae

Cyclical parthenogenesis, the alternation of sexual and parthenogenetic generations, is an ancestral feature of all Aphidoidea, with the additional refinement of the parthenogenetic generations being viviparous in Aphididae. Host alternation, where there is seasonal migration between a usually woody *primary* host, on which sexual reproduction occurs, and a usually herbaceous *secondary* host on which there is a series of parthenogenetic generations, has apparently evolved separately in many subfamilies of Aphididae, as well as in the adelgids and phylloxerids. In slightly different forms it is found in Hormaphidinae, Eriosomatinae and Anoeciinae, and probably in the past it has occurred in other subfamilies and species-groups and been lost secondarily. In the Aphidinae, however, the adoption of host alternation has led to the successful exploitation of northern temperate flowering plants on an unprecedented scale.

All host-alternating Aphidinae have a particular way of returning to their primary hosts in autumn. In other groups the migrants are all female and produce sexual morphs of both sexes – small oviparae that lay very few eggs, and small apterous males – on the leaves or bark of their primary hosts. But when the autumn migrant females of host-alternating Aphidinae arrive on their primary host they produce only oviparae, which usually mature into quite large adults and after mating lay at least 10-20 eggs. Alate males are produced on the secondary host, and migrate independently to locate and mate with the oviparae. This independent return migration of the sexes to the primary host presumably promotes outbreeding and results in more eggs being laid, but depends on the parthenogenetic generations on the secondary hosts producing sufficiently large numbers of return migrants for successful mate finding.

Many genera and species of Aphidinae no longer host-alternate; most of these have abandoned their original primary host and live all-year-round on herbaceous plants, producing sexual morphs, mating and laying overwintering eggs either on any foliage that is maintained through the winter, or in soil or leaf-litter. In some large genera such as *Acyrthosiphon*, *Macrosiphoniella* and *Uroleucon* this was evidently a very successful move resulting in rapid speciation that is still continuing to the present day. Other species have given up host alternation to return to life all-year-round on the original primary host.

Recognition of tribes within Aphidinae

Recent molecular studies (von Dohlen *et al.*, 2006) have supported the generally accepted view that there is a primary division of the Aphidinae between the group of genera centred on the enormous genus *Aphis*, and a group with many more genera and showing a great range of morphological variation, represented for example by *Macrosiphum*, *Myzus* and *Dysaphis*. This leaves the practical problem of distinguishing between these two tribes of subfamily Aphidinae; the Aphidini covered by Stroyan (1984) and the Macrosiphini which (apart from *Pterocomma* and *Plocamaphis*, see above) are the subject of this monograph. There have been several attempts to provide a key couplet to separate these two groups (Shaposhnikov, 1964; Eastop, 1966; Heie, 1980; Stroyan, 1984). These authors all use the most consistently discriminatory characters (distance apart of spiracles on abdominal segments 1 and 2, and the distribution, position and relative sizes of abdominal marginal tubercles), but these will usually need slide-mounted preparations, or at least examination with a stereomicroscope (in fact the positions of marginal tubercles in relation to spiracles can be better assessed with a stereomicroscope, in lateral rather than dorsoventral view). And even these characters are not wholly reliable when the full range of variation within species, and even within individuals, is taken into account (see Stroyan 1984, pp. 26-7).

In terms of a key couplet, I cannot find any way to improve on that provided by Stroyan (1984, p.26), the main part of which is therefore reproduced here:

- Distance between centres of spiracular pores of abdominal segments 2 and 3 typically not more than 2.1 times the distance between the centres of those on segments 1 and 2. If marginal tubercles are present on the abdomen, then those on segments 1 and 7 are usually larger, or at least not any smaller, than those on segments 2-5 (-6), which may be completely absent, and are never present in the absence of those on both 1 and 7. Those on segments 1 and 7, when present may lie posteroventral or posterodorsal to the spiracles of their respective segments (Fig. 7a, b) .... **Aphidini**

- Distance between centres of spiracular pores of abdominal segments 2 and 3 in morphs other than fundatrices typically more than 2.1 times the distance between the centres of those on segments 1 and 2 (e.g. Fig. 6a). If marginal tubercles are present on the abdomen, then those on segments 2-5 (-6) are usually larger, or at least not any smaller, than those on segments 1 and 7, which are often completely absent, and are never present in the absence of those on 2-5. Those on segments 1 and 2, and those on segment 7, when present, lie (postero-) dorsal to the spiracles of their respective segments (e.g. Fig. 7c) .... **Macrosiphini**

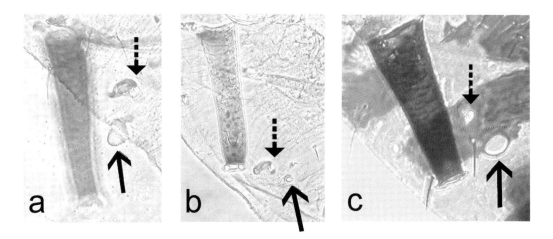

Figure 7. Position of marginal tubercle on abdominal segment 7 (solid arrow) in relation to position of spiracle (dotted arrow) as seen in ideal dorsoventral view, in (a) and (b) Aphidini and (c) Macrosiphini (when present). (a) *Aphis fabae* (note that in this photograph the ventral surface of the cuticle is in focus); (b) *Rhopalosiphum padi* (on its secondary host, where the marginal tubercles are generally smaller than on the primary host); (c) *Dysaphis anthrisci* (but absent in most Macrosiphini).

These are the only characters by which several genera of Macrosiphini can be recognised as belonging to that tribe. However, it may also be useful to list other characters that are possessed by a significant proportion of genera and species of Macrosiphini, but not found in any Aphidini. By checking through this list and finding that even one of these characters applies, it should be possible to recognise all the largest genera and more than 90% of the British species of Macrosiphini.

Character	Genera with species exhibiting character*
Siphunculi with distal polygonal reticulation	*Anthracosiphon, Aulacorthum*, Corylobium, Delphiniobium, Ericaphis*, Illinoia, Impatientinum, Linosiphon, Microsiphum, Macrosiphum, Macrosiphoniella, Metopeurum, Rhopalosiphoninus*, Sitobion, Staticobium, Uroleucon*
Head capsule at least partly spiculose	*Aulacorthum, Ceruraphis, Decorosiphon, Idiopterus, Jacksonia, Myzodium, Myzus, Neomyzus, Ovatus, Paramyzus, Pentalonia, Phorodon, Rhodobium, Rhopalomyzus*, Rhopalosiphoninus, Subacyrthosiphon, Tubaphis, Vesiculaphis*
Dorsal abdomen of *alate* vivipara with broad dark cross-bands leaving only very narrow intersegmental areas, or fused into a solid black patch extending over several tergites	*Anthracosiphon, Anuraphis, Aulacorthum*, Brachycaudus, Capitophorus, Cavariella, Ceruraphis, Chaetosiphon, Cryptomyzus, Dysaphis, Ericaphis, Eucarazzia, Impatientinum, Lipamyzodes, Lipaphis*, Longicaudus, Metopolophium*, Myzodium, Myzus, Nasonovia*, Nearctaphis, Neomyzus, Ovatomyzus, Paramyzus, Phorodon, Rhodobium*, Rhopalomyzus, Rhopalosiphoninus*, Wahlgreniella**
Dorsal hairs of *apterous* vivipara arise from small round sclerites (scleroites; Fig. 6a)	*Macrosiphoniella*, Nearctaphis, Staticobium, Uroleucon**
Antennae as long as or longer than body (more frequently exhibited by alatae than by apterae). (Note: body length not including cauda)	*Acyrthosiphon*, Amphorophora, Anthracosiphon, Aulacorthum, Capitophorus*, Chaetosiphon*, Corylobium, Cryptaphis, Cryptomyzus, Delphiniobium, Eucarazzia, Hyperomyzus*, Idiopterus, Illinoia, Impatientinum*, Linosiphon, Macrosiphoniella, Macrosiphum*, Megoura, Megourella, Metopeurum*, Metopolophium*, Microlophium, Microsiphum, Nasonovia*, Neomyzus, Ovatomyzus*, Ovatus*, Paramyzus, Pentalonia*, Pleotrichophorus, Rhodobium*, Rhopalomyzus*, Rhopalosiphoninus, Sitobion*, Subacyrthosiphon, Tubaphis, Uroleucon, Utamphorophora*, Wahlgreniella*

*Character not present in all species of genus, or not present in some individuals or morphs.

Character	Genera with species exhibiting character*
Antennal tubercles very well developed, so that there is a deep frontal sinus (e.g. Fig 6a)	*Acyrthosiphon*, Amphorophora, Anthracosiphon, Aulacorthum, Cryptaphis, Idiopterus, Illinoia, Impatientinum, Jacksonia, Linosiphon, Macrosiphoniella*, Macrosiphum, Megoura, Megourella, Metopolophium*, Microlophium, Myzotoxoptera, Myzus*, Neomyzus, Ovatomyzus, Ovatus, Paramyzus, Phorodon, Rhodobium, Rhopalosiphoninus, Subacyrthosiphon, Tubaphis, Uroleucon, Wahlgreniella*
Siphunculi mainly pale or dusky (not dark) **and** as long as or longer than the distance between their bases	*Acyrthosiphon*, Amphorophora*, Aulacorthum* Capitophorus, Chaetosiphon*, Corylobium, Illinoia, Ovatomyzus*, Ovatus*, Macrosiphum*, Metopolophium*, Microlophium, Myzus*, Paramyzus*, Phorodon, Rhodobium, Tubaphis, Wahlgreniella*
At least some of dorsal hairs in *apterae* capitate, fan-shaped, or otherwise expanded apically	*Capitophorus, Chaetosiphon, Coloradoa, Corylobium, Cryptaphis, Cryptomyzus, Idiopterus, Myzaphis*, Pleotrichophorus*
R IV+V more-or-less stiletto-shaped; some-what concave-sided and with pointed apex	*Capitophorus*, Coloradoa, Pleotrichophorus, Macrosiphoniella**
Siphunculi swollen on distal part to two or more times their minimal proximal diameter	*Amphorophora*, Cavariella*, Cryptomyzus*, Decorosiphon, Eucarazzia, Hyperomyzus, Illinoia*, Liosomaphis, Myzus*, Rhopalomyzus*, Rhopalosiphoninus, Wahlgreniella**
Siphunculi as raised pores or very low cones, or stump-like, not longer than their basal widths	*Aspidaphis*, Brachycolus*, Brachycorynella, Cryptosiphum, Diuraphis, Longicaudus, Microsiphum, Pseudobrevicoryne*
Cauda broadly rounded, semi-circular, helmet-shaped or bluntly triangular, not longer than its basal width (e.g. Fig. 6b)	*Acaudinum, Anuraphis, Brachycaudus, Dysaphis, Eucarazzia, Plocamaphis, Pterocomma*
Spiracular apertures large and rounded	*Brachycaudus, Delphiniobium, Hyperomyzus*, Nasonovia**
Spinal tubercles present on some segments (e.g. Fig.6b)	*Acyrthosiphon*, Anuraphis, Ceruraphis*, Corylobium, Dysaphis*, Illinoia, Macrosiphum* Metopolophium*, Myzus*, Pterocomma*, Wahlgreniella*
ABD TERG 8 with a backwardly-directed process	*Aspidaphis, Brachycolus*, Cavariella, Diuraphis*, Myzus**
First tarsal segments with more than 3 hairs	*Brachycaudus*, Chaetosiphon, Ericaphis*, Illinoia*, Longicaudus, Myzaphis, Nasonovia*, Uroleucon**
Cauda short with swollen basal part and narrow apical part, in combination with PT tapering to a point	*Aspidaphis, Decorosiphon, Muscaphis, Myzodium, Pseudacaudella* (moss-feeding aphids)

*Character not present in all species of genus, or not present in some individuals or morphs.

General characters of Macrosiphini

Morphological features typical of Macrosiphini are shown in Fig. 6 (p. 7). The two species shown represent major subdivisions within the tribe, and each have some of the features listed above. *Uroleucon* is allied to *Macrosiphum* and belongs to a group of 'macrosiphine aphids', which typically have long appendages and (when host-alternating) cause little or no deformation to their primary host plants. *Dysaphis* belongs to an 'anuraphidinae-myzine group' of genera with generally shorter appendages which typically deform the spring growth of their primary hosts. These groupings are supported by recent molecular studies (e.g. von Dohlen *et al.* 2006), but it is nonetheless difficult to define even these major subdivisons in strictly morphological terms. Various attempts have been made to subdivide the Macrosiphini further, and there are some clearly monophyletic groups of genera, but still no wholly satisfactory subtribal classification, perhaps because the extant genera are the result of large-scale speciation over a relatively short period of time in the mid-Tertiary. Another complicating factor is the scattered occurrence throughout the Macrosiphini of morphological adaptations for feeding on certain plants, or particular positions on the plant, or for attendance by ants.

Looking at host plant relationships, one thing that stands out is the number of genera with host-alternating species that have Rosaceae as their primary hosts, a biology that is shared with *Rhopalosiphum* and its relatives in the sister tribe Aphidini, and is found in evolutionarily divergent genera within the Macrosiphini, such as *Anuraphis*, *Myzus*, *Metopolophium* and *Macrosiphum*, so is probably the ancestral condition of the tribe. Switches of primary host to plants in other families that have occurred in the past are now particularly evident at the generic level – *Capitophorus* on Elaeagnaceae, *Cryptomyzus* on Grossulariaceae, *Cavariella* on Salicaceae, etc – whereas associations with secondary hosts tend to be more specific and show evidence of rapid and ongoing evolutionary change.

Loss of host alternation is also evidently a frequent event in Macrosiphini, many genera having host-alternating species with close relatives that stay all-year-round on what was originally either their primary or their secondary host. The consequences of past losses of host alternation, leading either to specialisation on the primary or the secondary host, are again most evident in present-day Macrosiphini at the level of the genus. A prime example is *Pterocomma* on Salicaceae, which have diverged considerably in morphology from the related host-alternating genus *Cavariella*. Specialisation on different groups of composite plants that were originally their secondary hosts has enabled genera such as *Macrosiphoniella* and *Uroleucon* to be highly successful in developing specific associations with their host plants and having large numbers of extant species.

Host-plants of British Aphidinae

This list excludes most non-indigenous garden and crop plants; for these consult the lists for the world fauna in Blackman & Eastop (2000, 2006). It is based on continental European as well as British records. Bracketed aphid species are those as yet unrecorded from Britain, and aphid species in italics are those not covered by this handbook (Aphidini, *Pterocomma* and *Plocamaphis*), having been keyed and reviewed by Stroyan (1984). Also included are some aphid species in other subfamilies (Chaitophorinae, Calaphidinae and Saltusaphidinae, reviewed by Stroyan, 1977) where these occur on the same plants as Aphidinae and might be confused with them. However, the root-feeding populations of the Eriosomatinae (e.g. *Pemphigus*, *Smynthurodes*, *Tetraneura*), Anoeciinae (*Anoecia*) and Lachninae (Tramini) are not included; these groups are easily recognised by their very short, peg-like ANT PT combined with siphunculi absent or reduced to shallow cones or pores. The list includes the very few common British plants that have no aphids recorded from them, and are thus possibly immune from attack even by polyphagous aphids.

Acaena novae-zelandiae: Acyrthosiphon malvae; Brachycaudus helichrysi; Macrosiphum euphorbiae

Achillea millefolium: *Aphis fabae, vandergooti*; Aulacorthum solani; Brachycaudus cardui, helichrysi; Coloradoa achilleae; Macrosiphoniella abrotani, millefolii, sejuncta, tanacetaria, tapuskae, usquertensis; Macrosiphum euphorbiae; Metopeurum fuscoviride; Microsiphum millefolii; Myzus ascalonicus, cymbalariae, ornatus, persicae; Neomyzus circumflexus; Uroleucon achilleae

Achillea ptarmica: *Aphis fabae, nasturtii, vandergooti*; Aulacorthum solani; Brachycaudus cardui, helichrysi; Macrosiphoniella millefolii, ptarmicae; Macrosiphum euphorbiae; Myzus cymbalariae

Acinos arvensis: *Aphis clinopodii, craccivora, fabae*; Ovatomyzus chamaedrys

Aconitum: Delphiniobium junackianum

Acorus calamus: *Rhopalosiphum nymphaeae, padi, rufulum*; *Schizaphis scirpi*

Actea spicata: *Aphis fabae*

Adiantum capillus-veneris: *Idiopterus nephrelepidis*

Aegopodium podagraria: Anuraphis subterranea; *Aphis fabae, podagrariae, sambuci*; Aulacorthum solani; Cavariella aegopodii, theobaldi; Dysaphis crataegi; Hyadaphis foeniculi; Myzus ornatus; Semiaphis dauci, pimpinellae

Aethusa cynapium: *Aphis fabae*; Dysaphis crataegi ssp. aethusae; Hyadaphis foeniculi; Macrosiphum euphorbiae, gei; Myzus ornatus

Agrimonia eupatoria: Acyrthosiphon malvae ssp. agrimoniae; Macrosiphum rosae; Sitobion fragariae

Agropyron see *Elymus*

Agrostis: Diuraphis agrostidis; *Melanaphis pyraria*; Metopolophium dirhodum, festucae; Rhopalomyzus poae; *Rhopalosiphum insertum, padi*; *Schizaphis agrostis, graminum ssp. gigjai* (?), *rufula*; Siphini spp. (see Stroyan, 1977); Sitobion avenae, fragariae

Ajuga: Myzus ajugae, ornatus, persicae; Ovatomyzus chamaedrys

Alcea rosea: Acyrthosiphon malvae; *Aphis fabae, gossypii, nasturtii, spiraecola, umbrella*; Aulacorthum solani; Macrosiphum euphorbiae; Myzus ornatus, persicae

Alchemilla: Acyrthosiphon malvae ssp. potha; Amphorophora gei; *Aphis fabae*; Aulacorthum solani; Brachycaudus helichrysi; Ericaphis wakibae; Myzus ascalonicus, ornatus, persicae; Macrosiphum euphorbiae; Neomyzus circumflexus

Alisma: *Aphis nasturtii*; Aulacorthum solani; *Rhopalosiphum nymphaeae*

Alliaria petiolata: Brevicoryne brassicae; Lipaphis erysimi; Myzus persicae; Nasonovia ribisnigri

Allium: Myzus ascalonicus, cymbalariae; Neotoxoptera formosana (but no aphid records from *A. oleraceum* or *A. ursinum*)

Alopecurus: Metopolophium dirhodum, festucae; Myzus persicae; *Rhopalosiphum insertum, padi*; *Schizaphis nigerrima*; Sitobion alopecuri, avenae, fragariae

Althaea officinalis: *Aphis fabae, gossypii, nasturtii, spiraecola, umbrella*

Amblystegium serpens: Muscaphis musci

Ammophila arenaria: *Hyalopterus pruni*; *Schizaphis rufula*; Siphini spp. (see Stroyan, 1977)

Anagallis arvensis: *Aphis craccivora, fabae, gossypii, nasturtii, nerii*; Myzus ascalonicus, persicae

Anchusa: *Aphis fabae, gossypii, symphyti*; Brachycaudus bicolor

Andromeda polifolia: *Aphis vaccinii*; Ericaphis scammelli; Illinoia azaleae

Anemone nemorosa: no aphid records

Angelica sylvestris: *Aphis fabae*; Cavariella archangelicae, konoi, pastinacae; Dysaphis angelicae; Hyadaphis foeniculi

Anthemis arvensis: *Aphis fabae*; Aulacorthum solani; Brachycaudus helichrysi; Macrosiphoniella tapuskae; Macrosiphum euphorbiae; Myzus persicae; Pleotrichophorus glandulosus

Anthemis cotula: *Aphis nasturtii, vandergooti*; Brachycaudus helichrysi, lateralis; Macrosiphoniella abrotani, millefolii, tapuskae; Macrosiphum euphorbiae; Myzus ornatus, persicae

Anthoxanthum odoratum: *Rhopalosiphum padi*; Sitobion avenae, fragariae

Anthriscus: *Aphis brohmeri, fabae*; Aulacorthum solani; Cavariella aegopodii, pastinacae; Dysaphis anthrisci, crataegi, hirsutissima; Hyadaphis foeniculi; Macrosiphum euphorbiae, gei; Myzus ornatus

Anthyllis vulneraria: Acyrthosiphon loti; *Aphis craccivora, klimeschi, loti*

Apera spica-venti: *Schizaphis rufula*

Apium graveolens: *Aphis fabae, gossypii, sambuci, spiraecola*; Aulacorthum solani; Brachycaudus helichrysi; Cavariella aegopodii, archangelicae, konoi, pastinacae, theobaldi; Dysaphis apiifolia; Hyadaphis foeniculi; Macrosiphum euphorbiae; Myzus ornatus, persicae; Neomyzus circumflexus; Rhopalosiphoninus latysiphon

Aquilegia vulgaris: *Aphis fabae, gossypii*; Aulacorthum solani; Longicaudus trirhodus; Macrosiphum euphorbiae; Myzus ascalonicus, persicae; Neomyzus circumflexus

Arabidopsis thaliana: *Aphis gossypii*; Brevicoryne brassicae; Lipaphis erysimi, rossi; Myzus ornatus, persicae

Arabis arenosa: Lipaphis erysimi; Myzus ascalonicus

Arabis glabra: Brevicoryne brassicae; Lipaphis turritella; Macrosiphum euphorbiae

Arabis hirsuta: Lipaphis rossi; Myzus persicae

Arbutus unedo: Wahlgreniella nervata ssp. arbuti

Arctium lappa: *Aphis fabae, gossypii, solanella*; Aulacorthum solani; Brachycaudus cardui, helichrysi; Capitophorus elaeagni; Dysaphis lappae; Macrosiphum euphorbiae; Myzus ornatus, persicae

Arctium minus: *Aphis fabae, fabae* ssp. *mordvilkoi, nasturtii, solanella*; Aulacorthum solani; Brachycaudus cardui, helichrysi; Dysaphis lappae

Arctostaphylos uva-ursi: *Aphis fabae, uvaeursi, vaccinii*; Aulacorthum solani; Brachycaudus helichrysi; Myzus ascalonicus, ornatus; Neomyzus circumflexus; Rhopalosiphoninus staphyleae; Wahlgreniella nervata, ossiannilssoni, vaccinii

Arenaria serpyllifolia: Myzus certus

Arrhenatherum elatius: Metopolophium albidum, dirhodum, fasciatum; *Rhopalosiphum padi*; *Sipha* spp. (see Stroyan, 1977); Sitobion avenae, fragariae

Artemisia absinthium: *Aphis fabae*; Aulacorthum solani; Coloradoa absinthii, angelicae, artemisiae, rufomaculata; Macrosiphoniella absinthii, artemisiae, oblonga, pulvera, tanacetaria; Macrosiphum euphorbiae; Myzus ascalonicus; Pleotrichophorus glandulosus

Artemisia campestris: Coloradoa artemisiae; Cryptosiphum artemisiae; Macrosiphoniella artemisiae, tapuskae, usquertensis; Macrosiphum euphorbiae; Myzus ornatus; (Pleotrichophorus persimilis)

Artemisia maritima see *Seriphidium maritimum*

Artemisia vulgaris: *Aphis fabae*; Aulacorthum solani; Brachycaudus cardui, helichrysi; Coloradoa artemisiae, rufomaculata; Cryptosiphum artemisiae; Macrosiphoniella absinthii, artemisiae, oblonga, pulvera, tanacetaria; Myzus ornatus, persicae; Pleotrichophorus glandulosus

Arundo donax: *Hyalopterus pruni*; Macrosiphum euphorbiae; *Melanaphis pyraria*; Metopolophium dirhodum; Myzus ornatus, persicae; *Rhopalosiphum padi*; *Sipha maydis* (see Stroyan, 1977)

Asarum europaeum: Brachycaudus cardui; Rhopalosiphoninus staphyleac

Asperula cynanchica: *Aphis galliiscabri*; Dysaphis pyri; Myzus cerasi

Asplenium: Amphorophora ampullata; Idiopterus nephrelepidis

Aster tripolium: *Aphis fabae, tripolii*; Brachycaudus helichrysi; Macrosiphoniella asteris; Myzus persicae

Astragalus: *Aphis craccivora*; *Therioaphis trifolii* (subfamily Calaphidinae; see Stroyan, 1977)

Athyrium filix-femina: Amphorophora ampullata

Atrichum see *Catharinaea*

Atriplex: *Aphis craccivora, fabae, gossypii*; Hayhurstia atriplicis; Myzus persicae

Avena (fatua, ludoviciana): *Aphis fabae*; Macrosiphum euphorbiae; Metopolophium dirhodum; Myzus persicae; *Rhopalosiphum padi*; *Schizaphis rufula*; *Sipha maydis* (see Stroyan, 1977); Sitobion avenae, fragariae

Azolla filiculoides: *Rhopalosiphum nymphaeae*

Ballota nigra; *Aphis balloticola*; Aulacorthum solani; Cryptomyzus alboapicalis, ballotae; Ovatomyzus sp. (chamaedrys?)

Barbarea: *Aphis triglochinis*; Aulacorthum solani; Brevicoryne brassicae; Macrosiphum euphorbiae; Myzus ascalonicus, ornatus, persicae; Pseudobrevicoryne buhri

Barbula: Muscaphis musci

Bellis perennis: Aulacorthum solani; Brachycaudus helichrysi; Macrosiphum euphorbiae; Myzus ascalonicus, ornatus, persicae; Neomyzus circumflexus

Beta vulgaris: *Aphis fabae, nasturtii, solanella*; Aulacorthum solani; Hayhurstia atriplicis; Macrosiphum euphorbiae, stellariae; Myzus antirrhinii, ascalonicus, persicae; Rhopalosiphum latysiphon, staphyleae

Bidens: *Aphis fabae, nasturtii*; Brachycaudus helichrysi; Macrosiphoniella tanacetaria; Myzus persicae

Brachypodium: *Melanaphis pyraria*; *Sipha maydis* (see Stroyan, 1977)

Brachythecium: Muscaphis musci

Briza: *Rhopalosiphum padi*; *Sipha maydis* (see Stroyan, 1977); Sitobion fragariae

Bromus: Hyalopteroides humilis; *Melanaphs pyraria*; Metopolophium dirhodum, festucae; Myzus persicae; *Rhopalosiphum padi*; Siphini spp. (see Stroyan, 1977); Sitobion avenae, fragariae

Bryonia dioica: Macrosiphum euphorbiae

Bryum: Muscaphis musci

Buddleja davidii: *Aphis fabae, verbasci*; Myzus antirrhinii, ornatus, persicae

Cakile maritima: Acyrthosiphon auctum; *Aphis fabae*; Brevicoryne brassicae; Lipaphis erysimi; Myzus persicae

Calamagrostis: (Diuraphis calamagrostis); *Hyalopterus pruni*; Metopolophium dirhodum; Siphini spp. (see Stroyan, 1977); Sitobion avenae, fragariae

Calamintha acinos see *Acinos arvensis*

Calla palustris: *Aphis nasturtii*; *Rhopalosiphum nymphaeae*

Calliergon cuspidatum: Muscaphis cuspidati

Calluna vulgaris: *Aphis callunae*; Ericaphis ericae, latifrons

Caltha palustris: *Aphis nasturtii*; Macrosiphum euphorbiae; Myzus ascalonicus, persicae; Rhopalosiphoninus calthae; *Rhopalosiphum nymphaeae*

Calystegia: *Aphis fabae*; Aulacorthum solani; Myzus persicae

Campanula glomerata: *Aphis fabae*; Uroleucon nigrocampanulae

Campanula latifolia: Uroleucon nigrocampanulae

Campanula persicifolia: Dysaphis sorbi; Myzus ascalonicus, ornatus; Neomyzus circumflexus; Uroleucon campanulae, nigrocampanulae

Campanula rapunculoides: *Aphis fabae*; Aulacorthum solani; Myzus ascalonicus, persicae; Uroleucon campanulae, nigrocampanulae, (rapunculoides)

Campanula rotundifolia: Dysaphis brevirostris, sorbi; Myzus ascalonicus; Rhopalosiphoninus staphyleae; Uroleucon campanulae

Campanula trachelium: *Aphis fabae*; Uroleucon campanulae, nigrocampanulae

Capsella bursa-pastoris: Acyrthosiphon pisum; *Aphis fabae, frangulae, nasturtii, sambuci, solanella*; Aulacorthum solani; Brachycaudus cardui, helichrysi; Brevicoryne brassicae; Lipaphis erysimi; Macrosiphum euphorbiae; Myzus antirrhinii, ascalonicus, certus, persicae; Nearctaphis bakeri; Neomyzus circumflexus; Rhopalosiphoninus staphyleae; *Rhopalosiphum padi, nymphaeae*; Sitobion avenae

Cardamine: *Aphis fabae, nasturtii, triglochinis*; Aulacorthum solani; Brevicoryne brassicae; Lipaphis erysimi; Macrosiphum euphorbiae; Myzotoxoptera wimshurstae; Myzus ascalonicus, cerasi, ornatus, persicae

Cardaria draba see *Lepidium draba*

Carduus: *Aphis fabae, solanella*; Brachycaudus cardui, helichrysi; Capitophorus carduinus, elaeagni; Myzus persicae; Uroleucon aeneum

Carex: *Aphis fabae*; Ceruraphis eriophori; Metopolophium dirhodum, festucae; *Rhopalosiphum insertum, padi*; Saltusaphidinae spp. (see Stroyan, 1977); *Schizaphis caricis, scirpi*; Siphini spp. (see Stroyan, 1977); Sitobion avenae, fragariae; Vesiculaphis theobaldi

Carlina vulgaris: Uroleucon helenae

Carum carvi: *Aphis brohmeri, fabae*; Cavariella aegopodii, theobaldi; Hyadaphis foeniculi; Myzus ornatus

Catabrosa aquatica: Cavariella aquatica; *Rhopalosiphum padi*

Catharinaea undulata: Decorosiphon corynothrix; Muscaphis musci; Myzodium modestum

Centaurea calcitrapa: *Aphis fabae*; Myzus persicae; Uroleucon jaceae

Centaurea nigra: Brachycaudus helichrysi; Uroleucon jaceae, jaceicola

Centaurea scabiosa: Acaudinum centaureae; *Aphis fabae*; Uroleucon jaceae (incl. ssp. henrichi), jaceicola

Centaurium erythraea: *Aphis gentianae*; Myzus cerasi

Cerastium: Aulacorthum solani; Brachycolus cerastii; Macrosiphum euphorbiae; Myzus ascalonicus, certus, cymbalariae, persicae

Chaerophyllum temulum: *Aphis fabae*; Cavariella aegopodii, pastinacae; Dysaphis chaerophylli; Macrosiphum gei

Chamaemelum nobile: *Aphis fabae*; Brachycaudus cardui, helichrysi; Macrosiphoniella tanacetaria

Chelidonium majus: *Aphis fabae*; Aulacorthum solani; Macrosiphum euphorbiae; Myzus persicae; Rhopalosiphoninus latysiphon

Chenopodium: *Aphis craccivora, fabae, gossypii, nasturtii, solanella*; Aulacorthum solani; Hayhurstia atriplicis; Macrosiphum euphorbiae; Myzus antirrhinii, ornatus, persicae (but no aphids recorded from *Ch. bonus-henricus* and *Ch. rubrum*)

Chrysanthemum segetum: *Aphis fabae, nasturtii*; Brachycaudus helichrysi, lateralis; Macrosiphoniella sanborni; Macrosiphum euphorbiae; Myzus ornatus, persicae; Uroleucon sonchi

Cichorium intybus: *Aphis fabae, gossypii*; Aulacorthum solani; Brachycaudus helichrysi; Hyperomyzus lactucae, picridis; Macrosiphum euphorbiae; Myzus ornatus, persicae; Nasonovia ribisnigri; Uroleucon cichorii, sonchi

Cicuta virosa: *Aphis fabae, nasturtii*; Cavariella aegopodii, konoi, pastinacae; Macrosiphum gei; *Rhopalosiphum nymphaeae*

Cirsium arvense: *Aphis fabae* ssp. *cirsiiacanthoidis, nasturtii, solanella*; Brachycaudus cardui, helichrysi; Capitophorus carduinus, elaeagni, gynoxanthus; Hyperomyzus lactucae; Macrosiphum euphorbiae; Myzus persicae; Nasonovia ribisnigri; Uroleucon aeneum, cichorii, cirsii, jaceae

Claytonia perfoliata: Myzus persicae

Clematis vitalba: Aulacorthum solani; Myzus varians

Clinopodium vulgare: *Aphis clinopodii, origani*; Myzus ornatus; Ovatomyzus chamaedrys

Cochlearia officinalis: Lipaphis cochleariae; Myzus ascalonicus

Colutea arborescens: Acyrthosiphon caraganae ssp. occidentale, pisum; *Aphis craccivora, cytisorum*; Myzus ascalonicus

Conium maculatum: Anuraphis subterranea; *Aphis fabae*; Aulacorthum solani; Cavariella aegopodii, pastinacae, theobaldi; Dysaphis apiifolia, crataegi, lauberti; Hyadaphis foeniculi, passerinii; Macrosiphum euphorbiae, gei; Myzus ornatus

Convallaria majalis: *Aphis gossypii*; Aulacorthum solani, speyeri; Macrosiphum euphorbiae; Metopolophium dirhodum; Myzus ascalonicus, persicae

Convolvulus arvensis: *Aphis fabae, gossypii, spiraecola*; Aulacorthum solani; Macrosiphum euphorbiae; Myzus persicae; Rhopalosiphoninus latysiphon

Conyza canadensis: *Aphis fabae, gossypii*; Aulacorthum solani; Brachycaudus helichrysi; Myzus persicae; Uroleucon erigeronense, simile

Cornus: *Anoecia* spp. (subfam. Anoeciinae); *Aphis salicariae, spiraecola*; Macrosiphum euphorbiae; Myzus ornatus, persicae

Coronilla varia: Acyrthosiphon caraganae ssp. occidentale, pisum; *Aphis coronillae, craccae*

Corylus avellana: Corylobium avellanae

Corynephorus canescens: Sitobion avenae

Crambe maritima: Brevicoryne brassicae

Crataegus: *Aphis fabae, pomi*; Aulacorthum solani; Dysaphis angelicae, apiifolia, crataegi, lauberti, ranunculi; Macrosiphum euphorbiae; Ovatus crataegarius, insitus; *Rhopalosiphum insertum*

Crepis biennis: *Aphis crepidis, fabae*; Aulacorthum solani; Brachycaudus helichrysi; Hyperomyzus picridis; Myzus ascalonicus; Uroleucon cichorii, grossum

Crepis capillaris: *Aphis crepidis, fabae*; Brachycaudus cardui; Macrosiphum euphorbiae; Myzus ornatus; Nasonovia ribsinigri; Uroleucon cichorii, grossum, murale, sonchi

Crepis paludosa: Nasonovia ribisnigri; Uroleucon cichorii, riparium

Crepis vesicaria: *Aphis crepidis*; Aulacorthum solani; Hyperomyzus lactucae; Myzus ornatus, persicae; Nasonovia ribisnigri; Uroleucon cichorii, grossum

Crithmum maritimum: *Aphis fabae*; Cavariella aegopodii; Dysaphis crithmi; Hyadaphis foeniculi

Cuscuta europea: *Aphis hederae*

Cymbalaria muralis: Brachycaudus helichrysi; Dysaphis gallica; Myzus ascalonicus, cymbalariae, ornatus, persicae

Cynodon dactylon: *Rhopalosiphum padi*; *Sipha maydis* (see Stroyan, 1977); Sitobion avenae

Cynoglossum officinale: Acyrthosiphum malvae; *Aphis symphyti*; Brachycaudus bicolor, cardui, helichrysi, lateralis; Myzus persicae

Cynosurus: *Atheroides serrulatus* (see Stroyan, 1977); Metopolophium fasciatum, festucae ssp, cerealium; *Rhopalosiphum padi*; Sitobion avenae

Cyperus longus: *Rhopalosiphum padi*; Sitobion avenae

Cytisus scoparius: Acyrthosiphon caraganae ssp. occidentale, pisum; *Aphis cytisorum* ssp. *sarothamni;* Aulacorthum solani; *Ctenocallis setosa* (see Stroyan, 1977); Myzus persicae

Daboecia cantabrica: Ericaphis ericae

Dactylis glomerata: Aulacorthum solani; Hyalopteroides humilis; Jacksonia papillata; *Melanaphis pyraria*; Metopolophium dirhodum; Myzus ornatus, persicae; Rhopalomyzus lonicerae, poae; *Rhopalosiphum insertum, padi*; Siphini spp. (see Stroyan, 1977); Sitobion avenae, fragariae; Utamphorophora humboldti

Daphne: Aulacorthum solani; Macrosiphum daphnidis, euphorbiae

Datura stramonium: *Aphis craccivora, fabae, gossypii*; Aulacorthum solani; Macrosiphum euphorbiae; Myzus ornatus, persicae; Nasonovia ribisnigri; Neomyzus circumflexus; Rhopalosiphoninus staphyleae

Daucus carota: *Aphis fabae, gossypii, lambersi*; Aulacorthum solani; Cavariella aegopodii; Dysaphis apiifolia, crataegi;Hyadaphis passerini; Myzus ornatus, persicae; Semiaphis dauci

Deschampsia: *Atheroides* spp. (see Stroyan, 1977); *Hyalopterus pruni*; Jacksonia papillata; Metopolophium festucae, tenerum; *Rhopalosiphum padi*; Sitobion avenae, fragariae

Descurainia sophia: *Aphis craccivora, fabae, solanella*; Brachycaudus helichrysi; Brevicoryne brassicae; Lipaphis erysimi

Dianthus deltoides: Aulacorthum solani; Macrosiphum euphorbiae; Myzus ascalonicus, certus, ornatus; Rhopalosiphoninus staphyleae

Dicranum scoparium: Jacksonia papillata; Muscaphis escherichi; Pseudocaudella rubida

Digitalis purpurea: Acyrthosiphon malvae; *Aphis armata, fabae*; Aulacorthum solani; Brachycaudus helichrysi; Macrosiphum euphorbiae; Myzus persicae

Digitaria: Myzus ornatus; *Rhopalosiphum padi*; Sitobion avenae

Diplotaxis: Brevicoryne brassicae

Dipsacus: *Aphis confusa, fabae, ochropus, solanella*; Macrosiphum rosae; Myzus persicae

Doronicum pardalianches: *Aphis fabae*; Brachycaudus helichrysi

Drepanocladus aduncus: Muscaphis cuspidati

Drosera: *Aphis nasturtii, triglochinis*; Myzus lythri; *Rhopalosiphum nymphaeae*

Dryas octopetala: Acyrthosiphon malvae

Dryopteris: Amphorophora ampullata; Idiopteris nephrelepidis

Echium vulgare: *Aphis fabae, solanella, symphyti*; Brachycaudus cardui, helichrysi; Myzus persicae

Elodea canadensis: *Rhopalosiphum nymphaeae*

Elymus: Diuraphis frequens; Metopolophium dirhodum, festucae; Myzus ascalonicus; *Rhopalosiphum padi*; *Schizaphis rufula*; *Sipha* spp. (see Stroyan, 1977); Sitobion avenae

Empetrum nigrum: Ericaphis latifrons, scammelli; Wahlgreniella nervata ssp. arbuti

Epilobium: *Aphis epilobiaria, epilobii, fabae, frangulae, gossypii, grossulariae, praeterita, salicariae*; Brachycaudus cardui; Macrosiphum euphorbiae, tinctum; Myzus ascalonicus, lythri, ornatus, persicae

Epipactis: *Aphis epipactis, fabae*

Equisetum: Neomyzus circumflexus; Sitobion avenae

Erica tetralix: Ericaphis ericae

Erigeron acer: Acyrthosiphon malvae; Aulacorthum solani; Brachycaudus helichrysi; Myzus ornatus; Uroleucon simile

Erodium: Acyrthosiphon malvae, Aulacorthum solani; Macrosiphum euphorbiae; Myzus ascalonicus, ornatus, persicae; Nasonovia ribisnigri

Erophila verna: No aphids recorded

Eriophorum: Cavariella aquatica; Ceruraphis eriophori; Metopolophium dirhodum; *Schizaphis scirpi* ssp. *eriophori*; Vesiculaphis theobaldi

Eruca vesicaria: *Aphis gossypii*; Brevicoryne brassicae; Lipaphis erysimi; Myzus persicae

Erucastrum gallicum: Brevicoryne brassicae

Eryngium maritimum: Aulacorthum solani; Cavariella aegopodii; Dysaphis apiifolia; Myzus ascalonicus

Erysimum cheiranthoides: Lipaphis turritella; Myzus persicae

Euonymus europaeus: *Aphis euonymi, fabae, solanella*; Macrosiphun euphorbiae

Eupatorium cannabinum: *Aphis frangulae, gossypii, spiraecola*; Brachycaudus cardui, helichrysi; Macrosiphum euphorbiae

Euphorbia: (Acyrthosiphon cyparissiae, euphorbiae); *Aphis euphorbiae*; Aulacorthum solani; Macrosiphum euphorbiae, euphorbiellum; Myzus persicae

Euphrasia: Brachycaudus helichrysi; Nasonovia ribisnigri

Eurynchium: Muscaphis cuspidati, escherichi, musci

Fallopia: *Aphis craccivora, fabae, gossypii, nasturtii, solanella*; Aulacorthum solani; Macrosiphum euphorbiae; Myzus persicae

Festuca: Cryptaphis poae; Jacksonia papillata; Metopolophium dirhodum, festucae, sabihae, tenerum; Rhopalomyzus poae; *Rhopalosiphum insertum, padi*; *Schizaphis nigerrima*; Siphini spp. (see Stroyan, 1977); Sitobion avenae, fragariae; Utamphorophora humboldti; Vesiculaphis theobaldi

Filago arvensis: (Pleotrichophorus filaginis)

Filago vulgaris: No aphids recorded

Filipendula ulmaria: Amphorophora gei; *Aphis ulmariae*; Macrosiphum cholodkovskyi

Foeniculum vulgare: *Aphis fabae*; Brachycaudus helichrysi; Cavariella aegopodii, konoi, pastinacae; Dysaphis apiifolia, lauberti; Hyadaphis foeniculi, passerinii; Myzus ascalonicus, persicae

Fragaria moschata: Acyrthosiphon malvae ssp. rogersii; Sitobion fragariae

Fragaria vesca: Aulacorthum solani; Chaetosiphon fragaefolii; Ericaphis wakibae; Macrosiphum euphorbiae; Myzus ascalonicus, ornatus, persicae; Neomyzus circumflexus;

Rhodobium porosum; Sitobion fragariae

Frangula alnus: *Aphis frangulae*

Fumaria: Acyrthosiphon malvae; *Aphis fabae, solanella*; Macrosiphum euphorbiae; Myzus persicae; Neomyzus circumflexus

Galanthus nivalis: No aphids recorded

Galega officinalis: Acyrthosiphon pisum; Aulacorthum solani; Macrosiphum euphorbiae

Galeopsis: *Aphis frangulae* ssp. *beccabungae, gossypii, nasturtii*; Aulcorthum solani; Cryptomyzus galeopsidis, ribis; Myzus padellus, persicae

Galinsoga parviflora: *Aphis fabae*; Aulacorthum solani; Brachycaudus cardui, helichrysi, lateralis; Macrosiphum euphorbiae; Myzus ornatus, persicae

Galium: *Aphis fabae, galiiscabri, solanella*; Aulacorthum solani; Brachycaudus helichrysi; Dysaphis pyri; Hydaphias hofmanni, mosana; Linosiphon galiophagum; Macrosiphum euphorbiae; Myzus ascalonicus, cerasi, cymbalariae, langei, ornatus, persicae; Neomyzus circumflexus; Sitobion fragariae; Staegeriella necopinata

Genista: Acyrthosiphon pisum; *Aphis craccivora, cytisorum, genistae*

Gentianella: No aphids recorded

Geranium: Acyrthosiphon malvae; Aulacorthum solani; Myzus ornatus

Geum: Acyrthosiphon malvae, malvae ssp. potha; Amphorophora gei; Aulacorthum solani; Macrosiphum euphorbiae, gei; Myzus ascalonicus, ornatus; Ovatomyzus boraginacearum

Glaucium flavum: *Aphis fabae*; Macrosiphum euphorbiae

Glechoma hederacea: Aulacorthum solani; Myzus ascalonicus; Ovatus glechomae; Rhopalosiphoninus staphyleae ssp. tulipaellus

Glyceria: *Melanaphis pyraria*; Metopolophium dirhodum; Rhopalomyzus lonicerae, poae; *Rhopalosiphum insertum, nymphaeae, padi*; *Sipha glyceriae* (see Stroyan, 1977); Sitobion avenae, fragariae

Gnaphalium sylvaticum: (Pleotrichophorus filaginis)

Gnaphalium uliginosum: *Aphis nasturtii*; Aulacorthum solani; Brachycaudus helichrysi; Myzus ornatus

Hedera helix: *Aphis fabae, gossypii, hederae*; Aulacorthum solani; Macrosiphum euphorbiae; Myzus ascalonicus, ornatus, persicae; Neomyzus circumflexus; Rhopalosiphoninus staphyleae

Helianthemum nummularium: *Aphis cliftonensis, helianthemi, nasturtii*; Myzus ornatus

Helleborus foetidus, H. viridis: Macrosiphum hellebori

Heracleum: Anuraphis subterranea; *Aphis bromeri, fabae*; Aulacorthum solani; Cavariella aegopodii, archangelicae, pastinacae, theobaldi; Dysaphis crataegi, lauberti, newskyi; Hyadaphis foeniculi; Macrosiphum euphorbiae, gei; Myzus ascalonicus, ornatus, persicae; Paramyzus heraclei

Hesperis matronalis: *Aphis gossypii*; Lipaphis erysimi; Myzus ascalonicus; Rhopalosiphoninus staphyleae

Hieracium: *Aphis fabae, pilosellae*; Aulacorthum solani; Brachycaudus cardui, helichrysi; Hyperomyzus hieracii; Macrosiphum euphorbiae; Myzus persicae; Nasonovia compositellae, pilosellae, ribisnigri; Uroleucon cichorii, obscurum, (pilosellae)

Hierochloe odorata: Sitobion fragariae

Hippocrepis comosa: Acythosiphon caraganae ssp. occidentale, loti, pisum

Hippophae rhamnoides: Capitophorus elaeagni, hippophaes, similis

Hippuris vulgaris: Brachycaudus helichrysi; Myzus lythri; *Rhopalosiphum nymphaeae*

Hirschfeldia incana: Brevicoryne brassicae; Lipaphis erysimi; Myzus persicae

Holcus: Cryptaphis poae; Diuraphis holci; Hyalopteroides humilis; *Melanaphis pyraria*; Metopolophium dirhodum, festucae; *Rhopalosiphum nymphaeae, padi*; *Schizaphis holci*; Siphini spp. (see Stroyan, 1977); Sitobion avenae, fragariae

Honkenya peploides: Acyrthosiphon auctum; Myzus ascalonicus, persicae

Hordeum murinum: Metopolophium dirhodum, fasciatum, festucae, festucae ssp. cerealium; *Rhopalosiphum padi*; Siphini spp. (see Stroyan, 1977); Sitobion avenae, fragariae

Hottonia palustris: *Rhopalosiphum nymphaeae*

Humulus lupulus: Macrosiphum euphorbiae; Myzus persicae; Phorodon humuli; Rhopalosiphoninus staphyleae

Hyacinthoides non-scripta: No aphids recorded

Hydrocharis morsus-ranae: *Rhopalosiphum nymphaeae*

Hydrocotyle vulgaris: Aulacorthum solani; *Rhopalosiphum nymphaeae*

Hylocomium: Muscaphis escherichi, musci; Pseudacaudella rubida

Hyoscyamus niger: *Aphis fabae*; Aulacorthum solani; Myzus persicae

Hypericum: *Aphis chloris, craccivora, fabae, gossypii, spiraecola*; Aulacorthum solani; Macrosiphum euphorbiae; Myzus persicae

Hypnum cupressiforme: Muscaphis escherichi

Hypochaeris: *Aphis fabae, gossypii, hypochoeridis, nasturtii*; Brachycaudus helichrysi; Macrosiphum euphorbiae; Myzus ascalonicus, cymbalariae, persicae; Nasonovia ribisnigri; Neomyzus circumflexus; Uroleucon cichorii, hypochoeridis, sonchi

Iberis amara: Lipaphis erysimi; Myzus persicae

Ilex aquifolium: *Aphis fabae, ilicis*; Aulacorthum solani; Illinoia lambersi; Macrosiphum euphorbiae, rosae

Impatiens glandulifera, parviflora: *Aphis fabae*; Impatientinum asiaticum

Impatiens noli-tangere: *Aphis fabae*; Impatientinum balsamines

Inula conyza: Capitophorus inulae; Ovatus inulae

Inula helenium: Brachycaudus cardui, helichrysi; Capitophorus pakansus; Ovatus inulae

Inula salicina: Brachycaudus helichrysi; Capitophorus inulae

Iris: *Aphis newtoni*; Dysaphis tulipae

Isatis tinctoria: Brevicoryne brassicae; Lipaphis erysimi; Myzus persicae

Jasione montana: Brachycaudus helichrysi; Dysaphis brevirostris, sorbi; Myzus ascalonicus; Uroleucon campanulae (but see text)

Juncus: Cavariella aquatica; *Rhopalosiphum insertum, nymphaeae, padi*; Saltusaphidinae spp. (see Stroyan, 1977); *Schizaphis palustris*; Siphini spp. (see Stroyan, 1977); Sitobion avenae, fragariae

Knautia arvensis: *Aphis confusa*; Aulacorthum knautiae, solani; Macrosiphum rosae; Ovatomyzus boraginacearum

Koeleria cristata: *Rhopalosiphum padi*

Lactuca: Acyrthosiphon lactucae; *Aphis fabae*; Aulacorthum solani; Hyperomyzus lactucae; Macrosiphum euphorbiae; Myzus persicae; Nasonovia ribisnigri; Uroleucon cichorii, sonchi

Lagurus ovatus: *Sipha maydis* (see Stroyan, 1977); Sitobion avenae, fragariae

Lamiastrum galeobdolon: *Aphis lamiorum*; Cryptomyzus maudamanti

Lamium: *Aphis frangulae, fabae, lamiorum*; Aulacorthum solani; Brachycaudus helichrysi; Cryptomyzus alboapicalis, ballotae, galeopsidis, korschelti, ribis, (ulmeri); Macrosiphum euphorbiae; Myzus ornatus, persicae; Rhopalosiphoninus staphyleae

Lapsana communis: *Aphis fabae*; Aulacorthum solani; Hyperomyzus lampsanae; Macrosiphum euphorbiae; Myzus ornatus; Nasonovia ribisnigri; Uroleucon cichorii

Lathyrus: Acyrthosiphon pisum; *Aphis craccivora, fabae, pseudocomosa*; Macrosiphum euphorbiae; Megoura viciae; Megourella purpureae

Lavatera arborea: *Aphis umbrella*; Myzus ornatus, persicae

Leersia oryzoides: *Rhopalosiophum nymphaeae*; *Sipha glyceriae* (see Stroyan, 1977)

Lemna: *Rhopalosiphum nymphaeae*

Leontodon: *Aphis fabae, nasturtii, striata*; Aulacorthum palustre, solani; Hyperomyzus lactucae; Nasonovia ribisnigri; Uroleucon cichorii, leontodontis

Lepidium: *Aphis fabae, frangulae, nasturtii*; Aulacorthum solani; Brevicoryne brassicae; Lipaphis erysimi; Macrosiphum euphorbiae; Myzus persicae

Leucanthemum vulgare: *Aphis fabae, solanella, vandergooti*; Aulacorthum solani; Brachycaudus cardui, helichrysi; Coloradoa tanacetina; Macrosiphoniella artemisiae, millefolii, oblonga, subterranea, tanacetaria; Metopeurum fuscoviride; Myzus ascalonicus; Uroleucon sonchi

Leymus arenarius: *Laingia psammae* (see Stroyan, 1977); Metopolophium dirhodum; *Rhopalosiphum padi*; *Schizaphis rufula*; Sitobion avenae

Ligustrum vulgare: Myzus ligustri

Lilium martagon: Myzus ascalonicus, persicae

Limonium: Staticobium staticis (see text)

Linaria vulgaris: Brachycaudus helichrysi, linariae; Macrosiphum euphorbiae; Myzus ascalonicus, persicae

Listera ovata: *Aphis fabae*; Aulacorthum solani

Lithospermum: *Aphis craccivora, fabae*; Brachycaudus cardui; Uroleucon jaceae

Lolium: Diuraphis frequens; Metopolophium dirhodum, festucae; Myzus persicae; *Rhopalosiphum padi*; Siphini spp. (see Stroyan, 1977); Sitobion avenae, fragariae

Lonicera periclymenum: Hyadaphis passerinii; Macrosiphum euphorbiae; Rhopalomyzus lonicerae

Lonicera xylosteum: Hyadaphis foeniculi; Rhopalomyzus lonicerae

Lotus: Acyrthosiphon caraganae ssp. occidentale, loti, pisum; *Aphis craccivora, fabae, loti, lotiradicis*; Megoura viciae; Nearctaphis bakeri

Luzula: *Melanaphis luzulella*; Sitobion avenae

Lychnis flos-cuculi: Myzus ascalonicus

Lychnis viscaria: Brachycaudus lychnidis

Lycium barbarum: Myzus persicae

Lycopus europaeus: Ovatus insitus

Lysimachia: *Aphis fabae, frangulae*; Aulacorthum solani; Macrosiphum euphorbiae; Myzus persicae

Lythrum salicaria: *Aphis fabae, grossulariae*; Myzus lythri

Mahonia aquifolia: Liosomaphis berberidis; Macrosiphum euphorbiae

Malus sylvestris: *Aphis fabae, pomi*; Dysaphis anthrisci, brancoi, chaerophylli, devecta, plantaginea; Macrosiphum euphorbiae, rosae; Myzus persicae; Ovatus insitus; *Rhopalosiphum insertum*

Malva: Acyrthosiphon malvae; *Aphis fabae, umbrella*; Aulacorthum solani; Brachycaudus helichrysi, malvae; Macrosiphum euphorbiae; Myzus persicae

Marrubium vulgare: *Aphis balloticola*; Aulacorthum solani; Cryptomyzus ballotae

Matricaria: *Aphis fabae, nasturtii, solanella, vandergooti*; Aulacorthum solani; Brachycaudus cardui, helichrysi, lateralis; Macrosiphoniella abrotani, tapuskae; Macrosiphum euphorbiae; Myzus ornatus, persicae

Meconopsis cambrica: *Aphis fabae*; Myzus ornatus

Medicago: Acyrthosiphon loti, pisum; *Aphis coronillae* (ssp. *arenaria*), *craccivora, fabae*; Brachycaudus helichrysi; Macrosiphum euphorbiae; Myzus ornatus, persicae; Nearctaphis bakeri; *Therioaphis* spp. (subfamily Calaphidinae; see Stroyan, 1977)

Melampyrum: Brachycaudus persicae; Macrosiphum melampyri

Melilotus: Acyrthosiphon pisum; *Aphis craccivora, fabae*; Macrosiphum euphorbiae; Nearctaphis bakeri; *Therioaphis* spp. (subfamily Calaphidinae; see Stroyan, 1977)

Mentha: *Aphis fabae, oregani*; Aulacorthum solani; Eucarazzia elegans; Myzus ornatus; Ovatus crataegarius, mentharius

Menyanthes trifoliata: *Aphis triglochinis*; *Rhopalosiphum nymphaeae*

Mercurialis annua: *Aphis fabae, nasturtii*; Aulacorthum solani; Myzus persicae

Mertensia maritima: Brachycaudus helichrysi

Meum athamanticum: Cavariella aegopodii

Milium effusum: Metopolophium dirhodum; *Rhopalosiphum padi*

Mnium: Muscaphis escherichi, musci; Pseudacaudella rubida

Moehringia trinervia: *Aphis sambuci*; Brachycolus stellariae; Macrosiphum stellariae; Myzus certus

Molinia caerulea: *Hyalopterus pruni*; Metopolophium dirhodum; Sitobion avenae, fragariae

Mycelis muralis: Uroleucon murale

Myosotis arvensis: *Aphis fabae*; Aulacorthum solani; Brachycaudus cardui, helichrysi, jacobi; Macrosiphum euphorbiae; Myzus ascalonicus, ornatus, persicae

Myosotis caespitosa: Brachycaudus helichrysi

Myositis scorpioides: *Aphis fabae, nasturtii, triglochinis*; Aulacorthum solani; Brachycaudus helichrysi; Macrosiphum euphorbiae, gei; Myzus myosotidis, ornatus, persicae

Myosotis sylvaticus: Brachycaudus helichrysi, jacobi; Myzus ornatus, persicae; Neomyzus circumflexus

Myosoton aquaticum: *Aphis nasturtii*; Aulacorthum solani

Myrica gale: Macrosiphum euphorbiae

Myriophyllum spicatum: *Rhopalosiphum nymphaeae*

Myrrhis odorata: *Aphis fabae*; Aulacorthum solani; Cavariella aegopodii, archangelicae, konoi; Dysaphis crataegi; Macrosiphum gei; Myzus ornatus

Najas flexilis: *Rhopalosiphum nymphaeae*

Nardus stricta: Metopolophium dirhodum, festucae ssp. cerealium

Narthecium ossifragum: No aphids recorded

Nepeta cataria: *Aphis fabae, frangulae, nasturtii*; Aulacorthum solani; Eucarazzia elegans; Myzus ornatus; Ovatus crataegarius

Nuphar lutea: Macrosiphum euphorbiae; *Rhopalosiphum nymphaeae*

Nymphaea alba: *Rhopalosiphum nymphaeae*

Nymphoides peltata: *Rhopalosiphum nymphaeae*

Oenanthe: Anuraphis subterranea; Aulacorthum solani; Cavariella aegopodii, theobaldi; Hyadaphis passerinii; Macrosiphum euphorbiae; Myzus persicae

Oenothera: *Aphis nasturtii*; Aulacorthum solani; Macrosiphum euphorbiae; Myzus ornatus, persicae

Onobrychis viciifolia: Acyrthosiphon pisum; *Aphis craccivora, pseudocomosa*; *Therioaphis trifolii* (subfamily Calaphidinae; see Stroyan, 1977)

Ononis: Acyrthosiphon ononis, pisum; *Aphis craccivora*; Brachycaudus helichrysi; Macrosiphum euphorbiae; *Therioaphis* spp. (subfamily Calaphidinae; see Stroyan, 1977)

Onopordon acanthium: *Aphis fabae, solanella*; Brachycaudus cardui, helichrysi; Capitophorus elaeagni; Myzus persicae; Uroleucon aeneum

Ophrys: *Aphis fabae*

Origanum vulgare: *Aphis fabae, nasturtii, origani*; Aulacorthum solani; Myzus ornatus, persicae; Ovatus crataegarius

Ornithopos perpusillus: Acyrthosiphon pisum; *Aphis craccivora*

Orobanche hederae: Macrosiphum euphorbiae

Osmunda regalis: Aulacorthum solani; Neomyzus circumflexus

Oxalis: *Aphis nasturtii*; Aulacorthum solani; Brachycaudus helichrysi; Macrosiphum euphorbiae; Myzus cymbalariae, persicae; Rhopalosiphoninus latysiphon, staphyleae

Papaver: *Aphis fabae,nasturtii, solanella*; Brachycaudus helichrysi; Macrosiphum euphorbiae; Myzus ascalonicus, persicae

Parentucellia viscosa: Brachycaudus helichrysi; Myzus persicae

Parietaria diffusa: *Aphis parietariae*

Paris quadfrolia: No aphids recorded

Parnassia palustris: No aphids recorded

Pastinaca sativa: Anuraphis subterranea; *Aphis brohmeri, fabae, gossypii*; Cavariella aegopodii, konoi, pastinacae, theobaldi; Dysaphis bonomii, crataegi ssp. kunzei, lauberti; Hyadaphis foeniculi, passerinii; Macrosiphum euphorbiae; Myzus ornatus, persicae

Pedicularis palustris: *Aphis nasturtii*; Ericaphis wakibae

Pentaglottis sempervirens: Ovatomyzus boraginacearum

Persicaria: *Aphis fabae, nasturii, solanella*; Aspidaphis adjuvans; Aulacorthum solani; Brachycaudus amygdalinus, rumexicolens; Capitophorus hippophaes; Macrosiphum euphorbiae; Myzus persicae

Petasites: Aulacorthum solani; Brachycaudus cardui, helichrysi; Capitophorus similis; Myzus ornatus; Uroleucon tussilaginis

Peucedanum: *Aphis fabae*; Aulacorthum solani; Cavariella aegopodii

Phalaris arundinacea: Metopolophium dirhodum; Myzus persicae; Rhopalomyzus lonicerae, poae; *Rhopalosiphum insertum, padi*; Siphini spp. (see Stroyan, 1977); Sitobion avenae, fragariae

Phleum: Diuraphis muehlei; Metopolophium dirhodum, tenerum; Rhopalomyzus lonicerae; *Rhopalosiphum padi*; *Sipha* spp. (Stroyan, 1977); Sitobion avenae

Phragmites: *Hyalopterus pruni*; *Melanaphis elizabethi*; *Rhopalosiphum padi*; Sitobion avenae

Picris: *Aphis fabae, nasturtii*; Aulacorthum palustre; Hyperomyzus lactucae, picridis; Myzus ornatus, persicae; Nasonovia ribisnigri; Uroleucon cichorii, picridis, sonchi

Pilosella see *Hieracium*

Pimpinella: Anuraphis catonii; Cavariella aegopodii, theobaldi; Hyadaphis foeniculi; Macrosiphum euphorbiae; Semiaphis pimpinellae

Pinguicula: No aphids recorded

Plantago: *Aphis fabae, longirostrata, nasturtii, plantaginis*; Aulacorthum solani; Brachycaudus helichrysi, lucifugus; Dysaphis aucupariae, maritima, plantaginea; Macrosiphum euphorbiae; Myzus ascalonicus, cymbalariae, ornatus, persicae

Pleurozium schreberi: Muscaphis escherichi; Pseudacaudella rubida

Poa: Cryptaphis poae; *Hyalopteryus pruni*; Jacksonia papillata; *Melanaphis pyraria*; Metopolophium dirhodum, festucae, festucae ssp. cerealium, frisicum; Myzus ascalonicus; Rhopalomyzus poae; *Rhopalosiphum insertum, padi*; *Schizaphis agrostis, palustris*; Siphini spp. (see Stroyan, 1977); Sitobion alopecuri, avenae, fragariae; Utamphorophora humboldti

Pogonatum urnigerum: Myzodium modestum

Pohlia: Muscaphis escherichi; Myzodium modestum

Polemonium caeruleum: Macrosiphum euphorbiae; Rhopalosiphoninus staphyleae

Polygonatum multiflorum: Aulacorthum speyeri; Metopolophium dirhodum; Myzus ascalonicus

Polygonum aviculare: *Aphis avicularis, nasturtii*; Aspidaphis adjuvans; Brachycaudus amygdalinus, rumexicolens; Capitophorus hippophaes; Macrosiphum euphorbiae; Myzus certus, persicae; Sitobion avenae

Polypogon monspelliensis: Metopolophium dirhodum; *Rhopalosiphum padi*; *Sipha maydis* (see Stroyan, 1977); Sitobion avenae, fragariae; Utamphorophora humboldti

Polytrichum: Decorosiphon corynothrix; Muscaphis escherichi, musci; Myzodium modestum; Pseudacaudella rubida

Populus: *Pterocomma populeum, tremulae*

Portulaca oleracea: *Aphis fabae, nasturtii*; Aulacorthum solani; Macrosiphum euphorbiae; Myzus certus, ornatus, persicae

Potamogeton: *Rhopalosiphum nymphaeae*

Potentilla: Acyrthosiphon boreale, malvae, malvae ssp. potha; Anthracosiphon hertae; *Aphis comari, nasturtii, solanella, tormentillae*; Aulacorthum solani; Chaetosiphon fragaefolii, potentillae; Longicaudus trirhodus; Macrosiphum euphorbiae, rosae; Myzaphis rosarum; Myzus ascalonicus, ornatus, persicae; Rhopalosiphoninus latysiphon

Primula: Acyrthosiphon primulae; Aulacorthum solani; Macrosiphum euphorbiae; Myzus ascalonicus, cymbalariae, ornatus, persicae

Prunella vulgaris: *Aphis brunellae, nasturtii*; Aulacorthum solani; Macrosiphum euphorbiae; Myzus ornatus, persicae

Prunus avium: *Aphis fabae*; Brachycaudus helichrysi; Myzus cerasi, persicae; *Rhopalosiphum nymphaeae*

Prunus insititia: Brachycaudus helichrysi, persicae; *Hyalopterus pruni*; Phorodon humuli; *Rhopalosiphum nymphaeae*

Prunus padus: *Hyalopterus pruni*; Myzus padellus; *Rhopalosiphum padi*

Prunus spinosa: Brachycaudus hclichrysi, prunifex; *Hyalopterus pruni*; Phorodon humuli; *Rhopalosiphum nymphaeae, padi*

Pseudoscleropodium purum: Muscaphis escherichi, musci; Pseudacaudella rubida

Pteridium aquilinum: Amphorophora ampullata; *Aphis nasturtii*; Idiopterus nephrelepidis; Macrosiphum ptericolens

Ptilium crista-castrensis: Muscaphis escherichi

Puccinellia: Siphini spp. (see Stroyan, 1977)

Pulicaria dysenterica: *Aphis fabae*; Aulacorthum solani; Brachycaudus helichrysi; Myzus ornatus, persicae; Ovatus inulae

Pulmonaria officinalis: *Aphis fabae, nasturtii*; (Aulacorthum langei); Brachycaudus cardui, helichrysi; Myzus ascalonicus, persicae

Pulsatilla vulgaris: Myzus ascalonicus

Radiola linoides: *Aphis fabae*

Ranunculus acris: *Aphis fabae, nasturtii*; Aulacorthum solani; Dysaphis ranunculi; Macrosiphum euphorbiae; Myzus ascalonicus, ornatus, persicae; Tubaphis ranunculina

Ranunculus bulbosus: *Aphis fabae*; Aulacorthum solani; Dysaphis ranunculi; Myzus ascalonicus, ornatus, persicae; Neomyzus circumflexus; *Rhopalosiphum padi*

Ranunculus flammula: *Aphis nasturtii*; Macrosiphum euphorbiae

Ranunculus fluitans: *Rhopalosiphum nymphaeae*

Ranunculus lingua: *Aphis nasturtii, triglochinis*

Ranunculus repens: *Aphis nasturtii*; Aulacorthum solani; Dysaphis ranunculi; Macrosiphum stellariae; Myzus ascalonicus; Tubaphis ranunculina

Ranunculus sceleratus: *Aphis nasturtii*; Macrosiphum euphorbiae; Myzus ornatus; *Rhopalosiphum nymphaeae*

Ranunuculus trichophyllus: *Rhopalosiphum nymphaeae*

Raphanus raphanistrum: *Aphis fabae, nasturtii*; Brevicoryne brassicae; Lipaphis erysimi; Macrosiphum euphorbiae; Myzus persicae; Neomyzus circumflexus

Rapistrum rugosum: Brevicoryne brassicae; Myzus persicae

Reseda lutea: *Aphis fabae*; Myzus persicae

Reseda luteola: Acyrthosiphon pisum; Cavariella aegopodii; Uroleucon cichorii

Rhamnus cathartica: *Aphis commensalis, frangulae, gossypii, nasturtii*

Rhinanthus minor: Brachycaudus helichrysi; Hyperomyzus rhinanthi

Rhodiola rosea: *Aphis sedi*; Brachycaudus sedi

Rhytidiadelphus: Decorosiphon corynothrix; Muscaphis escherichi

Rorippa: *Aphis fabae, nasturtii, triglochinis*; Lipaphis erysimi; Myzus ascalonicus, ornatus, persicae; Neomyzus circumflexus; *Rhopalosiphum nymphaeae*

Rosa: *Aphis fabae, gossypii, spiraecola*; Chaetosiphon tetrarhodum; Longicaudus trirhodus; Macrosiphum euphorbiae, rosae; *Maculolachnus submacula* (subfamily Lachninae); Metopolophium dirhodum; Myzaphis bucktoni, rosarum; Myzus ornatus, persicae; Rhodobium porosum; Sitobion fragariae

Rubia peregrina: *Aphis fabae*; Macrosiphum euphorbiae

Rubus caesius: Amphorophora rubi; *Aphis ruborum*; Brachycaudus helichrysi

Rubus chamaemorus: Amphorophora rubi; *Aphis frangulae, ruborum*; Macrosiphum euphorbiae

Rubus fruticosus: Amphorophora rubi; *Aphis ruborum*; Macrosiphum funestum, rosae; Sitobion fragariae

Rubus idaeus: Amphorophora idaei; *Aphis idaei, ruborum*; Macrosiphum euphorbiae; Myzus ornatus

Rubus saxatilis: *Aphis ruborum*; Myzus persicae; Sitobion fragariae

Rumex: *Aphis acetosae, etiolata, fabae, nasturtii, rumicis, sambuci, solanella*; Aulacorthum solani; Brachycaudus helichrysi, rumexicolens; Dysaphis radicola; Macrosiphum euphorbiae; Myzus antirrhinii, ascalonicus, cymbalariae, ornatus, persicae; Neomyzus circumflexus

Rumex sanguineus: *Aphis rumicis*

Ruppia maritima: *Rhopalosiphum nymphaeae*

Ruscus aculeatus: No aphids recorded

Sagina procumbens: Myzus ascalonicus, certus, cymbalariae, persicae

Sagittaria sagittifolia: *Aphis fabae, nasturtii*; Macrosiphum euphorbiae; *Rhopalosiphum nymphaeae*

Salix: *Aphis farinosa*; Cavariella aegopodii, aquatica, archangelicae, intermedia, konoi, pastinacae, theobaldi; *Plocamaphis amerinae, flocculosa* ssp. *brachysiphon*; *Pterocomma jacksoni, pilosum, rufipes, salicis*

Salvia verbenacea: *Aphis craccivora*; Brachycaudus helichrysi; Myzus ornatus, persicae

Sambucus nigra: *Aphis sambuci*

Samolus valerandi: *Aphis triglochinis*

Sanguisorba: Acyrthosiphon malvae ssp. poterii; *Aphis sanguisorbae*; Aulacorthum solani; Macrosiphum euphorbiae; Myzus ascalonicus, ornatus, persicae

Sanicula europaea: *Aphis fabae*; Aulacorthum solani; Cavariella aegopodii

Saxifraga: *Aphis sambuci*; Aulacorthum solani; Nasonovia dasyphylli, saxifragae

Scabiosa columbaria: *Aphis confusa*; Macrosiphum rosae, weberi; Ovatomyzus chamaedrys

Scandix pecten-veneris: *Aphis fabae*; Cavariella aegopodii; Myzus persicae; Semiaphis dauci

Schoenus nigricans: *Rhopalosiphum padi*; *Sipha glyceriae* (see Stroyan, 1977)

Scirpus: *Hyalopterus pruni*; Metopolophium dirhodum; *Rhopalosiphum nymphaeae, padi*; Saltusaphidinae spp. (see Stroyan, 1977); *Schizaphis caricis, scirpi*; Siphini spp. (see Stroyan, 1977); Sitobion avenae, fragariae; Vesiculaphis theobaldi

Scleranthus annuus: Myzus persicae

Scrophularia auriculata: Myzus persicae

Scutellaria galericulata: Macrosiphum euphorbiae

Sedum: *Aphis sedi*; Macrosiphum euphorbiae; Nasonovia dasyphylli

Sedum rosea = *Rhodiola rosea*

Selinum carvifolia: *Aphis fabae*; Aulacorthum solani; Cavariella aegopodii; Hyadaphis foeniculi

Senecio: Aphis fabae, jacobaeae, solanella; Aulacorthum solani; Brachycaudus cardui, helichrysi, lateralis; Macrosiphum euphorbiae; Myzus ascalonicus, ornatus, persicae; Neomyzus circumflexus; Uroleucon cichorii

Seriphidium maritimum: Coloradoa heinzei, submissa; Cryptosiphum artemisiae; Macrosiphoniella abrotani, absinthii, pulvera

Serratula tinctoria: Aulacorthum solani; Brachycaudus helichrysi; Uroleucon minor

Setaria: Myzus persicae; *Rhopalosiphum padi*; *Sipha* spp. (see Stroyan, 1977); Sitobion avenae

Sherardia arvensis: *Aphis fabae*; Brachycaudus helichrysi; Myzus ascalonicus, cerasi, persicae

Silaum silaus: *Aphis fabae*; Aulacorthum solani; Cavariella aegopodii; Myzus ascalonicus

Silene dioica: *Aphis fabae, sambuci*; Brachycaudus klugkisti, lychnidis; Myzus ornatus, persicae

Silene noctiflora: *Aphis sambuci*; Brachycaudus klugkisti, lychnidis; Macrosiphum euphorbiae; Myzus certus

Silene uniflora: Acyrthosiphon auctum; Brachycaudus klugkisti, lychnidis, populi; Macrosiphum euphorbiae, penfroense, stellariae; Myzus ornatus, persicae

Silene vulgaris: *Aphis fabae*; Brachycaudus lychnidis, populi; Brachycolus cucubali; Macrosiphum euphorbiae, stellariae; Myzus ascalonicus, certus, persicae

Silybum marianum: *Aphis fabae*; Brachycaudus cardui, helichrysi; Capitophorus elaeagni; Macrosiphum euphorbiae; Uroleucon aeneum

Sinapis: Brevicoryne brassicae; Lipaphis erysimi; Macrosiphum euphorbiae; Myzus persicae; Nasonovia ribisnigri

Sison amomum: *Aphis fabae*

Sisymbrium: *Aphis nasturtii*; Brevicoryne brassicae; Lipaphis erysimi; Myzus ascalonicus, persicae; Nasonovia ribisnigri

Sium latifolium: *Aphis fabae*; Cavariella aegopodii; Macrosiphum euphorbiae

Smyrnium olusatrum: *Aphis fabae*; Cavariella aegopodii; Dysaphis crataegi, lauberti; Hyadaphis foeniculi

Solanum (dulcamara, nigrum): *Aphis fabae, nasturtii, solanella*; Aulacorthum solani; Macrosiphum euphorbiae; Myzus ornatus, persicae; Neomyzus circumflexus

Solidago virgaurea: *Aphis fabae*; Brachycaudus helichrysi; Macrosiphum euphorbiae; Uroleucon solidaginis

Sonchus: Acyrthosiphon lactucae; *Aphis craccivora, fabae, gossypii*; Aulacorthum solani; Brachycaudus cardui, helichrysi; Hyperomyzus lactucae, pallidus; Macrosiphum euphorbiae; Myzus ornatus, persicae; Nasonovia ribinigri; Neomyzus circumflexus; Uroleucon cichorii, picridis, sonchi

Sorbus aucuparia: *Aphis pomi, spiraecola*; Brachycaudus helichrysi; Dysaphis sorbi; Myzus ornatus; Ovatus insitus; *Rhopalosiphum insertum*

Sorbus torminalis: Dysaphis aucupariae

Sparganium erectum: *Rhopalosiphum nymphaeae; Schizaphis scirpi*

Spartina maritima: *Sipha littoralis* (see Stroyan, 1977)

Spergula arvensis: *Aphis nasturtii, sambuci*; Sitobion avenae

Spergularia: *Aphis sambuci*; Macrosiphum euphorbiae; Myzus certus, persicae; Sitobion avenae

Sphagnum: Myzodium modestum

Spirodela polyrrhiza: *Rhopalosiphum nymphaeae*

Stachys arvensis: *Aphis gossypii*; Cryptomyzus ribis

Stachys palustris: Aulacorthum solani; Cryptomyzus ribis; Myzus persicae

Stachys sylvatica: Cryptomyzus korschelti

Stellaria: Acyrthosiphon auctum; *Aphis fabae, nasturtii, sambuci*; Aulacorthum solani; Brachycaudus helichrysi; Brachycolus stellariae; Macrosiphum euphorbiae, stellariae; Myzus ascalonicus, certus, cymbalariae, ornatus, persicae; Neomyzus circumflexus

Suaeda: Clypeoaphis suaedae

Succisa pratensis: Macrosiphum rosae, weberi

Symphytum: *Aphis fabae, symphyti*; Aulacorthum solani; Brachycaudus cardui, helichrysi; Macrosiphum euphorbiae; Myzus ascalonicus, ornatus, persicae; Ovatomyzus boraginacearum

Tanacetum parthenium: *Aphis fabae, gossypii*; Brachycaudus cardui, helichrysi; Macrosiphoniella artemisiae, oblonga, tanacetaria; Nasonovia ribisnigri; Uroleucon tanaceti

Tanacetum vulgare: *Aphis fabae, vandergooti*; Aulacorthum solani; Brachycaudus cardui, helichrysi; Coloradoa tanacetina; Macrosiphoniella millefolii, persequens, tanacetaria; Macrosiphum euphorbiae; Metopeurum fuscoviride; Pleotrichophorus glandulosus; Uroleucon tanaceti

Taraxacum officinale: *Aphis fabae, gossypii, taraxacicola, vandergooti*; Aulacorthum solani; Hyperomyzus lactucae; Macrosiphum euphorbiae; Myzus ascalonicus, cymbalariae, ornatus, persicae; Neomyzus circumflexus; Uroleucon cichorii, taraxaci

Teucrium: *Aphis aliena*; Aulacorthum solani; Ovatomyzus chamaedrys

Thalictrum: *Aphis thalictri*; Aulacorthum solani; Longicaudus trirhodus; Myzus persicae

Thelypteris palustris: Amphorophora ampullata

Thlaspi arvense: Aulacorthum solani; Lipaphis erysimi; Myzus persicae; Neomyzus circumflexus

Thuidium tamariscinum: Pseudacaudella rubida

Thymus: *Aphis serpylli*

Tordylium maximum: *Aphis fabae*

Torilis: *Aphis fabae*; Aulacorthum solani; Cavariella aegopodii; Dysaphis apiifolia, crataegi; Hyadaphis foeniculi; Macrosiphum euphorbiae, gei; Myzus ornatus, persicae

Tortula muralis: Muscaphis musci

Tragopogon pratensis: *Aphis fabae*; Brachycaudus tragopogonis; Macrosiphum euphorbiae; Myzus persicae

Trifolium: Acyrthosiphon pisum; *Aphis coronillae, craccivora, fabae, nasturtii*; Aulacorthum solani; Brachycaudus helichrysi; Macrosiphum euphorbiae; Megoura viciae; Myzus ornatus, persicae; Nearctaphis bakeri; Neomyzus circumflexus; Subacyrthosiphon cryptobium; *Therioaphis* spp. (subfamily Calaphidinae; see Stroyan, 1977)

Triglochin maritimum: *Aphis triglochinis*; *Rhopalosiphum nymphaeae, padi*; Sitobion avenae

Triglochin palustre: *Schizaphis palustris*

Tripleurospermum inodorum: *Aphis fabae, vandergooti*; Aulacorthum solani; Brachycaudus cardui, helichrysi, lateralis; Macrosiphoniella abrotani, millefolii, oblonga, tanacetaria, tapuskae; Macrosiphum euphorbiae; Myzus persicae

Trisetum flavescens: *Rhopalosiphum padi*; *Sipha maydis* (see Stroyan, 1977); Sitobion avenae, fragariae

Trollius europaeus: Aulacorthum solani

Tulipa sylvestris: Dysaphis tulipae; Myzus ascalonicus

Tussilago farfara: Anuraphis farfarae; *Aphis fabae*; Aulacorthum solani; Brachycaudus cardui, helichrysi; Capitophorus similis; Macrosiphum euphorbiae; Myzus ascalonicus, ornatus, persicae; Uroleucon tussilaginis

Typha: Ceruraphis eriophori; *Hyalopterus pruni*; *Rhopalosiphum nymphaeae, padi*; *Schizaphis scirpi*; *Sipha glyceriae* (see Stroyan, 1977); Sitobion avenae, fragariae

Ulex europaeaus: *Aphis fabae, ulicis*

Umbilicus rupestris: *Aphis sedi*

Urtica dioica: *Aphis fabae, urticata*; Macrosiphum euphorbiae; Microlophium carnosum, Microlophium sp. (see text); Myzus ascalonicus, ornatus, persicae; Neomyzus circumflexus; Rhopalosiphoninus latysiphon, staphyleae

Urtica urens: Acyrthosiphon malvae; *Aphis fabae, urticata*; Aulacorthum solani; Microlophium carnosum; Myzus ascalonicus, cymbalariae, persicae

Utricularia vulgaris: *Rhopalosiphum nymphaeae*

Vaccaria hispanica: Brachycaudus lychnidis

Vaccinium: *Aphis vaccinii*; Aulacorthum rufum; Ericaphis latifrons; scammelli, Macrosiphum euphorbiae; Myzus ornatus; Neomyzus circumflexus; Wahlgreniella vaccinii

Valeriana officinalis: *Aphis fabae, gossypii*; Dysaphis brancoi ssp. rogersoni; Macrosiphum centranthi, euphorbiae, rosae

Verbascum: *Aphis fabae, verbasci*; Aulacorthum solani; Brachycaudus helichrysi

Verbena officinalis: *Aphis fabae, gossypii, solanella*; Brachycaudus helichrysi

Veronica: *Aphis frangulae* ssp. *beccabungae, gossyppi, nasturtii, triglochinis*; Aulacorthum solani; Brachycaudus helichrysi; Cryptomyzus galeopsidis; Dysaphis gallica; Macrosiphum euphorbiae; Myzus ascalonicus, cerasi, cerasi ssp. veronicae, ornatus, persicae; Nasonovia ribisnigri; Nearctaphis bakeri

Viburnum: *Aphis fabae, fabae* ssp. *mordvilkoi, lantanae, spiraecola, viburni*; Aulacorthum solani; Ceruraphis eriophori; Myzus ornatus, persicae

Vicia: Acyrthosiphon loti, pisum; *Aphis craccae, craccivora, fabae, nasturtii*; Aulacorthum solani; Macrosiphum euphorbiae; Megoura viciae; Megourella tribulis; Myzus ornatus, persicae

Vinca: Aulacorthum solani; Brachycaudus helichrysi; Macrosiphum euphorbiae; Myzus ornatus, persicae; Neomyzus circumflexus

Viola: *Aphis violae*; Aulacorthum solani; Brachycaudus helichrysi; Myzus ascalonicus, certus, cymbalariae, ornatus, persicae; Neomyzus circumflexus; Rhopalosiphoninus latysiphon, staphyleae

Vulpia: Metopolophium festucae ssp. cerealium, sabihae; Sitobion avenae, fragariae

Checklist of British Macrosiphini

Some of the more polyphagous and cosmopolitan species carry very long lists of synonyms. The synonymy given here is confined to the western palaearctic literature. Full synonymies for all Aphididae are given by Remaudière & Remaudière (1997).

ACAUDINUM Bomer, C., 1930
> *centaureae* (Koch, C.L., 1854) – TYPE-SPECIES (Aphis)
>> *dolychosiphon* (Mordviliko, 1928) (Anuraphis)
>> *scabiosae* Hille Ris Lambers, 1959
>> *scabiosae* (Koch, in litt. 1854, nec Scopoli, 1763; Schrank, 1801) (Aphis)

ACYRTHOSIPHON Mordviliko, 1914
> TLJA Mordviliko, 1914
> MACCHIATIELLA Del Guercio, 1917, non 1909
> MIROTARSUS Börner, 1939
> LACTUCOBIUM Hille Ris Lambers, 1947
> TENUISIPHON Mordvilko in Tarbinski & Plavilshchikov, 1948
> HOTTESINA Börner, 1950
>> *auctum* (Walker, 1849) (Aphis)
>>> *silenicola* Hille Ris Lambers, 1955
>>> *shawi* Stroyan, 1957
>> *auriculae* Martin, 1981
>> *boreale* Hille Ris Lambers, 1952
>> [*caraganae* (Cholodkovsky, 1907) (Siphonophora) (non-British)]
>> *caraganae* subsp. *occidentale* Hille Ris Lambers, 1947
>> *lactucae* (Passerini, 1860) (Siphonophora)
>>> *barri* (Essig, 1949) (Macrosiphum)
>>> *lactucarium* (Borner, C., 1931) (Macrosiphum)
>> *loti* (Theobald, 1912) (Macrosiphum)
>>> *anthyllidis* Börner, 1950
>>> *gracilipes* (Börner, 1950) (Metopolophium)
>> *malvae* (Mosley, 1841) (Aphis)
>>> *erigeroniellus* (Theobald, 1926) (Myzus)
>>> *geranicola* Hille Ris Lambers, 1935
>>> *geranii* (Kaltenbach, 1862) (Aphis)
>>> *pelargonii* (Kaltenbach, 1843) (Aphis)
>>> *sodalis* (Walker, 1848) (Aphis)
>> *malvae* subsp. *agrimoniae* (Börner, 1940) (Aulacorfhum)
>> *malvae* subsp. *poterii* Prior & Stroyan, 1964
>> *malvae* subsp. *potha* (Börner, 1950) (Acyrthosiphon (Metopolophium))
>> *malvae* subsp. *rogersii* (Theobald, 1913) (Macrosiphum)
>> *ononis* (Koch, 1855) (Siphonophora)
>>> *ononis* (Ferrari, 1872) (Siphonophora)
>> *pisum* (Harris, 1776) (Aphis)
>>> *basalis* (Walker, 1848) (Aphis)
>>> *onobrychis* (Boyer de Fonscolombe, 1841) (Aphis)
>>> *onobrychis* subsp. *galegae* Börner, 1952
>>> *pisi* (Kaltenbach, 1843) – TYPE-SPECIES (Aphis) by designation
>>> *pisi* subsp. *turanicum* Mordviliko, 1914

pisi subsp. *ussuriensis* Mordviliko, 1914
promedicaginis (Del Guercio, 1930) (Anuraphis (Macchiatiella))
spartii (Koch, 1855) (Siphonophora)
spartii subsp. *nigricantis* Börner, 1952
trifolii (Del Guercio, 1917) (Macchiatiella)
trifolii (Theobald, 1913) (Macrosiphum)
primulae (Theobald, 1913) (Macrosiphum)

AMPHOROPHORA Buckton, 1876
EUNECTAROSIPHON Del Guercio, 1913
RHOPALOSIPHUM van der Goot, 1913, nec Koch, C.L, 1854, nec Passerini, 1860
ampullata Buckton, 1876 – TYPE-SPECIES
gei (Börner, 1939) (Nectarosiphon)
franzi (Börner, 1942) (Hyperomyzus)
idaei (Börner, 1939) (Nectarosiphon)
rubi (Kaitenbach, 1843) (Aphis)
conjuncta (Walker, 1848) (Aphis)
cynoglossi (Walker, 1848) (Aphis)
digitalisii Theobald, 1928
fragariella (Theobald, 1905) (Siphonophora)
rubi subsp. *zhuravlevi* (Mordvilko, 1919) (Acyrthosiphon (Amphorophora))
tuberculata Brown & Blackman, 1985

ANTHRACOSIPHON Hille Ris Lambers, 1947
hertae Hille Ris Lambers, 1947 – TYPE-SPECIES

ANURAPHIS Del Guercio, 1907
catonii Hille Ris Lambers, 1935
farfarae (Koch, C.L, 1854) (Aphis)
kochi Del Guercio, 1930
kochi (Schouteden, 1903) (Aphis)
pyri (Koch, 1854, nec Boyer de Fonscolombe, 1841) – TYPE-SPECIES (Aphis)
pyriella Theobald, 1929
?*vacillans* (Walker, 1849) (Aphis)
subterranea (Walker, 1852) (Aphis)
heraclei (Koch, 1854) (Aphis)

ASPIDAPHIS Gillette, 1917
adjuvans (Walker, 1848) (Aphis)
polygoni Gillette, 1917 – TYPE-SPECIES by designation
polygoni (Schouteden, 1907) (Sipha)
polygoni (Walker, 1848) (Aphis)
porosiphon Börner, 1950

AULACORTHUM Mordviliko, 1914
NEOMACROSIPHUM van der Goot, 1915
DYSAULACORTHUM Börner, 1939
MELANOSIPHUM Börner, 1944
knautiae Heie, 1960
palustre Hille Ris Lambers. 1947

rufum Hille Ris Lambers, 1947
>   ?*pirolacearum* Szelegiewicz, 1967
solani (Kaltenbach, 1843) - TYPE-SPECIES (Aphis)
>   *antirrhinii* (Theobald, 1926, nec Macchiati, 1883) (Myzus/Siphonophora)
>   *aquilegiae* (Theobald, 1913) (Macrosiphum)
>   *atropae* (Mordviliko, 1895) (Siphonophora)
>   *begoniae* (Schouteden, 1901) (Macrosiphum)
>   *boerneri* (F.P. Müller, 1952) (Dysaulacorthum)
>   *chelidonii* (Theobald, 1913) (Macrosiphum)
>   *convolvuli* (Buckton. 1876, nec Kaltenbach, 1843) (Siphonophora/Aphis)
>   *diplanterae* (Koch, 1855) (Siphonophora)
>   *doronici* Börner, 1950
>   *duffieldii* (Theobald, 1913) (Macrosiphum)
>   *gei* (Theobald, 1919) (Myzus)
>   *glaucii* (Theobald, 1923) (Myzus)
>   *hederae* (Theobald, 1915) (Macrosiphum)
>   *hydrocotylei* (Theobald, 1925) (Myzus)
>   ?*incertum* (Walker, 1849) (Aphis)
>   ?*indecisum* (Walker, 1849) (Aphis)
>   *lamii* (Theobald, 1915) (Macrosiphum)
>   *menthae* (Buckton, 1876) (Siphonophora)
>   *mercurialis* (Theobald, 1919) (Myzus)
>   *neogei* (Theobald, 1926) (Myzus)
>   *pallidum* (Walker, 1848) (Aphis)
>   *pelargonii* auctt. nec (Kaltenbach, 1843)
>   *piceaellum* (Theobald, 1916) (Macrosiphum)
>   *polyanthi* (Theobald, 1926) (Myzus)
>   *prasinum* Börner, 1950
>   *pseudolamii* (Theobald, 1926) (Myzus)
>   *pseudosolani* (Theobald, 1922) (Myzus)
>   *ranunculi* Mordviliko, 1914 (Acyrthosiphon (Metopolophium))
>   *rosaeollae* Theobald, 1915 (Macrosiphum)
>   *veronicae* (Del Guercio, 1900) (Myzus)
>   *veronicellum* (Theobald, 1926) (Myzus)
>   *vincae* (Walker, 1848) (Aphis)
speyeri Börner, 1939

BRACHYCAUDUS van der Goot, 1913
>   NEOACAUDUS Theobald. 1927
>   *helichrysi* (Kaitenbach, 1843) (Aphis)
>   *abrotaniella* (Theobald, 1919) (Anuraphis)
>   *adjecta* (Walker, 1849) (Aphis)
>   *adscita* (Walker, 1848) (Aphis)
>   *apposita* (Walker, 1850) (Aphis)
>   *bartsiae* (Walker, 1849) (Aphis)
>   *bellis* (Buckton, 1879) (Aphis)
>   *bipapillatus* (Theobald, 1923) (Acaudus)
>   *brevisiphon* (Del Guercio, 1930) (Anuraphis)
>   *centauriella* (Theobald, 1921) (Anuraphis)
>   *chrysanthemi* (Walker, 1849) (Aphis)
>   *cinerariae* (Theobald. 1923) (Anuraphis)

   consumpta (Walker, 1849) (Aphis)
   convecta (Walker, 1849) (Aphis)
   conviva (Walker, 1849) (Aphis)
   cyani (Theobald, 1923) (Anuraphis)
   detracta (Walker, 1849) (Aphis)
   ?*diminuta* (Walker, 1850) (Aphis)
   familiaris (Walker. 1848) (Aphis)
   fasciatus (Del Guercio, 1920) (Anuraphis)
   filaginis var. *anthemidis* (Del Guercio, 1930) (Anuraphis)
   flavescens (Del Guercio, 1930) (Anuraphis)
   glaucifolia (Theobald, 1923) (Anuraphis)
   incumbens (Walker, 1849) (Aphis)
   insessa (Walker, 1849) (Aphis)
   insititiae (Koch, 1854) (Aphis)
   insititiella (Del Guercio, 1930) (Anuraphis)
   leontopodii (Schouteden, 1903) (Aphis)
   myosotidis (Koch, 1854) – TYPE-SPECIES by designation (Aphis)
   nociva (Walker, 1849) (Aphis)
   padi auctt. div. nec (Linnaeus, 1758) (Aphis)
   persorbens (Walker, 1849) (Aphis)
   poae (Del Guercio, 1916) (Anuraphis)
   pruni (Del Guercio, 1930) (Anuraphis)
   prunina (Walker, 1848) (Aphis)
   sherardiae (Theobald, 1926) (Anuraphis)
   ?*similis* (Walker, 1848) (Aphis)
   socia (Walker. 1848) (Aphis)
   verbenae Macchiati, 1884 (Aphis)
  spiraeae Borner, C., 1932
Subgenus ACAUDUS van der Goot, 1913
 BRACHYCAUDINA Borner, C., 1950
 BRACHYCAUDUS subgen. SCROPHULAPHIS Andreev, 1982
 NEOBRACHYCAUDUS Narzikulov, 1965
 PRUNAPHIS Shaposhnikov. 1964
  cardui (Linnaeus, 1758) (Aphis)
   asselbergsi Hille Ris Lambers, 1931
   capsellae (Koch, 1854, nec Kaltenbach, 1843) (Aphis)
   cardui subsp. *turanica* (Mordvilko ex Nevsky, 1929 (Anuraphis)
   chamomillae (Koch, 1854) (Aphis)
   chrysanthemi (Koch, 1854, nec Walker, 1849) (Aphis)
   cnici (Schrank, 1801) (Aphis)
   flavicephalus (Del Guercio, 1930) (Anuraphis (Macchiatiella))
   insitus (Walker, 1852, non 1849) (Aphis)
   instabilis (Buckton, 1879) (Aphis)
   latus (Walker, 1850) (Aphis)
   leucanthemi (Scopoli, 1763) (Aphis)
   onopordi (Schrank, 1801) (Aphis)
   opimus (Buckton, 1879) (Aphis)
   ?*pectinata* (Del Guercio, 1930) (Anuraphis (Macchiatiella))
   petherbridgei (Theobald, 1929) (Anuraphis)
   ?*phelipaeae* (Passerini, 1879) (Aphis)

    projacobaeae (Del Guercio, 1930) (Anuraphis (Macchiatiella))

    pruni (Koch, 1854, nec Geoffroy, 1762, nec Scopoli, 1763) (Aphis)

    pruniphila (Del Guercio, 1930) (Anuraphis (Macchiatiella))

    pruniphila var. *cefaliflava* (Del Guercio, 1930) (Anuraphis)

    senecii (Del Guercio, 1930) (Anuraphis (Macchiatiella))

jacobi Stroyan, 1957

klugkisti (Borner, C., 1942) (Acaudus)

lateralis (Walker, 1848)

linariae Stroyan, 1950

lucifugus Muller, F.P., 1955

lychnidis (Linnaeus, 1758) – TYPE-SPECIES of subgenus Acaudus (Aphis)

    lychnidis dioicae (Cederhjelm, 1798) (Aphis)

    melampyri (Del Guercio, 1911) (Anuraphis)

malvae Shaposhnikov, 1964 (Brachycaudus (Prunaphis))

persicae (Passerini, 1860) (Myzus)

    depressa (Del Guercio, 1930) (Anuraphis (Macchiatiella))

    massei (Theobald, 1927) (Anuraphis)

    ?*mimeuri* Remaudière, 1952

    nitidus Hille Ris Lambers, 1935

    oblonga (Del Guercio, 1930) (Anuraphis (Macchiatiella))

    ?*persicaecola* (Boisduval, 1867) (Aphis)

    ?*semisubterraneus* Börner, 1951

populi (Del Guercio, 1911) (Anuraphis)

Subgenus APPELIA Börner, 1930

    prunifex (Theobald, 1926) (Anuraphis)

    schwartzi (Börner, 1931) (Appelia)

        persicae (Boyer de Fonscolombe, 1841; Kaltenbach, 1843; Koch, 1854, nec Sulzer, 1776) (Aphis)

    tragopogonis (Kaltenbach, 1843) – TYPE-SPECIES of subgenus Appelia (Aphis)

Subgenus NEVSKYAPHIS Shaposhnikov, 1950

    bicolor (Nevsky, 1929) – TYPE-SPECIES of subgenus Nevskyaphis (Dentatus)

Subgenus THULEAPHIS Hille Ris Lambers, 1960

    amygdalinus (Schouteden, 1905) (Aphis)

    rumexicolens (Patch, 1917) (Aphis)

    sedi Jacob, 1964

BRACHYCOLUS Buckton, 1879

    cerastii (Kaitenbach, 1846) (Aphis)

    cucubali (Passerini, 1863) (Aphis)

        melanocephalus (Buckton, 1879)

        sileneus (Ferrari, 1872) (Aphis)

    stellariae (Hardy, 1850) – TYPE-SPECIES (Aphis)

BREVICORYNE van der Goot, 1915

    BOZHKOJA Shaposhnikov, 1964

    brassicae (Linnaeus, 1758) – TYPE-SPECIES (Aphis)

        dusmeti (Gomez-Menor, 1950, partim) (Brachycolus)

        florisrapae (Curtis, 1842) (Aphis)

        isatidis (Boyer de Fonscolombe, 1841) (Aphis)

        raphani (Schrank, 1801) (Aphis)

CAPITOPHORUS van der Goot, 1913
    CAPITOPHORINUS Börner, 1931
        carduinus (Walker, 1850) – TYPE-SPECIES (Aphis)
            flaveolus Theobald, 1926, nec (Walker, 1849) (Aphis)
        elaeagni (Del Guercio, 1894) (Myzus)
            carthusianus (Haviland, 1918) (Myzus)
            cynariellus Theobald, 1923
            elaeagni van der Goot, 1913
            viridis (Craveri, 1915) (Aphis)
        gynoxanthus Hille Ris Lambers, 1953 ex subsp. of *horni* Börner, 1931
        hippophaes (Walker, 1852) (Aphis)
            gillettei Theobald, 1926
            hippophaes (Koch, 1854) (Rhopalosiphum)
        inulae (Passerini, 1860) (Phorodon)
        pakansus Hottes & Prison, 1931
            vandergooti Hille Ris Lambers, 1947
        similis van der Goot, 1915

CAVARIELLA Del Guercio, 1911
    CAVARAIELLOPSIS Heinze, 1960
    CORYNOSIPHON Mordviliko, 1914
        aegopodii (Scopoli, 1763) (Aphis)
            capreae auctt. nec (Fabricius, 1775) (Aphis)
            umbellatarum (Koch, 1854), description, not figures (Aphis)
        archangelicae (Scopoli, 1763) (Aphis)
            fusca (Macchiati, 1881) (Toxoptera)
            gigliolii Del Guercio, 1911
        intermedia Hille Ris Lambers, 1969
        konoi Takahashi, 1939
            archangelicae (Oestlund, 1886, nec Scopoli, 1763) (Siphocoryne/Aphis)
        pastinacae (Linnaeus, 1758) – TYPE-SPECIES (Aphis)
            capreae (Fabricius, 1775) (Aphis)
            rumicis (Theobald, 1925) (Rhopalosiphum)
        saxifragae Remaudière, 1959
        theobaldi (Gillette & Bragg, 1918) (Aphis)
            glauciiphaga Theobald, 1923
            umbellatarum Theobald, 1927, nec (Koch, C.L., 1854) (Aphis)
  Subgenus CAVARAIELLIA Heinze, 1960
        aquatica (Gillettte & Bragg, 1916) (Siphocoryne)
        hillerislambersi Ossiannilsson, 1959 – TYPE-SPECIES of subgenus Cavaraiellia

CERURAPHIS Borner, C, 1926
    NEOCERURAPHIS Shaposhnikov, 1956
        eriophori (Walker, 1848) (Aphis)
            eriophori (Haliday ex Buckton, 1877) (Hyalopterus)
            junci (Kaltenbach, 1875) (Aphis)
            lantanaella (Theobald, 1925) (Aphis)
            luzulae (Kaltenbach, 1862) (Aphis)
            viburni (Schrank, 1801, nec Scopoli, 1763) (Aphis)
            viburniana (Franssen, 1928) (Aphis)
            viburnicola (Börner, 1916, nec Gillette, 1909) – TYPE-SPECIES (Aphis)

CHAETOSIPHON Mordviliko, 1914, in Nevsky, 1929
Subgenus PENTATRICHOPUS Börner, 1930
  fragaefolii (Cockerell, 1901) (Myzus)
    fragariae (Theobald, 1912) (Myzus)
  potentillae (Walker, 1850) (Aphis)
  tetrarhodus (Walker, 1849) – TYPE-SPECIES of subgenus Pentatrichopus (Aphis)
    neorosarum (Theobald, 1915) (Myzus)
    rosarum (Koch, 1855) (Siphonophora)

CLYPEOAPHIS Soliman, 1937
  suaedae (Mimeur, 1934) (Longicaudus)
    suaedae Soliman, 1937 (Clypeoaphis) – TYPE SPECIES by designation

COLORADOA Wilson, 1910
  CAPITOPHORAPHIS Blanchard, E.E, 1944
  LIDAJA Börner, 1952
  NEAPHIS Nevsky, 1929
  absinthii (Lichtenstein, 1885) (Rhopalosiphum)
    lydiae Börner, 1932
  achilleae Hille Ris Lambers, 1939
    achilleae Börner, 1940
  angelicae (Del Guercio, 1911) (Siphocoryne)
    absinthiella Ossiannilsson, 1962
  artemisiae (Del Guercio, 1913) (Siphocoryne)
  bournieri Remaudière & Leclant, 1969
  heinzei (Börner, 1952) (Lidaja)
  rufomaculata (Wilson, 1908) – TYPE-SPECIES (Aphis)
  submissa Doncaster, 1961
  tanacetina (Walker, 1850) (Aphis)
    ?tanaceticola (Del Guercio, 1930) (Anuraphis (Macchiatiella))

CORYLOBIUM Mordviliko, 1914
  avellanae (Schrank, 1801) – TYPE-SPECIES (Aphis)
    coryli (Mosley, 1841, nec Goeze, 1778) (Aphis)

CRYPTAPHIS Hille Ris Lambers, 1947
  NEODECOROSIPHON Heinze. 1960
  poae (Hardy, 1850) (Aphis)
    muscicolens (Heinze, 1960) (Neodecorosiphon)
    ?pilosa (Walker, 1849, nec Zetterstedt, 1840) (Aphis)
    setiger Hille Ris Lambers, 1947 – TYPE-SPECIES by designation

CRYPTOMYZUS Oestlund, 1922
  MYZELLA Börner, 1930
  alboapicalis (Theobald, 1916) (Siphocoryne)
    ulmeri (Börner, 1952) (Myzella)
  ballotae Hille Ris Lambers, 1953
  galeopsidis (Kaltenbach, 1843) (Aphis)
    lamii (van der Goot, 1912) (Myzus)
    quaerens (Walker, 1849) (Aphis)
    scrophulariae (Buckton, 1876) (Siphonophora)

whitei (Theobald, 1912) (Myzus)
galeopsidis subsp. *citrinus* Hille Ris Lambers, 1953
galeopsidis subsp. *dickeri* Hille Ris Lambers, 1953
korschelti Börner, 1938
    elaeagni Borner, C., 1950
maudamanti Guldemond, 1990
ribis (Linnaeus, 1758) – TYPE-SPECIES (Aphis)
    ribis (O.F. Müller, 1776) (Aphis)

CRYPTOSIPHUM Buckton, 1879
    artemisiae Buckton, 1879 – TYPE-SPECIES
        artemisiae (Passerini, 1860, nec Boyer de Fonscolombe, 1841) (Aphis)
        gallarum (Kaltenbach, 1856, nec Gmelin, J.F., 1790) (Aphis)

DECOROSIPHON Borner, C., 1939
    corynothrix Börner, 1939 – TYPE-SPECIES

DELPHINIOBIUM Mordviliko, 1914
    junackianum (Karsch, 1887) (Myzus)
        aconiti (van der Goot, 1912) – TYPE-SPECIES by designation (Rhopalosiphum)

DIURAPHIS Aizenberg, 1935
    CAVAHYALOPTERUS Mimeur, 1941
    CUERNAVACA J. McV. Baker , 1934, nec Kirkaldy, 1913
    muehlei (Börner, 1950) (Brachycolus)
Subgenus HOLCAPHIS Hille Ris Lambers, 1939
    agrostidis (Muddathir, 1965) (Holcaphis)
    frequens (Walker, 1848) (Aphis)
        korotnewi (Mordviliko, 1901) (Brachycolus)
    holci (Hille Ris Lambers, 1939) (Holcaphis)
        holci (Hardy, 1850, nomen nudum, in Hille Ris Lambers, 1939) – TYPE-SPECIES of subgenus Holcaphis by designation (Holcaphis)

DYSAPHIS Borner, C, 1931
    DENTATUS van der Goot, 1913, nec Gray, 1847
    SAPPAPHIS: Hille Ris Lambers, 1945, nec Matsumura, 1918
    YEZABURA: Börner, 1930, nec Matsumura, 1917

Subgenus DYSAPHIS sensu stricto
    ANNAJA Börner, C, 1952
    CRATAEGARIA Shaposhnikov, 1964
    UMBELLIFERARIA Shaposhnikov, 1964
    angelicae (Koch, C.L, 1854) – TYPE-SPECIES (Aphis)
    anthrisci Börner, 1950
        communis: Börner, 1932, nec Mordviliko, 1928 (Dentatus)
    apiifolia (Theobald, 1923) (Anuraphis)
        inculta (Börner, 1950, nec Walker, 1849) (Yezabura/Aphis)
        kunzei (Börner, 1950), partim ('Lectotypus', unpublished) (Yezabura)
        lappae (Davidson, J., 1925, nec Koch, C.L., 1854) (Anuraphis/Aphis)
        nudicaulium (Börner, 1950) (Yezabura)
        petroselini (Börner, 1950) (Yezabura)

bonomii (Hille Ris Lambers, 1935) (Yezabura)
[*brancoi* (Börner, 1950) (Yezabura) (non-British)]
brancoi subsp. *rogersoni* (Stroyan, 1955) (Sappaphis)
chaerophylli (Börner, 1940) (Yezabura)
    stroyani Shaposhnikov, 1956
crataegi (Kaltenbach, 1843) (Aphis)
    crataegi subsp. *aegopodii* (Börner, 1950) (Yezabura)
    crataegi subsp. *anthrisci* (Börner, 1950) (Yezabura)
    dauci (Goureau, 1867) (Forda)
    dauci (Theobald, 1927, nec Fabricius, 1775) (Anuraphis/Aphis)
crataegi subsp. *aethusae* (Börner, 1950) (Yezabura)
crataegi subsp. *kunzei* (Börner, 1950) (Yezabura)
crithmi (Buckton, 1886) (Aphis)
devecta (Walker, 1849) (Aphis)
    communis (Mordviliko, 1928) (Dentatus)
    pyri (Buckton. 1879, nec Boyer de Fonscolombe, 1841) (Aphis)
hirsutissima (Börner, 1940) (Yezabura)
lappae (Koch, C.L. 1854) (Aphis)
    mira (Börner, 1952, nec Mordviliko, 1928) (Chomaphis)
    prolappae (Del Guercio, 1930) (Anuraphis (Macchiatiella))
lappae subsp. *cirsii* (Börner, 1950) (Chomaphis)
lauberti (Börner, 1940) Yezabura)
    heraclei (Theobald, 1927, nec Koch, 1854) (Anuraphis/Aphis)
newskyi (Börner, 1940) (Neanuraphis)
    sphondylii (Stroyan, 1952) (Sappaphis)
radicola (Mordviliko, 1897) (Aphis)
    communis Börner, 1950, nec (Mordviliko, 1928) (Dentatus)
    lapathi (Börner & Blunck, 1916) (Aphis)
    leontodoniella (Theobald, 1915) (Aphis)
    radicicola (Schouteden, 1906) (Aphis)
    rumicella (Theobald, 1924), partim (Anuraphis)
ranunculi (Kaitenbach, 1843) (Aphis)
    bulbosi (Börner, 1950) (Yezabura)
    crataegi (van der Goot, 1915, nec Kaltenbach, 1843) (Dentatus/Aphis)
    nigra Theobald, 1916 (Aphis)
    oxyacanthae (Koch, 1854, nec Schrank, 1801) (Aphis)
tulipae (Boyer de Fonscolombe, 1841) (Aphis)
    gladioli (Felt, 1908) (Aphis)
    iridis (Del Guercio, 1900) (Aphis)
    palaestinensis (Hille Ris Lambers, 1948) (Sappaphis)
Subgenus POMAPHIS Börner, 1939
    SAPPAPHIS Börner, 1950, nec Matsumura, 1918
      aucupariae (Buckton, 1879) (Aphis)
        appelii (Börner, 1926) (Anuraphis)
      brevirostris (Börner, 1950) (Myzodes (Myzodium))
      gallica (Hille Ris Lambers, 1955) (Sappaphis)
        linariae (Lichtenstein, 1884) nomen nudum, sensu Börner, 1952 (Aphis)
      maritima (Hille Ris Lambers, 1955) (Sappaphis)
      plantaginea (Passerini, 1860) (Myzus)
        lentiginis (Buckton, 1879) (Aphis)

mali (Ferrari, 1872) (Myzus)
malicola (Mordviliko, 1928) (Dentatus)
malifoliae auctt. nec (Fitch, 1855) (Aphis)
padi (Del Guercio, 1930) (Anuraphis (Macchiatiella))
pyri (Hartig, 1841, nec Boyer de Fonscolombe, 1841) (Aphis)
sorbi (van der Goot, 1915, nec Kaltenbach, 1843) (Dentatus/Aphis)
pyri (Boyer de Fonscolombe, 1841) (Aphis) TYPE SPECIES of subgenus Pomaphis
hirta (Del Guercio, 1930) (Anuraphis (Macchiatiella))
kochi (Theobald, 1916, partim, nec Schouteden, 1903) (Aphis)
malus (Nevsky, 1929) (Dentatus)
oxyacanthae (Del Guercio, 1930) (Anuraphis)
piri (Börner, 1952, nec Matsumura, 1918) (Sappaphis)
reaumuri (Börner, 1952, pp. 317, 461, nec Mordvilko, 1928)
 (Sappaphis/Dentatus)
sorbi (Kaltenbach, 1843) (Aphis)

ELATOBIUM Mordviliko, 1914
NEOMYZAPHIS Theobald, 1926
abietinum (Walker, 1849) – TYPE-SPECIES (Aphis)

ERICAPHIS Börner, 1939
BOREAMYZUS Shaposhnikov, 1964
FIMBRIAPHIS Richards, 1959
PLACOAPHIS Richards, 1961
ericae (Börner, 1933) - TYPE-SPECIES (Myzaphis)
ericae (Kloet & Hincks, 1945. nec Walker, 1852) (Ericaphis/Aphis)
latifrons (Börner, 1942 (Ovatus)
empetri Ossiannilsson, 1954 (Ericaphis)
lagarriguei (Remaudière, 1952) (Myzodium)
scammelli (Mason, 1942) (Myzus)
fimbriata subsp. *pernettyae* Prior, 1971
wakibae (Hottes, 1934) (Dactynotus)

EUCARAZZIA Del Guercio, 1921
elegans (Ferrari, 1872) – TYPE SPECIES (Rhopalosiphum)

HAYHURSTIA Del Guercio, 1917
atriplicis (Linnaeus, 1761) (Aphis)
chenopodii (Schrank, 1801) (Aphis)
deformans Del Guercio, 1917 – TYPE-SPECIES by designation
mercurialis (Balachowsky & Cairaschi, 1941) (Pergandeida)

HYADAPHIS Kirkaldy, 1904
MIRAPHIS Nevsky, 1928
NEOHAYHURSTIA Aizenberg, 1956
SIPHOCORYNE Passerini, 1863, non 1860
foeniculi (Passerini, 1860) (Siphocoryne)
?*apii* Hall, 1932
coniella Theobald, 1925
linicerae (Mosley, 1841, nec Siebold, 1839) (Aphis)

    lonicerae (Boyer de Fonscolombe, 1841, nec Siebold, 1839) (Aphis)
    schranki Hille Ris Lambers, 1931
    xylostei (Schrank, 1801, nec De Geer, 1773) – TYPE-SPECIES by
      designation (Aphis)
passerinii (Del Guercio, 1911) (Siphocoryne)
    lonicerae Börner, 1939

HYALOPTEROIDES Theobald 1916
    HAYHURSTIA Mordviliko, 1921, nec Del Guercio, 1917
    humilis (Walker, 1852) (Aphis)
      dactylidis (Hayhurst, 1909) (Hyalopterus)
      pallidus Theobald, 1916 – TYPE-SPECIES by designation
      ?*slavae* (Mordviliko, 1921) (Brachycolus)

HYDAPHIAS Börner, 1930
    hofmanni Börner, 1950
    mosana Hille Ris Lambers, 1956

HYPEROMYZUS Börner, 1933
    lactucae (Linnaeus, 1758) – TYPE-SPECIES (Aphis)
      erraticus (Koch, 1854) (Rhopalosiphum)
      triticum (Theobald, 1923) (Amphorophora)
    lampsanae (Börner, 1932) (Rhopalosiphoninus)
      lactucae (Passerini, 1874, nec Linnaeus, 1758) (Rhopalosiphum/Aphis)
    pallidus Hille Ris Lambers, 1935
Subgenus HYPEROMYZELLA Hille Ris Lambers, 1949
    rhinanthi (Schouteden, 1903) – TYPE-SPECIES of subgenus Hyperomyzella
      (Nectarosiphon)
      affinis (Börner, 1921) (Rhopalosiphum)
      britteni (Theobald, 1913) (Rhopalosiphum)
      erraticus (Börner, 1952, nec Koch, 1854) (Hyperomyzella/Rhopalosiphum)
      tuberculatus (Theobald, 1929) (Rhopalosiphoninus)
Subgenus NEONASONOVIA Hille Ris Lambers, 1949
    hieracii (Börner, 1939) (Rhopalosiphoninus)
    picridis (Börner & Blunck, 1916) – TYPE-SPECIES of subgenus Neonasonovia
      (Rhopalosiphum)
      hieracioides (Theobald, 1926) (Amphorophora)
      crepidis Heinze, 1961
    thorsteinni Stroyan, 1960

IDIOPTERUS Davis, 1909
    FULLAWAYELLA Del Guercio, 1911
    nephrelepidis Davis, 1909 – TYPE-SPECIES

ILLINOIA Wilson, 1910
    azaleae (Mason, 1925) (Amphorophora)
    goldamaryae (Knowlton, 1938) (Amphorophora)
    morrisoni (Swain, 1918) (Nectarosiphon)
Subgenus MASONAPHIS Hille Ris Lambers, 1939
    lambersi (MacGillivray, 1960) (Masonaphis

IMPATIENTINUM Mordviliko, 1914
    asiaticum Nevsky, 1929
    balsamines (Kaltenbach, 1862) (Aphis)
       fuscum Mordviliko, 1928 – TYPE-SPECIES

JACKSONIA Theobald, 1923
    papillata Theobald, 1923
       morrisoni (Laing, 1928) (Myzus)

LINOSIPHON Börner, 1944
    galiophagum (Wimshurst, 1923) – TYPE-SPECIES (1950) (Macrosiphum)

LIOSOMAPHIS Walker, 1868
    berberidis (Kaitenbach, 1843) – TYPE-SPECIES (Aphis)
    berberidis (Narzikulov, 1957) (Rhopalomyzus)

LIPAMYZODES Heinze, 1960
    matthiolae (Doncaster, 1954) – TYPE-SPECIES (Lipaphis)

LIPAPHIS Mordviliko, 1928
  LIPAPHIDOIDES Borner, C., 1939
    cochleariae Jacob, 1956
    erysimi (Kaltenbach, 1843) – TYPE-SPECIES (Aphis)
       contermina (Walker, 1849) (Aphis)
       ?*sisymbrii* (Del Guercio, 1913) (Rhopalosiphum)
    rossi Börner, 1939
    turritella (Wahlgren, 1938) (Brachycolus)

LONGICAUDUS van der Goot, 1913
  HEMIAPHIS Börner, 1926
    trirhodus (Walker, 1849) – TYPE-SPECIES (Aphis)
       aquilegiae (Koch, 1854) (Hyalopterus)
       dilineatus (Buckton, 1879) (Hyalopterus)
       flavus (Schouteden, 1906) (Hyalopterus)

MACROSIPHONIELLA Del Guercio, 1911
  DIELCYSMURA Mordviliko, 1914
  MEDIOSIPHUM Wojciechowski, 1993
  PYRETHROMYZUS Börner, 1950
    abrotani (Walker, 1852) (Aphis)
    absinthii (Linnaeus, 1758) (Aphis)
       fasciata Del Guercio, 1913
       lineata Del Guercio, 1913
    artemisiae (Boyer de Fonscolombe, 1841) (Aphis)
       inflata (Theobald, 1928) (Neocaudus)
    millefolii (DeGeer, 1773) (Aphis)
    ptarmicae Hille Ris Lambers, 1956
    pulvera (Walker, 1848) (Aphis)
       arnica (Walker, 1848) (Aphis)
       atomaria (Walker, 1849) (Aphis)
       collega (Walker, 1848) (Aphis)

           reducta (Walker, 1848) (Aphis)

       sanborni (Gillette, 1908) (Macrosiphum)

            bedfordi Theobald, 1914

            chrysanthemi Del Guercio, 1913

            chrysanthemi var. *brevicauda* Del Guercio, 1913

       sejuncta (Walker, 1848) (Aphis)

            formicaria (Theobald, 1913) (Macrosiphum)

       subterranea (Koch, 1855) (Siphonophora)

            trimaculata Hille Ris Lambers, 1938

       tanacetaria (Kaltenbach, 1843) (Aphis)

            lilacina (Ferrari, 1872) (Siphonophora)

       tapuskae (Hottes & Frison, 1931) (Macrosiphum)

            cerata (Börner, 1940) (Phalangomyzus)

            chamomillae Hille Ris Lambers, 1947

            gulbenkiani (llharco, 1968) (Uroleucon)

       usquertensis Hille Ris Lambers, 1935

Subgenus ASTEROBIUM Hille Ris Lambers, 1938

       asteris (Walker, 1849) - TYPE-SPECIES of subgenus Asterobium (Aphis)

Subgenus PHALANGOMYZUS Börner, 1939

       oblonga (Mordviliko, 1901) (Siphonophora)

            lineata (van der Goot, 1912) (Macrosiphum)

       persequens (Walker, 1852) (Aphis)

            pseudolineata Hille Ris Lambers, 1931

MACROSIPHUM Passerini, 1860

    NECTAROPHORA Oestlund, 1887

    PASSERINIA Macchiati, 1882

    SIPHONOPHORA Koch, C.L, 1855, nec Fischer, 1823

       albifrons Essig, 1911

       centranthi Theobald, 1915

       cholodkovskyi (Mordvilko, 1909) (Siphonophora)

            corallinum Theobald, 1925

            ?*portschinskyi* (Mordvilko, 1909) (Siphonophora)

            ?*rushkovskii* Mordvilko, 1919

       daphnidis Börner, 1950

            daphnes Ossiannilsson, 1959

       euphorbiae (Thomas, C., 1878) (Siphonophora)

            cyparissiae var. *cucurbitae* Del Guercio, 1913

            koehleri Börner, 1937

       euphorbiellum Theobald, 1917

            amygdaloides Theobald, 1925

       funestum (Macchiati, 1885) (Siphonophora)

            rubi var. *rufum* (Buckton, 1883) (Siphonophora)

            rubifolium Theobald, 1917

            funestum subsp. *shelkovnikovi* Mordviliko, 1919

       gei (Koch, 1855) (Siphonophora)

       hellebori Theobald & Walton, 1923

       melampyri Mordviliko, 1919

       penfroense Stroyan, 1979

       ptericolens Patch, 1919

       rosae (Linnaeus, 1758) – TYPE-SPECIES (Aphis)

dipsaci (Schrank, 1801) (Aphis)
fragariae (Koch, 1855) (Siphonophora)
rosae (Macchiati, 1882) (Passerinia)
rosae subsp. *fragaricola* Hille Ris Lambers, 1939
rosae var. *glaucum* (Buckton, 1876) (Siphonophora)
rosaecola (Passerini, 1871) (Siphonophora)
scabiosae (Scopoli, 1763) (Aphis)
stellariae Theobald, 1913
?incertum Mordviliko, 1919
sileneum Theobald, 1913
tinctum (Walker, 1849) (Aphis)
epilobii Theobald ,1919
epilobiellum Theobald, 1923
weberi Börner, 1933

MEGOURA Buckton, 1876
DREPANIELLA Del Guercio, 1913
viciae Buckton, 1876 – TYPE-SPECIES
kaltenbachi Hille Ris Lambers, 1938
papilionacearum (Lindinger, 1932) (Rhopalosiphum)
viciae (Kaltenbach, 1843, nec Fabricius, 1781) (Aphis)

MEGOURELLA Hille Ris Lambers, 1949
purpurea Hille Ris Lambers, 1949
tribulis (Walker, 1849) – TYPE-SPECIES (Aphis)

METOPEURUM Mordviliko, 1914
PHARALIS auctt. nec Leach, 1826 (invalid: nomen nudum)
fuscoviride Stroyan, 1950
tanaceti (sensu Mordvilko, 1914 nec Linnaeus, 1758) – TYPE-SPECIES
by designation (Aphis)

METOPOLOPHIUM Mordviliko, 1914
GOIDANICHIELLUM Martelli, 1950
albidum Hille Ris Lambers, 1947
dirhodum (Walker, 1848) – TYPE-SPECIES (Aphis)
arundinis (Theobald, 1913) (Macrosiphum)
gracilis (Buckton, 1876) (Myzus)
graminum (Theobald, 1913) (Macrosiphum)
longipennis (Buckton, 1876) (Siphonophora)
fasciatum Stroyan, 1982
festucae (Theobald, 1917) (priority established by Opinion 1353 of I.C.Z.N.) (Myzus)
myrmecophilum (Theobald, 1916) (Macrosiphum)
festucae subsp. *cerealium* Stroyan, 1982
graminearum Börner, C., 1952, nec Mordviliko, 1919
montanum Hille Ris Lambers, 1966, partim (apterous alienicolae)
frisicum Hille Ris Lambers, 1947
sabihae Prior, 1976
tenerum Hille Ris Lambers, 1947

MICROLOPHIUM Mordviliko, 1914
    carnosum (Buckton, 1876) (Siphonophora)
        urticae (Schrank, 1801, nec Linnaeus, 1758) – TYPE-SPECIES (Aphis)
        evansi (Theobald, 1923) (Amphorophora)
        schranki (Theobald, 1927) (Macrosiphum)

MICROSIPHUM Cholodkovsky, 1902
    millefolii Wahlgren, 1914

MUSCAPHIS Börner, 1933
    ASPIDAPHIUM Börner, 1939
    TOXOPTERELLA Hille Ris Lambers, 1960
    TOXOPTERELLA subgen. SORBOBIUM MacGillivray & Bradley, 1961
    cuspidati Stroyan, 1955
    escherichi Börner, 1939
        jeschkei Börner, 1939
    musci Börner, 1933 – TYPE-SPECIES
        stammeri Börner, 1952

MYZAPHIS van der Goot, 1913
    FRANCOA Del Guercio, 1917
    bucktoni Jacob, 1946
        dilineata (Buckton, 1879, partim) (Hyalopterus)
    rosarum (Kaltenbach, 1843) (Aphis) – TYPE-SPECIES
        elegans (Del Guercio, 1917) (Francoa)
        rhodolestes (Wood-Baker, 1943) (Trilobaphis)

MYZODIUM Börner, 1950
    modestum (Hottes, 1926) (Carolinaia)
        rabeleri (Börner, 1950) – TYPE-SPECIES (Myzodes)

MYZOTOXOPTERA Theobald, 1927
    wimshurstae Theobald, 1927 – TYPE-SPECIES

MYZUS Passerini, 1860
    MYZOIDES van der Goot, 1913
    PRUNOMYZUS Hille Ris Lambers & Rogerson, 1946
    SPINASPIDAPHIS Heinze, 1961
    cerasi (Fabricius, 1775) – TYPE-SPECIES (Aphis)
        alectorolophi Heinze, 1961
        aparines (Kaltenbach, 1843, nec Fabricius, 1775) (Aphis)
        asperulae (Walker, 1848) (Aphis)
        cerasi (O.F. Müller, 1776) (Aphis)
        euphrasiae (Walker, 1849) (Aphis)
        galiifolium Theobald, 1919
        molluginis (Koch, 1854) (Aphis)
        pruniavium Börner, 1926
        quasipyrinus Theobald, 1929
    cerasi subsp. *veronicae* (Walker, 1848) (Aphis)

lythri (Schrank, 1801) (Aphis)

 droserae (Heinze, 1961) (Spinaspidaphis)

 mahaleb (Koch, 1854) (Aphis)

 pruni (Ferrari, 1872) (Phorodon)

 pruni mahaleb (Boyer de Fonscolombe, 1841) (Aphis)

ornatus Laing, 1932

padellus Hille Ris Lambers & Rogerson, 1946

varians Davidson, 1912

Subgenus GALIOBIUM Börner, 1933

 langei (Börner, 1933) – TYPE-SPECIES of subgenus Galiobium (Trilobaphis (Galiobium))

Subgenus NECTAROSIPHON Schouteden, 1901

 AMYZUS Hille Ris Lambers, 1946

 IDIOVATUS Börner, C., 1944

 MACROSIPHUM Del Guercio, 1900, nec Passerini, 1860

 MYZODES Mordviliko, 1914

 RHOPALOSIPHUM Passerini, 1860, nec Koch, C.L., 1854

 ajugae Schouteden, 1903

 antirrhinii (Macchiati, 1883) (Siphonophora)

 certus (Walker, 1849) (Aphis)

  auctus subsp. *pseudopersicae* (Börner, 1952) (Myzodes)

  caryophyllacearum Hille Ris Lambers, 1946

  persicae var. *cerastii* Theobald, 1926

 dianthicola Hille Ris Lambers, 1966

 ligustri (Mosley, 1841) (Aphis)

  ligustri (Kaitenbach, 1843) (Aphis)

 myosotidis (Börner, 1950) (Myzodes)

 persicae (Sulzer, 1776) (Aphis)

  betae (Theobald, 1913) (Rhopalosiphum)

  callae (Koch, 1854 in litt. syn. of *dianthi* Schrank) (Rhopalosiphum)

  consors (Walker, 1848) (Aphis)

  convolvuli (Kaltenbach, 1843) - TYPE-SPECIES of subgenus Nectarosiphon (Aphis)

  cymbalariae (Schouteden, 1900) (Aphis)

  cynoglossi (Williams, 1911) (Phorodon)

  dianthi (Schrank, 1801) (Aphis)

  depositus (Walker, 1848) (Aphis)

  derelictus (Walker, 1849) (Aphis)

  egressus (Walker, 1849) (Aphis)

  galeactitis (Macchiati, 1883) (Rhopalosiphum)

  lactucellus (Theobald, 1914) (Rhopalosiphum)

  lophospermum (Theobald, 1914) (Macrosiphum)

  lycopersicellus (Theobald, 1914) (Macrosiphum)

  nasturtii (Koch, 1855) (Siphonophora)

  particeps (Walker, 1848) (Aphis)

  persicae subsp. *dyslycialis* F.P. Müller, 1955

  persicae var. *portulacella* Theobald, 1926

  persicae var. *sanguisorbiella* Theobald, 1926

  persicae var. *tuberoscellae* Theobald, 1922

  persicophila (Rondani in Scheda, Passerini, 1860) (Aphis)

  ?*persolus* (Walker, 1848) (Aphis)

    redundans (Walker, 1849) (Aphis)

    tabaci (Mordvilko, 1914) (Myzodes)

    trilineatus (Del Guercio, 1920) (Rhopalosiphum)

  persicae subsp. *nicotianae* Blackman, 1987

Subgenus SCIAMYZUS Stroyan, 1954

  ascalonicus Doncaster, 1946

  cymbalariae Stroyan, 1954 – TYPE-SPECIES of subgenus Sciamyzus

    cymbalariellus Stroyan, 1967

NASONOVIA Mordviliko. 1914

  SUBMACROSIPHUM Hille Ris Lambers, 1931

    compositellae (Theobald, 1924) (Aphis)

    compositellae subsp. *nigra* (Hille Ris Lambers, 1931) (Submacrosiphum)

      hieracii (Kaitenbach, 1843, partim, nec Schrank, 1801) (Aphis)

    pilosellae (Börner, 1933) (Impatientinum)

    ribisnigri (Mosley, 1841) (Aphis)

      agrostemnium (Theobald, 1913) (Macrosiphum)

      alliariae (Koch, 1855, p.177 nec p.160) (Siphonophora)

      hieracii (Kaltenbach, 1843, partim, nec Schrank, 1801) (Aphis)

      hieracii subsp. *teriolana* (Hille Ris Lambers, 1931) (Submacrosiphum)

      kaltenbachi (Schouteden, 1906) (Macrosiphum)

      polygoni (Buckton, 1876) (Siphonophora)

      pseudohieracii (Theobald, 1912) (Macrosiphum)

      ribicola (Kaltenbach, 1843) - TYPE-SPECIES (Aphis)

      ribis var. *bucktoni* (Del Guercio, 1894) (Myzus)

      ribis var. *trifasciata* (Del Guercio, 1894) (Myzus)

  Subgenus KAKIMIA Hottes & Frison, 1931

    NEOKAKIMIA Doncaster & Stroyan, 1952

    dasyphylli Stroyan, 1957 (Nasonovia (Neokakimia))

    saxifragae (Doncaster & Stroyan, 1952) (Kakimia (Neokakimia))

NEARCTAPHIS Shaposhnikov, 1950

  AMELANCHIERIA Shaposhnikov, 1950

  FITCHIELLA Shaposhnikov, 1950

  MAMONTOVA Shaposhnikov, 1964

  bakeri (Cowen, 1895) – TYPE-SPECIES (Aphis)

NEOMYZUS van der Goot, 1915

  circumflexus (Buckton, 1876) – TYPE-SPECIES (Siphonophora)

    callae (Henrich, 1909) (Siphonophora)

NEOTOXOPTERA Theobald, 1915

  formosana (Takahashi, 1921) (Fullawayella)

OVATOMYZUS Hille Ris Lambers, 1947

  boraginacearum Eastop, 1952

  chamaedrys (Passerini, 1879) (Phorodon)

    calaminthae (Macchiati, 1885) (Phorodon)

    minutus (Börner ex Eggler, 1951) (Ovatus)

    pusillus (Börner, 1950) (Ovatus)

  stachyos Hille Ris Lambers, 1947 – TYPE-SPECIES

OVATUS van der Goot, 1913
  OVATOPHORODON Aizenberg, 1966
      crataegarius (Walker, 1850) (Aphis)
          crataeginus (Walker MS) Theobald, 1926
          melissae (Walker, 1852) (Aphis)
          menthae (Walker, 1852) (Aphis)
          ?*mespiliellus* (Theobald, 1920) (Myzus)
      glechomae Hille Ris Lambers, 1947
      insitus (Walker, 1849) (Aphis)
          mespili van der Goot, 1913 – TYPE-SPECIES by designation
      mentharius (van dcr Got, 1913) (Phorodon)
          menthastri Hille Ris Lambers, 1947
  Subgenus OVATOIDES Börner, 1939
          inulae (Walker, 1849) – TYPE-SPECIES of subgenus Ovatoides (Aphis)

PARAMYZUS Börner, 1933
  NEOTOXOPTERA: Kloet & Hincks, 1945, nec Theobald. 1915
      heraclei Börner, 1933 – TYPE-SPECIES

PENTALONIA Coquerel, 1859
      caladii van der Goot, 1917
          ?*nigronervosa* Coquerel, 1859 – TYPE-SPECIES

PHORODON Passerini, 1860
      humuli (Schrank, 1801) – TYPE-SPECIES (Aphis)
          pruni (Scopoli, 1763; Fabricius, 1775, nec Geoffroy, 1762) (Aphis)
          ?*secunda* (Walker, 1849) (Aphis)

PLEOTRICHOPHORUS Börner, 1930
      chrysanthemi (Theobald, 1920) (Capitophorus)
      duponti Hille Ris Lambers, 1935
      glandulosus (Kaltenbach, 1846) – TYPE-SPECIES (Aphis)
          pilosus (van der Goot, 1912) (Myzus)

PSEUDACAUDELLA Börner, 1950
  (genus described in 1944 but validated in 1950 by designation of type species)
  SCHIZOMYZUS Börner, 1950
      rubida (Börner, 1939) – TYPE-SPECIES (Acaudella)
          lindneri (Börner, 1950) (Schizomyzus)

PSEUDOBREVICORYNE Heinze, 1960
      buhri (Börner, 1952) – TYPE-SPECIES (Brevicoryne)

RHODOBIUM Hille Ris Lambers, 1947
      porosum (Sanderson, 1900) (Myzus)
          rosaefoliae (Theobald, 1915) – TYPE-SPECIES (Macrosiphum)
          viride (van der Goot, 1917) (Aulacorthum)

RHOPALOMYZUS Mordviliko, 1921
      poae (Giltette, 1908) – TYPE-SPECIES (Rhopalosiphum)
          alpigenae (Börner, 1914) (Rhopalosiphum)

Subgenus JUDENKOA Hille Ris Lambers, 1949
> *lonicerae* (Siebold, 1839) – TYPE-SPECIES of subgenus Judenkoa (Aphis)

RHOPALOSIPHONINUS Baker, 1920
> *latysiphon* (Davidson, 1912) – TYPE-SPECIES (Amphorophora)
> *ribesinus* (van der Goot, 1912) (Rhopalosiphum)

Subgenus MYZOSIPHON Hille Ris Lambers, 1946
> ARTHROMYZUS Börner, 1950
>> *staphyleae* (Koch, C.L., 1854) – TYPE-SPECIES of subgenus Myzosiphon
>> (Rhopalosiphum)
>>> *latysiphon* Theobald, 1924, nec (Davidson, 1912) (Amphorophora)
>>> *lupulinus* Theobald, 1926
>>> *theobaldi* (Börner, 1950) (Hyperomyzus)
>>> *waltoni* Theobald & Walton, 1923
>> *staphyleae* subsp. *tulipaellus* (Theobald, 1916) (Rhopalosiphum)
>>> *pseudorumicis* Theobald, 1926

Subgenus PSEUDORHOPALOSIPHONINUS Heinze, 1961
> RHOPALOMYZUS Börner, 1950, nec Mordviliko, 1921
>> *calthae* (Koch, 1854) – TYPE-SPECIES of subgenus Pseudorhopalosiphoninus
>> (Rhopalosiphum)

Subgenus SUBMEGOURA Hille Ris Lambers, 1953
> *heikinheimoi* (Börner, 1952) – TYPE-SPECIES of subgenus Submegoura
> (Myzotoxoptera)
>> *obscuratus* Hille Ris Lambers in Stroyan. 1950, nomen nudum

SEMIAPHIS van der Goot, 1913
> *dauci* (Fabricius, 1775) (Aphis)
>> *carotae* (Koch, 1854) – TYPE-SPECIES by designation (Aphis)
> *pimpinellae* (Kaltenbach, 1843) (Aphis)
>> *escherichi* Börner, 1931

SITOBION Mordviliko, 1914
> ANAMESON Mordviliko, 1914
> APHIDIELLA Theobald, 1923
>> *alopecuri* (Takahashi, 1921) (Macrosiphum)
>> *avenae* (Fabricius, 1775) (Aphis)
>>> *adjutum* (Walker, 1848) (Aphis)
>>> *caianense* (Del Guercio, 1900) (Siphonophora)
>>> *cereale* (Kaltenbach, 1843) (Aphis)
>>> *consuetum* (Walker, 1848) (Aphis)
>>> *gnaphalii* (Walker, 1849) (Aphis)
>>> *granarium* (Kirby, 1798) – TYPE-SPECIES by designation (Aphis)
>>> *secretocauda* (Theobald, 1923) (Aphidiella)
>>> *triglochiniellum* (Theobald, 1928) (Macrosiphoniella)
>> *fragariae* (Walker, 1848) (Aphis)
>>> *avenae* Börner, 1952, nec (Fabricius, 1775) (Aphis)
>>> *avenivorum* (Kirkaldy, 1905) (Macrosiphum)
>>> *dallmani* (Theobald, 1924) (Aphis)
>>> *granarium* (Buckton, 1876, nec Kirby, 1798) (Siphonophora/Aphis)
>>> *laricellum* (Theobald, 1926) (Myzus)
>>> *molluginellum* (Theobald, 1924) (Myzus)

    poae (Macchiati, 1885) (Siphonophora)

    rubiellum (Theobald, 1913) (Macrosiphum)

  luteum (Buckton, 1876) (Siphonophora)

    aurantiacum (Del Guercio, 1913) (Macrosiphoniella)

    polystachyae (Franssen & Tiggelovend, 1935) (Macrosiphum)

Subgenus METOBION Heikinheimo, 1990

    scoticum (Stroyan, 1969) (Macrosiphum (Sitobion))

STAEGERIELLA Hille Ris Lambers, 1947

    necopinata (Börner, 1939) – TYPE-SPECIES (Hydaphias)

      galii (Theobald, 1927, nec Kaltenbach, 1843) (Pergandeida/Aphis)

STATICOBIUM Mordviliko, 1914

    staticis (Theobald, 1923) (Macrosiphoniella)

      limonii (Walker, 1852, nec Contarini, 1847) (Aphis)

SUBACYRTHOSIPHON Hille Ris Lambers, 1947

    cryptobium Hille Ris Lambers, 1947 – TYPE-SPECIES

TRICHOSIPHONAPHIS Takahashi, 1922

    polygonifoliae (Shinji, 1944) (Myzus)

TUBAPHIS Hille Ris Lambers, 1947

  OVATOPSIS Aizenberg, 1954

    ranunculina (Walker, 1852) – TYPE-SPECIES (Aphis)

      ranunculi {Aizenberg, 1954) (Ovatopsis)

      ranunculi (Del Guercio. 1900) (Myzus)

UROLEUCON Mordviliko, 1914

  DACTYNOTUS auctt. nec Rafinesque, 1818 (invalid)

  EURYTHAPHIS Mordviliko, 1914

  MEGALOSIPHUM Mordviliko, 1919

    achilleae (Koch, 1855) (Siphonophora)

    cichorii (Koch, 1855) (Siphonophora)

      phillipsii (Theobald, 1925) (Macrosiphum)

      sisymbrii (Buckton, 1876) (Siphonophora)

    cirsii (Linnaeus, 1758) (Aphis)

      marcatum (Hille Ris Lambers, 1931) (Dactynotus)

      olivatum (Buckton, 1876) (Siphonophora)

      serratulae (Kaltenbach, 1843) (Aphis)

    grossum (Hille Ris Lambers, 1939) (Dactynotus)

      picridicola (Hille Ris Lambers, 1939) (Dactynotus)

    hypochoeridis (Fabricius, 1779) (Aphis)

      hypochoeridis (Hille Ris Lambers, 1939) (Dactynotus)

    jaceicola (Hille Ris Lambers, 1939) (Dactynotus)

    leontodontis (Hille Ris Lambers, 1939) (Dactynotus)

    murale (Buckton, 1876) (Siphonophora)

    obscurum (Koch, C.L., 1855) (Siphonophora)

      picridis (Schrank, 1801, nec Fabricius, 1775) (Aphis)

    picridis (Fabricius, 1775) (Aphis)

    [?*pilosellae* (Börner, 1933) (Dactynotus) (British status uncertain)]

    sonchi (Linnaeus, 1767) - TYPE-SPECIES (Aphis)
        alliariae (Koch, 1855, p. 160, non p. 177) (Siphonophora)
    tanaceti (Linnaeus, 1758) (Aphis)
        tanaceticola (Kaltenbach, 1843) (Aphis)
    tussilaginis (Walker, 1850) (Aphis)
        basale (Börner, 1952, nec Walker, 1848) (Dactynotus/Aphis)
Subgenus LAMBERSIUS Olive, 1965
    erigeronense (Thomas, 1878) – TYPE-SPECIES of subgenus Lambersius
    (Siphonophora)
Subgenus UROMELAN Mordviliko, 1914
    aeneum (Hille Ris Lambers, 1939) (Dactynotus (Uromelan))
    campanulae (Kaltenbach, 1843) (Aphis)
    helenae (Hille Ris Lambers, 1950) (Dactynotus (Uromelan))
    jaceae (Linnaeus, 1758) – TYPE-SPECIES of the subgenus Uromelan (Aphis)
        jaceae subsp. *henrichi* (Börner, 1950) (Dactynotus)
        jaceae subsp. *scabiosae* (Börner, ex Franz, 1949) (Dactynotus)
    minor (Börner, 1940) (Dactynotus)
    nigrocampanulae (Theobald, 1928) (Macrosiphum)
        glomeratae (Börner, 1950) (Dactynotus)
        trachelii (Börner, 1939) (Dactynotus)
    riparium (Stroyan, 1955) (Dactynotus (Uromelan))
    simile (Hille Ris Lambers, 1935) (Dactynotus)
    solidaginis (Fabricius, 1779) (Aphis)
    taraxaci (Kaltenbach, 1843) (Aphis)

UTAMPHOROPHORA Knowlton, 1947
    humboldti (Essig, 1941) (Myzus)

VESICULAPHIS Del Guercio, 1911
  TRILOBAPHIS Theobald, 1922
    theobaldi Takahashi, 1930
        caricis (Theobald, 1922) (Trilobaphis)

WAHLGRENIELLA Hiile Ris Lambers, 1949
    nervata (Gillette, 1908) (Rhopalosiphum)
    nervata subsp. *arbuti* (Davidson, W.M., 1910) – TYPE-SPECIES (Rhopalosiphum)
        henryi (Balachowsky & Cairaschi, 1941) (Amphorophora)
    ossiannilssoni Hille Ris Lambers, 1949
    vaccinii (Theobald, 1924) (Myzus)

Keys to genera of British Macrosiphini

Apterous viviparae

(I am grateful to Paul Brown of the Entomology Department of the Natural History Museum for his help in compiling an early version of this key.)

1. Siphunculi with a subapical zone of polygonal reticulation (Fig. 8), generally comprising more than 10 closed cells (sometimes less in *Impatientinum*, which has an extensive black dorsal shield). Siphunculi tapering, cylindrical or slightly to moderately clavate, but never markedly inflated 2

- Siphunculi without a subapical zone of polygonal reticulation (unless this is on a cylindrical part distal to a balloon-like swelling); sometimes with a few rows of transverse striae at apex that may include some closed cells (less than 10), but then there is no extensive black shield. Siphunculi of various shapes; sometimes markedly clavate 15

2. ANT III never with rhinaria. Siphunculi cylindrical or only very slightly swollen.. *Linosiphon* (p. 249)

- ANT III with 1 or more rhinaria (sometimes very small, and occasionally missing from one antennae, but very rarely from both, and then the siphunculi are distinctly swollen) 3

3. Siphunculi with a swollen region, the maximum width of the swollen part being 1.05 or more times greater than the narrowest width of the part proximal to the swelling (Figs 9a, 10) 4

- Siphunculi cylindrical or tapered, sometimes with the reticulated part somewhat constricted, but without any swollen part exceeding the width proximal to it 5

4. Siphunculi (Fig. 9a) smooth, swollen on distal two-thirds, less than twice length of cauda. Longest hairs on ANT III more than 0.5 times basal diameter of segment. PT 9-12 times longer than base of ANT VI, which is less than 5 times longer than wide. Thoracic spiracles much larger than abdominal spiracles (Fig. 9b) .... ***Delphiniobium*** (p. 190)

- Siphunculi (Fig. 10) imbricated, slightly to distinctly swollen on distal half, more than twice length of cauda. Longest hairs on ANT III less than 0.5 times basal diameter of segment. PT 4-6 times longer than base of ANT VI, which is more than 5 times longer than wide. Thoracic spiracles similar in size to abdominal spiracles .... ***Illinoia*** (p. 244)

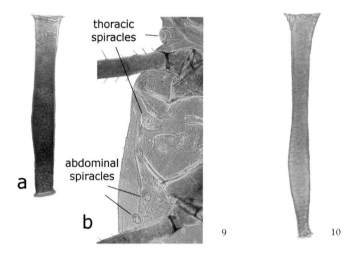

5. Anal plate conical, protruding backward below cauda (Fig. 11). Cauda triangular, less than 1.5 times longer than its basal width (Fig.12). Antennal tubercles very low, so that front of head is straight or shallowly concave in dorsal view .... ***Metopeurum*** (p.287)

- Anal plate normal, not protruding. Cauda more than 1.5 times longer than its basal width. Antennal tubercles variably developed, but if very low then median tubercle is also somewhat developed 6

6. Siphunculi (Fig. 13a) short and thick, 1.1-1.4 times longer than cauda, with basal, unreticulated part ornamented with separate spinules. Spiracles covered by opercula (Fig. 13b) .... ***Staticobium.*** (p.362)

- Siphunculi various, 0.7-3.5 times longer than cauda, with basal, unreticulated part smooth or imbricated. Spiracles not covered by opercula 7

a   b

13

7. Hairs on dorsal body and antennae very short; longest hairs on ANT III less than 0.5 times basal width of segment 8

- Hairs on dorsal body and antennae longer; longest hairs on ANT III more than 0.5 times basal width of segment 10

8. Head with minute spicules, at least ventrally. Antennal tubercles well developed, steep-sided .... ***Aulacorthum*** (part; p.128)

- Head smooth. Antennal tubercles variably developed, usually rather low, with inner faces broadly divergent 9

9. Siphunculi 2.7-3.5 times longer than cauda. R IV+V 1.2-1.5 times longer than HT II. Dorsal cuticle not sclerotic .... ***Macrosiphum*** (part; *ptericolens*; p.2 282)

- Siphunculi 1.1-2.7 times longer than cauda. R IV+V 0.6-1.1 times longer than HT II. Dorsal cuticle usually completely sclerotic, but with varying pigmentation .... ***Sitobion*** (p.356)

10. Dorsum with an extensive black sclerotic shield 11

- Dorsum without an extensive black sclerotic shield; at most with black bars and/or patches 12

11. Head with minute spicules. Dorsal hairs usually slightly knobbed. R IV+V longer than HT II. Cauda black .... ***Anthracosiphon*** (p. 122)

- Head smooth. Dorsal hairs acute. R IV+V shorter than HT II. Cauda pale .... ***Impatientinum*** (p. 247)

12. Dorsal body hairs capitate, arising from tuberculate bases (Fig. 14). R IV+V very long, and with numerous accessory hairs (Fig. 15a). Cauda short, triangular (Fig. 15b) .... *Corylobium* (p. 179)

- Body hairs with acute or blunt apices. R IV+V of various shapes. Cauda tongue- or finger-shaped 13

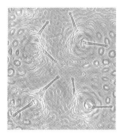

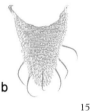

a   b

14

15

13. Siphunculi usually without a flange or lip at apex, and polygonal reticulation usually extending over distal 0.4-0.7 of length; if less, then siphunculi are very long and have distinctly flared (but flangeless) apices (Fig. 16). Crescent-shaped antesiphuncular sclerites are frequently present, but rarely postsiphuncular sclerites. R IV+V often (but not always) more-or-less stiletto-shaped, with concave sides, extended apex and/or long, fine accessory hairs on basal half (Fig. 17). First tarsal segments each with 3 hairs (i.e., a short subapical trichoid sensilla with a longer hair on each side of it) .... *Macrosiphoniella* (p. 256)

- Siphunculi usually with a distinct flange or small lip at apex. Polygonal reticulation extends over distal 0.1-0.4 of length of siphunculus, and apices are never distinctly flared but flangeless. Antesiphuncular sclerites are rarely present and then only in association with postsiphuncular sclerites. R IV+V never stiletto-shaped, and accessory hairs are never long and fine. First tarsal segments each with 3 or 5 (sometimes 4) hairs 14

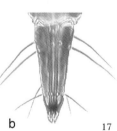

a   b

16

a   b   17

14. First tarsal segments each with 3 hairs. Cauda pale or dusky, never black. Dorsal abdominal hairs never with dark spots (scleroites) at their bases. Siphunculi reticulated over distal 0.08-0.25 of length .... *Macrosiphum* (p. 271)

- First tarsal segments usually with 5 hairs (i.e. a pair of lateral hairs in addition to the 3 apical ones – see Fig. 4); if with only the 3 apical hairs then the cauda is black and/or dorsal abdominal hairs have dark spots (scleroites) at their bases. Siphunculi reticulated over distal 0.15-0.35 of length .... *Uroleucon* (p. 366)

15. Siphunculi very small, about as long as wide and only 0.20-0.33 times length of cauda, with 1-2 rows of polygonal reticulation distally (Fig. 18) .... ***Microsiphum*** (p. 279)

- Siphunculi ranging from merely slightly elevated pores to tubes up to 4.9 times longer than cauda, but if shorter than cauda then they have no discernible polygonal reticulation 16

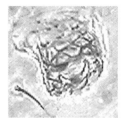

18

16. Antennae arising from well-developed antennal tubercles, which have inner faces that are either divergent, parallel or convergent in dorsal view, or bear rounded or finger-like projections (e.g. Fig.19). Front of head between antennal tubercles either concave, or with a median tubercule that is considerably smaller than the antennal tubercles. Antennae often as long as or longer than body (but sometimes much shorter) 17

- Antennal tubercules absent, or very low, or developed in association with a medial frontal tubercle of similar size. Front of head between antennae therefore flat, convex or sinuate, or with a prominent medial tubercle, or with three similar–sized tubercles (e.g. Fig.20). Antennae not longer than body 58

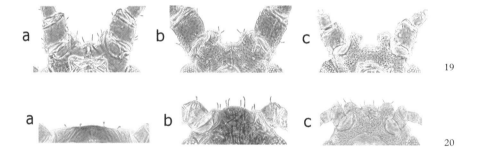

17. Siphunculi only 0.3-0.4 of length of cauda (Fig. 1c) .... ***Hyalopteroides*** (p. 232)

- Siphunculi at least 0.8 of length of cauda 18

18. Hairs on front of head longer than basal diameter of ANT III, with distinctly expanded (capitate, fan-shaped or spatulate) apices, and usually with tuberculate bases 19

- If frontal hairs are longer than basal diameter of ANT III then they have blunt or pointed apices 24

19. ANT III bearing one or more rhinaria (exceptionally without rhinaria on one antenna) 20

- ANT III without rhinaria 23

20. Siphunculi black at base and contrastingly pale distally (Fig. 1r). Dorsal abdominal hairs arising from large sclerotic warts (Fig. 21) .... *Idiopterus* (p. 243)

- Siphunculi entirely pale or only dark at apices. Dorsal abdomen without large sclerotic warts 21

21

21. R IV+V stiletto-shaped, and usually with a pair of long hairs on basal part that are much longer than any of the subapical (primary) hairs (Fig. 22) .... *Pleotrichophorus* (p. 339)

- R IV+V not stiletto-shaped, and with one of the primary pairs of hairs longest 22

22

22. Siphunculi tapering or cylindrical on distal half, with weak imbrication, and a large flange (Fig. 23). ANT PT 4.2-5.9 times longer than base of last antennal segment ....*Cryptaphis* (p. 180)

23

- Siphunculi cylindrical or somewhat swollen on distal half, smooth, and with a small or moderate flange (Fig. 24). ANT PT 6-13 times longer than base of last antennal segment .... *Cryptomyzus* (p. 180)

a   b

24

23. ANT PT usually less than 5 (2.0-5.1) times longer than base of last antennal segment. First tarsal segments with 5 hairs; that is, a pair of lateral hairs in addition to the subapical group of two hairs plus a sense peg (as in Fig. 4) ....*Chaetosiphon* (part; p. 169)

- ANT PT usually more than 5 (4.6-11) times longer than base of last antennal segment. First tarsal segments with 3 hairs (no lateral hairs) .... *Capitophorus* (p. 153)

24. Thoracic spiracles very large and rounded (Fig. 25a), more than twice as large as abdominal spiracles (e.g. Fig. 25b) 25

- Thoracic spiracles not much larger than abdominal spiracles 26

a   b

25

25. Siphunculi cylindrical or tapering .... *Nasonovia* (p. 320)

\- Siphunculi swollen .... *Hyperomyzus* (p. 236)

26. Antennal tubercles with inner faces smooth (e.g. Fig. 19a), and usually divergent (never with processes). Inner sides of ANT I and II usually also smooth. Dorsal cuticle of head smooth or only slightly rough; spicules absent, or small and few in number (although they may be present on ventral side of head) 27

\- Antennal tubercles with inner faces scabrous or at least bearing a few spicules, and usually steep-sided or convergent, or bearing rounded or finger-like processes (e.g. Fig. 19b,c). Inner sides of ANT I and II also scabrous or spiculose. Dorsal as well as ventral cuticle of head usually ornamented with nodules and/or spicules (but sometimes these are limited to the inner sides of the antennal tubercles) 37

27. Siphunculi considerably inflated on distal half, with maximum width of swollen part 2-3 times their narrowest width on basal half. Cauda very short, not longer than its basal width. ANT III often with rhinaria on distal half .... *Eucarrazzia* (p. 229)

\- Siphunculi cylindrical or swollen to a lesser degree. Cauda longer than its basal width. If there are rhinaria on ANT III then they are usually on basal half 28

28. Cauda tongue-shaped, rather short, with a distinct constriction at base (Fig. 26). ANT II bearing a large dorsal tubercle (Fig. 27). Antennal tubercles with inner faces steep-sided, parallel or apically convergent and bearing rather long stiff hairs with slightly thickened apices (e.g. Fig. 28). ANT III thickened basally and without rhinaria. Siphunculi tapering, cylindrical or slightly swollen on distal third, with a small flange or almost flangeless .... *Ovatomyzus* (p. 328)

\- Cauda elongate triangular, tongue- or finger-shaped, without a distinct basal constriction. ANT II without a large tubercle. Antennal tubercles with diverging inner faces, and with hairs often shorter than the basal diameter of ANT III (if longer then ANT III has rhinaria and/or siphunculi are distinctly swollen over about half of length). ANT III with or without rhinaria, and siphunculi tapering, cylindrical or swollen, with a small or large flange 29

26   27   28

29. Siphunculi with distinct swelling 30

\- Siphunculi tapering or cylindrical 34

30. Siphunculi dark, swollen in middle, and often with crescent-shaped sclerites just in front of their bases (Fig. 29). Head and antennal bases also dark 31

- Siphunculi pale, or only dark distally, and swollen on distal part. No antesiphuncular sclerites. Head and antennal bases not dark 32

a

b

29

31. Most dorsal abdominal hairs arising from dark sclerites. Cauda pale or dark with distal hairs thick and blunt (Fig. 30) .... *Megourella* (p. 285)

- Dorsal abdominal hairs not mostly arising from dark sclerites. Cauda black with distal hairs fine-pointed (Fig. 31) .... *Megoura* (p. 284)

30

31

32. Siphunculi 0.12-0.14 times body length and 1.3-1.6 times cauda length. R IV+V 0.6-0.7 times longer than second segment of hind tarsus .... *Rhopalomyzus (Judenkoa)* (p. 345)

- Siphunculi much longer, 0.18-0.35 times body length and 1.9-3.1 times cauda length. R IV+V 0.9-1.5 times longer than second segment of hind tarsus 33

33. ANT III usually with rhinaria. Cauda with 7-21 hairs (10-19 hairs if ANT III is without rhinaria) .... *Amphorophora* (p. 117)

- ANT III without rhinaria, except in alatiform specimens. Cauda with 5 or 6 hairs .... *Wahlgreniella* (p. 391)

34. Hairs on ANT III 25-40 µm, more than 0.5 of basal diameter of segment, and those on anterior abdominal tergites 30-60µm, 0.8-1.5 times that diameter. Siphunculi flared apically and with a large flange (Fig. 32) .... *Microlophium* (p. 296)

- Hairs on ANT III 7-20 µm, not more than 0.5 of basal diameter of segment, and those on anterior abdominal tergites 8-25 µm, 0.3-0.8 of that diameter. Siphunculi not distinctly flared apically and with small to moderate flange (e.g. Fig. 33) 35

32

33

35. ANT III with 8-17 rhinaria over basal 0.5-0.6 of length. R IV+V 0.6-0.7 times longer than HT II, with only 2 accessory hairs. Siphunculi heavily imbricated and with some indistinct subapical reticulation at apex (Fig. 34) .... **Sitobion (Metobion)** (p. 356)

-   ANT III with 0-24 rhinaria, but if with more than 8 then R IV+V is more than 0.7 times longer than HT II, and/or bears more than 2 accessory hairs. Siphunculi moderately imbricated and without any subapical reticulation (e.g. Fig. 33) 36

34

36. Front of head with median tubercle generally well developed (Fig. 35a). ANT III with 0-4 rhinaria. R IV+V with 0-8 accessory hairs .... **Metopolophium** (p. 288)

-   Median tubercle hardly evident (Fig. 35b). ANT III with 1-24 rhinaria. R IV+V with 3-25 accessory hairs ....**Acyrthosiphon** (p. 108)

a ↓

b

35

37. Cauda pentagonal, a little shorter than its basal width (Fig. 36) .... **Myzotoxoptera** (p. 304)

-   Cauda triangular or tongue-shaped, longer than its basal width ... 38

36

38. Siphunculi clavate; i.e. slightly to markedly swollen on distal part, with a narrower section proximal and distal to the swelling 39

-   Siphunculi not clavate; tapering or cylindrical for most of length ... 48

39. Hairs on antennae and legs very long and erect; those on third antennal segment many times longer than basal diameter of segment (Fig. 37). Siphunculi markedly clavate and strongly squamous, even on swollen part (Fig. 38) .... **Decorosiphon** (p. 189)

-   Hairs on antennae and legs short and blunt, or apically expanded; those on third antennal segment much shorter than its basal diameter. Siphunculi smooth or imbricated, not squamous 40

37

38

40. Siphunculi markedly clavate, the maximum width of the swollen part 1.6-4.8 times the minimum width proximal to the swelling (Fig. 39). Dorsum usually with dark markings, e.g. an extensive shield, or sclerites at bases of siphunculi .... **Rhopalosiphoninus** (p. 348)

-   Siphunculi less clavate; maximum width of swollen part less than 1.6 times the minimum proximal width. Dorsum without dark markings 41

a   b

39

41. Dorsal body hairs fan-shaped, or with apices expanded to more than twice their basal diameters 42

- Dorsal body hairs very short, rod-shaped, with blunt, unexpanded apices 43

42. Antennal tubercles small, widely separated. Siphunculi strongly imbricated, with distal half dark and basal half paler (Fig. 40a). Cauda constricted at base, and bearing 4 hairs (Fig. 40b) .... ***Pentalonia*** (p. 337)

- Antennal tubercles well-developed, not widely separated. Siphunculi smooth, uniformly pigmented (Fig. 41a). Cauda not or hardly constricted at base, with 5-7 hairs (Fig. 41b) .... ***Rhopalomyzus*** (p. 345)

43. ANT III with 6-19 rhinaria (Fig. 42). R IV+V 1.4-1.7 times longer than HT II .... ***Paramyzus*** (p. 336)

- ANT III with 0-3 rhinaria. R IV+V 0.7-1.5 times longer than HT II 44

44. Dorsal cuticle of head mostly without spicules or nodules, scabrosity being confined to antennal tubercles. ANT III with 0-3 rhinaria near base. R IV+V 0.7-0.9 times longer than HT II .... ***Utamphorophora*** (p. 389)

- Dorsal cuticle of head with numerous spicules and/or nodules. ANT III without rhinaria. R IV+V 0.8-1.5 times longer than HT II 45

45. Siphunculi 0.84-1.34 times longer than ANT III 46

- Siphunculi 0.45-0.81 times as long as ANT III 47

46. Siphunculi bearing some very small hairs, and slightly swollen only on about subapical 0.2 of length (Fig. 43). Cauda with 8-14 hairs .... ***Trichosiphonaphis*** (*polygonifoliae;* p. 364)

- Siphunculi without hairs; slightly to moderately swollen on distal 0.33-0.5 of length. Cauda with 5-9 hairs ....
.... ***Myzus (Nectarosiphon)*** (p. 305)

47. Head, ANT I and II, coxae and most of femora pale or dusky. ANT PT 2.5-3.5 times longer than base of ANT VI .... *Myzus* (*Sciamyzus*; p. 305)

- Head, ANT I and II, coxae and most of femora dark to blackish. ANT PT 3.2-4.5 times longer than base of ANT VI .... *Neotoxoptera* (*formosana*; p. 327)

48. ANT III almost always with at least one rhinarium (occasional specimens have none, and if there is only one then it is often small and situated on the outside near base of segment). Antennal tubercles with inner faces parallel or slightly divergent, rarely apically convergent, and never with processes 49

- ANT III always without any rhinaria. Antennal tubercles sometimes parallel or slightly divergent but usually with convergent apices and/or bearing processes 52

49. Dorsal abdomen with small dusky/dark antesiphuncular and postsiphuncular sclerites .... *Subacyrthosiphon* (p. 363)

- Dorsal abdomen either without dark sclerites, or with more extensive dorsal markings 50

50. Dorsal abdomen with a large distinctive roughly U-shaped black mark, and thoracic tergites with black cross bands or paired patches (Fig. 44) .... *Neomyzus* (p. 326)

- Dorsum without or with different dark markings 51

44

51. ANT III often with up to 18 (range 0-18, commonly 6-9) rather large rhinaria spaced out along its length (Fig. 45). Median frontal tubercle distinctly developed (Fig. 46). Dorsum never with dark markings. Cauda with four long hairs plus 0-4 (usually 1-2) much shorter, blunt hairs near apex .... *Rhodobium* (p. 344)

- ANT III with 0-6 (usually 1-2) small rhinaria on one side near the base (Fig. 47). Median frontal tubercle not distinctly developed (Fig. 48). Dorsum with or without dark markings. Cauda with 4-8 (usually 7) hairs all of similar length .... *Aulacorthum* (p. 128)

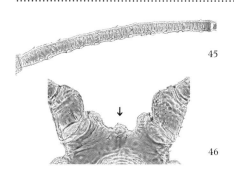

45

46

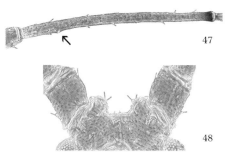

47

48

52. Siphunculi flangeless; very scabrous, tapering from broad base to narrower middle section, then slightly flared at apex (Fig. 49) ....*Jacksonia* (p. 248)

- Siphunculi with a distinct flange 53

49

53. Inner faces of antennal tubercles themselves divergent, but bearing rounded or finger-like processes that project forward, and slightly upward and inward 54

- Inner faces of antennal tubercles without processes 55

54. Processes on inner sides of antennal tubercles finger-like, longer than their basal widths and projecting almost to apex of first antennal segment (Fig. 50). Antennae 0.5-0.85 times length of body .... *Phorodon* (p. 338)

- Processes on inner sides of antennal tubercles rounded, shorter than their basal widths and not projecting beyond half the length of the first antennal segment (Fig. 51). Antennae 0.9-1.5 times length of body .... *Ovatus* (p. 331)

50

51

55. Dorsal cuticle of head mainly smooth, with sparse, small spicules or nodules, any scabrosity on the dorsal surface being confined to inner sides of the slightly divergent, rather low antennal tubercles .... *Dysaphis* (*Pomaphis*, part; p. 194)

- Dorsal cuticle of head rather densely spiculose/nodulose 56

56. Cauda with a basal constriction, and bearing 4 hairs (Fig. 52) .... *Tubaphis* (p. 365)

- Cauda without any basal constriction, tongue-shaped or triangular, and bearing 4-9 hairs (e.g. Fig. 53) 57

52

a

57. Antennae longer than body .... *Ericaphis* (*wakibae*; p. 228)

- Antennae shorter than body .... *Myzus* (**s. str.**; p. 305)

53

b

58. Siphunculi pore-like or mammariform, or tubular, with the aperture not surrounded by a lip or flange 59

- Siphunculi conical or tubular, with the aperture surrounded by an outwardly-projecting transparent lip or flange 71

59. Siphunculi as pores or very short cones or tubes, not more than 0.6 of length of cauda 60

- Siphunculi more than 0.7 of length of cauda 68

60. Siphunculi as very small pores, hardly visible (Fig. 54a). Body globular. Cauda broadly rounded. Antenna only about 0.25 of body length, with PT 0.3-0.7 times length of base of last antennal segment. R IV+V stilletto-shaped (Fig. 54b) .... *Cryptosiphum* (p. 188)

a   b   54

- Siphunculi distinct, even if only as pores. Body oval to elongate oval. Cauda tongue-shaped or triangular. Antenna more than 0.25 of body length, with PT 0.9 or more times longer than base of last antennal segment. R IV+V not stilletto-shaped 61

61. ABD TERG 8 with a broad-based triangular prolongation, almost pointed at apex and wholly or partially covering the cauda (Fig. 55a, b) .... *Aspidaphis* (p. 126)

- ABD TERG 8 without any prolongation, or with only a small medial process that does not extend over cauda 62

a

b   55

62. ANT III bearing 1-8 rhinaria 63

- ANT III without rhinaria 64

63. Rhinaria on ANT III situated on basal half, and none on ANT IV. Siphunculi and cauda much longer than their basal diameters (Fig. 56) .... *Hyalopteroides* (p. 232)

56

- Rhinaria on ANT III situated on distal half, and some rhinaria also usually present on ANT IV. Siphunculi and cauda not longer than their basal diameters (Fig. 57) .... *Pseudobrevicoryne* (p. 343)

57

64. ABD TERG 8 with a medial process that is at least as long as its basal width and at least 0.25 of length of cauda (Fig. 58) .... *Diuraphis* (**s.str.**; p. 190)

- ABD TERG 8 without a medial process, or with a small process that is shorter than its basal width and less than 0.2 of length of cauda 65

58

65. Cauda long and finger-like, more than twice as long as its basal width ....
.... ***Brachycorynella*** (p. 151)

-   Cauda tongue-shaped or triangular, less than twice as long as its basal width 66

66. ANT PT 1.0-1.5 times length of base of last antennal segment. Siphunculi as thick-rimmed raised pores or shallow cones shorter than their basal widths, situated on ABD TERG 6 (Fig. 59) ....
.... ***Diuraphis*** (***Holcaphis***; p. 190**)**

59

-   ANT PT 2.0-3.0 times length of base of last antennal segment. Siphunculi as short or very short tubes, cylindrical, tapering or slightly swollen and often somewhat asymmetrical, as long as or longer than their basal widths, with thin apical rims, situated on ABD TERG 5, or on the border beteen 5 and 6 67

67. Siphunculi more than 1.5 times longer than their basal widths, often curved with aperture directed inward (Fig. 60). Spiracular pores on abdominal segments I and II close together, the distance between them not more than the basal width of the hind femur
.... ***Semiaphis*** (p. 354)

a   b

60

-   Siphunculi usually less than 1.5 times longer than their basal widths (Fig. 61). Distance between spiracular pores on abdominal segments I and II more than the basal width of the hind femur .... ***Brachycolus*** (part; p. 149)

61

68. BL 3.0-4.5 mm. Body and appendages clothed with long fine hairs. Cauda hardly longer than its basal width and bearing 20-35 hairs .... ***Plocamaphis*** (see Stroyan, 1984)

-   BL 0.5-2.6 mm. Body and appendages with rather sparse short hairs. Cauda distinctly longer than its basal width and bearing 4-22 hairs ... 69

69. Siphunculi somewhat swollen on distal part, thin on basal part (Fig. 62). ABD TERG 8 with a short backward-pointed hair-bearing process above the cauda, which is finger-like, tapering, and bears 6-11 hairs (Fig. 63) ....
.... ***Cavariella*** (***Cavaraiella***; p. 161)

62

-   Siphunculi tapering or cylindrical. ABD TERG 8 without a hair-bearing process. Cauda if finger-like and tapering then with more than 12 hairs 70

63

70. Siphunculi very scabrous, sometimes with aperture subapical; more than twice as long as the short cauda (Fig. 64). Cauda has a swollen basal part and a narrower distal part, and bears only 4 hairs (Fig. 65). ANT III without rhinaria .... **Muscaphis** (p. 298)

- Siphunculi normally imbricated, often curved inwards, with aperture always apical (Fig. 66); not longer than cauda, which is tongue- or finger-shaped and bears more than 12 hairs (Fig. 67). ANT III with 2-9 rhinaria on distal part .... **Hydaphias** (p. 233)

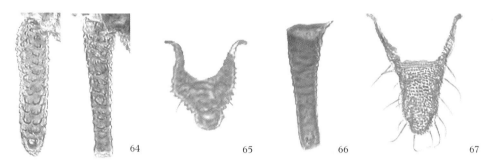

64   65   66   67

71. Cauda extremely short and broad, semicircular or crescent-shaped (often deflected forward or upward in slide preparations, e.g. Fig. 68); length about 0.15-0.6 of basal width 72

- Cauda rounded, helmet-shaped, triangular, tongue- or finger-shaped, with length at least 0.7 of its basal width 73

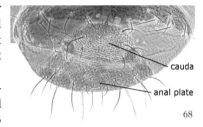

cauda

anal plate

68

72. Siphunculi long, black, imbricated, 0.20-0.25 of length of body (Fig. 69). Cauda with about 15 hairs. ANT PT 4.5-6.9 times longer than base of ANT VI .... **Acaudinum** (p. 107)

- Siphunculi very short, conical, rather dark but not black, and without imbrication (Fig. 70); 0.03-0.04 of body length. Cauda with 4-8 hairs. ANT PT 1.6-2.5 times longer than base of ANT VI ....
.... **Brachycaudus** (**Thuleaphis**; p. 148)

69

73. Body and appendages densely covered in long fine hairs. Cauda broadly rounded, not longer than its basal width and bearing 20-60 hairs ....
.... **Pterocomma** (see Stroyan, 1984)

- Body and appendages more sparsely hairy, if hairs are conspicuous then they are not long and fine. Cauda if short then with less than 20 hairs 74

70

74. Front of head and dorsal body with long, thick, distinctly capitate hairs arising from tuberculate bases (e.g. Fig. 71), those on front of head being 1.5-3 times longer than basal diameter of third antennal segment. Basal antennal segments with some similar, shorter capitate hairs, also with tuberculate bases (Fig. 72) .... *Chaetosiphon* (part; p. 169)

71

- Dorsal body hairs with pointed, blunt, fan-shaped or capitate apices; if capitate then shorter and without or with only small tuberculate bases. Hairs on antennae never thick and capitate 75

72

75. ABD TERG 8 with a distinct backward-pointing finger-like, triangular or quadrangular process above the cauda, usually longer than its basal width (Fig. 73) ... *Cavariella* **s. str.** (p. 161)

- ABD TERG 8 without any distinct backward-pointing process; sometimes with a low, broad-based protuberance less than half as long as its basal width 76

73

76. Dorsum with an extensive dark sclerotic shield that is solid at least over ABD TERG 1-5. Siphunculi dark 77

- Dorsum membranous or sclerotic but if with extensive dark pigmentation then either the siphunculi are pale (sometime dusky at apices), or ABD TERG 1-5 have dark patches or cross-bands that are separated at least partially between segments 80

77. Cauda with a broad basal part and a narrower apical part (Fig. 74). PT tapering almost to a point at apex 78

- Cauda tongue-shaped, triangular, semicircular or helmet-shaped, without a narrower apical part. PT with normal apex 79

a   b   74

78. Very small aphids (body length 0.7-1.0 mm). ANT III constricted at base, to less than half apical width of ANT II (Fig. 75). Cuticle of front of head rough, but without distinct warts, and antennal tubercles not at all developed .... *Pseudacaudella* (p. 342)

75

- Body length 1.2-2.0 mm. Basal diameter of ANT III more than half apical width of ANT II. Head with low rounded antennal tubercles covered in warts (Fig. 76) .... *Myzodium* (p. 303)

76

79. Cauda triangular or tonguc-shaped (Fig. 77a). Siphunculi jet black, darker than dorsal sclerotisation, and very rugose (Fig. 77b). Abdominal spiracular apertures reniform .... *Ceruraphis* (p. 168)

a   b

77

- Cauda semi-circular or helmet-shaped (Fig. 78a). Siphunculi pale or dark, but not darker than dorsal sclerotisation, and smooth or only moderately imbricated (e.g. Fig. 78b). Abdominal spiracular apertures rather large and rounded .... *Brachycaudus* (part; p. 133)

a   b

78

80. Siphunculi very scabrous, strongly wrinkled on the dorsal surface and densely scaly on the ventral surface; curved inwards at base and outwards at apex into a shallow 'S' shape, thick and cylindrical or somewhat swollen for most of length, narrowing or constricted just proximal to the flange (Fig. 79) 81

- Siphunculi straight or if somewhat curved then not very scabrous; smooth or with similar imbrication on dorsal and ventral surfaces 82

a   b   79

81. Front of head with three large, rounded processes (the middle one situated more ventrally), each bearing rather long, almost spine-like hairs (Fig. 80) .... *Vesiculaphis* (p. 390)

- Front of head without large processes and frontal hairs minute .... *Myzus* (*Galiobium*; p. 305)

80

82. Siphunculi ornamented with blunt spinules, arranged in transverse rows (Fig. 81). Cauda short, shorter than basal width or only a little longer 83

- Siphunculi smooth or imbricated, sometimes with small spinules but these are associated with the imbrications. Cauda short or long 84

a

b

81

83. ANT PT 3.0-4.4 times longer than base of last antennal segment. Rostrum very long (Fig. 82), with R IV+V 1.5-2.0 times longer than HT II. Most segments with rather large flat spinal as well as marginal tubercles .... ***Anuraphis*** (p. 123)

82

- ANT PT 1.8-3.0 times longer than base of last antennal segment. R IV+V 1.0-1.1 times longer than HT II (Fig. 83). Spinal tubercles absent, and marginal tubercles are small ... ***Nearctaphis*** (p. 325)

83

84. Cauda rounded or helmet-shaped, a little shorter than its basal width (Fig. 84) 85

- Cauda triangular, tongue-shaped or thumb- or finger-shaped, as long as or longer than its basal width 86

a   b   84

85. Spiracular apertures widely open, circular or almost circular. Head without spinal tubercles, small spinal tubercles occasionally present on ABD TERG 8 only, and marginal tubercles if present are also small. Siphunculi pale and smooth, with an annular incision below the flange (Fig. 85) ....
.... ***Brachycaudus*** (part; p. 133)

85

- Spiracular apertures small oval or bean-shaped. Head with a pair of spinal tubercles, and ABD TERG 8, or 7 and 8, usually with well-developed spinal tubercles. Marginal tubercles usually present on most segments, and often large (see Fig. 6b). Siphunculi pale or dark, imbricated, usually without any distinct annular incision below the flange .... ***Dysaphis*** (part; p. 194)

86. Front of head with a strongly projecting rounded or quadrate median tubercle, bearing 2-4 hairs with slightly capitate apices (Fig. 86). Antennal tubercles much more weakly developed. Dorsum sclerotic, with numerous shallow depressions ....
.... ***Myzaphis*** (p. 301)

- Front of head convex, straight or sinuous; if with a well-developed median tubercle then the antennal tubercles are developed to the same or to a greater extent. Dorsum sclerotic or membranous 87

86

87. Siphunculi 0.8-1.0 times the broad, triangular cauda, which is not longer than its basal width. Dorsal abdomen with some dark markings including transverse bars on ABD TERG 7 and 8 (Fig. 87). Dorsal body hairs pointed and mostly longer than basal diameter or ANT III .... **_Brevicoryne_** (p. 152)

87

- Siphunculi longer or shorter than cauda, but if shorter then cauda is clearly longer than its basal width. Dorsal abdomen with or without dark markings. Dorsal body hairs usually short; if longer than basal diameter of ANT III then they are expanded at apices 88

88. Cuticle of head spinulose both dorsally and ventrally, with spinulosity extending dorsally into region between eyes. Front of head with both median and antennal tubercles well developed and bearing slightly capitate hairs, the longest of which are 0.5-1.4 longer than basal diameter of ANT III (Fig. 88) ....
.... **_Lipamyzodes_** (p. 251)

88

- Cuticle of head smooth or wrinkled, or spinulose ventrally with only a scattering of spinules dorsally, the region between the eyes being almost smooth. If both median and antennal tubercles are well developed then the frontal hairs are less than 0.7 of basal diameter of ANT III, and pointed or blunt, not capitate 89

89. Clypeus enlarged, dark and bulbous, protruding beyond front of head (Fig. 89). ANT PT a little shorter than base of last antennal segment .... **_Clypeoaphis_** (p. 172)

89

- Clypeus not enlarged. ANT PT as long as or longer than base of last antennal segment 90

90. Siphunculi smooth and strongly swollen over distal two-thirds of length, with maximum width of swollen part about twice that of narrowest basal part (Fig. 90). ANT PT 1.0-1.3 times longer than base of last antennal segment .... **_Liosomaphis_** (p. 250)

- Siphunculi cylindrical, conical, tapering or not so strongly or extensively swollen. ANT PT 1.0-4.5 times longer than base of last antennal segment 91

90

91. Siphunculi as short truncate cones, only about 0.3 of length of the long finger-like cauda which bears 14-19 hairs (Fig. 91). ANT PT 1.0-1.3 times longer than base of last antennal segment. First tarsal segments each with 6 hairs .... *Longicaudus* (p. 255)

- Siphunculi tapering, cylindrical or swollen, or if short truncate cones then more than 0.4 of length of cauda and cauda bearing 5-7 hairs. ANT PT 1.0-4.5 times longer than base of last antennal segment 92

91

92. ANT PT 1.0-1.6 times longer than base of last antennal segment. Siphunculi long, almost cylindrical (Fig. 92), 1.7-2.3 times longer than the cauda .... *Elatobium* (p. 224)

- ANT PT 1.4-4.5 times longer than base of last antennal segment, but if less than 1.6 times longer then siphunculi are somewhat swollen and shorter than cauda 93

92

93. Siphunculi 0.4-0.8 times longer than cauda 94

- Siphunculi 0.9-3.7 times longer than cauda 97

94. Dorsal body hairs with fan-shaped apices (Fig. 93)..................... .... *Coloradoa* (part; p. 173)

- Dorsal body hairs short, rather inconspicuous 95

93

95. Siphunculi 3-4 times longer than their basal widths, and slightly clavate (Fig. 94) .... *Hayhurstia* (p. 229)

- Siphunculi less than twice as long as their basal widths 96

94

96. Siphunculi truncate, heavily imbricated (Fig. 95). HT I with 2 hairs .... *Staegeriella* (p. 361)

95

- Siphunculi barrel-shaped, lightly imbricated (Fig. 96). HT I with 3 hairs .... *Brachycolus* (*cucubali*; p.151)

96

97. Siphunculi 0.9-1.4 times longer than cauda, which is finger-like, more than 1.6 times its basal width (Fig. 97) ....
. ... *Hyadaphis* (p. 230)

- Siphunculi 1.2-3.7 times longer than cauda, but if 1.2-1.4 times longer than cauda then the cauda is triangular and less than 1.5 times its basal width 98

97

98. Siphunculi 2.5-3.7 times longer than cauda ....
.... *Dysaphis* (*Pomaphis*; part; p. 194)

- Siphunculi 1.2-2.0 times longer than cauda 99

99. Front of head convex, with antennal tubercles not developed (Fig. 98). Triommatidium in ventral position relative to compound eye, so that it does not project as an 'ocular tubercle' at the posterior margin of the eye in dorsal view ....
.... *Coloradoa* (part; p. 173)

98

- Front of head sinuate, with both median and antennal tubercles developed to some extent. Triommatidium projecting as an 'ocular tubercle' at posterior margin of compound eye (see Fig. 6a) 100

100. Siphunculi pale, tapering or cylindrical (Fig. 99). Dorsal abdomen without any dark markings ....
.... *Ericaphis* (part; p.225)

a   b

99

- Siphunculi pale or dark, with slightly swollen distal part (Fig. 100). Dorsal abdomen with at least transverse dark bars on posterior tergites .... *Lipaphis* (p. 252)

a   b

100

Alate viviparae

1. Forewing veins fuscous-bordered, with radius fused to media for most of length so that it either appears to be missing or forms a closed 4-sided cell beneath the pterostigma (Fig. 101 a & b) 2

- Forewing with radius always separate from media, and veins not usually all fuscous-bordered 3

a

b   101

2. Siphunculi tapering/cylindrical, pale distally, black on about basal third (e.g. Fig. 1r). Femora wholly pale .... ***Idiopterus*** (p. 243)

- Siphunculi slightly swollen distally, wholly dark or paler towards base. Femora dark distally .... ***Pentalonia*** (p. 337)

3. Large aphids (BL more than 2.5 mm) with body and appendages clothed in long, fine hairs. Cauda broadly rounded with more than 20 hairs 4

- If BL more than 2.5 mm then body and appendages not clothed in long fine hairs, or cauda not broadly rounded 5

4. Siphunculi with terminal aperture surrounded by a small but distinct flange. Dorsal abdomen often with dark segmental cross-bands ...... ***Pterocomma*** (see Stroyan, 1984)

- Siphunculi without an apical flange. Dorsal abdomen without cross-bands ....
.... ***Plocamaphis*** (see Stroyan, 1984)

5. Siphunculi poriform, tubular, conical, barrel-shaped or mammariform, 0.08 of length of body or shorter, and abdomen is without a dark central dorsal patch 6

- Siphunculi short or long, tubular; cylindrical, tapering or swollen on distal part. If less than 0.09 of length of body then abdomen has a dark central dorsal patch 21

6. ABD TERG 8 with a median tubercle or conical process 7

- ABD TERG 8 without a median tubercle or process 8

7. Antennae 5-segmented, with secondary rhinaria only on ANT III. Siphunculi poriform or finger-like with a small subterminal aperture .... *Aspidaphis* (p. 126)

- Antennae usually 6-segmented, with secondary rhinaria on ANT III and IV. Siphunculi tubular with wide terminal aperture .... *Diuraphis* (**s. str.**; p. 190)

8. Antennae as long as or longer than body, arising from broadly divergent antennal tubercles. Siphunculi cylindrical, not longer than wide, with traces of reticulation. Cauda triangular with 9-30 hairs .... *Microsiphum* (p. 297)

- Antennae shorter than body. Siphunculi without reticulation. Cauda if triangular then with fewer hairs 9

9. Secondary rhinaria on ANT III in a row along one side, or with only 1-2 rhinaria displaced from a single row 10

- Secondary rhinaria on ANT III not in a row, dispersed over segment 17

10. Siphunculi more than half of length of cauda 11

- Siphunculi not more than half of length of cauda 14

11. Siphunculi cylindrical, flangeless, often curved towards midline. Cauda with 12-22 hairs .... *Hydaphias* (*mosana*; (p. 235)

- Siphunculi swollen, and with a flange. Cauda with less than 10 hairs 12

12. Clypeus greatly enlarged, globose, projecting in front of head in dorsal view. ANT PT shorter than base of last antennal segment .... *Clypeoaphis* (p. 172)

- Clypeus not enlarged. ANT PT longer than base of last antennal segment 13

13. Dorsal abdomen with dark cross bars. ANT III with 8-17 rhinaria, IV and V with 0. ANT PT 2.1-3.7 times longer than base of last segment .... *Hayhurstia* (p. 229)

- Dorsal abdomen without dark markings. ANT III with 3-9 rhinaria, IV with 2-5, V with 0-1. ANT PT 1.2-1.6 times longer than base of last segment ....
.... *Coloradoa* (*heinzei*; p. 177)

14. Siphunculi thin, pale, tubular, more than 1.4 times longer than their basal widths. ANT III with 11-20 rhinaria .... **Hyalopteroides** (p. 232)

- Siphunculi dusky or dark and less than 1.4 times longer than their basal widths. ANT III with 1-16 rhinaria 15

15. Siphunculi as short truncated cones. Hairs on ABD TERG 8 only 6-10 m long .... **Brachycorynella** (p. 151)

- Siphunculi either as short, asymmetric tubes, or mammariform, or poriform or barrel-shaped. Hairs on ABD TERG 8 are 13-36 μm long 16

16. ANT PT 1.4-2.1 times longer than base of ANT VI. Longest hairs on ABD TERG 8 are 24-36 μm long, with pointed apices .... **Diuraphis** (**Holcaphis**; p. 190)

- ANT PT 2.4-4.5 times longer than base of ANT VI. Longest hairs on ABD TERG 8 are 13-33 μm long, usually with blunt apices .... **Brachycolus** (p. 149)

17. Cauda crescent-shaped. Siphunculi as small raised pores. ANT PT 1.0-1.5 times longer than base of ANT VI .... **Cryptosiphum** (p. 188)

- Cauda triangular or tongue-shaped. Siphunculi as short tubes. ANT PT more than twice as long as base of ANT VI 18

18. Siphunculi more than half of length of cauda, somewhat swollen, and with a flange ... 19

- Siphunculi less than half of length of cauda, not swollen, without a flange 20

19. Dorsal abdomen with dark spinal transverse bars. Cauda triangular, about as long as its basal width. ANT III with 50-70 rhinaria, IV with 0-1 .... **Brevicoryne** (p. 152)

- Dorsal abdomen without dark spinal transverse bars. Cauda finger-like, longer than basal width. ANT III with 10-19 rhinaria, IV with 0-5 .... **Staegeriella** (p. 361)

20. Dorsal abdomen with dark spinal transverse bars, partly fragmented. Siphunculi only about as long as their basal widths. Cauda triangular, about as long as its basal width .... **Pseudobrevicoryne** (p. 343)

- Dorsal abdomen without any dark spinal markings anterior to siphunculi. Siphunculi longer than their basal widths. Cauda elongate triangular or tongue-shaped, longer than basal width .... **Semiaphis** (p. 354)

21. Siphunculi with a subapical zone of polygonal reticulation, generally comprising more than 10 closed cells (if a little less than 10 then there is a large black dorsal abdominal patch). Siphunculi tapering, cylindrical or slightly to moderately swollen distally, but never very markedly inflated 22

- Siphunculi without a distinct subapical zone of polygonal reticulation (except when they have a balloon-like inflated middle section); sometimes with a few (less than 10) closed polygonal cells or some interconnected striae at apex, but then there is no large black dorsal abdominal patch. Siphunculi of various shapes 37

22. Siphunculi 3.3-5.5 times longer than the short triangular cauda. Abdominal tergites with variably developed spinopleural or pleural markings 23

- Siphunculi less than 3.3 times longer than the triangular, tongue- or finger-shaped cauda. Dorsal abdomen with or without dark dorsal markings 24

23. Siphunculi pale/dusky with only about distal 0.1 reticulated. Cauda only about as long as its basal width. R IV+V with numerous (about 20) accessory hairs ....
.... ***Corylobium*** (p. 179)

- Siphunculi dark with at least distal 0.15 reticulated. Cauda longer than its basal width. R IV+V with only a few (5-8) accessory hairs .... ***Anthracosiphon*** (p. 122)

24. Dorsal abdomen anterior to siphunculi with extensive dark dorsal markings, either as cross bars or fused into a central patch. Siphunculi 1.5-3 times longer than cauda with reticulation limited to subapical part 25

- Dorsal abdomen anterior to siphunculi without dark markings or with small flecks, dots or patches, or if with short cross bars then siphunculi are shorter and reticulated over about half of length 27

25. Dorsal abdomen with narrow cross-bands not fused between tergites ....
.... ***Metopolophium*** (gynoparae of *fasciatum;* p. 294)

- Dorsal abdomen with broad cross-bands fused to form a large central sclerite at least between ABD TERG 4 and 5 26

26. Siphunculi 2-3 times longer than cauda which has a midway constriction ....
.... ***Ericaphis*** (*wakibae;* p. 228)

- Siphunculi 1.5-1.9 times cauda which is without any constriction ....
.... ***Impatientinum*** (p. 247)

27. Hairs on ANT III evident at low magnifications, the longest more than 0.5 times longer than basal articular diameter of segment 28

- Hairs on ANT III inconspicuous, not exceeding 0.5 times the basal articular diameter of segment 34

28. Cauda triangular, about 1.5 times its basal width .... *Metopeurum* (p. 287)

- Cauda finger-shaped or elongate triangular, more than 1.5 times longer than its basal width 29

29. Siphunculi 0.65-1.2 times longer than cauda, with reticulation extending over distal 0.25-0.81 of length .... *Macrosiphoniella* (part; p. 259)

- Siphunculus 1.2-2.8 times longer than cauda, with reticulation extending over distal 0.08-0.60 of length 30

30. ANT III with only 1-6 rhinaria confined to basal half. Spiracular pores covered by raised dark opercula .... *Staticobium* (p. 362)

- ANT III with 8-130 rhinaria usually extending onto distal half. Spiracular pores not covered by opercula 31

31. First tarsal segments usually with 5 hairs (a pair of lateral hairs as well as the 3 apical ones), rarely with 3 hairs but then dorsal hairs all arise from small dark spots (scleroites). Reticulation of siphunculi extends over distal 0.15-0.40 of length (0.21-0.40 in species with 3 hairs on first tarsal segments) .... *Uroleucon* (p. 372)

- First tarsal segments with just the 3 apical hairs. Dorsal hairs not usually arising from dark scleroites (but if they do then the reticulation of siphunculi extends over less than 0.21 or more than 0.50 of length) 32

32. Siphunculi dilated at base and flared (trumpet-shaped) at apex, but with flange reduced or absent, and either with reticulation extending over distal 0.45-0.60 of length, or on about subapical 0.20 (in which case siphunculi are mainly dark with pale bases and cauda is pale) .... *Macrosiphoniella* (*Phalangomyzus*; p. 259)

- Siphunculi cylindrical, tapering or slightly swollen on distal half, with a well-developed flange. Reticulation extending over distal 0.08-0.35 of length. If siphunculi are mainly dark with pale bases and reticulated for about 0.2 of length then cauda is also dark ... 33

33. Cauda dark. Siphunculi mostly dark with pale bases, and usually slightly thickened on distal half. ANT PT 10-13 times longer than base of ANT VI. Thoracic spiracular apertures much larger than abdominal ones .... ***Delphiniobium*** (p. 190)

- Cauda pale, dusky or dark. Siphunculi pale or either wholly or apically dark, tapering or cylindrical (sometimes with reticulated part somewhat constricted). ANT PT less than 8 times longer than base of ANT VI .... ***Macrosiphum*** (p. 274)

34. Siphunculi swollen on distal half, to a diameter at least 1.05 times greater than minimum diameter on basal half .... ***Illinoia*** (p. 244)

- Siphunculi tapering or cylindrical 35

35. Siphunculi darker than cauda and reticulated over distal 0.15-0.45 of length .... ***Sitobion*** (p. 357)

- Siphunculi and cauda similarly pigmented, with siphunculi reticulated over 0.08-0.18 of length 36

36. ANT III with 38-62 secondary rhinaria extending over most of segment .... ***Macrosiphum*** (*ptericolens*; p. 282)

- ANT III with 5-17 rhinaria usually extending onto distal half of segment .... ***Aulacorthum*** (*rufum*; p.131)

- ANT III with 3-6 rhinaria, usually all on basal half .... ***Linosiphon*** (p. 249)

37. ABD TERG 8 with a wart-like median process bearing two hairs .... ***Cavariella*** (p. 162)

- ABD TERG 8 without a median hair-bearing process 38

38. Siphunculi slightly to markedly swollen, with narrower part proximal to swelling 39

- Siphunculi tapering, cylindrical, sometimes appearing slightly swollen proximal to a subapical constriction, but without a narrower more proximal part 71

39. Abdomen with a dark dorsal patch anterior to siphunculi, often containing 'windows', but fused for the most part between ABD TERG 4 and 5 40

- Dorsal abdomen with or without segmental flecks or bars of varying width, sometimes well-developed but not or only partly fused between ABD TERG 4 and 5 56

40. Hairs on antennae very long, more than twice as long as basal diameter of ANT III. Cauda with apical part distinctly narrower .... ***Decorosiphon*** (p. 189)

- Hairs on antennae inconspicuous or at most about equal in length to basal diameter of ANT III. Cauda without distinctly narrower apical part 41

41. Secondary rhinaria only present on ANT III (occasionally with 1-2 on IV) 42

- Secondary rhinaria present on ANT III-IV or III-V 45

42. Siphunculi very strongly swollen on distal part, with maximum width of swollen part much greater than that of widest part of hind femur .... ***Rhopalosiphoninus*** (part; p. 350)

- Siphunculi only slightly to moderately swollen, to a width less than that of widest part of hind femur 43

43. ANT PT 1.5-1.9 times longer than base of last segment. ANT III with 14-32 protruberant rhinaria distributed over entire surface .... ***Myzaphis*** (*rosarum*; p. 303

- Terminal process of antenna more than 2.5 times longer than base of last segment. Antennal segment III with 6-32 rhinaria along one side of segment 44

44. Dorsal abdominal patch almost straight-sided, with only weak indentations. ABD TERG 8 usually with 5-6 rather long hairs. ANT III with 18-32 rhinaria, not in a single row .... ***Lipamyzodes*** (p. 251)

- Dorsal abdominal patch with deep lateral indentations. ABD TERG 8 usually with 2-4 short hairs. ANT III with 6-24 rhinaria mostly forming a single row .... ***Myzus*** (part; p. 309)

45. Siphunculi 5.0-6.5 times longer than cauda, with narrow stem and very markedly inflated distal part. Wing veins all ending in dark triangles (Fig. 102a) ... ***Eucarazzia*** (p. 229)

- Siphunculi less than 4 times longer than cauda, of varying degrees of inflation. Wing veins not ending in dark triangles 46

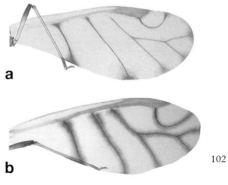

a

b

102

46. All forewing veins strongly and thickly bordered with fuscous. Radial sector (R$_S$) very strongly arched into a semicircle (Fig. 102b) .... *Neotoxoptera* (p. 327)

- Forewing veins not bordered with fuscous or only narrowly and weakly bordered, or only the proximal cubital vein (Cu$_{1b}$) strongly and thickly bordered 47

47. Proximal cubital vein (Cu$_{1b}$) more strongly and thickly bordered with fuscous than other veins. Siphunculi slightly swollen. R IV+V 1.5-1.75 times longer than HT II .... *Paramyzus* (p. 336)

- Forewing veins unbordered or with all veins rather similarly bordered. Siphunculi variously swollen. R IV+V usually less than 1.5 times longer than HT II 48

48. ANT PT 1.5-5.3 times longer than base of last segment; if more than 4.9 times then siphunculi are markedly swollen 49

- ANT PT 4.9-10+ times longer than base of last segment, but if less than 5.4 times then siphunculi are only slightly swollen 53

49. Siphunculi small, thin and flangeless, less than 0.1 of body length. ANT PT 1.5-2.4 times longer than base of last antennal segment ....*Jacksonia* (p. 248)

- Siphunculi more than 0.13 of body length, with an apical flange. ANT PT 2.4-5.3 times longer than base of last antennal segment 50

50. Siphunculi only slightly swollen. Cauda with broad rounded basal part and apical papilla. Terminal process of antenna tapering almost to a point ...... *Myzodium* (p. 303)

- Siphunculi distinctly swollen. Cauda without narrow apical part. Terminal process not tapering to a point 51

51. Siphunculi rather thin, maximum width of swollen part less than 0.15 of length of siphunculus. R IV+V with 7-15 accessory hairs .... *Myzus* (*ascalonicus*; p. 313)

- Siphunculus thick and markedly swollen, maximum width of swollen part more than 0.2 of length of siphunculus. R IV+V with 2-5 accessory hairs 52

52. ANT IV with 4-32 rhinaria, not in a row .... *Rhopalomyzus* (p. 346)

- ANT IV with 0-8 rhinaria, in a row .... *Rhopalosiphoninus* (part; p. 350)

53. Siphunculi thick and markedly swollen, with maximum width of swollen part 0.2 or more of length of siphunculus .... *Hyperomyzus* (part; p.237)

- Siphunculi with maximum width of swollen part less than 0.15 of length of siphunculus 54

54. ABD TERG 7 with a broad dark band .... *Ovatomyzus* (part; p. 329)

- ABD TERG 7 without a broad dark band 55

55. Siphunculi asymmetrically swollen on distal third. Cauda elongate, with pointed apex. Dorsal patch almost parallel-sided, almost without any indentation of lateral margins (Fig. 103a) .... *Capitophorus* (*hippophaes;* p. 158)

- Siphunculi rather symmetrically swollen on distal half. Cauda rounded at apex and usually rather short. Dorsal patch trapezoid, narrowing posteriorly and/or with marked lateral indentations (Fig. 103b) .... *Cryptomyzus* (part; p. 183)

103

56. R IV+V concave-sided. Dorsal abdominal hairs, especially those on abdominal tergites 7 and 8, spatulate, fan- or rod-shaped .... *Coloradoa* (part; p. 175)

- R IV+V straight-or convex-sided. Hairs on abdominal tergites 7 and 8 blunt or pointed 57

57. Siphunculi 0.8-1.55 times as long as cauda (*if* more than 1.45 times longer *then* antennae are shorter than body) 58

- Siphunculi 1.45-3.6 times longer than cauda (if 1.45-1.55 times longer *then* antennae are longer than body) 61

58. Antennal tubercles well developed, divergent, antennae longer than body. Siphunculi and cauda black, siphunculi cigar-shaped. Body length more than 2.6 mm .... *Megoura* (p. 284)

- Antennal tubercles undeveloped or weakly developed, and antennae shorter than body. Siphunculi and cauda pale, dusky or dark, siphunculi slightly to moderately swollen on distal part. Body length less than 2.6 mm 59

59. ANT PT only 1.3-1.5 times longer than base of last segment. ANT III with 10-14 secondary rhinaria, IV with 0-3 and V with 0 .... *Myzaphis* (*bucktoni*; p. 302)

- ANT PT 1.9-4.4 times longer than base of last segment. ANT III with 9-75 secondary rhinaria, IV with 2-28 and V with 0-5 60

60. ANT PT 1.9-2.6 times longer than base of last segment. ANT III with 9-32 secondary rhinaria, IV with 2-10 and V with 0-3. Siphunculi only slightly swollen .... *Lipaphis* (part; p. 253)

- ANT PT 2.7-4.4 times longer than base of last segment. ANT III with 24-75 secondary rhinaria, IV with 5-28 and V with 0-5. Siphunculi very distinctly clavate .... *Hyadaphis* (*foeniculi;* p. 231)

61. ANT PT only about as long as (0.9-1.2 times) base of last antennal segment .... *Liosomaphis* (p. 250)

- ANT PT at least 1.5 times longer than base of last antennal segment 62

62. Siphunculi very scaly, and swollen over most of length, without a distinct stem. ABD TERG 8 dark and forming conical projection over base of cauda. Antennal segment III with 15-33 small but very markedly tuberculate rhinaria distributed over entire surface, IV with 8-16 and V with 4-9. Terminal process 1.5-2.4 times longer than base of last antennal segment .... *Vesiculaphis* (*theobaldi*; p. 390)

- Siphunculi not very scaly, swollen distally, with a distinctly narrower more basal part. ABD TERG 8 not forming a conical projection. Antenna with different rhinariation and terminal process more than 2.5 times base of last segment 63

63. Siphunculi very markedly swollen on distal half, with maximum width of swollen part distinctly greater than that of distal part of hind femur and more than 0.2 of length of siphunculus 64

- Siphunculi not so swollen, maximum width of swollen part not more than that of distal part of hind femur, and less than 0.2 of length of siphunculus 65

64. Femora spinulose. Cauda usually with 5 hairs .... *Rhopalosiphoninus* (part; p. 350)

- Femora not spinulose. Cauda usually with 7 hairs .... *Hyperomyzus* (part; p. 237)

65. R IV+V short and stubby, hardly longer than its basal width. ANT III with 15-29 mostly large rhinaria, the largest having their maximum diameters similar to that of basal diameter of segment. ANT IV with 0-5 much smaller rhinaria ....
.... ***Utamphorophora*** (p. 389)

- R IV+V distinctly longer than its basal width, or if rather short then with rhinaria on ANT III-IV not as above 66

66. Siphunculi uniformly darker than cauda. Dorsal abdomen with mostly separate spinal and pleural sclerites forming longitudinal rows of dark spots. Crescent-shaped antesiphuncular sclerites present. Antennal hairs mostly as long as or longer than basal diameter of ANT III .... ***Megourella*** (p. 285)

- Siphunculi not uniformly darker than cauda; sometimes pale at base and darker towards apices. Dorsal abdomen with or without various sclerotic markings, but not as above. Antennal hairs usually much shorter than basal diameter of ANT III, and never longer
.... 67

67. Siphunculi more than 0.50 mm long. Secondary rhinaria usually only along one side of ANT III 68

- Siphunculi less than 0.45 mm long. Secondary rhinaria usually not restricted to one side of ANT III and often also on IV and V 69

68. Cauda with 7-21 hairs. Forewing vein Cu_{1b} not dark bordered .... ***Amphorophora*** (p. 119)

- Cauda with 4-6 hairs, rarely 7. Forewing vein Cu_{1b} dark bordered ....
.... ***Wahlgreniella*** (p. 392)

69. Dorsal abdomen without dark cross-bands. Siphunculi with very dark apices, swollen over only about distal 0.2-0.3, and usually bearing a few very small hairs ....
.... ***Trichosiphonaphis*** (*polygonifoliae*; p. 365)

- Dorsal abdomen with dark cross-bands. Siphunculi without very dark apices, swollen over distal 0.4-0.7 of length, without hairs 70

70. Hairs on front of head and antennae conspicuous, the longest of them similar in length to basal diameter of ANT III .... ***Cryptomyzus*** (*galeopsidis*, part; p. 185)

- Hairs of front of head and antennae inconspicuous, 0.2-0.4 of length of basal diameter of ANT III .... ***Myzus*** (*cymbalariae*; p. 315)

71. Dorsal hairs long (45-90 μm) with expanded apices, the longest more than twice as long as basal diameter of ANT III .... ***Cryptaphis*** (part; p. 180)

-   Dorsal hairs if with expanded apices then much shorter, the longest less than 1.5 times as long as basal diameter of ANT III 72

72. Abdomen with a dark dorsal patch anterior to siphunculi, often perforated and/or with lateral indentations but fused for the most part at least between ABD TERG 4 and 5 73

-   Dorsal abdomen either without dorsal sclerotisation or with segmental flecks or bars of varying width, sometimes well-developed but not fused, or only fused partially or laterally, between ABD TERG 4 and 5 88

73. Siphunculi less than half of length of the long thin cauda. ANT III about a long as IV and V together and bearing 45-117 rhinaria, IV and V without any .... ***Longicaudus*** (p.255)

-   Siphunculi more than half of length of cauda. ANT III relatively much shorter and if with numerous rhinaria then these are also present on IV and V 74

74. Siphunculi ornamented with close-set transverse rows of minute spicules. Lateral abdominal tubercles evident. Cauda short 75

-   Siphunculi smooth or imbricated, not with close-set rows of minute spicules. Lateral abdominal tubercles present or absent. Cauda long or short 76

75. Spinal tubercles present on most abdominal segments. ANT III with 55-105 rhinaria, IV with 3-39, V with 0-4. Cauda with 9-18 hairs .... ***Anuraphis*** (p. 124)

-   Spinal tubercles absent. ANT III with 18-38 rhinaria, IV with 3-11, V with 0-4. Cauda with 5-7 hairs .... ***Nearctaphis*** (p. 325)

76. Dorsal patch almost square, solid, almost straight-sided with very little lateral indentation (e.g. Fig. 104a). Hairs within patch do not have tuberculate bases. Most of remainder of tergum membranous. R IV+V pointed, with terminal part clearly demarcated. Siphunculi long and thin, 0.19-0.26 times body length .... ***Capitophorus*** (p. 155)

-   Dorsal patch usually irregular in outline with lateral indentations, and tergites anterior and/or posterior to the patch usually with some sclerotisation; if not (*Chaetosiphon fragaefolii*) then the hairs within the patch have tuberculate bases. R IV+V usually blunt with terminal part not clearly demarcated. Siphunculi 0.07-0.25 times body length ... 77

77. Cauda shorter than or as short as its basal width; broadly rounded, helmet-shaped, triangular or shortly tongue-shaped 78

- Cauda longer than its basal width; triangular or tongue or finger-shaped 79

78. Spiracular apertures broadly oval or circular. Siphunculi smooth or rather weakly imbricated, usually with a distinct annular incision below the flange. Head without spinal tubercles, small spinal tubercles occasionally present on ABD TERG VIII only, and marginal tubercles if present are usually small. ANT IV with 0-18 rhinaria (often 0) .... ***Brachycaudus*** (part; p. 137)

- Spiracular apertures kidney-shaped. Siphunculi with normal imbrication, usually without an annular incision below the flange. Head and posterior abdominal tergites usually with well-developed spinal tubercles, and marginal tubercles often large, but sometimes small or absent. ANT IV with 3-70 rhinaria (never 0) ...... ***Dysaphis*** (p. 202)

79. First tarsal segments with 5 hairs (a lateral pair in addition to the 3 subapical hairs). ANT III with 20-59 rhinaria. Spinal hairs often arising from tuberculate bases .... ***Chaetosiphon*** (p. 170)

- First tarsal segments with 2-5 hairs (but if with 5 then ANT III only has 7-10 rhinaria in a row along one side). Spinal hairs never with tuberculate bases 80

80. ANT III with 4-28 rhinaria all or mostly in a single row along one side of segment, and ANT IV 0-11 (often 0) rhinaria 81

- ANT III with 17-58 rhinaria, not in a single row. ANT IV with 0-31 rhinaria 83

81. Antennae longer than body. ANT IV with 0-11 rhinaria .... ***Neomyzus*** (p. 326)

- Antennae shorter than body. ANT IV with 0(-1) rhinaria 82

82. Cauda finger-shaped, usually with a distinct mid-way constriction, and more than 0.1 of body length. Rhinaria on ANT III with fimbriate or striated rims (needs high power) .... ***Ericaphis*** (p. 226)

- Cauda tapering or tongue-shaped, without any evident constriction, and less than 0.1 of body length. Rhinaria on ANT III with naked sclerotic rims .... ***Myzus*** (part; p.309)

83. Thoracic spiracular apertures much larger than abdominal ones. R IV+V 1.5-2.3 times longer than HT II and bearing 11-24 accessory hairs ..... ***Nasonovia (Kakimia***; p. 322**)**

- Thoracic spiracular apertures similar in size to abdominal ones. R IV+V 0.9-1.7 times longer than HT II and bearing 2-12 accessory hairs 84

84. Last segment of rostrum with 8-12 accessory hairs ....
.... ***Acyrthosiphon*** (*primulae*, part; p. 117)

- Last segment of rostrum with 2-4 accessory hairs 85

85. ABD TERG 3-7 with an extensive dark sclerotic shield, almost solid except sometimes for pale lines of intersegmental demarcation, and ornamented with a reticulate pattern of spicules. Siphunculi coarsely imbricated, black, darker than dorsal shield ....
.... ***Ceruraphis*** (p. 168)

- Dorsal abdominal patch centred on ABD TERG 3-4 or 3-5, with or without distinctly separate cross-bands on ABD TERG 7 and 8, and without spiculose ornamentation. Siphunculi weakly to moderately imbricated and not darker than dorsal patch 86

86. Siphunculi thin and cylindrical, thinner than hind tibiae at their respective midlengths. ANT PT 4.9-5.9 times longer than base of last antennal segment ....
.... ***Ovatomyzus*** (*stachyos*; p.331)

- Siphunculi thicker than hind tibiae at their respective midlengths. ANT PT 2.3-4.9 times longer than base of last antennal segment 87

87. Siphunculi 0.17-0.23 of body length. ANT PT 3.4-4.9 times longer than base of ANT VI .... ***Phorodon*** (*humuli*; p. 339)

- Siphunculi 0.11-0.15 of body length. ANT PT 2.3-3.4 times longer than base of ANT VI .... ***Myzus*** (*padellus;* p. 318)

88. Cauda very short, broad and rounded, less than 0.5 times its basal width and less than 0.1 of length of the thin black siphunculi. ANT III with 28-40 rhinaria along one side, IV and V without any .... ***Acaudinum*** (p. 107)

- Cauda triangular, helmet-, tongue- or finger-shaped, at least 0.8 times longer than its basal width. ANT III with 3-79 rhinaria, but if with more than 27 then they are dispersed around segment and there are usually also some on IV and/or V 89

89. Antennae shorter than body (excluding cauda); usually less than 0.8 of body length, but *if* 0.8-1.0 times length of body *then* ANT IV always has rhinaria 90

- Antennae as long as or longer than body, or *if* only 0.8-1.0 times length of body *then* ANT IV has no rhinaria 96

90. Siphunculi flangeless 91

- Siphunculi with a reflexed flange 92

91. Cauda tapering, tongue- or finger-shaped, with 12-16 hairs. Secondary rhinaria not or hardly tuberculate, distributed ANT III 10-16, IV 0-2, V 0 .... *Hydaphias* (*hofmanni*; p. 234)

\-   Cauda with narrow, papillate apical part, and only 4 hairs. Secondary rhinaria distinctly tuberculate, distributed ANT III 15-24, IV 4-16, V 5-11 .... *Muscaphis* (p. 299)

92. Siphunculi thin and cylindrical, 0.22-0.29 of body length .... *Elatobium* (p. 224)

\-   Siphunculi 0.10-0.16 of body length 93

93. Siphunculi cylindrical/tapering. ANT PT 3.9-6.0 times base of last antennal segment. Abdominal spiracular apertures rather large and rounded .... *Brachycaudus* (part; p. 137)

\-   Siphunculi usually appearing somewhat thickened on distal part. ANT PT 1.1-3.7 times longer than base of last antennal segment. Abdominal spiracles reniform 94

94. ANT PT tapering to a narrow, pointed apex. Media of forewing usually only once-branched .... *Pseudacaudella* (p. 342)

\-   ANT PT with normal rounded/truncate apex. Media of forewing usually twice-branched 95

95. ANT PT 1.1-2.0 times longer than base of last antennal segment. R IV+V with concave sides .... *Coloradoa* (part; p. 175)

\-   ANT PT 2.0-3.7 times longer than base of last antennal segment. R IV+V with convex sides .... *Lipaphis* (part; p. 253)

96. Cauda short, helmet-shaped, not longer than its basal width, with 4 hairs. Dorsal abdomen with a conspicuous pattern of transverse dark cross bars and large dark marginal and postsiphuncular sclerites .... *Myzotoxoptera* (p. 304)

\-   Cauda distinctly longer than its basal width, with 4-16 hairs. Dorsal abdomen without or with various dark markings 97

97. Hairs on front of head about as long as basal diameter of ANT III, with expanded apices. R IV+V with a pair of hairs near base that are much longer than any of the other rostral hairs .... *Pleotrichophorus* (p. 340)

\-   Hairs on front of head short and blunt or if long then with pointed apices. R IV+V without a pair of unusually long basal hairs 98

98. ANT IV (and sometimcs V) with 1 or more secondary rhinaria (sometimes 0 on one side) 99

- ANT IV without secondary rhinaria (rarely 1 on one side) 102

99. Dorsal abdomen with a well-developed pattern of dark pleurospinal, marginal and postsiphuncular sclerites. Thoracic spiracular apertures much larger than abdominal ones .... *Nasonovia* (**s.str.**; p. 322)

- Dorsal abdomen with only faint or dusky markings. Thoracic spiracular apertures similar in size to abdominal ones 100

100. ANT III with 11-22 rhinaria along one side. Forewing veins very dark .... *Rhodobium* (p. 344)

- ANT III with 10-79 rhinaria not restricted to one side. Forewing veins pale or dark 101

101. Siphunculi thin and cylindrical for most of length, thinner than hind tibia at their respective midlengths. R IV+V about as long as HT II. Cauda short with 4 hairs. Secondary rhinaria distributed III 23-48, IV 0-10, V 0-6 .... *Tubaphis* (p. 365)

- Siphunculi tapering gradually from base to apex, thicker than hind tibia at their respective midlengths (except in one species that has R IV+V more than twice as long as HT II and a finger-like cauda). Cauda with 4-7 hairs. Secondary rhinaria distributed III 10-79. IV 2-57, V 0-24 .... *Ovatus* (p. 333)

102. Dorsal abdomen with a pattern of dark spinopleural segmental spots or cross-bands between the marginal sclerites and in addition to the intersegmental muscle plates 103

- Dorsal abdomen without a pattern of dark spinopleural markings; with or without dark marginal sclerites and pigmented intersegmental muscle plates 105

103. ANT III with 29-55 rhinaria. R IV+V with 8-12 accessory hairs .... *Acyrthosiphon* (*primulae*, part; p. 117)

- ANT III with 3-30 rhinaria. R IV+V with 0-11 accessory hairs 104

104. Antennae not longer than body (excluding cauda). R IV+V 0.6-1.1 times as long as HT II. Siphunculi 1.1-2.7 times longer than cauda .... *Metopolophium* (part; p. 290)

- Antennae longer than body. R IV+V 1.0-1.7 times longer than HT II. Siphunculi 2.1-2.6 times longer than cauda .... *Aulacorthum* (part; p. 129)

105. R IV+V 1.2-1.7 times longer than HT II. ANT III with 4-13 rhinaria ....
.... *Aulacorthum* (*knautiae*, part; p. 130)

- R IV+V 0.6-1.5 times longer than HT II, but if more than 1.1 times longer then ANT III has 18-30 rhinaria 106

106. R IV+V with (0-)2 accessory hairs 107

- R IV+V with 3-25 accessory hairs 109

107. ANT III with 2-11 rhinaria. R IV+V 1.0-1.1 times longer than HT II ....
.... *Subacyrthosiphon* (*cryptobium*; p. 364)

- ANT III with 13-36 rhinaria. R IV+V 0.6-0.95 of length of HT II 108

108. Siphunculi 2.2-2.7 times longer than cauda. R IV+V 0.75-0.95 of length of HT II ......
.... *Metopolophium* (*frisicum*, part; p. 295)

- Siphunculi 1.3-1.6 times longer than cauda. R IV+V 0.6-0.7 of length of HT II ....
.... *Sitobion* (*scoticum*; p. 361)

109. Longest hair on antennal tubercle pointed, longer than basal diameter of ANT III. Siphunculi 0.8-1.2 mm long, 2.3-3.0 times longer than cauda, with flared apices. ANT PT 5.7-7.5 times longer than base of ANT VI .... *Microlophium* (p. 296)

- Longest hair on antennal tubercle blunt-ended and not exceeding basal diameter of ANT III. If siphunculi are more than 0.8 mm long then they are less than 1.8 times longer than cauda, and ANT PT is less than 5 times longer than base of ANT VI ....
.... 110

110. R IV+V with 15-25 accessory hairs .... *Acyrthosiphon* (part; p. 111)

- R IV+V with 3-14 accessory hairs 111

111. Base of ANT VI 0.24-0.39 mm long, 2-3 times longer than R IV+V ....
.... *Acyrthosiphon* (part; p. 111)

- Base of ANT VI 0.09-0.24 mm long, if more than 0.22 mm long then less than 2 times longer than R IV+V 112

112. Siphunculi 0.11-0.14 of body length, 1.09-1.35 times length of cauda 113

- Siphunculi 0.14-0.30 of body length, 1.35-2.30 times length of cauda 114

113. ANT PT 2.9-3.6 times longer than base of ANT VI. Cauda with 5-7 hairs ....
.... *Metopolophium* (part; p. 290)

- ANT PT 2.0-2.3 times longer than base of ANT VI. Cauda with 9-10 hairs ....
.... *Acyrthosiphon* (part; p. 111)

114. R IV+V 0.9-1.5 times as long as HT II .... *Acyrthosiphon* (part; p. 111)

- R IV+V 0.6-0.9 of length of HT II 115

115. ANT III with 3-19 rhinaria usually confined to basal half of segment ....
.... *Acyrthosiphon* (part; p. 111)

- ANT III with (3-) 8-30 rhinaria usually extending over most of segment ....
.... *Metopolophium* (part; p. 290)

Alate males

This key is designed for use with specimens trapped in flight and is therefore limited to genera containing species with alate males. In some cases the number of specimens available was very small, which may affect its reliability.

1. Siphunculi pore-like or as very short tubes, less than 0.06 of body length 2

- Siphunculi more than 0.06 of body length 9

2. Siphunculi as pores .... *Cryptosiphum* (*artemisiae*; p. 188)

- Siphunculi as short tubes 3

3. Cauda tongue-shaped or elongate triangular, longer than its basal width and longer than siphunculi 4

- Cauda broadly rounded or bluntly triangular, not longer than its basal width and usually shorter than siphunculi 8

4. Siphunculi less than 0.4 of length of cauda. ANT IV with 1-3 rhinaria close to apex. Body elongate .... *Hyalopteroides* (*humilis*; p. 232)

- Siphunculi more than 0.4 of length of cauda. ANT IV either without rhinaria or with rhinaria distributed over length of segment. Body oval 5

5. ABD TERG 3-6 with or without faint markings apart from the marginal sclerites 6

- ABD TERG 3-6 with short dark spinal cross-bands 7

6. Secondary rhinaria distributed ANT III 16-27, IV 6-12, V 10-14. Siphunculi more than half of length of cauda .... *Hayhurstia* (*atriplicis*; p. 230)

- Secondary rhinaria distributed ANT III 24-30, IV 5-10, V 4-6. Siphunculi about half of length of cauda .... *Semiaphis* (*dauci*; p. 355)

7. ANT III about as long as IV plus V together and bearing 81-94 rhinaria, IV with 0 and V with 3-8. Siphunculi pale, with weak normal imbrication ....
.... *Longicaudus* (*trirhodus*; p. 255)

- ANT III shorter than IV plus V and bearing 28-45 rhinaria, IV 13-24 and V with 7-9. Siphunculi dusky/dark, with rows of spicules .... *Nearctaphis* (*bakeri*; p. 326)

8. Dorsal abdomen with well-separated cross-bands. Siphunculi slightly swollen, barrel-shaped. Spiracular apertures reniform .... *Brevicoryne* (*brassicae*; p. 152)

- Dorsal abdomen with broad cross-bands at least partially coalesced between tergites. Siphunculi tapering. Spiracular apertures large and rounded ....
.... *Brachycaudus* (part; p. 140)

9. Siphunculi with a subapical zone of polygonal reticulation 10

- Siphunculi without a subapical zone of polygonal reticulation 21

10. Siphunculi 3.5-5.0 times longer than cauda. Abdominal tergites with variably developed spinopleural or pleural markings 11

- Siphunculi less than 3.5 times longer than cauda. Dorsal abdomen with or without dark dorsal markings 13

11. Siphunculi very long with basal half thin and cylindrical, and distal half distinctly swollen proximal to the subapical reticulated region .... *Illinoia* (*lambersi*; p. 246)

- Siphunculi tapering from base to apex 12

12. R IV+V very long and narrow, about twice as long as HT II or longer ....
.... *Corylobium* (*avellanae*; p. 179)

- R IV+V 1.2-1.3 times longer than HT II .... *Anthracosiphon*(*hertae*; p. 122)

13. Dorsal abdomen anterior to siphunculi with an extensive spinopleural pattern of dark sclerotisation involving broad cross-bands partly linked between segments and also often merged with intersegmental muscle-plates 14

- Dorsal abdomen anterior to siphunculi without dark markings except for the intersegmental muscle plates and rows of marginal sclerites, or with segmentally separated short bars, flecks, dots or patches 16

14. Siphunculi about twice as long as cauda. R IV+V shorter than HT II ....
.... ***Impatientinum*** (p. 247)

- Siphunculi more than 2.5 times longer than cauda. R IV+V as long as or longer than HT II 15

15. Secondary rhinaria distributed ANT III 20-29, IV 0, V 6-12. Siphunculi with only 1-4 subapical rows of polygonal cells .... ***Ericaphis*** (*wakibae*; p. 228)

- Secondary rhinaria distributed ANT III 30-85, IV 0-25, V 6-21. Siphunculi with more extensive subapical polygonal reticulation .... ***Macrosiphum*** (part; p. 277)

16. Siphunculi usually shorter than, and not more than 1.1 times longer than cauda ....
.... ***Macrosiphoniella*** (p. 261)

- Siphunculi 1.4 or more times longer than cauda 17

17. Hairs on ANT III conspicuous, the longest of them at least half as long as basal diameter of the segment 18

- Hairs on ANT III not conspicuous, all less than half as long as diameter of segment ... 20

18. ANT IV without secondary rhinaria or, if with 1-9 rhinaria then with many fewer than on ANT V (which has 8-19) .... ***Macrosiphum*** (part; p. 277)

- ANT IV with 2-19 secondary rhinaria, and ANT V with a similar number (2-20) 19

19. Siphunculi slightly swollen on distal half. Thoracic spiracles very large, much larger than abdominal spiracles .... ***Delphiniobium*** (*junackianum*; p. 190)

- Siphunculi cylindrical or tapering. Thoracic and abdominal spiracles similarly small and reniform .... ***Uroleucon*** (p. 375)

20. Siphunculi usually pale at least basally. R IV+V longer than HT II ....
.... ***Macrosiphum*** (*ptericolens*; p. 282)

-   Siphunculi uniformly dark. R IV shorter than HT II .... ***Sitobion*** (p. 358)

21. ABD TERG 8 with a wart-like median process bearing two hairs .... ***Cavariella*** (p. 163)

-   ABD TERG 8 without a median hair-bearing process 22

22. Siphunculi black and similar in length to (not more than 1.2 times longer than) the equally black elongate triangular cauda. Dorsal abdomen with a complete series of black segmental cross-bands extending laterally to touch the large marginal and presiphuncular sclerites .... ***Megoura*** (*viciae*; p. 285)

-   Siphunculi pale or dark, more than 1.2 times longer than cauda. Dorsal abdomen with less extensive markings 23

23. Siphunculi slightly to markedly swollen on distal part, with distinctly narrower part proximal to swelling 24

-   Siphunculi tapering, cylindrical, or thinnest in middle and flared at apex, or sometimes appearing slightly swollen throughout and constricted at apex, but without a distinctly narrower more proximal part 37

24. ANT IV without any rhinaria (although ANT V has 10-24) .... ***Amphorophora*** (p. 119)

-   ANT IV always with rhinaria, often with more than on ANT V (which has 1-20) 25

25. Dorsal abdomen anterior to siphunculi without any distinct dark spino-pleural sclerotic markings. ANT III with 100 or more rhinaria, and IV with about 40-60. Siphunculi with dark apices, slightly swollen over only about distal 0.2-0.3 of length, and usually bearing a few very small hairs .... ***Trichosiphonaphis*** (*polygonifoliae*; p. 365)

-   Dorsal abdomen with a pattern of dusky to dark spino-pleural sclerotic markings anterior to siphunculi. ANT III with 15-80 rhinaria, and IV with 5-40. Siphunculi slightly to markedly swollen over at least 0.33 of length, and hairless 26

26. Cauda triangular or rounded at apex, not more than 1.2 times as long as its basal width 27

-   Cauda tongue-shaped, often with a slight midlength constriction, distinctly longer than (more than 1.2 times) its basal width 34

27. Dorsal abdomen with sclerites at least partially fused between ABD TERG 4 and 5 or 3-5, usually forming a central patch perforated with "windows" 28

- Dorsal abdomen with all spino-pleural sclerites separated between segments 29

28. ANT PT more than 8 times longer than base of ANT VI .... *Cryptomyzus* (p. 184)

- ANT PT less than 6 times longer than base of ANT VI .... *Myzus* (part; p. 311)

29. Siphunculi rather short, less than 0.15 of body length 30

- Siphunculi more than 0.15 of body length 33

30. Dorsal abdomen anterior to siphunculi with a series of paired pleural sclerites leaving a wide gap in the mid-line .... *Utamphorophora* (*humboldti*; p. 389)

- Dorsal abdomen anterior to siphunculi with a series of transverse bands or bars crossing the mid-line 31

31. Siphunculi less than 0.1 of BL, and flangeless .... *Jacksonia* (p. 248)

- Siphunculi more than 0.1 of BL, with a small but distinct apical flange 32

32. ANT PT more than 4 times longer than base of ANT VI. ANT III with 50-75 rhinaria .... *Rhopalomyzus* (*lonicerae, poae*; p. 347)

- ANT PT less than 4 times longer than base of ANT VI. ANT III with 30-52 rhinaria .... *Myzus* (*cymbalariae*; p. 315)

33. ABD TERG 3-7 with short broad spino-pleural bars, but marginal sclerites and intersegmental sclerites indistinct or absent. R IV+V with a needle-like tip .... *Capitophorus* (*hippophaes*; p. 158)

- ABD TERG 3-7 with spino-pleural, marginal and intersegmental sclerites all similarly developed. R IV+V without a needle-like tip ... *Rhopalosiphoninus* (*staphyleae*; p. 353)

34. Siphunculi rather thin, pale and only slightly swollen .... *Paramyzus* (*heraclei*; p. 337)

- Siphunculi rather thick, pale or dark, and very markedly swollen 35

35. ANT III with 29-80 secondary rhinaria, IV with 9-20 and V with 3-12 ....
.... ***Hyperomyzus*** (p. 238)

- ANT III with 19-29 secondary rhinaria, IV with 1-10 and V with 5-9 36

36. Antennal tubercles undeveloped. ANT PT less than 1.5 times longer than base of ANT VI. Siphunculi symmetrically swollen, with a small apical flange. ANT IV with 5-10 rhinaria .... ***Liosomaphis*** (*berberidis*; p. 250)

- Antennal tubercles well developed. ANT PT more than 4 times longer than base of ANT VI. Siphunculi asymmetrically swollen, with a well-developed apical flange. ANT V with 1-3 rhinaria (based on one specimen) .... ***Wahlgreniella*** (*ossiannilssoni*; p. 393)

37. Siphunculi 0.06-0.17 of body length. Cauda very short, triangular, helmet-shaped or semi-circular, not longer than its basal width. Dorsal abdomen always with dark spino-pleural sclerotisation anterior to siphunculi, often merged between segments 38

- Siphunculi 0.14-0.25 of body length, but if less than 0.17 of body length then either cauda is distinctly longer than its basal width or dorsal abdomen has little or no spino-pleural sclerotisation anterior to siphunculi 40

38. Spiracular apertures large and rounded. Siphunculi smooth or rather weakly imbricated, usually with a distinct annular incision below the flange. Head without spinal tubercles, small spinal tubercles occasionally present on ABD TERG 8 only, and marginal tubercles if present are usually small .... ***Brachycaudus*** (part; p. 140)

- Spiracular apertures kidney-shaped. Siphunculi with normal or spiculose imbrication, usually without an annular incision below the flange. Head and at least posterior abdominal tergites usually with well-developed spinal tubercles, and marginal tubercles often large, but sometimes small or absent 39

39. ANT III with about 120-150 rhinaria (IV with 28-51 and V with 5-29). R IV+V more than 1.5 times longer than siphunculi which are ornamented with close-set rows of spicules .... ***Anuraphis*** (*farfarae, subterranea*; p. 126)

- ANT III with 25-104 rhinaria (IV with 3-42 and V with 1-17). R IV+V less than 1.5 times longer than siphunculi which have normal non-spiculose imbrication ....
.... ***Dysaphis*** (p. 208)

40. ANT IV without secondary rhinaria, rarely with 1-3 but far less than on ANT V (which has 5-25) 41

- ANT IV with 3-47 secondary rhinaria (in one species occasionally with only 1 or 2 on one side), ANT V often having less (range 2-30) 43

41. Dorsal abdomen usually with only small and indistinct sclerites in the spinal region, and intersegmental and marginal sclerites also tend to be weakly pigmented .... *Acyrthosiphon* (p. 112)

- ABD TERG 1-5 or 2-5 with well-developed dark spino-pleural cross-bands in addition to dark intersegmental and marginal sclerites 42

42. Siphunculi with a very well-developed flange, and more than 3 times longer than cauda, which bears 10-15 hairs. R IV+V longer than HT II .... *Microlophium* (*carnosum*; p. 297)

- Siphunculi with a moderate flange, and less than 3 times longer than cauda, which bears 6-9 hairs. R IV+V longer or shorter than HT II .... *Metopolophium* (part; p. 292)

43. ANT PT less than 2.5 times longer than base of ANT VI 44

- ANT PT more than 2.5 times longer than base of ANT VI 46

44. Siphunculi dark and very scaly, appearing slightly swollen over most of length but constricted and narrow at apex ('sausage-shaped') .... *Vesiculaphis* (*theobaldi*; p 390)

- Siphunculi pale or dark, smooth to moderately imbricated, tapering gradually or cylindrical, not constricted at apex 45

45. Siphunculi about 0.25 of body length. Cauda broad at base and slightly constricted at about midlength .... *Elatobium* (*abietinum*; p. 224)

- Siphunculi about 0.16 of body length. Cauda constricted near base .... *Tubaphis* (*ranunculina*; p. 365)

46. Dorsal abdomen without any distinct sclerotic markings (apart from pale marginal sclerites) anterior to siphunculi .... *Ovatus* (p. 334)

- Dorsal abdomen anterior to siphunculi with a pattern of dusky/dark spino-pleural and/or intersegmental sclerotisation 47

47. Dorsal abdomen anterior to siphunculi with a spinal row of separate short bars or patches leaving a large gap in pleural region between them and the marginal sclerites. Siphunculi thin and pale 48

- Dorsal abdomen anterior to siphunculi either with cross-bands extending into the pleural region (often partially fused between segments), or a series of well-developed intersegmental pleural sclerites, or both 49

48. ANT IV with 5-10 secondary rhinaria (III with 17-30 and V with 5-12). Hairs on dorsal abdominal sclerites with tuberculate bases. First tarsal segments with 5 hairs .... ***Chaetosiphon*** (*fragaefolii*; p. 170)

- ANT IV with 14-50 rhinaria (III with 20-80 and V with 6-30). Hairs on abdominal sclerites without tuberculate bases. First tarsal segments with 3 hairs .... ***Capitophorus*** (p. 156)

49. Spino-pleural cross-bands on ABD TERG 3-5 partially fused between segments to form a central patch perforated with "windows" 50

- Spino-pleural cross-bands either segmentally separated or absent, with pattern of scleritosation mainly formed by well-developed pairs of intersegmental sclerites 52

50. Cauda tongue-shaped with a slight midlength constriction. R IV+V 0.9-1.0 of length of HT II. Secondary rhinaria with fimbriate rims (needs high magnification) .... ***Ericaphis*** (*scammelli*; p. 227)

- Cauda triangular. R IV+V 1.0-1.4 times longer than HT II. Secondary rhinaria with naked rims 51

51. Siphunculi paler than or at least not darker than the dorsal patch, and 0.50-0.65 of length of ANT III .... ***Phorodon*** (*humuli*; p. 339)

- Siphunculi darker than the dorsal patch, or if paler then they are more than 0.8 of length of ANT III .... ***Myzus*** (*cerasi, varians*; p. 311)

52. Siphunculi dark. ANT III with 50-70 rhinaria. Thoracic spiracular apertures much larger than abdominal ones which are themselves circular or subcircular, not partially occluded by opercula .... ***Nasonovia*** (*ribisnigri*; p. 324)

- Siphunculi pale or only dark at apices (or bases and apices). ANT III with 20-43 rhinaria. Thoracic and abdominal spiracles of similar size, those on abdomen reniform due to partial occlusion by opercula 53

53 ANT PT 2.6-3.1 times longer than base of ANT VI .... ***Metopolophium*** (*tenerum*; p. 296)

- ANT PT 3.9-6.1 times longer than base of ANT VI .... ***Aulacorthum*** (p. 130)

Systematic account of genera

There follows a systematic account of the British aphid genera in alphabetical order, including keys to species for apterous and alate parthenogenetic females, and to alate males for those genera where they are produced. Abbreviations for morphological characters are probably self-explanatory, but any clarification required of these characters and the way to measure them can be obtained by consulting pages 3-7 and 399 and Figs 2-6. No scales are provided on the photographs because the body size of aphids can vary by a factor of 2; the recorded size range for at least the apterous parthenogenetic female morph of each species is given in the text, and any other morphs illustrated are reproduced at the same scale as the aptera.

Acaudinum Börner, 1930

Medium-sized dark brown to blackish broadly oval aphids related to *Macrosiphum* but with morphology modified for ant-attendance, and a specific association with the composite genus *Centaurea*. The head is broad and lacks antennal or median tubercles, so that the outline of the front of the head is straight or slightly convex in dorsal view. Antennae have many rhinaria on segment III in apterae as well as alatae, and a long PT. Siphunculi are long, tapering and dark, with a small or indistinct flange. The cauda is very short and broadly rounded, almost indiscernible in unmounted specimens, and bears numerous hairs.

There are 5 species in the world, all living on *Centaurea* spp. in Europe and western Asia. Holman (1991) provided a revision and a key to species.

Figure 104. Aptera and alata of *Acaudinum centaureae*.

Acaudinum centaureae (Koch, 1854) Figs 69, 104

The only British species. It lives without host alternation on *Centaurea scabiosa*. It is found at or near ground level in earthen shelters at bases of leaf stalks, assiduously attended by ants, usually *Lasius niger* (L.). Apterae are broadly oval, shiny blackish green to black with dark appendages, and ANT III bearing 15-27 rhinaria along one side; BL 1.8-2.6 mm.

Fundatrices are rather large (2.4-2.9 mm) with shorter, blacker appendages than apterae. Alatae are similar to apterae but with large marginal sclerites on ABD TERG 2-4, and ANT III with 22-40 rhinaria; BL 1.6-2.5 mm. Sexual morphs are produced in October. Oviparae (BL 1.6-2.4 mm) have a cauda bearing up to 28 hairs (15-18 in apterae), and hind tibia only slightly swollen on basal half and bearing 2-16 scent glands. Males are small (BL c.1.5 mm) and apterous, with secondary rhinaria distributed III 32-34, IV 11-13, V 2-4, and broad sclerotic cross-bands on all abdominal tergites (based on 1 specimen, coll. F.H. Jacob, Fox Hill, Cambs., 12.x.1944). In southern England (Cambs, Suffolk, Beds, Herts, Oxon, Surrey, Kent) and South Wales (Baker, 2009); widely distributed in rest of Europe.

Acyrthosiphon Mordvilko, 1914

Medium-sized to large, usually pale-coloured, often slightly waxy aphids with spindle-shaped body and long appendages, living without host alternation on various dicots. *Acyrthosiphon* has close affinities with several other genera such as *Metopolophium* and *Microlophium*; an inclusive generic diagnosis that excludes some species in related genera is not possible. The head usually has well-developed antennal tubercles, with inner faces smooth and divergent, but in contrast to *Metopolophium* the median tubercle is always low or undeveloped. Antennae of apterae have a few small rhinaria on segment III near the base. Alatae usually have secondary rhinaria on segment III only, males (which may be apterous or alate) have them on III and V only, or on III, IV and V. In several species (*caraganae*, *malvae*, *pisum*) males are predominantly apterous in maritime western Europe but alate in a more continental climate. Hairs on the dorsal body and antennae are short and blunt. First tarsal segments usually all have 3 hairs. The dorsal abdomen is membranous in apterae, and usually also in alatae. Siphunculi are usually long, broad-based, tapering or cylindrical, usually pale, with a rather well-developed flange, and without subapical polygonal reticulation (sometimes with a few interconnected striae). The cauda is pale, tongue- or finger-shaped, and often large and long.

There are about 80 species in the world, mostly palaearctic. Their hosts are mainly Leguminosae, Rosaceae and Euphorbiaceae. They are not visited by ants, and often fall off the plant readily when disturbed. Eastop (1971) reviewed the genus, and Heie (1994) provided accounts of the Scandinavian species. Nine species are recorded from Britain. The key includes three more continental European species (*cyparissiae*, *euphorbiae* and *ignotum*) that may turn up here in future.

Key to apterous viviparae of British *Acyrthosiphon*

1. R IV+V very short and stubby, only 0.4-0.6 of HT II 2

- R IV+V not short and stubby, 0.6-1.5 of length of HT II 3

2. Front of head, ANT I to VI, distal 0.7 of siphunculi, tarsi and apices of femora and tibiae dark. First tarsal segments with 5(-7) hairs (usually 3 short blunt spine-like hairs flanked by 2 longer, finer ones) .... ***cyparissiae*** (Koch, 1855)

- Front of head and appendages all pale. First tarsal segments normally with 3 hairs (only one of them short, blunt and spine-like) .... ***euphorbiae*** (Börner, 1949)

3. Siphunculus 0.12-0.20 of length of body excluding cauda, and 0.85-1.33 of length of cauda. Antennal PT 1.6-2.9 times longer than base of ANT VI ... ***auctum*** (Walker, 1849)

- Siphunculus 0.20-0.33 of length of body excluding cauda, and 1.25-2.5 times longer than cauda. PT 2.8-8.0 times longer than base of ANT VI 4

4. R IV+V only 0.60-0.75 of length of HT II yet bearing 16-24 accessory hairs .... ***lactucae*** (Passerini, 1860)

- If R IV+V bears more than 12 accessory hairs then it is at least 0.9 of length of HT II 5

5. Base of ANT VI 0.23-0.42 mm long, 1.6-2.9 times longer than R IV+V. Cauda 4.1-5.9 times longer than R IV+V. ANT I bearing 9-23, usually 12 or more, hairs 6

- Base of ANT VI 0.11-0.20 mm long, 0.9-1.9 times longer than R IV+V. Cauda 1.3 –4.5 times longer than R IV+V. ANT I bearing 5-11 hairs 7

6. Base of ANT VI 1.6-1.9 times longer than R IV+V, which is 0.75-0.95 times longer than HT II and bears 6-12 accessory hairs (2-8 on dorsal side). Cauda bears 11-23 hairs .... ***ononis*** (Koch, 1855)

- Base of ANT VI 1.9-2.9 times longer than R IV+V, which is 0.63-0.85 times longer than HT II and bears 3-8 accessory hairs (0-4 on dorsal side). Cauda bears 7-14 hairs .... ***pisum*** (Harris, 1776)

7. R IV+V 0.6-0.9 times as long as HT II, if more than 0.85 times then PT is less than 4 times longer than base of ANT VI 8

- R IV+V 0.9-1.5 times longer than HT II, if less than 1.0 times then PT is more than 4 times longer than base of ANT VI 10

8. Siphunculi 0.40-0.72 mm long, 3.5-5.5 times longer than R IV+V and 1.2-1.7 times longer than cauda. PT 3.2-4.0 times longer than base of ANT VI which is 0.13-0.17 mm long .... ***loti*** (Theobald, 1913)

- Siphunculi 0.69-1.00 mm long, 5.6-7.7 times longer than R IV+V and 1.5-2.1 times longer than cauda. PT 4.0-6.0 times longer than base of ANT VI which is 0.16-0.21 mm long 9

9. Base of ANT VI 1.17-1.41 times longer than R IV+V. ABD TERG 8 with 7-10 hairs, usually at least 8 .... ***caraganae*** ssp. ***occidentale*** Hille Ris Lambers, 1947

- Base of ANT VI 1.43-1.75 times longer than R IV +V. ABD TERG 8 with 6-8 hairs, usually 6 .... ***ignotum*** Mordvilko, 1914

10. R IV+V bearing 25-31 accessory hairs. PT 3.4-4.9 times longer than base of ANT VI. ANT III with 7-19 rhinaria spaced out along its length .... *auriculae* Martin, 1981

- R IV+V bearing 6-23 accessory hairs, but if more than 20 then PT is more than 5 times longer than base of ANT VI. ANT III with 1-24 rhinaria, mainly on basal half 11

11. Cauda is 1.3-1.6 times longer than base of ANT VI, bears 6-8 hairs and has a slight mid-way constriction. Siphunculi 2.2-3.1 times longer than cauda. Median frontal tubercle somewhat developed .... *primulae* (Theobald, 1913)

- Cauda is 1.8-2.6 times longer than base of ANT VI, bears 6-12 (rarely 6 or 7) hairs, and has no mid-way constriction. Siphunculi 1.5-2.6 times longer than cauda. Median frontal tubercle little developed 12

(The remaining couplets are an attempt to separate the species/subspecies of the malvae group, including *boreale*. The identification will probably only be reliable if several specimens – ideally at least 10 – are available to assess the range of variation in the sample. The host plant can of course provide useful confirmation of identity.)

12. ANT PT usually more than 6 times (4.8-7.5 times) longer than base of ANT VI, only less than 6 times in early spring populations. (R IV+V usually bearing 13-18 accessory hairs.) .... *malvae* (Mosley, 1841) **s.str**.

- ANT PT rarely more than 6 times (3.4-6.4 times) longer than base of ANT VI 13

13. R IV+V with 12-23 accessory hairs. ANT III of aptera with 6-21 rhinaria .... ssp. *agrimoniae* (Börner, 1940)

- R IV+V with 6-15 accessory hairs. ANT III of aptera with 1-19 rhinaria 14

14. R IV+V usually more than 1.1 times (1.0-1.4 times) longer than HT II .... ssp. *rogersii* (Theobald, 1913)

- R IV+V usually less than 1.1 times (0.9-1.2 times) longer than HT II 15

15. Longest hairs on front of head and antennal tubercles 12-25 µm long. R IV+V 1.0-1.2 times longer than HT II .... ssp. *poterii* Prior & Stroyan, 1964

- Longest hairs on front of head and antennal tubercles 17-50 µm long. R IV+V 0.9-1.1 times longer than HT II 16

16. ANT III of aptera with 1-9 (rarely more than 5) rhinaria. On *Alchemilla* spp. .... ssp. *potha* Börner, (1940) 1950

- ANT III of aptera with 2-14 (rarely less than 5) rhinaria. On *Potentilla* spp. .... *boreale* Hille Ris Lambers, 1952

Key to alate viviparae of British *Acyrthosiphon*

Three other continental European *Acyrthosiphon* species (*cyparissiae, euphorbiae* and *ignotum*) are again included.

1. R IV+V very short and stubby, only 0.4-0.6 of HT II 2

- R IV+V not short and stubby, 0.6-1.5 of length of HT II 3

2. First tarsal segments with 5(-7) hairs (usually 3 short blunt spine-like hairs flanked by 2 longer, finer ones). ANT III with 4-12 rhinaria. Siphunculi much darker than cauda .... ***cyparissiae***

- First tarsal segments normally with 3 hairs (only one of them short, blunt and spine-like). ANT III with 11-25 rhinaria. Siphunculi and cauda pale .... ***euphorbiae***

3. Dorsal abdomen with an extensive pattern of dark spinopleural sclerotisation between the marginal sclerites and in addition to the intersegmental muscle plates (see Fig. 109). ANT III with 29-55 rhinaria .... ***primulae***

- Dorsal abdomen without a pattern of dark spinopleural markings; with or without dark marginal sclerites and pigmented intersegmental muscle plates. ANT III with 3-31 rhinaria ... 4

4. R IV+V only 0.60-0.75 of length of HT II yet bearing 16-24 accessory hairs ..... ***lactucae***

- If last R IV+V bears more than 12 accessory hairs then it is at least 0.9 of length of HT II 5

5. Siphunculus 0.10-0.12 of body length (excluding cauda), and 1.1-1.3 times longer than cauda. PT less than 3 times longer than base of ANT VI .... ***auctum***

- Siphunculus at least 0.15 of body length and more than 1.35 times longer than cauda. PT 3-6 times longer than base of ANT VI 6

6. Base of ANT VI 0.24-0.39 mm long, 1.6-2.9 times longer than R IV+V. Cauda 3.4-5.0 times longer than R IV+V. ANT I bearing 11-21 hairs 7

- Base of ANT VI 0.12-0.24 mm long, 0.8-1.9 times longer than R IV+V. Cauda 1.4-3.5 times longer than R IV+V. ANT I bearing 5-11 hairs 8

7. R IV+V 0.80-0.95 of length of HT II, and bearing 8-12 accessory hairs. Cauda with 12-16 hairs .... ***ononis***

- R IV+V 0.65-0.85 of length of hind tarsus, and bearing 5-7 accessory hairs. Cauda with 7-16 hairs (usually 7-12) .... ***pisum***

8. R IV+V 0.6-0.9 times as long as HT II, if more than 0.85 times then PT is less than 4.5 times longer than base of ANT VI. ANT III bearing 3-19 rhinaria 9

- R IV+V 0.9-1.5 times longer than HT II, if less than 1.0 times then PT is more than 4.5 times longer than base of ANT VI. ANT III bearing 12-31 rhinaria 11

9. Siphunculi 0.30-0.69 mm long, 1.35-1.67 times longer than cauda and 3.0-3.7 times longer than HT II, and with midlength diameter always less than 1.5 times the midlength diameter of the hind tibia .... *loti*

- Siphunculi relatively longer and thicker; 0.62-0.93 mm long, 1.62-2.25 times longer than cauda and 3.5-4.7 times longer than HT II, and with midlength diameter often more than 1.5 times that of hind tibia 10

10. PT 1.75-2.2 times longer than cauda. Siphunculus 1.6-2.0 times longer than cauda (usually less than 1.9 times). ABD TERG 8 bearing (6-) 7-10 hairs, usually 7-8 ....
.... *caraganae* ssp. *occidentale*

- PT 2.1-3.1 times longer than cauda. Siphunculus 1.8-2.2 times longer than cauda (rarely less than 1.9 times). ABD TERG 8 bearing 4-7 hairs, often 6 .... *ignotum*

11. R IV+V with 24-30 accessory hairs. PT 3.65-4.4 times longer than base of ANT VI ......
.... *auriculae*

- R IV+V with 6-17 accessory hairs. PT (4.3-) 5.1-8.25 times longer than base of ANT VI .... *malvae* group including *boreale*

Key to alate males of British *Acyrthosiphon*

1. R IV+V very short and stubby, about 0.5 of length of HT II .... *cyparissiae*

- R IV+V 0.6 or more of length of HT II 2

2. Siphunculi attenuate distally, thinner on distal half than hind tibiae at midlength. Cauda more than twice as long as R IV+V .... *pisum*

- Siphunculi not attenuate distally, similar in thickness to hind tibiae at midlength. Cauda less than twice as long as R IV+V 3

3. R IV+V 0.6-0.8 of length of HT II and bearing 16-24 accessory hairs .... *lactucae*

- R IV+V 1.0-1.4 times longer than hind tarsus, and bearing 8-15 accessory hairs ....
.... *malvae*

Acyrthosiphon auctum (Walker, 1849)

Apterae are pale yellowish green, green or pink in life, wax-dusted; BL 1.9-2.8 mm. Alatae (as yet unrecorded from UK) have a dark head and thorax and reddish abdomen. It is found mainly in sand dune habitats on such plants as sea sandwort, *Honkenya peploides* and sea campion, *Silene uniflora* (Caryophyllaceae), and sea rocket, *Cakile maritima* (Cruciferae), feeding inconspicuously on leaves close to the stem. Oviparae and apterous males (with secondary rhinaria distributed III 13-21: IV 8-13, V 4-10) are produced in September-October in Scotland (BMNH colln, leg. H.L.G. Stroyan). In northern England (Newcastle area) and Scotland, northern Europe including Iceland, and in Greenland.

Acyrthosiphon auriculae Martin, 1981

Apterae are pale to bright green in life, BL 1.8-2.9 mm, found on upper surfaces of young apical leaves of a cultivated hybrid *Primula* (section Auricula); experimental host transfers indicated specificity to this section of the genus (Martin, 1981). Oviparae and apterous males (with secondary rhinaria distributed III 34-40, IV 0-2, V 7-12) are produced in October. Only known from England, although alatae of a possible geographic variant of this species have been trapped in Corsica.

Acyrthosiphon boreale Hille Ris Lambers, 1952

Apterae are green with anterior part of body yellowish; BL 2.7-3.2 mm. They live on *Potentilla* spp. Males are apterous with secondary rhinaria distributed III 28-42, IV 5-19, V 11-13. In England, northern Europe, Greenland and Canada (Baffin I), and there are also records from Switzerland, Hungary and Kazakhstan, although the distinction from other members of the *malvae* group is not clear enough to be certain about the extent of its distribution.

Acyrthosiphon caraganae (Cholodkovsky, (1907) 1908) Fig. 105

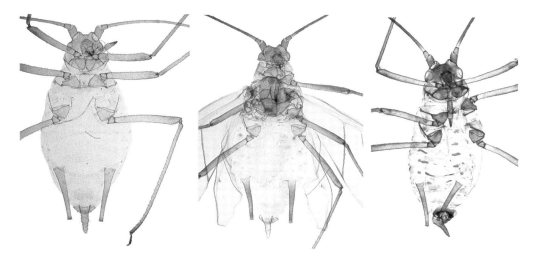

Figure 105. Aptera, alata and male of *Acyrthosiphon caraganae*.

Apterae are yellowish or greyish-green to very dark apple-green in life, with variably-developed pale grey cross-bands of powdery wax and/or a brighter green spinal stripe; BL 2.6-4.3 mm. They feed on leaves and young growth of woody Leguminosae, especially

Caragana arborescens, Coronilla spp. and *Colutea* spp., often forming large colonies. Yellowish-green oviparae and dull reddish apterous males (with secondary rhinaria distributed III 39-65, IV 12-28, V 10-25) occur in September-October in western Europe. Probably originating in Central Asia, it now occurs in parks and gardens in temperate regions throughout much of the Northern Hemisphere, although in Britain it is only so far recorded from southern England. In other parts of the world males are usually alate with darker and more extensive dorsal abdominal markings, and for this reason western European populations are regarded as a subspecies, ***A. caraganae* ssp. *occidentale*** Hille Ris Lambers, 1947.

Acyrthosiphon cyparissiae (Koch, 1855)

Apterae are green in life with mainly dark appendages; BL 2.4-3.4 mm. It occurs on *Euphorbia* spp. (*cyparissias, esula, sequieriana*), feeding mainly on upper sides of upper leaves, often in large numbers. Oviparae and alate males (with secondary rhinaria distributed III 25-33, IV 0, V 10-17) occur in late September in the Netherlands (Hille Ris Lambers, 1947a). In Europe (but UK records so far apply to other species), Middle East, Central Asia and China.

Acyrthosiphon euphorbiae (Börner, 1949)

Apterae are green in life, tinged with yellow; BL 2.3-4.4 mm. It occurs on *Euphorbia* spp., in small colonies on upper sides of leaves, sometimes mixed with *E. cyparissiae*. Life cycle is apparently unknown. In Europe (not yet in UK), North Africa and the Middle East. Dutch specimens described as ssp. *neerlandicus* Hille Ris Lambers are probably only a local variant.

Acyrthosiphon ignotum Mordvilko, 1914

Apterae are pale green to yellowish-green in life, with brownish legs and antennae; BL 2.2-3.4 mm. It feeds at the shoot tips of *Spiraea* spp., often in large colonies. Widespread in gardens and parks of continental western Europe and across Asia, but not yet recorded from UK.

Acyrthosiphon lactucae (Passerini, 1860)

Apterae are pale yellowish green or pink, with pale grey wax bloom; BL 1.7-2.9 mm. Alatae are also pale. It colonises stems and the undersides of leaves of *Lactuca* spp. Oviparae and alate males (with secondary rhinaria distributed III 30-37, IV 0-3, V 11-14) occur in October (BMNH collection, leg. V.F. Eastop). Widely distributed in Europe, Middle East, and introduced to North America. In Britain it has only been found in southern England (Cambridge, Bucks, Essex).

Acyrthosiphon loti (Theobald, 1913) Fig. 106

Apterae are green in life, frequently with faint greyish cross-bands of wax powder, or more rarely pink; BL 1.7-3.3 mm. They live all-year-round on bird's foot trefoils, *Lotus* spp., colonising young shoots, upper parts and flowers, and sometimes found on certain other herbaceous Leguminosae (e.g. *Anthyllis vulneraria, Hippocrepis comosa, Medicago sativa, Onobrychis viciifolia*). Sexual morphs occur in October in continental Europe, but have not yet been collected in Britain; small narrow-bodied greyish red apterous males, with secondary rhinaria distributed III 40-50, IV 12-20, V 10-20, were described from the Netherlands (Hille Ris Lambers, 1947a), and both apterous and alate males occur in Switzerland (Meier, 1958). In England, Scotland, Wales, Ireland, and Europe eastward to Turkey.

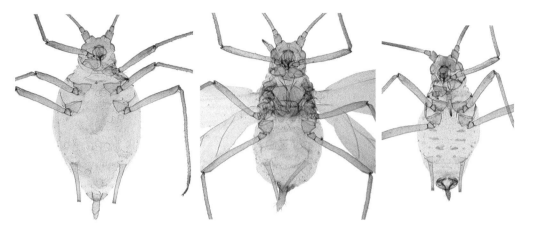

Figure 106. Aptera, alata and male of *Acyrthosiphon loti*.

Acyrthosiphon malvae (Mosley, 1841) Fig. 107

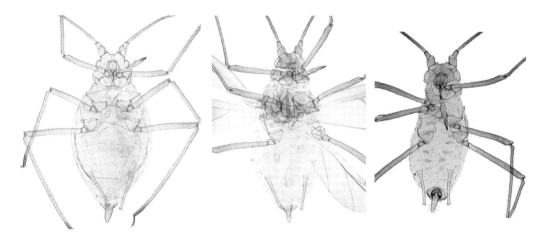

Figure 107. Aptera and alata of *Acyrthosiphon malvae* (s.str.) and apterous male of ssp. *rogersii*.

Apterae are pale green, yellowish or greyish green, or pinkish red in life; BL 1.5-3.2 mm. They feed on many plants, but particularly herbaceous Rosaceae. This is a complex taxon, in which several forms with more specific host plant associations are recognised as subspecies. Slide-mounted specimens cannot usually be identified to subspecies level unless large samples are available. Populations of pale green or red aphids on many Geraniaceae (*Geranium*, *Pelargonium*, *Erodium*) and Malvaceae (*Alcea*, *Malva*), as well as many plants in other families, are regarded as ***A. malvae*** (Mosley, 1841) s. str. (with *geranii* Kaltenbach, 1862 and *pelargonii* Kaltenbach, 1843 as synonyms), and are of almost world-wide distribution, with anholocycly in warmer climates and indoor populations. ***A. malvae* ssp. *agrimoniae*** (Börner, 1940) is yellowish green and found in flowerheads or on undersides of leaves of *Agrimonia* spp. in Europe and W Asia. ***A. malvae* ssp. *poterii*** Prior & Stroyan, 1964 is bright salmon pink, yellowish or green and found on *Sanguisorba minor* (= *Poterium sanguisorba*) in England. ***A. malvae* ssp. *potha*** Börner, (1943) 1950 is pale yellowish or greyish green and associated with *Alchemilla* spp. - and possibly also occurs sometimes on

Acaena spp. *Potentilla* spp. and *Geum rivale* - throughout Europe. Records of ssp. *potha* from *Potentilla* may be due to confusion with the almost indistinguishable *A. boreale* (q.v.). **A. malvae ssp. rogersii** (Theobald, 1913) is green or yellow-green, often shiny, and may form large colonies on young leaves of *Fragaria* in northern and western Europe (Blackman & Eastop, 2000). From the key it can be seen that *poterii* is relatively short -haired, *boreale* and *potha* have a relatively short R IV+V, and *agrimoniae* and *malvae* s. str. often have many more accessory hairs on R IV+V than the other subspecies. The recognised subspecies apparently live all-year-round on their respective host plants; males are usually apterous, with secondary rhinaria distributed III 28-60, IV 0 (-14) V 5-20, but ssp. *poterii* and *rogersii* sometimes have alate males, and occasional hybridisation may occur between host-specific and more polyphagous populations, further confusing the taxonomic situation (Prior & Stroyan, 1964; Müller, 1983).

Acyrthosiphon ononis (Koch, 1855)

Apterae are green or pinkish red in life: BL 2.7-3.9 mm. They feed only on restharrows, *Ononis* spp. Oviparae and apterous males (with secondary rhinaria distributed III 50-74, 0-14, V 17-24) occur in late September to October. Oviparae often have less swollen hind tibiae with fewer scent glands than *A. pisum*. This species is closely related to *A. pisum*, and has often been regarded as a subspecies. In England, Wales, Scotland, and most of Europe.

Acyrthosiphon pisum (Harris, 1776) **Pea Aphid** Figs 1n, 35b, 108

Apterae are green or pink in life, with dark antennal joints; BL 2.5-4.3 mm. Immatures are dusted with wax. Alatae have head and thorax only slightly less pale than abdomen. *A. pisum* feeds on many genera and species of herbaceous Leguminosae, and is an important pest of peas, clover and lucerne. Distribution is world-wide. Oviparae and males occur in late September to October. British populations usually have apterous males (with secondary rhinaria distributed III 37-79, IV 0-20, V 14-24), but alate males are common in some parts of the world. For further information see Blackman & Eastop (2000, 2006).

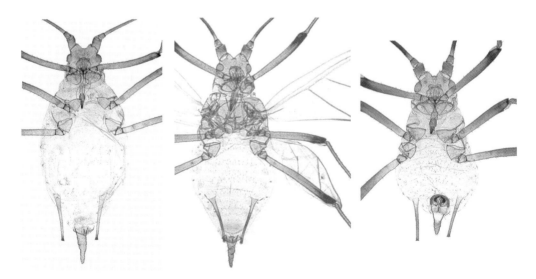

Figure 108. Aptera, alata and apterous male of *Acyrthosiphon pisum*.

Acyrthosiphon primulae (Theobald, 1913) Figs 19a, 109

Apterae are shiny pale yellow to greenish-yellow in life, with dark tips to antennae and legs; BL 2.0-2.5 mm. Alatae have dark dorsal cross-bands and post-siphuncular sclerites, and resemble those of *Microlophium*, in which genus it has sometimes been placed (e.g. Heie, 1994). It is found on the undersides of leaves of *Primula* spp., (*veris, kewensis*). No sexual morphs have ever been recorded. In England, Scotland and Ireland; apparently rare elsewhere in Europe, but it has been introduced to Tasmania, New Zealand and California.

Figure 109. Aptera and alata of *Acyrthosiphon primulae*.

Amphorophora Buckton, 1876

Medium-sized to large, usually pale-coloured aphids with spindle-shaped body and long appendages, similar to *Macrosiphum* but with swollen ('amphora-like') siphunculi lacking any subapical reticulation. The antennae of apterae as well as alatae often have many rhinaria on ANT III. Males have numerous rhinaria on ANT III and V, but none on IV. Hairs on the dorsal body and antennae are blunt, of short to medium length. First tarsal segments all have 3 hairs. The siphunculi are long and distinctly swollen on the distal part, usually pale with dark tips; they lack subapical polygonal reticulation. The cauda is pale, and tongue- or finger-shaped, or triangular.

The genus is holarctic, with 28 species. They live without host alternation, mainly on Rosaceae (especially *Rubus*), but a few species feed on ferns. They are not visited by ants.

There are 5 British species.

Key to apterous viviparae of British *Amphorophora*

1. Apices of tibiae very dark with scaly imbrication (Fig. 110). Siphunculi usually dark distally and very dark at apices (Fig. 112). Base of ANT VI 1.7-2.1× HT II, which is 0.14-0.19 mm long .... ***ampullata*** Buckton, 1876

- Apices of tibiae pale, dusky or dark, without imbrication. Siphunculi pale or dusky, or with dusky apices. Base of ANT VI 1.0-2.3× HT II (less than 1.7× unless HT II is 0.1 mm long or less) 2

 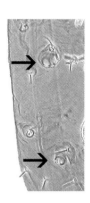

110   111

2. Well-developed marginal tubercles regularly present on ABD TERG 2-5 (Fig. 111). R IV+V bearing 21-28 accessory hairs, and 1.9-2.6× longer than HT II, which is 0.1 mm long or less. ANT III with 0-2 secondary rhinaria ....
.... ***tuberculata*** Brown and Blackman, 1985

- Marginal tubercles usually absent from abdomen, if present then very small in size and few in number. R IV+V with 8-16 accessory hairs, and less than 1.5× longer than HT II which is more than 0.1 mm long. ANT III with 1-30 rhinaria 3

3. ANT III bearing 1-10 rhinaria and with its longest hairs 17-30 μm long. Siphunculi 2.2-3.1× cauda which bears 7-9 hairs .... ***gei*** (Börner, 1939)

- ANT III bearing 2-44 rhinaria and with its longest hairs 26-48 μm long. Siphunculi 2.1-2.6× cauda which bears 8-21 hairs 4

4. Base of ANT VI 0.95-1.25× length of R IV+V (if necessary examine several specimens). Value of function (length of R IV+V)[3] divided by length of ANT III greater than 3925 in c.90% of specimens (both measurements in μm) .... ***rubi*** (Kaltenbach, 1843)

- Base of ANT VI 1.10-1.52× length of R IV+V. Value of function (length of R IV+V)[3] divided by length of ANT III less than 3925 in c.90% of specimens ....
.... ***idaei*** (Börner, 1939)

Key to alate viviparae of British *Amphorophora*

1. Apices of tibiae very dark with scaly imbrication (see Fig. 110). Forewing vein Cu_{1b} distinctly darker than other veins, and with a dark triangle at base (Fig. 112) ... ***ampullata***

- Apices of tibiae dusky or dark without scaly imbrication. Forewing vein Cu_{1b} not distinctly darker than other veins, and without a dark triangle at base 2

2. ANT III with 11-19 rhinaria, and IV with 0-3. Base of ANT VI 1.9-2.5× length of HT II, which is 0.08-0.10 mm. Marginal tubercles regularly present on prothorax and ABD TERG 2-5. R IV+V bearing 21-27 accessory hairs .... ***tuberculata***

- ANT III with 19-67 rhinaria, IV with 0. Base of ANT VI 1.1-1.5× length of HT II, which is 0.11-0.16 mm. Marginal tubercles only sporadically present on ABD TERG 2-5. R IV+V bearing 8-16 accessory hairs 3

3. ANT III with 19-32 rhinaria. Siphunculus with maximum width of swollen part more than 1.7× narrowest width of stem, which is similar to that of middle part of hind tibia (Fig. 113). Cauda with 7-9 hairs .... ***gei***

- ANT III with 23-83 rhinaria. Siphunculus with maximum width of swollen part less than 1.6× narrowest width of stem, which is thicker than middle part of hind tibia. Cauda with 10-21 hairs 4

4. ANT III with 39-83 rhinaria, at a density usually greater than 43 per mm. Cauda with 8-19 hairs (usually 11-14). Base of ANT VI 0.95-1.25× length of R IV+V .... ***rubi***

- ANT III with 23-60 rhinaria, at a density usually less than 43 per mm. Cauda with 11-21 hairs (usually 13-17). Base of ANT VI 1.15-1.47× length of R IV+V .... ***idaei***

Key to alate males of British *Amphorophora*

1. Dorsal abdomen without spinal sclerites and with only faint marginal sclerites. Secondary rhinaria distributed ANT III 21-32, IV 15-30, V 6-16. Marginal tubercles regularly present on prothorax and ABD TERG 2-5 .... ***tuberculata***

- Dorsal abdomen with longitudinal rows of dusky/dark spinal and marginal sclerites. Secondary rhinaria distributed III 30-85, IV 0 (-5), V 10-24 2

2. Apices of tibiae very dark with scaly imbrication (see Fig. 110). Forewing vein Cu_{1b} with a dark triangle at base. (Fig. 112) R IV+V about equal in length to HT II ..... ***ampullata***

- Apices of tibiae dusky or dark without scaly imbrication. Forewing vein Cu_{1b} without a dark triangle at base. R IV+V 1.1-1.3 times longer than HT II 3

3. Base of ANT VI 1.29-1.82 times longer than R IV+V .... *idaei*

- Base of ANT VI less than 1.3 times longer than R IV+V (based on 3 specimens) ...... *rubi*

Amphorophora ampullata Buckton, 1876 Fig. 112

Apterae are green in life, with dark apices to antennae, legs and siphunculi, and pale cauda; BL 3.0-5.0 mm. Apterae have 5-23 rhinaria on ANT III, and alatae have 25-51. They colonise the undersides of fronds of ferns in numerous genera (*Asplenium, Athyrium, Cystopteris, Dryopteris, Polystichum*). Oviparae and alate males (the latter having dark spinal and marginal abdominal sclerites) occur in October-November. Widely distributed in Britain, Ireland, and throughout Europe, Asia and North America. However, the name may be being applied to more than one species. Populations on lady fern (*Athyrium filix-femina*) in Britain have a different chromosome number (2n=10 as opposed to 2n=12 on other ferns), and are probably a biologically distinct but morphologically very similar taxon.

Figure 112. Aptera, alata and male of *Amphorophora ampullata*.

Amphorophora gei (Börner, 1939) Fig. 113

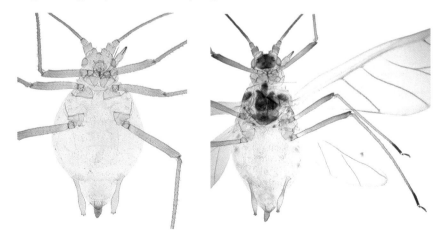

Figure 113. Aptera and alata of *Amphorophora gei*.

Apterae in life are pale grcen or yellowish green with dusky or dark siphunculi and cauda; BL 2.2-3.9 mm. It is found on the undersides of the leaves of *Geum* spp., especially water avens, *G. rivale*, in moist, shady places. There are also records from *Alchemilla vulgaris* and *Filipendula ulmaria*. Presumably sexuales and overwintering eggs are produced on *Geum*, as Hille Ris Lambers (1947a) described the fundatrix from the Netherlands, but the sexual morphs are as yet undescribed. In England, Scotland and Wales, but found rather infrequently; widespread in continental Europe, and introduced to western USA.

Amphorophora idaei (Börner, 1939) **Large Raspberry Aphid** Fig. 114

Apterae in life are pale green, rather shiny, with pale siphunculi; BL 2.6-4.1 mm. They are found on the undersides of leaves of raspberry, *Rubus idaeus* s.str., and cultivated varieties derived from it. Oviparae and alate males appear in October-November. In Britain, Ireland and throughout the rest of Europe. This species has been confused in the past with *A. rubi*, for example in pre-1975 British work on the genetics of host plant resistance and virus transmission.

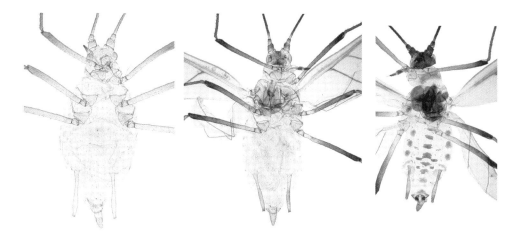

Figure 114. Aptera, alata and male of *Amphorophora idaei*.

Amphorophora rubi (Kaltenbach, 1843) **Large Blackberry Aphid**

Apterae in life are shiny pale yellowish green to green with pale siphunculi; BL 2.2-4.7 mm. They feed on the undersides of leaves of *Rubus* spp., esp. blackberry, *R. fruticosus* s. lat. Oviparae and alate males appear in late October-November, but a proportion of the population also overwinters by continued parthenogenetic reproduction. Morphologically it is very similar to the raspberry aphid *A. idaei*, but differs in chromosome number (Blackman *et al.*, 1977). It is a common species in Britain and Ireland, throughout Europe, and introduced to New Zealand.

Amphorophora tuberculata Brown and Blackman, 1985

Apterae in life are shining deep green; BL 2.2-3.4 mm. It was first found on the leaves and flowerheads of the common garden plant *Geranium macrorrhizum* in south-east England (Brown and Blackman, 1985), and is specific to this host, so it was presumably introduced from montane areas of continental Europe where this plant is native, and it has in fact subsequently been found in Bulgaria (J. Holman, pers. comm.). Oviparae and both apterous and alate males occur in autumn.

Anthracosiphon Hille Ris Lambers, 1947

Medium-sized shiny black aphids, oval-bodied with long appendages, related to *Macrosiphum* but apterae have an extensive dark sclerotic dorsal shield, and the inner faces of the well-developed antennal tubercles are spiculose and only slightly divergent. Hairs on the dorsal body and antennae are of moderate length, and have blunt or slightly capitate apices. First tarsal segments vary in number of hairs, from 2 to 5. Alatae have a dark central patch or broad cross bars. Siphunculi are long, dark, almost cylindrical, with subapical polygonal reticulation and a well-developed flange. The cauda is dark and rather short, tongue-shaped or triangular.

There are 2 species in the world, one European and one North American, both living on *Potentilla* and related Rosaceae. They are not visited by ants.

Anthracosiphon hertae Hille Ris Lambers, 1947 Fig. 115

The only British species. Apterae are shiny black dorsally, lead-coloured with rosy hue ventrally, with blackish appendages; BL 2.3-2.8 mm. Immatures are pinkish brown dusted with grey wax. Alatae have large marginal sclerites and broad dorsal cross-bands sometimes merging into a solid patch. The antennae of apterae have 2-11 rhinaria along one side of ANT III, those of alatae have 20-34. *A. hertae* lives without host alternation on marsh cinquefoil, *Potentilla palustris* (= *Comarum palustre*), silverweed, *P. anserina* (Hille Ris Lambers, 1947a), and perhaps other *Potentilla* spp., colonising runners just above soil or water level. Oviparae (BL 1.9-2.5 mm, with hind tibia slightly swollen on basal half and bearing 30-100 scent glands) and grey-brown alate males (BL 1.7-2.2 mm, with secondary rhinaria distributed III 29-50, IV 0-20, V 10-18, base VI 0-1) appear in September to November. In Britain it has only been collected in Yorkshire and North Wales (Prior, 1971), but alatae have been trapped in Scotland; also recorded from Scandinavia, Netherlands, Germany and Czech Republic.

Figure 115. Aptera, alata and male of *Anthracosiphon hertae*.

Anuraphis del Guercio, 1907

Medium-sized, broadly oval, dull olive-green to brown aphids with short appendages, related to *Dysaphis*, distinguished from that genus by the closely spaced rows of spinules on their siphunculi, the large flattish marginal and spinal tubercles on most abdominal segments, the elongate R IV+V and the hairy cauda. The head is broad, without antennal or median tubercles in apterae, so that the outline of the front of the head is almost straight (but alatae have antennal tubercles somewhat developed). Antennae of apterae have many rhinaria on segment III, not in a row, and some also usually on IV. Alatae have antennae swollen with numerous rhinaria on III and IV. Hairs on the dorsal body and appendages are very short. First tarsal segments usually all have 3 hairs. The dorsal abdomen has dark sclerotic markings in both apterae and alatae, especially marginally and on posterior segments. Siphunculi are short, tapering, ornamented with close-set rows of spinules, and end with a well-developed flange. The cauda is short, semicircular or helmet-shaped, with numerous hairs.

There are 9 species in the world, all palaearctic, typically host-alternating between leaf pseudo-galls on *Pyrus* and subterranean parts of Umbelliferae, or Compositae of the *Tussilago* group, where they are attended by ants. Populations on pear in spring consist of fundatrices and their all-alate progeny. These alate fundatrigeniae or spring migrants have fewer secondary rhinaria and a shorter last rostral segment than those produced on the secondary host plants.

There are 3 British species, one of which is only known from populations on its secondary hosts.

Key to fundatrices of British *Anuraphis*

- Head, thorax and abdomen often with spinal tubercles. Siphunculi 1.35-2.20 times longer than PT, which is 0.6-1.15 times longer than base of last antennal segment. Antennae 5-segmented ....*farfarae* (Koch, 1854)

- Head and thorax without spinal tubercles which are also absent or sparse (1-2) on abdomen. Siphunculi 0.85-1.25 times longer than PT, which is 1.2-1.5 times longer than base of last antennal segment. Antennae 5- or 6-segmented, but when 5-segmented the point of fusion between segments III and IV is often apparent ....*subterranea* (Walker, 1852)

Key to apterous viviparae of British *Anuraphis* on secondary hosts

1. Marginal tubercles present on ABD TERG 1-5, absent from 6 and 7 ....*farfarae*

- Marginal tubercles usually present on ABD TERG 6 and 7 as well as 1-5 (Fig. 116) 2

2. Body length almost always less than 2.3 mm (range 1.63-2.37 mm). R IV+V 0.18-0.24 mm long, and bearing 4-6 accessory hairs .... *catonii* Hille Ris Lambers, 1935

- Body length almost always more than 2.3 mm (range 2.32-3.46 mm). R IV+V 0.24-0.34 mm long and bearing 5-11, but rarely less than 7, accessory hairs .... *subterranea*

Key to alate viviparae of British *Anuraphis*

1. Marginal tubercles usually present on all of ABD TERG 1-7 (see Fig. 116) 2

- Marginal tubercles always absent from ABD TERG 6 and 7 4

2. ABD TERG 8 bearing 6 or 7 hairs which are only 15-20 µm long. ANT IV 1.1-1.3 times longer than HT II which is usually less than 0.14 mm long. Secondary rhinaria distributed III 55-65, IV 12-22, V 0-1 .... ***catonii***

- ABD TERG 8 bearing 8-14 hairs which are 40-65 µm long. ANT IV 1.3-2.2 times longer than HT II which is usually more than 0.14 mm long. Secondary rhinaria distributed III 70-135, IV 4-46, V 0-1 3

3. R IV+V 0.21-0.23 mm long, 1.2-1.4 times longer than HT II. ANT IV 0.23-0.29 mm long, 1.3-1.6 times longer than HT II, and bearing only 4-17 rhinaria .... spring migrants of ***subterranea*** from pear

- R IV+V 0.23-0.36 mm long, 1.6-2.0 times longer than HT II. ANT IV 0.30-0.40 mm long, 1.7-2.3 times longer than HT II, and bearing 28-46 rhinaria .... exules and autumn migrants (gynoparae) of ***subterranea*** from secondary host plants

4. R IV+V 0.23-0.27 mm long, 1.4-1.6 times longer than HT II. ANT IV 0.31-0.36 mm long, 1.9-2.3 times longer than HT II. Secondary rhinaria distributed III 61-76, IV 5-21, V 0-2 .... spring migrants of ***farfarae*** from pear

- R IV+V 0.28-0.33 mm long, 1.8-2.2 times longer than HT II. ANT IV 0.25-0.30 mm long, 1.6-1.9 times longer than HT II. Secondary rhinaria distributed III 76-100, IV 22-42, V 0-10 ... exules and autumn migrants (gynoparae) of ***farfarae*** from secondary host plants

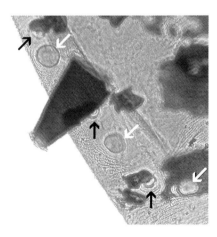

Figure 116. Marginal tubercles of aptera of *Anuraphis subterranea*; black arrows indicate spiracles and white arrows ndicate marginal tubercles on segments 5, 6 and 7.

Key to alate males of British *Anuraphis*

- Marginal tubercles present on ABD TERG 1-7 (rarely missing from 7). Siphunculi 1.0-1.15 times longer than HT II. ANT V with 5-12 secondary rhinaria .... ***subterranea***

- Marginal tubercles on ABD TERG 1-5 only. Siphunculi 1.2 or more times longer than HT II. ANT V with 13-29 secondary rhinaria .... ***farfarae***

Anuraphis catonii Hille Ris Lambers, 1935 Fig. 82

Apterae are bright yellowish and greenish in life, with brown legs and antennae; BL 1.6-2.4 mm. They colonise ground-level parts of burnet-saxifrage, *Pimpinella saxifraga*, and other *Pimpinella* spp. Alatae are much darker, with a large dark dorsal patch. In England south of the Wash, and widely distributed in Europe, but the sexual generation on *Pyrus* is only known from Crimea (Kolesova, 1972). In western Europe it seems to reproduce parthenogenetically on *Pimpinella* throughout the year. The single available male, collected in October in Switzerland, was much smaller than males of the other two British species (BL 1.6 mm) and had secondary rhinaria distributed III 61-78, IV 22-24, V 7, base VI 4-5.

Anuraphis farfarae (Koch, 1854) **Pear-Colt's-Foot Aphid** Figs 1h, 117

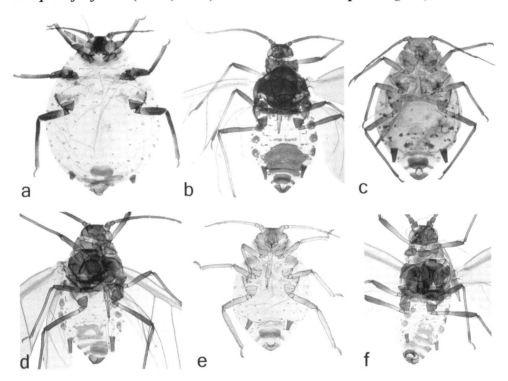

Figure. 117. *Anuraphis farfarae*: (a) fundatrix from pear ; (b) spring migrant alata; (c) aptera from Tussilago; (d) autumn return migrant alata; (e) ovipara from pear; (f) male.

Large (BL 2.7-3.7 mm), plump-bodied brown fundatrices of this species roll and fold the leaves of pear trees (*Pyrus communis*) in spring, producing green progeny that all develop into alatae, for migration to the subterranean parts of colt's-foot (*Tussilago farfara*) and sometimes butterburs (*Petasites* spp.). Apterae on secondary hosts are dark greyish green often tinged with red laterally and with a yellowish spinal stripe, and with dark antennae, legs and siphunculi; BL 2.2-3.2 mm. Immatures are paler, yellowish white, reddish, or pale green with a yellowish white spinal stripe. Alatae have a broad dark patch on ABD TERG 4-6, almost solid in spring migrants but smaller and with a large window in alatae produced on the secondary host. The oviparae on pear in autumn, which have not yet been recorded in Britain, are relatively small and pale, BL 1.6-1.8 mm, with hind tibiae swollen along the entire length and bearing numerous scent glands. Males are relatively large, BL 2.3-2.6 mm, with secondary rhinaria distributed III c.140-150, IV 42-51, V 13-29, base VI 0-1. Part of the population probably also overwinters parthenogenetically on *Tussilago* roots (Shaposhnikov and Sharov, 1977). *A. farfarae* occurs in England, Scotland, Wales and Ireland, throughout Europe and in Central Asia.

Anuraphis subterranea (Walker, 1852) **Pear-Hogweed Aphid** Fig. 81a

Plump-bodied brown fundatrices (BL 2.6-3.0 mm) roll and crumple the leaves of pear trees in spring like *A. farfarae*, but their progeny are brown, developing as alatae which migrate in May to certain Umbelliferae, especially hogweed *Heracleum sphondylium*, wild parsnip *Pastinaca sativa* and alexanders, *Smyrnium olusatrum*, where large ant-attended colonies develop on the lower part of the stem under sheathing leaves. Apterae on secondary hosts are brown, BL 2.3-3.5 mm, and their immature progeny are pale brown. Alatae have a similar dorsal sclerotic pattern to *A. farfarae*. The return migration to pear occurs in September. Oviparae on pear are small (BL 1.4-1.8 mm), relatively pale, with strongly swollen hind tibiae bearing numerous scent glands. Males are relatively large, 2.3-2.7 mm, with secondary rhinaria distributed III c.120-140, IV 28-57, V 5-12, base VI 0-2. *A. subterranea* is found in England, Scotland, Wales, Ireland, throughout Europe and in Central Asia.

Aspidaphis Gillette, 1917

Small, dull green or yellowish brown aphids characterised by the cowl-like backward projection of ABD TERG 8, the short 5-segmented antennae in both apterae and alatae, and the reduced flangeless siphunculi. Antennae of apterae lack secondary rhinaria; those of alatae have secondary rhinaria on segment III or III-IV. The hairs on the dorsal body and appendages are very short. First tarsal segments have 3-3-2 hairs. The dorsum of the aptera is sclerotic, granulate or warty. Siphunculi are either short, with aperture positioned subapically on inner side, or reduced to slightly elevated pores.

There are 2 species in the world, living without host alternation, one on *Polygonum* and the other on *Festuca*. Possibly they do not really belong in the same genus (Stroyan, 1966). They are not attended by ants. Both species occur in Britain, and both apterous and alate viviparae are easily separated by the following key:

- Siphunculi as small thin tubes, 0.03-0.04 of body length, swollen distally and with subapical aperture (Fig. 118). (ABD TERG 8 of aptera pitted) .... *adjuvans* (Walker, 1848) 118

- Siphunculi as small pores with partly sclerotised rims hardly raised above the body surface (Fig. 119). (ABD TERG 8 of aptera rugose, not pitted) .... *porosiphon* Börner, 1950 119

Aspidaphis adjuvans (Walker, 1848) Figs 55a, 120

Apterae are elongate oval, somewhat flattened, yellowish, brownish yellow or pale bluish green; BL 1.3-2.0 mm. Alatae have 4-8 rhinaria spaced out on ANT III, and a small backwardly-pointed projection of ABD TERG 8. *A. adjuvans* lives on knotgrass, *Polygonum aviculare*, and redshank, *Persicaria maculosa*, and is most often found on plants growing in disturbed situations, at roadsides or on paths. The body colour and form make it difficult to detect except by shaking plants over a beating tray. Sexual morphs occur in late September to October. Oviparae are dirty yellowish brown, BL 1.5-1.9 mm, with hind tibiae swollen and bearing c.20-40 rather large and well-formed scent glands. Males are apterous, narrow-bodied and dark, BL 1.1-1.4 mm, with small secondary rhinaria distributed III 15-36, IV 6-17. In Britain it is only recorded from England, but it occurs widely in continental Europe, Asia, and North America.

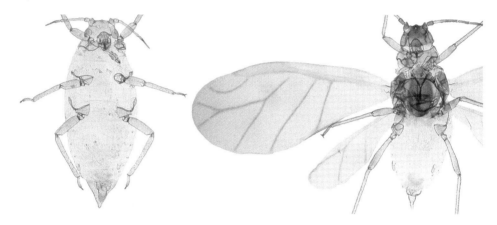

Figure 120. Aptera and alata of *Aspidaphis adjuvans.*

Aspidaphis porosiphon Börner, 1950 Figs 55b, 121

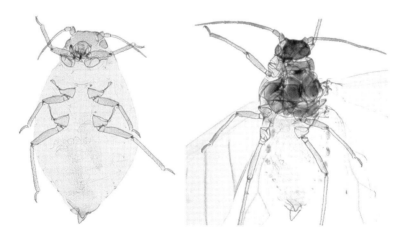

Figure 121. Aptera and alata of *Aspidaphis porosiphon.*

Apterae are dull pale green, oval, with dorsum domed; BL 1.2-1.9 mm. The fundatrices (reared from eggs by H.L.G. Stroyan) are almost identical to apterae of later generations. Alatae have the abdomen pale green apart from dusky marginal sclerites, and secondary rhinaria distributed III 9-17, IV 0-1. This species lives singly on leaf blades of *Festuca rubra* growing in lush herbage (Stroyan, 1966). Sexual morphs occur in October. Oviparae are pale green, BL 1.3-1.9 mm, with yellow eggs visible through cuticle, and have swollen basal two-thirds of hind tibia bearing c.20-50 small, rather ill-formed scent glands. Males are apterous, small and slender, BL 0.9-1.4 mm, brownish green with dusky dorsal abdominal markings, and secondary rhinaria distributed III 24-31, IV 6-12. *A. porosiphon* has been found in England, Wales, Sweden, Germany and Czech Republic.

Aulacorthum Mordvilko, 1914

Medium-sized oval aphids, the apterae usually rather pale with a shiny, sclerotic dorsum, but sometimes there are extensive black markings. Frequently there is a conspicuous spot of internal pigment at the base of each siphunculus. The genus is most clearly defined by the well-developed, spiculose antennal tubercles with their steep-sided, almost parallel inner faces, along with the presence in apterae of 1-3 small rhinaria near the base of ANT III. Alatae have much darker appendages than apterae, and almost always have a pattern of segmentally-divided dark dorsal pigmentation; unlike *Myzus*, they never have a solid black dorsal patch. The hairs on the dorsal body and antennae are very short, and blunt or slightly capitate. First tarsal segments all have 3 hairs. The siphunculi are quite long, tapering or cylindrical, usually pale with darker apices, and end with a rather well-developed flange; they usually lack subapical polygonal reticulation, but in some species there are up to six rows of hexagonal cells. The cauda is pale and tongue-shaped, and most often with 7 hairs.

There are about 40 species in the world, mostly in eastern palaearctic and oriental regions. They all live without host alternation on herbaceous plants. Males may be apterous or alate, even within one species. Most species are host specific, yet there is no clear pattern of host association for the genus as a whole, many different plant families being utilised.

There are five British species.

Key to apterous viviparae of British *Aulacorthum*

1. Dorsum with extensive dark sclerotisation. Siphunculi with basal part usually dark ....
.... ***speyeri*** Börner, 1939

- Dorsum pale. Siphunculi basally pale 2

2. Head spiculose dorsally as well as ventrally. Apices of siphunculi dark without any polygonal reticulation .... ***solani*** (Kaltenbach, 1843)

- Head with very few spicules on dorsal side, usually restricted to inner faces of antennal tubercles. Apices of siphunculi pale or dusky, or if dark then with some distinct polygonal reticulation 3

3. Base of ANT VI 1.6-2.0 times longer than R IV+V, which is 1.0-1.2 times longer than HT II .... ***rufum*** Hille Ris Lambers, 1947

- Base of ANT VI 1.2-1.5 times longer than R IV+V, which is 1.1-1.7 times longer than HT II 4

4. Base of ANT VI 1.8-2.1 times longer than HT II. R IV+V (1.2-)1.3-1.7 times longer than HT II .... ***knautiae*** Heie, 1960

- Base of ANT VI 1.4-1.7 times longer than HT II. R IV+V 1.1-1.3 times longer than HT II .... ***palustre*** Hille Ris Lambers, 1947

Key to alate viviparae of British *Aulacorthum*

Note: The separation of alatae of *A. knautiae* is based on the assumption that *A. sedens* Müller is a synonym.

1. Siphunculi dark on basal part and at apex, with pale middle section. Cross bands on ABD TERG 4 and 5 partially fused between segments .... ***speyeri***

- Siphunculi pale or only dark at apices. If with dark dorsal abdominal cross bands on ABD TERG 4 and 5 then these are not fused between segments 2

2. Outer side of ANT I usually with only 1 hair, occasionally with 0 or 2 (Fig. 122). Some or all of ABD TERG 1-5 usually with transverse cross bands, sometimes reduced or fragmented .... ***solani***

- Outer side of ANT I usually with 2-4 hairs (Fig. 123). ABD TERG 1-5 with variable dark sclerotic markings, sometimes forming cross-bands but often not fused across midline 3

122   a   b   123

3. Base of ANT VI 1.6-2.0 times longer than R IV+V, which is 1.0-1.2 times longer than HT II .... ***rufum***

- Base of ANT VI 1.2-1.5 times longer than R IV+V, which is 1.1-1.7 times longer than HT II 4

4. ANT III with 5-13 rhinaria. Base of ANT VI 2.0-2.5 times longer than HT II. R IV+V 1.4-1.8 times longer than HT II .... **knautiae**

- ANT III with 15-26 rhinaria. Base of ANT VI 1.5-1.9 times longer than HT II. R IV+V 1.1-1.3 times longer than HT II .... **palustre**

Key to alate males of British *Aulacorthum*

(Alate males of *solani* are rare, and insufficient specimens are available to include alate males of *knautiae* and *speyeri*, which have in any case not been recorded in Britain.)

- Secondary rhinaria distributed III 42-46, IV 15-23, V 15-18. Spino-pleural sclerites on ABD TERG 4 and 5 not joined across midline .... **palustre**

- Secondary rhinaria distributed III 19-27, IV 10-12, V 10-12. Spino-pleural sclerites on at least ABD TERG 4 and 5 may be joined across midline to form cross-bands .... **solani**

Aulacorthum knautiae Heie, 1960 Fig. 124

Apterae are yellowish white to pale green, often shiny, without pigment spots at bases of siphunculi; BL 2.3-2.9 mm. Alatae have the abdomen yellowish green with fragmented dark cross-bands and spots. This aphid lives all-year-round on field scabious, *Knautia arvensis*, feeding on undersides of lower leaves, with usually only one or a few specimens per leaf (Heie, 1960). Oviparae and males occur in late September and October in continental Europe, but have not yet been recorded in Britain. Males found in Denmark were apterous (Heie, 1960), but they were alate in Germany (Müller, 1966, as *A. sedens*, which is here regarded as a synonym). In England this species has been found in a few localities south of the Wash, and it is also known from Denmark, Germany, Czechoslovakia and Switzerland.

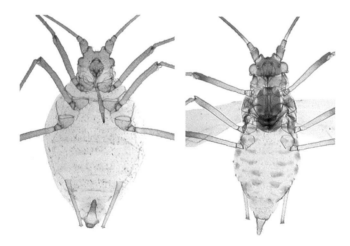

Figure 124. Aptera and alata of *Aulacorthum knautiae*.

Aulacorthum palustre Hille Ris Lambers, 1947 Fig. 123a, 125

Apterae are pinkish, pale green or whitish green, with black tips to antennae and legs, and often with rust-coloured or darker green spots around bases of siphunculi; BL 2.4-3.2 mm.

Alatae have a reddish or greenish abdomen with variably fragmented cross bands or paired spots. Immatures have cross-bands of wax powder. It lives on undersides of leaves of liguliflorous Compositae such as *Hypochaeris*, *Leontodon*, *Picris* and *Taraxacum*. Alate males have been trapped in England in October, but oviparae have never been described and this species may usually overwinter parthenogenetically; apterous and alate viviparae have been found on underside of rosette leaves of *Taraxacum* in England in February (BMNH colln, coll. J.H. Martin). In England, Scotland, Wales and Ireland, and in continental Europe east to Poland and Czech Republic, and south to Italy.

Figure 125. Aptera, alata and male of *Aulacorthum palustre*.

Aulacorthum rufum Hille Ris Lambers Fig. 123b, 126

Apterae are green or dirty reddish brown, slightly wax-powdered laterally and ventrally; BL 2.0-2.7 mm. It lives all-year-round on young shoots and undersides of leaves of *Vaccinium* spp., usually bilberry (*V. myrtillus*). The sexual morphs have not been described, but apterous males have been found in Germany (Börner, 1952), and England (Derbyshire, 8.x.1978; BMNH collection, leg. J.H.Martin) and an ovipara was collected along with viviparae in Scotland (Aberdeenshire, 18.viii.1971; BMNH collection, leg. H.L.G. Stroyan). In England, Scotland and Wales, and through northern and central Europe.

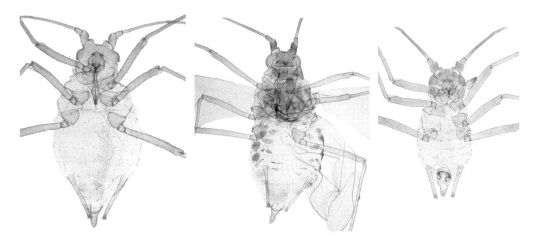

Figure 126. Aptera, alata and male of *Aulacorthum rufum*.

Aulacorthum solani (Kaltenbach, 1843). **Glasshouse-Potato Aphid** Figs 47, 48, 122, 127

Apterae are usually shining pale whitish or yellowish green with darker green, orange or rust-coloured spots at bases of siphunculi, but sometimes dull green or greenish brown; BL 1.8-3.0 mm. Alatae have a dark head and thorax and a variably-developed pattern of dark dorsal abdominal cross-bands. This is an extremely polyphagous aphid, colonising plants in many different families of both dicots and monocots. Probably of European origin, it is now almost world-wide. In countries such as Britain with mild climates and in glasshouses it overwinters parthenogenetically, but it also has the unusual ability to go through the sexual phase on many different plant species, producing both apterous and (much more rarely) alate males. In continental Europe, but not so far recognised in Britain, there are a number of taxa that are morphologically similar to *A. solani* and often regarded as subspecies, but they have specific host associations (e.g. *A. aegopodii* Börner, 1939 on *Aegopodium podagraria* and *A. langei* Börner, 1939 on *Pulmonaria officinalis*) and are clearly functioning as distinct biological species.

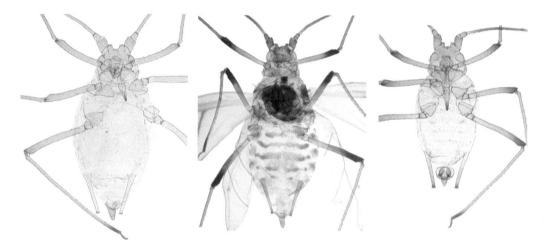

Figure 127. Aptera, alata and apterous male of *Aulacorthum solani*.

Aulacorthum speyeri Börner, 1939 Fig. 128

Apterae are shiny black except for pale yellow areas on mesonotum and ABD TERG 1 and 5, with mainly pale antennae and legs, siphunculi dark at base and apex, and dark cauda. Alatae have extensive black dorsal sclerotic markings (Fig. 128); BL 1.9-2.9 mm. On undersides of leaves of lily-of-the-valley *Convallaria majalis*, solomon's-seal *Polygonatum multiflorum*, and some other Convallariaceae. It is also sometimes found in small numbers in concealed situations on certain other plants (*Anthericum, Lycopus, Potentilla*). Infested leaves of *Convallaria* develop large yellow spots and become desiccated. Oviparae (which have strongly swollen hind tibiae bearing numerous scent glands and lack dark dorsal abdominal pigmentation) and alate males occur in October in northern Europe. In England, Scotland, north-west Europe, Italy, Hungary, and eastward to Iran. Müller (1979) gave an account of this aphid.

Figure 128. Aptera and alata (with two variants of abdominal sclerotisation) of *Aulacorthum speyeri*.

Brachycaudus van der Goot, 1914

Small to medium-sized shiny green, brown or black aphids with rather short appendages. Characteristic features of species in this genus are the rounded spiracular apertures, short cauda, and the short, often rather smooth-surfaced siphunculi which have a subapical annular incision below the flange. The head is broad, with median and antennal tubercles only weakly developed. Antennae are usually 6-segmented but shorter than body; those of apterae lack secondary rhinaria (except in alatiform individuals), those of alatae have them on III or III-IV, or more rarely on III-V. Hairs on the dorsal body and appendages vary greatly in length between species. First tarsal segments have 3-3-3(2) or 4-4-4 hairs (the latter in subgenus *Appelia*). Apterae often have very extensive dark dorsal sclerotisation (subgenera *Acaudus* and *Appelia*), and alatae almost always have a large dark dorsal abdominal patch. The cauda is semicircular or helmet-shaped, or (in apterae of subgenus *Thuleaphis*) extremely short and broadly rounded.

There are 45 species in the world, 44 in the palaearctic and one nearctic. Fourteen species belonging to four of the 5-6 recognised subgenera live on *Prunus* or use this as their primary host, but secondary host associations seem to be evolutionarily labile. Andreev (2004) revised the subgeneric classification, but recent molecular work by Couer-d'Acier *et al.* (2008) has shown that further clarification of relationships within the genus is needed, and the subgeneric names used here reflect their findings. Colonies are regularly visited by ants.

There are 19 British species.

Key to apterous viviparae of British *Brachycaudus*

1. R IV+V 0.6-1.15 times as long as HT II, if 1.0-1.15 times then dorsal abdomen always has extensive dark sclerotisation 2

- R IV+V 1.0-2.0 times as long as HT II, but if 1.0-1.2 times then dorsal abdomen lacks any dark sclerotisation 10

2. Cauda very short and broadly rounded, hardly developed, usually less than half as long as its basal width (e.g. Fig. 129). Siphunculi also very short, 0.03-0.07 of body length. PT 1.6-3.6 times longer than base of last antennal segment, (subgenus *Thuleaphis*) 3

129

- Cauda semi-circular or helmet-shaped, usually more than half as long as its basal width (e.g. Figs 130, 135). Siphunculi 0.04-0.20 of body length. PT 2.2-5.9 times longer than base of last antennal segment 6

130

3. Siphunculi 0.09-0.12 mm long, longer than their basal width, similar in length to HT II. Longest hair on ANT III 15-35μm, 0.8-1.3 times basal diameter of segment. Usually with a dark patch (often fragmented) on ABD TERG 3-5, but ABD TERG 6-8 pale or with only small sclerites (Fig. 142a) .... spring generations of ***amygdalinus*** (Schouteden, 1905) on *Prunus*

- Siphunculi 0.04-0.07 mm long, not longer than their basal width, less than 0.6 of length of HT II. Longest hair on ANT III 4-10 μm, 0.3-0.7 times basal diameter of segment. With or without dark sclerotisation of ABD TERG 3-5, but ABD TERG 6-8 almost always with dark cross bands (Figs 142c, 152, 154) 4

4. Antennae not or hardly any longer than width of head across (and including) eyes. Dorsal abdomen usually with dark cross bands on ABD TERG 6-8, but no pigmentation on ABD TERG 1-5 (Fig. 142c) .... ***amygdalinus*** on secondary hosts (Polygonaceae)

- Antennae distinctly longer than head width across eyes. Dorsal abdomen with a dark cross band on ABD TERG 5 (or 4-5) as well as 6-8, and often with some smaller dark sclerites on more anterior tergites (Figs 152, 154) 5

5. Longest hair on ANT III 4-7 μm, 0.3-0.5 times basal diameter of segment. R IV+V 1.3-2.0 times longer than siphunculi, which are 0.46-0.62 of length of HT II .... ***rumexicolens*** (Patch, 1917)

- Longest hair on ANT III 7-10 μm, 0.5-0.7 times basal diameter of segment. R IV+V 1.9-2.6 times longer than siphunculi, which are 0.29-0.40 of length of HT II .... ***sedi*** (Jacob, 1964)

6. Longest hair on spinal region of ABD TERG 3 is 39-65 μm, and on ANT III 31-42 μm, as long as or longer than basal diameter of ANT III. PT 3.4-5.9 times longer than base of last segment .... ***populi*** (del Guercio, 1911)

- Longest hair on spinal region of ABD TERG 3 is 4-32 μm, and on ANT III 6-24 μm, usually shorter than and often much shorter than basal diameter of ANT III. PT 2.2-4.8 times longer than base of last segment 7

7. First tarsal segments with 3 hairs on fore and mid tarsi and 2 hairs on hind tarsi. Dorsal sclerotisation present or absent but never very clearly defined (see Fig. 155), except in alatiform specimens with secondary rhinaria. No marginal abdominal tubercles. PT 2.2-3.0 times longer than base of last segment .... ***spiraeae*** Börner, 1932

- First tarsal segments all with 4 hairs (Fig. 131). Dorsum with extensive clearly-defined dark sclerotisation, usually consisting of broad cross-bands fused or partly fused between tergites. Marginal abdominal tubercles usually present on most of segments 1-5. PT 2.3-4.8 times longer than base of last segment (subgenus *Appelia*) 8

131

8. Longest hairs on marginal sclerites of ABD TERG 2-4 are 12-60 μm long, often longer than diameter of marginal tubercle (if present) on same sclerite (Fig. 132, white arrows). Longest hair on inner side of ANT II 16-56 μm, 0.8-1.6 times longer than basal diameter of ANT III. Dorsal cross-bands usually fused into a solid patch on ABD TERG 2-5 that connects on each side with marginal sclerites (Fig. 151) .... ***prunifex*** Theobald, 1926

- Longest hairs on marginal sclerites of ABD TERG 2-4 are 4-15 μm long, usually less than half diameter of marginal tubercle (if present) on same sclerite (Fig. 133, white arrows). Longest hair on inner side of ANT II 10-32 μm, 0.4-1.0 times longer than basal diameter of ANT III. Dorsal cross-bands often not completely fused intersegmentally and/or with a spinal gap, and not connected to marginal sclerites, at least on ABD TERG 2-3 9

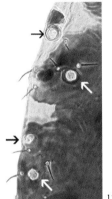

132

9. Marginal abdominal tubercles on ABD TERG 2-4 (circular membranous areas, indicated by white arrows in Fig. 133) mostly less than diameter of spiracles (black arrows) on same segments. R IV+V 0.75-1.0 times length of HT II, which is 0.13-0.175 mm. Dorsal abdominal sclerotisation variable but often with cross-bands divided spinally as well as intersegmentally into paired pleural patches (Fig. 156) ...... ***tragopogonis*** (Kaltenbach, 1843)

- Marginal abdominal tubercles on ABD TERG 2-4 mostly greater than 18 μm in diameter, often as large as or larger than spiracles (Fig. 134). R IV+V 0.9-1.15 times length of HT II, which is 0.12-0.15 mm. Dorsal cross-bands on ABD TERG 3-5 usually fused intersegmentally and rarely divided spinally (Fig. 153) .... ***schwartzi*** (Börner, 1931)

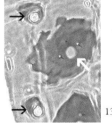

133

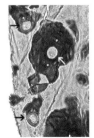

134

10. Dorsum without dark sclerotisation (Fig. 145c) .... ***helichrysi*** (Kaltenbach, 1843)

- Dorsum with extensive dark sclerotisation 11

11. Longest hairs on ABD TERG 3 as long as or longer than basal diameter of ANT III
.... 12

- Longest hairs on ABD TERG 3 very short, usually much shorter than basal diameter of ANT III 13

12. ANT III with 6-15 hairs, the longest 17-29 μm long, 0.5-1.3 of length of basal diameter of ANT III, and 0.29-0.56 of length of the longest spinal hair on ABD TERG 3. Cauda about as long as its basal width, usually with a distinct basal constriction, and bearing 6-12 hairs (Fig. 135) .... *klugkisti* (Börner, 1942)

135

- ANT III with 15-24 hairs, the longest 32-53 μm long, 1.1-2.8 of length of basal diameter of ANT III, and 0.63-1.4 of length of the longest spinal hair on ABD TERG 3. Cauda shorter than its basal width, not or only slightly constricted at base, and bearing 11-17 hairs (Fig. 136) .... *lychnidis* (Linnaeus, 1758)

136

13. ABD TERG 8 bearing 10-14 short hairs, not in a single row (e.g. Fig. 137) 14

- ABD TERG 8 bearing 4-8 short or long hairs in a single row (e.g. Fig. 138) 15

137

138

14. R IV+V 0.165-0.190 mm. Cauda with 5-9 hairs, and anterior half of subgenital plate with 12-17 hairs. Marginal tubercles often absent, if present then usually only on prothorax and ABD TERG 2-4 .... *malvae* Shaposhnikov, 1964

- R IV+V 0.135-0.160 mm. Cauda with 10-16 hairs, and anterior half of genital plate with 2-9 hairs. Medium to large flat marginal tubercles usually present on pronotum and some or all of ABD TERG 1-5 .... *linariae* Stroyan, 1950

15. Hairs on ABD TERG 8 very short, less than 10 μm long, like the dorsal hairs on more anterior segments (Fig. 138) .... *lucifugus* F.P.Müller ex Börner, 1952

- Hairs on ABD TERG 8 are 30-113 μm long, much longer than the dorsal hairs on more anterior segments (e.g. Fig. 139) 16

139

16. ANT III bearing 4-11 rhinaria (3-6 in oviparae) .... *jacobi* Stroyan, 1957

- ANT III without rhinaria except in clearly alatiform specimens 17

17. R IV+V 0.130-0.165 mm, 1.2-1.5 times longer than HT II. Mesosternal tubercles rather low and inconspicuous .... *persicae* (Passerini, 1860)

- R IV+V 0.180-0.225 mm, 1.3-2.0 times longer than HT II. Semi-globular mesosternal tubercles often quite evident (Fig. 140, 144) 18

140

18. Conspicuous flat marginal tubercles usually present on all segments from pronotum to ABD TERG 7 (Fig. 141), and spinal tubercles on pronotum and ABD TERG 7 and 8. Siphunculi pale or dusky... *bicolor* (Nevsky, 1929)

141

- Marginal tubercles absent or present on ABD TERG 2-4 only, if present then small and inconspicuous, and spinal tubercles usually absent. Siphunculi dark 19

19. Longest hairs on ABD TERG 8 are 20-61 μm long. Longest hairs on hind femur are 10-25μm long .... *lateralis* (Walker, 1848)

- Longest hairs on ABD TERG 8 are at least 70μm long. Longest hairs on hind femur are more than 25μm long .... *cardui* (Linnaeus, 1758)

Key to alate viviparae of British *Brachycaudus*

1. R IV+V 0.6-1.05 times as long as HT II 2

- R IV+V 1.1-2.0 times as long as HT II 9

2. Siphunculi very short, 0.02-0.06 of body length. PT 1.7-3.2 times longer than base of ANT VI (subgenus *Thuleaphis*) 3

- Siphunculi 0.06-0.18 of body length. PT 2.8-7.8 times longer than base of ANT VI 5

3. PT 1.5-1.7 times length of HT II, which is 0.145-0.16 mm .... *sedi*

- PT 1.7-2.5 times length of HT II, which is 0.10-0.13 mm 4

4. Siphunculi usually longer than their basal width, which is 2-3 times the length of the longest hair (18-30 µm) on the ante-siphuncular (marginal) sclerite. ABD TERG 8 bearing 9 -12 hairs. Hind tibia usually 2.2-2.6 times longer than ANT III (but up to 2.9 times in small specimens on *Polygonum*). Marginal abdominal tubercles variably present on segments 1-5 .... ***amygdalinus***

- Siphunculi about as long as their basal width, which is 4-8 times the length of the longest hair (10-15 µm) on the ante-siphuncular (marginal) sclerite. ABD TERG 8 bearing 5 -11 hairs (usually 6-8). Hind tibia 2.6-3.4 times longer than ANT III. Marginal abdominal tubercles absent .... ***rumexicolens***

5. First tarsal segments with 3 hairs on fore and mid tarsi, and 2-3 hairs on hind tarsi 6

- First tarsal segments all with 4 hairs 7

6. Hairs on ANT III all less than 0.5 of basal diameter of segment. PT 2.8-3.8 times longer than base of ANT VI. ANT IV with 4-14 secondary rhinaria, and V with 0-2. HT I with 2 hairs .... ***spiraeae***

- Longest hairs on ANT III longer than basal diameter of segment. PT 4.7-7.5 times longer than base of ANT VI. ANT IV with 0-3 secondary rhinaria, ANT V with 0. HT I with 3 hairs .... ***populi***

7. Hairs on marginal sclerites of ABD TERG 2-4 are 25-60 µm long, usually as long as or longer than diameter of marginal tubercle (if present) on same sclerite (see Fig. 132). Longest hair on inner side of ANT II 16-56 µm, 0.8-1.6 times longer than basal diameter of ANT III. Dorsal patch usually solid over ABD TERG 3-6 (Fig. 151) .... ***prunifex***

- Hairs on marginal sclerites of ABD TERG 2-4 are 4-12 µm long, less than half diameter of marginal tubercle (if present) on same sclerite (see Fig. 133). Longest hair on inner side of ANT II 8-32 µm, 0.4-1.0 times longer than basal diameter of ANT III. Dorsal patch with a narrow intersegmental division between ABD TERG 3 and 4, and at least with a narrow window between ABD TERG 5 and 6 (Figs 153, 156) 8

8. Marginal abdominal tubercles (circular membranous areas) on ABD TERG 2-4 (if present) mostly not larger than spiracles on same segments (see Fig. 133). Dorsal patch often divided or with a window between ABD TERG 4 and 5 as well as 5 and 6 (Fig. 156) .... ***tragopogonis***

- Marginal abdominal tubercles on ABD TERG 2-4 mostly as large as or larger than spiracles (see Fig. 134). Dorsal patch usually solid between ABD TERG 4 and 5 (Fig. 153) .... ***schwartzi***

9. Siphunculi 0.9-1.6 times longer than R IV+V 10

- Siphunculi 1.6-2.3 times longer than R IV+V 16

10. Dorsal abdomen without broad cross-bands or a large dark patch, sometimes with broken sclerites on ABD TERG 4-5 only (Fig. 148). Hairs on ABD TERG 8 very short, less than 10 µm long .... *lucifugus*

- Dorsal abdomen with broad dark cross-bands usually fused into a large black patch, Hairs on ABD TERG 8 much longer 11

11. PT 5.0-7.3 times longer than base of ANT VI. Longest hairs on ABD TERG 3 are 35-55 µm. Cauda with 8-17 hairs 12

- PT 3.0-5.0 times longer than base of ANT VI. Longest hairs on ABD TERG 3 are 7-23 µm. Cauda with 4-8 hairs 13

12. ANT III 21-28 times longer than the longest hair borne upon it (20-25 µm). Cauda usually with a distinct basal constriction .... *klugkisti*

- ANT III 12-17 times longer than the longest hair borne upon it (27-43 µm). Caudanot or only slightly constricted at base .... *lychnidis*

13. Siphunculi 0.07-0.11 of body length, 0.8-2.0 times longer than cauda .... *helichrysi*

- Siphunculi 0.12-0.16 of body length, 1.9-3.4 times longer than cauda 14

14. Conspicuous marginal tubercles usually present on all segments from pronotum to ABD TERG 7, and spinal tubercles on pronotum and ABD TERG 7 and 8. ANT IV usually with 1-8 rhinaria .... *bicolor*

- Marginal tubercles absent or present on ABD TERG 2-4 only, if present then small and inconspicuous; spinal tubercles absent. ANT IV usually without rhinaria, or with only 1 15

15. Longest hairs on ABD TERG 8 are 60-70 µm long. Longest hairs on hind femur are 20-30 µm long .... *lateralis*

- Longest hairs on ABD TERG 8 are 85-110 µm long. Longest hairs on hind femur are 40-80 µm long .... *cardui*

16. Dorsal abdominal sclerotisation divided intersegmentally and covering ABD TERG 4-5 or 4-6 only. ANT IV with 6-9 secondary rhinaria .... *linariae*

- Dorsal abdomen with an almost solid black patch usually extending over ABD TERG 3-6. ANT IV with either 0-3 or 10-21 rhinaria 17

17. Secondary rhinaria very protuberant and distributed ANT III 26-45, IV 10-21, V 0-6 .... *persicae*

- Secondary rhinaria less protruberant and distributed ANT III 6-30, IV 0-3, V 0 18

18. Siphunculi 2.1-2.3 times longer than R IV+V. ANT III with 6-16 rhinaria .... *jacobi*

- Siphunculi 1.6-1.8 times longer than R IV+V. ANT III with 21-30 rhinaria ...... *malvae*

Key to alate males of British *Brachycaudus*

1. R IV+V 1.2-1.4 times longer than HT II .... *helichrysi*

- R IV+V 0.7-1.0 of length of HT II 2

2. Siphunculi very short, 0.03-0.04 of body length .... *amygdalinus*

- Siphunculi 0.05 or more of body length 3

3. First tarsal segments with 3 hairs on fore and mid tarsi, and 2-3 hairs on hind tarsi 4

- First tarsal segments all with 4 hairs 5

4. Hairs on ANT III all less than 0.5 of basal diameter of segment. PT less than 5 times longer than base of ANT VI. HT I with 2 hairs .... *spiraeae*

- Longest hairs on ANT III longer than basal diameter of segment. PT more than 6 times longer than base of ANT VI. HT I with 3 hairs .... *populi*

5. Hairs on marginal sclerites of ABD TERG 2-4 are 20-50 µm long, usually as long as or longer than diameter of marginal tubercle on same sclerite. Longest hair on inner side of ANT II more than 16 µm long, at least 0.8 times longer than basal diameter of ANT III .... *prunifex*

- Hairs on marginal sclerites of ABD TERG 2-4 are 4-12 µm long, less than half diameter of marginal tubercle on same sclerite (if present). Longest hair on inner side of ANT II less than 0.8 times longer than basal diameter of ANT III 6

6. Marginal abdominal tubercles on ABD TERG 2-4 (if present) mostly not larger than spiracles on same segments .... *tragopogonis*

- Marginal abdominal tubercles on ABD TERG 2-4 mostly as large as or larger than spiracles .... *schwartzi*

Brachycaudus (Thuleaphis) amygdalinus (Schouteden, 1905) Fig. 142

Apterae on *Prunus* are squat-bodied with rather short pale legs and antennae, green with variably developed dark dorsal markings, often comprising a small fragmented black patch; BL 1.3-2.1 mm. Alatae have a dark dorsal central abdominal patch and 9-21 secondary rhinaria on ANT III. Host-alternating between *Prunus dulcis* or *P. persica* and certain Polygonaceae (*Polygonum aviculare, Persicaria maculosa*). Colonies in spring cause rolling of young almond or peach leaves and stunting of new growth. The leaves are rolled somewhat obliquely with respect to the mid-rib, rather than perpendicularly to the mid-rib as in *B. helichrysi*. Darwish (1983) described the morphology of the spring generations. Apterae on *Polygonum* are more narrow-bodied and often much smaller (0.8-2.0 mm) and feed hidden under the thin bracts surrounding the nodes (Talhouk, 1977). In Europe, Middle East, Pakistan and South Africa. In Britain it is only known from southern England; an autumn population (gynoparae and oviparae) on peach at Harpenden, Herts (Stroyan, 1980), a collection from *P. aviculare* at Chiswick, London (BMNH collection, V.F. Eastop, 23.vii.1995), and alate males (with secondary rhinaria distributed III 37-45, IV 11-17, V 8-13, VI base 1-6) caught in suction traps in October. In milder climates it frequently overwinters in the parthenogenetic phase on Polygonaceae, even where primary hosts are available.

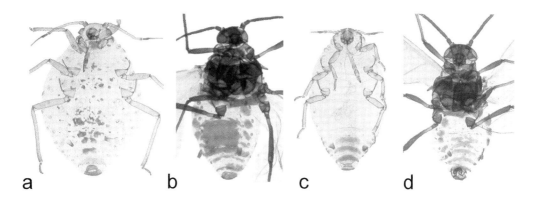

a　　　　b　　　　c　　　　d

Figure 142. *Brachycaudus amygdalinus*; (a) aptera on peach, (b) spring migrant alata, (c) aptera on *Polygonum*, (d) male.

Brachycaudus (Nevskyaphis) bicolor (Nevsky, 1929) Fig. 130, 141, 143

Apterae are shining yellowish tinged with pink, to pale green, with a variably-developed shiny black dorsal abdominal patch, and pale/dusky siphunculi (but this seems to be a feature only of British populations, elsewhere the siphunculi are normally quite dark); BL c.2.1-2.4 mm. Alatae have secondary rhinaria distributed III 28-52, IV 3-8. *B. bicolor* lives in ant-attended colonies on root collars, and at bases of leaves near ground level, of hound's-tongue, *Cynoglossum officinale*. Outside Britain (but see below) it is recorded from other Boraginaceae (*Anchusa, Cerinthe, Heliotropium, Lindelofia, Myosotis*) and from *Codocephalum* (Compositae). Sexual morphs are unrecorded, and overwintering in the parthenogenetic phase has been noted in Italy (Barbagallo & Patti, 1998). In England (Stroyan, 1955), South Wales (Baker, 2009) southern Europe (Madeira, Portugal, Spain, Italy), Egypt, Caucasus, Tajikistan, Uzbekistan and Afghanistan. [The disjunct distribution and pale siphunculi suggest that the British population is perhaps a distinct native taxon, possibly specific to *Cynoglossum*.]

Figure 143. Apterae (with less and more dorsal sclerotisation) and alata of *Brachycaudus bicolor*.

Brachycaudus (Nevskyaphis) cardui (Linnaeus, 1758) **Thistle Aphid** Figs 78, 140, 144

Apterae are shiny black dorsally, light green to yellowish or reddish ventrally (imm. green or reddish); BL 1.9-2.3 mm. Alatae have secondary rhinaria distributed III 15-36, IV 0(-4). It lives in dense ant-attended colonies on stems and leaves of many species of Compositae (e.g. *Arctium, Carduus, Cirsium, Cynara, Chrysanthemum, Tanacetum, Matricaria, Senecio*) and Boraginaceae (e.g *Borago, Cynoglossum, Echium, Symphytum*), and also frequently on other plants, e.g. *Capsella*. In Britain it seems to live all year round on Compositae, but in continental Europe there is a sexual phase on *Prunus*, esp. *P. domestica*. In England, Scotland, Wales, Ireland, throughout Europe, and in Asia, North Africa and North America.

Figure 144. Aptera (with mesosternal tubercles arrowed) and alata of *Brachycaudus cardui*.

Brachycaudus helichrysi (Kaltenbach, 1843) **Leaf-curling Plum Aphid** Figs 84a, 85, 145

Apterae are very variable, pale green, pale yellow, whitish or pinkish; BL 0.9-2.0 mm. Alatae have secondary rhinaria distributed III 13-46, IV 0-18. *B. helichrysi* is a very common aphid on stems and in flowerheads of numerous plant species, esp. Compositae (e.g. *Achillea, Ageratum, Aster, Bidens, Chrysanthemum, Cineraria, Erigeron, Gnaphalium, Helianthus, Matricaria, Senecio*) and Boraginaceae (e.g. *Anchusa, Cynoglossum, Myosotis, Symphytum*), but also many others incl. *Rumex, Saxifraga, Trifolium, Veronica*. It has a sexual phase on *Prunus* spp. (esp. *domestica*, *insititia, spinosa*), spring colonies causing leaves to roll up tightly perpendicular to the mid-rib. Migration to secondary hosts occurs mostly in May, with the return in September-October. The small (BL c.1 mm) yellow green oviparae lay non-diapausing eggs that hatch in November-December in England (Bennett, 1955) and Northern Ireland (Bell, 1983). Parthenogenetic reproduction continues all-year-round in mild climates and in glasshouses. World-wide, and a major pest (see Blackman & Eastop, 2000).

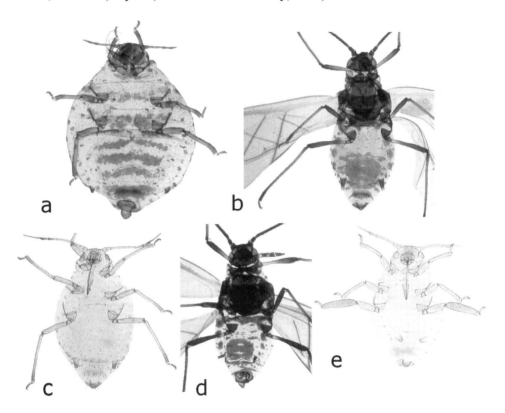

Figure 145. *Brachycaudus helichrysi*: (a) fundatrix on plum, (b) spring migrant alata, (c) aptera on composite secondary host, (d) male, (e) ovipara on plum.

Brachycaudus (Nevskyaphis) jacobi Stroyan, 1957

Apterae are black and shiny dorsally, olive green ventrally; BL 1.4-2.0 mm. Alatae have secondary rhinaria distributed III 6-16, IV 0-2. It lives all-year-round at base of stem or on roots of *Myosotis* and *Pulmonaria* spp., attended by ants. Males are apterous (Müller, 1975a). In England, Scotland (trap records) and continental Europe (Netherlands, Germany, Italy).

Brachycaudus (Acaudus) klugkisti (Börner, 1942) Figs 135,146

Apterae are shining black dorsally, red-brown ventrally; BL 1.5-2.5 mm. Alatae have secondary rhinaria distributed III 11-31 (in a row), IV 0-8. *B. klugkisti* colonises the upper parts of *Silene* (incl. *Melandrium*) spp. Oviparae, with hind tibiae narrow at base and rather abruptly swollen on glandular part in middle, and small dark apterous males (BL c.1 mm) with unusually short, 5-segmented antennae, are produced in October. Stroyan (1950) compared *klugkisti* with *lychnidis*. In England, Scotland, Wales, Shetland Isles, Channel Isles, and most of Europe.

Figure 146. Aptera, alata and male of *Brachycaudus klugkisti*.

Brachycaudus (*Nevskyaphis*) *lateralis* (Walker, 1848)

Apterae are shining black on dorsum, ventrally green or reddish; BL 1.6-2.6 mm. Alatae have secondary rhinaria distributed III 18-35, IV 0. It is found on stems and leaves, usually close to ground, of numerous Compositae incl. *Anthemis*, *Chrysanthemum*, *Galinsoga*, *Matricaria* and *Senecio*. Also found on *Capsella*. Mainly anholocyclic, although a sexual phase may sometimes occur on *Prunus* (Müller & Horatschek, 1979). Closely related to *B. cardui*, and recent DNA studies (Jousselin *et al.*, 2009) indicate that it may just be a variant form of that species. In England and much of continental Europe.

Brachycaudus (*Nevskyaphis*) *linariae* Stroyan, 1950 Figs 137, 147

Apterae are deep blackish green, shiny (imm. pale green); BL 1.4-1.9 mm. Alatae have secondary rhinaria distributed III 11-33, IV 6-9, V 0-2. It lives on the basal parts of *Linaria* spp., attended by ants. In England, Denmark, Sweden, Finland, France, Germany and most of eastern Europe. Sexual morphs are not yet known from UK, but oviparae very similar to apterous viviparae with hardly swollen hind tibia bearing 2-8 scent glands were collected in October in Slovakia (BMNH colln, leg. J. Holman).

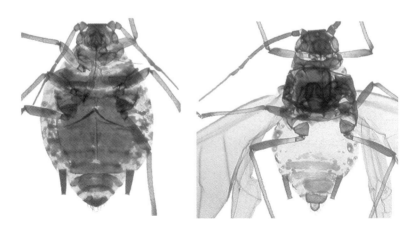

Figure 147. Aptera and alata of *Brachycaudus linariae*.

Brachycaudus (Nevskyaphis) lucifugus F.P.Müller ex Börner, 1952 Figs 138, 148

Apterae are yellowish green with shiny dark brown to black dorsum, the dorsal patch often broken into cross-bands; BL 1.3-2.2 mm. Alatae have secondary rhinaria distributed III 15-30, IV 2-9, V 0-1. It lives without host alternation in ant-attended colonies on roots and at leaf bases of *Plantago lanceolata*. Males are small and apterous. In Europe (southern England, Wales, Channel Isles, Germany, Hungary, Switzerland). See also Stroyan (1964).

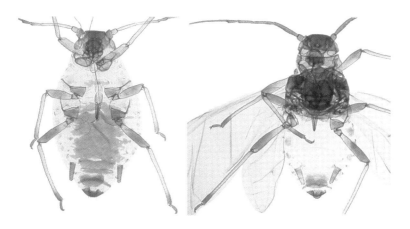

Figure 148. Aptera and alata of *Brachycaudus lucifugus*.

Brachycaudus (Acaudus) lychnidis (Linnaeus, 1758) Figs 136, 149

Apterae are reddish brown with shining brown-black dorsal shield; BL 1.8-2.9 mm. Alatae have secondary rhinaria distributed III 15-34, IV 0-4. It lives without host alternation on stems, leaves and flowers of *Lychnis* and *Silene* (incl. *Melandrium*) spp. Males are apterous (Heie, 1992). In England, Wales, Ireland, most of Europe, eastward to western Siberia, Turkey and Caucasus.

Figure 149. Aptera and alata of *Brachycaudus lychnidis*.

Brachycaudus (Nevskyaphis) malvae Shaposhnikov, 1964

Apterae are shining blackish green; BL 1.8-2.3 mm. Alatae have secondary rhinaria distributed III 21-30, IV 0-3. It lives on *Malva* spp., in ant-attended colonies at the base of the stem and on the lower leaves. Stroyan (1979) provided a redescription based on British specimens of apterae and alatae. Sexual morphs have apparently not been described. In England, South Wales (Baker, 2009), Spain, southern Russia, Ukraine, and China.

Brachycaudus (*Nevskyaphis*) *persicae* (Passerini, 1860) **Black Peach Aphid**
Fig. 139

Apterae have a shiny brown-black dorsum; BL 1.4-2.4 mm. Alatae have secondary rhinaria distributed III 26-45, IV 10-21, V 0-5. *B. persicae* is mostly known as a cosmopolitan pest of peach (Blackman & Eastop, 2000). In Europe, and possibly also in Australia, there seems to be a facultative host alternation from *Prunus* spp. (*domestica, insititia, spinosa, persica*) to Scrophulariaceae. Colonies on plum, damson and blackthorn occur on shoots and suckers near ground level in spring and on roots from summer through autumn and winter. No sexual morphs have been described. However populations on peach are commonly also found on the twigs and are perhaps a distinct species from those on the other *Prunus* species, but there are no reliable morphological discriminants. Apterae on Scrophulariaceae (*Euphrasia, Melampyrum, Rhinanthus*) are smaller than those on *Prunus* and live on the above-ground parts (Burger, 1975; Heie, 1992). In England, Scotland and almost world-wide.

Brachycaudus (*Acaudus*) *populi* (del Guercio, 1911) Fig. 150

Apterae are red-brown with shiny black dorsal shield; BL 1.6-2.9 mm. Alatae have secondary rhinaria distributed III 19-36, IV 0-3. It lives without host alternation on the upper parts of *Silene* spp. Oviparae are produced from the end of August (in Denmark; Heie, 1992). Males can be apterous or alate. In England, Scotland, Wales, Ireland, Channel Isles, and widely distributed in Europe, eastward to Crimea.

Figure 150. Aptera, alata and male of *Brachycaudus populi*.

Brachycaudus (*Appelia*) *prunifex* (Theobald, 1927) Figs 132, 151

Apterae shiny black, dark green or deep yellow-green with black cross-bands; BL 1.4-2.4 mm. Alatae have secondary rhinaria distributed III 25-41, IV 6-13, V 0(-1). It lives all-year-round on *Prunus spinosa*, in spring causing severe leaf curl and discoloration to new growth. There is also a record from *P. atropurpurea*. Suggestions of a facultative host alternation to *Tragopogon* do not appear to be substantiated. Alate males have been collected in September (BMNH collection), but oviparae are not yet recorded. In England, Wales, Ireland, and northern France. This species has been synonymised previously with *B. prunicola*

(Kaltenbach, 1843), which occurs on the same host throughout the rest of Europe and in Central Asia, but it can be distinguished from that species (and from *B. schwartzi*) by the longer hairs on the antennae and anterior abdominal tergites.

Figure 151. Aptera, alata and male of *Brachycaudus prunifex*.

Brachycaudus (Thuleaphis) rumexicolens (Patch, 1917) Figs 129, 152

Apterae are reddish with variably developed dark dorsal markings; BL 1.3-2.1 mm. Alatae have more-or-less fused cross-bands on posterior abdominal tergites and 8-22 secondary rhinaria on ANT III. In summer it is found in inflorescences of *Rumex acetosella*, and sometimes on other Polygonaceae (*Persicaria*, *Polygonum*). It is said to have a sexual phase on *Rumex*, but sexual morphs have not been collected in Britain; males from Turkey and Iran are apterous but alatiform (Tuatay & Remaudière, 1965, and BMNH colln). In England, Scotland, continental Europe, western and Central Asia, India, Australia, North and South America.

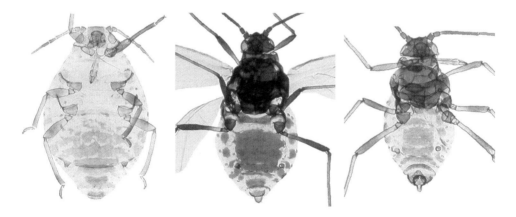

Figure 152. Aptera, alata and (alatiform) male of *Brachycaudus rumexicolens*.

Brachycaudus (Appelia) schwartzi (Börner, 1931) **Peach Aphid** Figs 134, 153

Apterae of BL 1.4-2.1 mm, shiny yellow-brown to dark brown with extensive dorsal black sclerotization; immatures are yellow-brown. Alatae have secondary rhinaria distributed III 25-37, IV 7-14, V 0-1. Living without host alternation on *Prunus persica*; spring colonies cause severe curling and distortion of peach leaves. *P. serotina* is the only other recorded host.

Darwish (1983) gave descriptions of all developmental stages. Males are alate. Records of *B. tragopogonis* from peach in the literature are this aphid. In England, Scotland, continental Europe, Iran, India, South America and California.

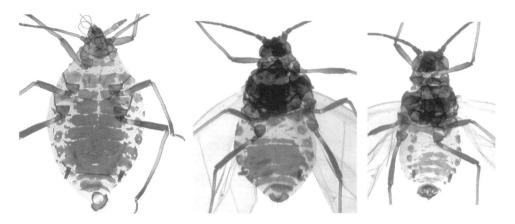

Figure 153. Aptera, alata and male of *Brachycaudus schwartzi.*

Brachycaudus (Thuleaphis) sedi (Jacob, 1964) Figs 68, 70, 154

Apterae are yellowish green, with dark cross-bands on posterior abdomen; B: 1.0-2.1 mm. Alatae have secondary rhinaria distributed III 11-19, IV 0-4, V 0(-1), VI base 0(-1). *B. sedi* lives without host alternation on *Rhodiola* (= *Sedum*) *rosea*, causing distortion of stem apices and flowers in spring and summer. Small apterous males and oviparae are produced in August-September (Jacob, 1964). In Wales, Scotland, Iceland and western Siberia.

Figure 154. Aptera, alata and male of *Brachycaudus sedi.*

Brachycaudus spiraeae Börner, 1932 Fig. 155

Apterae are light green to greyish brown with variable dark dorsal sclerotisation; BL 1.2-1.8 mm. Apterae are often alatiform with up to 11 secondary rhinaria on ANT III and 0-1 on IV. Alatae have secondary rhinaria distributed III 23-34, IV 6-14, V 0-2. It lives all-year-round on *Spiraea* spp., rolling leaves in spring and curling them into narrow 'pods'. Oviparae (BL c.1.2-1.3 mm) and alate males are produced in October. In Scotland and Wales (not yet recorded from England); Europe and Asia.

Figure 155. Aptera and alata of *Brachycaudus spiraeae*.

Brachycaudus (*Appelia*) *tragopogonis* (Kaltenbach, 1843) Figs 133, 156

Apterae are shining grey-brown to dark brown; BL 1.4 –2.3 mm. Alatae have secondary rhinaria distributed III 27-49, IV 13-19, V 0-4. Extent of dorsal sclerotisation of both morphs is very variable. Colonies occur on the aerial parts of *Tragopogon* spp. There is apparently no host alternation. Oviparae and alate males appear in September in Germany (Mostafawy, 1967), but are as yet unknown in Britain. In southern England, Europe, and introduced to South America.

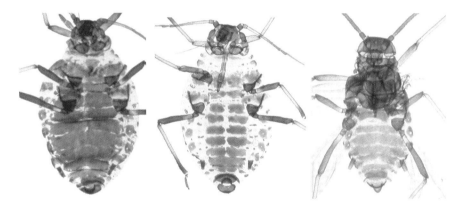

Figure 156. Apterae (with more and less dorsal sclerotisation) and alata of *Brachycaudus tragopogonis*.

Brachycolus Buckton, 1879

Rather small, wax-powdered, narrowly oval aphids similar to *Diuraphis* and *Hayhurstia* but with a specialised association with Caryophyllaceae. The head lacks antennal or median tubercles, and the antennae are 6-segmented but much shorter than body; those of apterae lack secondary rhinaria, those of alatae have only a few large ones. First tarsal segments have 3-3-2 hairs. The dorsum of the aptera is membranous, and the alata has only weakly pigmented marginal sclerites, and bands on posterior abdominal tergites. Siphunculi are very short, flangeless or with a very small flange. The cauda is triangular or tongue-shaped, much longer than the siphunculi, and has 5-6 hairs.

There are 5 species in the world, living without host alternation on Caryophyllaceae and affecting the growth of the plant to form galls or pseudogalls. They are not visited by ants.

There are 3 British species, both apterous and alate viviparae of which can be separated by the following key:-

1. Siphunculi much longer than their basal width, about 0.5 of length of cauda, with a small flange and normal-sized aperture (Fig. 157). Alatae have 9-16 rhinaria on ANT III .... ***cucubali*** (Passerini, 1863)

157

- Siphunculi shorter than or about as long their basal width, less than 0.33 of length of cauda, flangeless and with a reduced aperture. Alatae have 3-9 rhinaria on ANT III 2

2. R IV+V 0.9-1.1 times longer than HT II. Siphunculi pigmented and shorter than their basal widths (Fig. 158). Antenna of aptera only 0.3-0.4 of body length. PT 2.2-2.7 times longer than base of ANT VI in apterae and 2.8-3.3 times longer in alatae .... ***cerastii*** (Kaltenbach, 1846)

158

- R IV+V 0.55-0.72 times longer than HT II. Siphunculi unpigmented, short, cylindrical, about as long as their basal widths (Fig. 159). Antenna of aptera 0.48-0.65 of body length. PT 2.4-3.6 times longer than base of ANT VI in apterae and 3.2-4.5 times longer in alatae .... ***stellariae*** (Hardy, 1850)

159

Brachycolus cerastii (Kaltenbach, 1846) Figs 158, 160

Apterae are dirty green, powdered with wax; BL 1.2-1.7 mm. Alatae have 3-6 rhinaria on ANT III. They live on *Cerastium* spp., esp. *C. arvense*, causing shoots to be stunted and deformed into gall-like structures. Monoecious holocyclic; fundatrices, which lack siphunculi, have been collected in Italy (BMNH collection), but sexual morphs do not seem to have been described. In England, Scotland (one trapped alata), and widely distributed in Europe, but rarely collected.

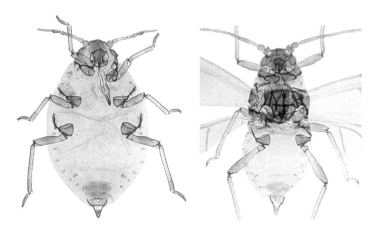

Figure 160. Aptera and alata of *Brachycolus cerastii*.

Brachycolus cucubali (Passerini, 1843) Figs 157, 161

Apterae are whitish yellow to pale green, wax-powdered, with dark appendages; BL 1.4-2.2 mm. Alatae have 9-16 rhinaria on ANT III and 0-2 on IV. It lives on *Silene* spp., feeding on the leaves and rolling them into elongate pseudogalls. Monoecious holocyclic, but the sexual morphs have apparently not been described. In England, throughout most of Europe, and North Africa.

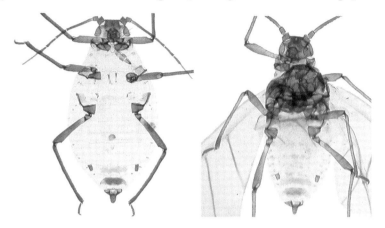

Figure 161. Aptera and alata of *Brachycolus cucubali.*

Brachycolus stellariae (Hardy, 1850) Figs 159, 162

Apterae are pale green, powdered with wax; BL 1.1-2.0 mm. Alatae have 4-9 rhinaria on ANT III and 0-1 on IV. Colonies occur on upper sides of leaves of *Stellaria* spp., which are rolled into oblong pseudogalls. Also recorded from *Moehringia trinervia*. Monoecious holocyclic with oviparae and small, apterous males produced in September. In England, Scotland, Wales, and through north-west, central and eastern Europe.

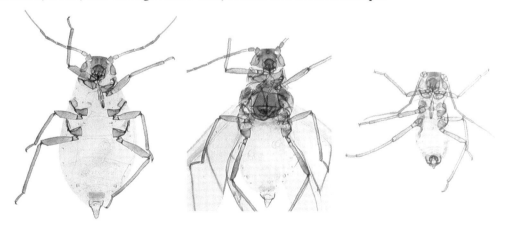

Figure 162. Aptera, alata and male of *Brachycolus stellariae*

Brachycorynella Aizenburg, 1954

Small, wax-covered, long-bodied green aphids with short appendages. The head lacks antennal or median tubercles. The antennae are 6-segmented, much shorter than body, with a short PT. Antennae of apterae lack secondary rhinaria, those of alatae have only a few large ones. Hairs on dorsal body and appendages are very short. First tarsal segments have 3-3-2 hairs. Siphunculi are very short, mammariform, and placed on ABD TERG 6 as in *Diuraphis*. The cauda is long and finger-like.

The genus has only two species, neither of which are found in Britain, but ***Brachycorynella asparagi*** (Mordvilko, 1929) is included here as it has recently expanded its range in Europe. It lives without host alternation on *Asparagus*, causing severe stunting of growth and 'rosetting' of the leaves. In continental Europe, and introduced to North America and China. For further information see Heie (1992).

Brevicoryne van der Goot, 1915

Medium-sized wax-powdered, oval aphids characterised by the short dark barrel-shaped siphunculi and broad-based triangular cauda. The head has very low smoothly rounded antennal and median tubercles, so that the outline of the front of the head is sinuous. Antennae are 6-segmented (occasionally 5-segmented in apterae) but much shorter than body, with an unusually long ANT III. Antennae of apterae lack secondary rhinaria, those of alatae have numerous rhinaria on segment III but usually none on IV. Dorsal body hairs are pointed and moderately long. First tarsal segments have 3-3-2 or 3-3-3 hairs. The dorsum has dark segmentally-divided sclerites in both apterae and alatae.

There are 7 species in the world, living without host alternation on dicotyledons, primarily Cruciferae. They are not visited by ants.

Brevicoryne brassicae (Linnaeus, 1758) **Mealy Cabbage Aphid** Figs 1f, 87, 163

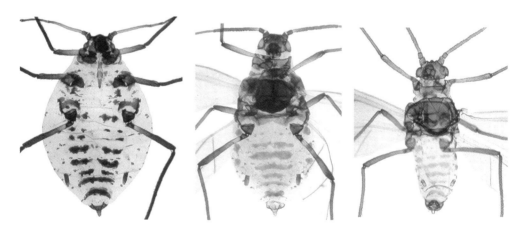

Figure 163. Aptera and alata of *Brevicoryne brassicae*.

The one British species, *Brevicoryne brassicae*, is an important cosmopolitan pest of cruciferous crops. Apterae are greyish-green or dull mid-green, with dark head and dark dorsal thoracic and abdominal markings, BL 1.6-2.6 mm, the body covered with greyish-white wax meal that is also secreted onto the surface of the plant and extends throughout the colony. Alatae have a dark head and thorax, dark transverse bars on the dorsal abdomen, and 50-70 rhinaria on ANT III. *B. brassicae* lives without host alternation on *Brassica*,

Capsella, Lepidium, Sinapis, Raphanus and many other Cruciferae, and also on *Tropaeolum.* Oviparae, with strongly swollen hind tibiae bearing numerous scent glands, and small, thin alate males (BL 1.2-1.5 mm), appear in autumn and give rise to overwintering eggs, but part of the population also overwinters parthenogenetically.

Capitophorus van der Goot, 1913

Apterae are small to medium-sized, usually very pale aphids with slender body and very long almost colourless legs and antennae. Alatae look very different with extensive black dorsal pigmentation and darker appendages. The head has well-developed antennal tubercles with divergent inner faces. Antennae are usually 6-segmented, with a very long PT; apterae lack secondary rhinaria, but alatae have numerous rhinaria on segments III-IV, and usually also on V. Males have numerous rhinaria on ANT III-V. The genus name refers to the dorsal hairs of the apterae which are typically thick and conspicuously capitate, and arise from tuberculate bases, but in several British species such hairs are restricted to the head and posterior abdomen, other segments having smaller hairs. Capitate hairs also sometimes occur on the antennae and legs. Alatae have much shorter, blunt or less capitate hairs. R IV+V is another distinctive feature of the genus; it has a pointed apex, and there are always only two (shortish) accessory hairs on the basal part. First tarsal segments have 3-3-3 hairs. The dorsal abdomen is membranous in apterae, but alatae have a very clearly demarcated black quadrangular patch, and in males there are separate segmental cross-bands. The siphunculi are long and slender, cylindrical or with slight swelling of distal part, pale or with dark tips in apterae, shorter and often darker in alatae. The cauda is pale in apterae, but darker in alatae; tongue-shaped or triangular, much shorter than the siphunculi.

There are 30 species, 25 palaearctic and 5 nearctic. They either have host alternation, with Elaeagnaceae as the primary hosts and Compositae (mainly subtribe Carduinae) or Polygonaceae as secondary hosts, or live all-year-round on Compositae or Polygonaceae. Males are alate in most species, and tend to be small and slender. They are not usually visited by ants.

There are 7 British species. Detailed descriptions of biology and all morphs are given by Hille Ris Lambers (1953).

Key to apterous viviparae of British *Capitophorus*

1. Siphunculi distinctly swollen distally on inner sides (Fig 164). R IV+V similar in length to HT II .... ***hippophaes*** (Walker, 1852)

- Siphunculi cylindrical or thin in middle and broadest at base and apex, not swollen distally or with only very slight subapical swelling (Fig. 165a-b). R IV+V distinctly longer than HT II 2

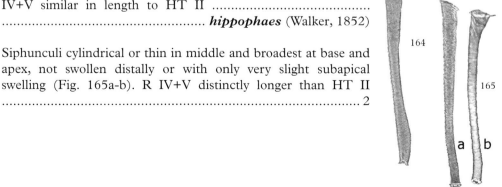

2. ABD TERG 1-4 each with a transverse row of 6-8 hairs (2 spinal, 2 pleural and 2-4 marginal) (Fig. 166) 3

- ABD TERG 1-4 with at least the spinal hairs duplicated 4

3. Spinal abdominal hairs gradually increasing in length from tergites 1 to 8, those on tergite 5 being more than half as long as those on tergite 6 (Fig. 166). ANT PT 6.0-9.2 times longer than base of ANT VI. Siphunculi dusky to dark at apices. R IV+V 1.4-1.5 times longer than HT II. Cauda pointed at apex, with 7-13 hairs (Fig. 167) .... *elaeagni* (del Guercio, 1894)

- Spinal abdominal hairs long only on tergites 6-8, those on tergites 1-5 being much shorter (less than half as long), and often absent or inconspicuous on more anterior tergites (Fig. 168). ANT PT 4.5-6.3 times longer than base of ANT VI. Siphunculi not dark at apices. R IV+V 1.5-1.8 times longer than HT II. Cauda blunt at apex, with 5-8 hairs (Fig. 169) .... *carduinus* (Walker, 1850)

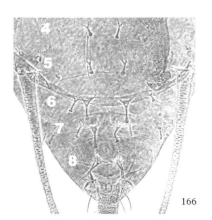

166

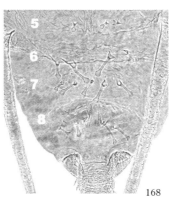

168

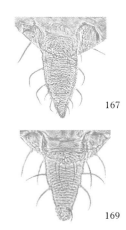

167

169

4. ABD TERG 1-4 each with numerous (18-28) long thick capitate hairs, arranged in paired groups on large pleurospinal and marginal protruberances (Fig. 170). ANT III with 2-5 long thick capitate hairs, some of which are longer than basal diameter of the segment (Fig. 171). R IV+V 2.2-2.5 times longer than HT II .... *pakansus* Hottes & Frison, 1931

- ABD TERG 1-4 each with 10-14 thick capitate hairs (4 spinal, 2-4 pleural and 4-6 marginal), with tuberculate bases but not grouped on large protruberances. If ANT III has 1-5 capitate hairs then these are rarely longer than basal diameter of the segment. R IV+V 1.3-2.3 times longer than HT II 5

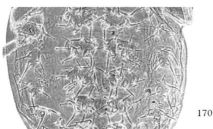

170

171

5. R IV+V 1.33-1.45 times longer than HT II. ABD TERG 1-4 each often with only one pleural hair (arrowed), and 2 marginal hairs (of different lengths) on each side (i.e. 10, or maximally 12, hairs per segment) (Fig. 172). Cauda with 8-13 hairs (5 long and 3-8 shorter) .... ***gynoxanthus*** Hille Ris Lambers, 1953

- R IV+V 1.6-2.3 times longer than HT II. ABD TERG 1-4 each with 2 pleural hairs (arrowed) and (usually) 3 marginal hairs on each side (i.e. usually 14 hairs per segment; Fig. 173). Cauda with 5-8 hairs 6

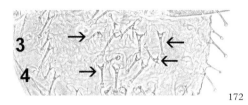 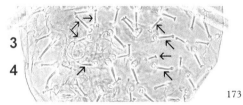

172   173

6. ANT III with 1-5 capitate hairs 0.35-1.15 times diameter of base of segment (Fig. 174). R IV+V 1.8-2.3 times longer than HT II .... ***similis*** van der Goot, 1915

- ANT III with 1-3 very short and inconspicuous blunt hairs, only about 0.15-0.33 of basal diameter of segment (Fig. 175). R IV+V 1.6-1.8 times longer than HT II .... ***inulae*** (Passerini, 1860)

174   175

Key to alate viviparae of British *Capitophorus*

1. Siphunculi distinctly swollen on distal half .... ***hippophaes***

- Siphunculi not swollen on distal half; cylindrical, or thin in middle and broadest at base and apex 2

2. Anterior part of central abdominal sclerite with only 2 spinal hairs and 2 pleural hairs per segment 3

- Anterior part of central abdominal sclerite with at least 4 spinal hairs and 2 pleural hairs per segment (Figs. 178-180) 4

176

3. Siphunculi mainly pale, dusky or dark only at apices. ANT PT 4.5-6.8 times longer than R IV+V, which tapers almost to a point (Fig. 176). Secondary rhinaria distributed III 30-75, IV 10-48, V 3-22 .... ***elaeagni***

- Siphunculi rather uniformly dusky or dark. ANT PT 3.1-4.3 times longer than R IV+V, which ends more abruptly (Fig. 177). Secondary rhinaria distributed III 21-39, IV 8-20, V 0-6 .... ***carduinus***

177

4. R IV+V shorter than cauda, less than 1.5 times longer than HT II. ABD TERG 4 on central abdominal sclerite with 6 hairs, 2 spinal and 1 pleural (arrowed) on each side (Fig. 178) .... *gynoxanthus*

- R IV+V longer than cauda and more than 1.5 times longer than HT II. ABD TERG 4 central abdominal sclerite usually with at least 7-8 hairs (2 spinal and 1-2 pleural on each side), rarely with only 6 (Figs 179, 180) 5

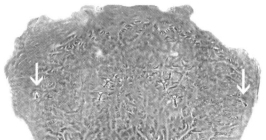

5. Siphunculi with basal half more usually pale and only distal part dark. ABD TERG 4 on central abdominal sclerite with 8 or more spino-pleural hairs, often varying greatly in size, arranged in two widely separated groups (in Fig. 179) .... *pakansus*

- Siphunculi uniformly dusky or dark. ABD TERG 4 on central abdominal sclerite with 2 spinal and (1-) 2 pleural hairs on each side, the spinal hairs being well separated from the pleural ones (arrowed in Fig. 180) 6

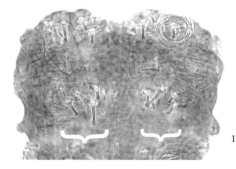 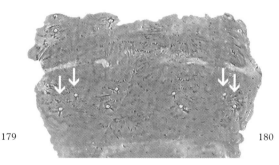

6. Siphunculi longer than (1.05-1.35 times) ANT III. R IV+V 1.8-2.0 times longer than HT II .... *similis*

- Siphunculi usually a little shorter than (0.85-1.02 times) ANT III. R IV+V 1.5-1.8 times longer than HT II .... *inulae*

Key to alate males of British *Capitophorus*

1. Siphunculi distinctly swollen on distal half .... *hippophaes*

- Siphunculi not swollen on distal half; cylindrical, or thin in middle and broadest at base and apex 2

2. ABD TERG 2 and 3 each with one pair of spinal hairs (and one pair of pleural hairs) 3

-   ABD TERG 2 and 3 each with two or more pairs of spinal hairs, and sometimes with more pleural hairs 4

3. Secondary rhinaria distributed ANT III 23-42, IV 18-30, V 6-16 .... *carduinus*

-   Secondary rhinaria distributed ANT III 60-80, IV 20-50, V 15-30 .... *elaeagni*

4. R IV+V less than 1.5 times longer than HT II. ABD TERG 3 and 4 each usually with 6 hairs per segment (2 spinal pairs and 1 pleural pair). Secondary rhinaria distributed ANT III 18-34, IV 9-21, V 8-14 .... *gynoxanthus*

-   R IV+V more than 1.7 times longer than HT II. ABD TERG 3 and 4 each with at least 7-8 spino-pleural hairs per segment (including usually at least two pairs of pleural hairs). Secondary rhinaria distributed ANT III 32-65, IV 14-31, V 8-18 5

5. Siphunculi with basal half more usually pale and only distal part dark. Cross-band on ABD TERG 4 with 8 or more spino-pleural hairs, the hair-bases conspicuously large and the hairs often varying greatly in size, arranged in two widely separated groups .... *pakansus*

-   Siphunculi uniformly dusky or dark. Cross-band on ABD TERG 4 with 2 spinal and (1-) 2 pleural hairs on each side, the spinal hairs being close together and well separated from the pleural ones .... *similis*

Capitophorus carduinus (Walker, 1850) Figs 168, 169, 177, 181

Apterae are pale greenish white to yellowish green, almost translucent, often with two indistinct darker green longitudinal stripes; BL 1.6-2.2 mm. They feed on *Carduus* and *Cirsium* spp., mainly on undersides of lower leaves. It lives all year round on thistles, with oviparae and alate males appearing in September-October. In England, Scotland, Wales, Ireland, and across Europe and Asia.

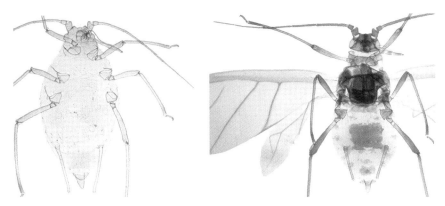

Figure 181. Aptera and alata of *Capitophorus carduinus*.

Capitophorus elaeagni (del Guercio, 1894) Fig. 165a, 176

Apterae are pale greenish white to yellowish green with dark tips to siphunculi; BL 1.4-2.5 mm. It lives on plants in several genera of Compositae, mostly in the sub-tribe Carduinae (*Arctium, Carduus, Cirsium, Cynara, Gerbera, Silybum*), feeding on the undersides of lower leaves. In England, Scotland, and widely distributed through the temperate regions of all continents. The sexual phase that occurs on Elaeagnaceae in continental Europe has not yet been recorded in Britain.

Capitophorus gynoxanthus Hille Ris Lambers, 1953 **(stat. nov.)** Figs 172, 178, 182

Apterae are pale greenish, often with two rather indistinct brighter green longitudinal dorsal stripes; BL 1.6-2.5 mm. It lives all the year round on *Cirsium* spp., especially creeping thistle *C. arvense*, feeding between young leaves at stem apices and on undersides of leaves in spring. Later in summer apterae are found living singly on undersides of radical leaves, and give rise in autumn to the oviparae and alate males. In England, Scotland, Wales, and widely distributed in Europe. [This species was described and hitherto regarded as a subspecies of *C. horni* Börner, 1931, which lives on *Cirsium oleraceum* in continental Europe. However it differs not only in host plant but in colour in life, R IV+V/ HT II ratio (this is less than 1.3 in *horni*), and distribution of rhinaria in both alate viviparae and males (more rhinaria on ANT IV in both morphs of *gynoxanthus*). These differences when considered in relation to the relatively sedentary habits and overlapping distributions of the two taxa provide ample evidence that they are functioning as distinct species.]

Figure 182. Aptera, alata and male of *Capitophorus gynoxantha*.

Capitophorus hippophaes (Walker, 1852) Figs 103a, 183

Fundatrices on Elaeagnaceae (*Elaeagnus, Hippophae*) in April-May are greenish with reddish spots, BL 1.5-1.9 mm. All their progeny develop into alatae which migrate at the end of May to form colonies on the undersides of leaves of *Polygonum* and *Persicaria* spp. Apterae in these colonies are very pale, translucent greenish to yellowish white, sometimes with longitudinal rows of green spots; BL 1.7-2.4 mm. Alate viviparae (gynoparae) and males are produced in September. Immature males have a broad red spinal band, and adult males have a reddish ground colour. Migration back to the primary host occurs in September-October. Oviparae are greenish to orange-red becoming dark red to greenish-black with age. In England, Scotland, Wales, rest of Europe, Asia, North Africa, North and South America.

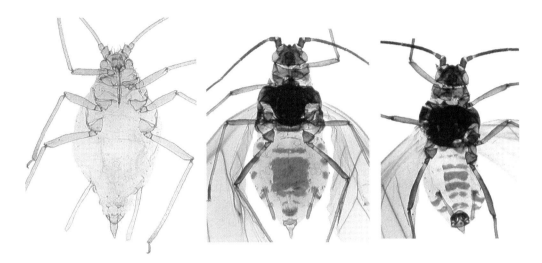

Figure 183. Aptera, alata and male of *Capitophorus hippophaes.*

Capitophorus inulae (Passerini, 1860) Figs 173, 175, 180, 184

Apterae are translucent yellowish white; BL 1.1-1.6 mm. The only host recorded in Britain is ploughman's spikenard, *Inula conyza*, but it has been found on certain other *Inula* spp. in Europe, and around the Mediterranean it is also found on *Dittrichia viscosa* and *Pulicaria* spp. Sexual morphs and life cycle are unknown, and at least in England it probably overwinters in the parthenogenetic phase. In England and Wales, continental Europe, Middle East, central Asia, and introduced to Australia.

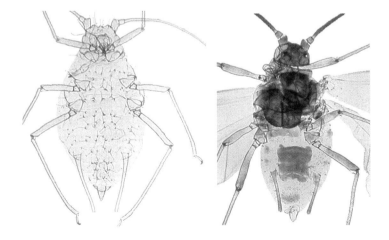

Figure 184. Aptera and alata of *Capitophorus inulae.*

Capitophorus pakansus Hottes & Frison, 1931 Figs 170, 171, 179

Apterae are white or greenish yellow; BL 1.3-2.2 mm. They feed on the undersides of leaves of elecampane, *Inula helenium*; in continental Europe *C. pakansus* is also recorded from other *Inula* spp. (but not *I. conyza*) and from *Telekia speciosa*. Only the secondary host populations have been found in England, but elsewhere there is a sexual phase on *Elaeagnus*. In England, Scotland (one trapped alata), Europe from Norway to Ukraine, and in eastern North America, whence it probably originates. Hille Ris Lambers (1953) provided a detailed account of this species as *C. vandergooti*.

Capitophorus similis van der Goot, 1915 Figs 165b, 174, 185

Fundatrices maturing on Elaeagnaceae (*Elaeagnus*, *Hippophae*) in May are pale green with dorsal longitudinal rows of brighter green spots, BL 1.4-2.2 mm. Alatae are produced in the second and third generations and migrate in June to found colonies on colt's-foot, *Tussilago farfara*, and *Petasites* spp. Apterae on *Tussilago* are translucent yellowish white to white, BL 1.5-2.6 mm, and sit unobtrusively on the undersides of the leaves along veins and leaf margins. Migration of alate viviparae (gynoparae) and males back to the primary host occurs in September-October. Male ground colour is cream to ivory, and oviparae are yellowish green mottled with darker green and orange-yellow. In England, Scotland, Wales, Ireland, rest of Europe, and Asia to eastern Himalayas. In warm climates this species can overwinter parthenogenetically on secondary hosts (Patti, 1983).

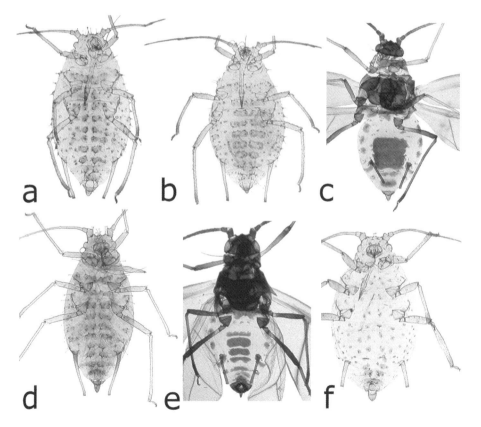

Figure 185. *Capitophorus similis*: (a) fundatrix on sea buckthorn, (b) second generation aptera on sea buckthorn, (c) spring migrant alata, (d) aptera on *Tussilago*, (e) male, (f) ovipara on sea buckthorn.

Cavariella del Guercio, 1911

Small to medium-sized matt green, yellowish or reddish oval aphids, somewhat flattened dorsoventrally and with rather short appendages. Apart from the distinctive host associations (see below), the most characteristic feature of apterae of *Cavariella* is the backwardly-directed process on ABD TERG 8, which always bears two hairs. This process is reduced and wart-like in alatae. The head has no antennal tubercles, so that the outline of the front of the head is convex. Antennae are usually 6-segmented, sometimes 5-segmented in apterae in summer, shorter than the body, with PT very variable in length in different species. Antennae of apterae lack secondary rhinaria; those of alatae have numerous often rather protruberant rhinaria on ANT III, and sometimes also on IV and V. Dorsal body hairs are very short. First tarsal segments all have 3 hairs. The dorsal cuticle of apterae is sclerotic (but not dark) and roughened, usually with numerous small roundish shallow depressions. Alate viviparae have broad abdominal segmental sclerotic cross-bands, usually dark green in life, often fused into a solid patch. Siphunculi are well developed, usually clavate, with the swelling asymmetrical and the flange directed slightly outwards. The cauda is tongue-shaped, with 4-11 hairs. The surprisingly close relationship recently revealed by molecular studies between this genus and another, morphologically very different genus, *Pterocomma*, is discussed on page 9.

There are 32 species in the world, half of them in east Asia. Most have host alternation from *Salix* spp. to Umbelliferae. They are not visited by ants. There are 8 British species.

Key to apterous viviparae of British *Cavariella*

This key is not applicable to fundatrices on *Salix* in early spring.

1. PT less than 1.3 times longer than base of last antennal segment 2

- PT more than 1.3 times longer than base of last antennal segment 5

2. Siphunculi flangeless, with a small aperture (Fig. 186). Cauda with 5-12 hairs .... ***aquatica*** Gillette & Bragg, 1916

- Siphunculi with a distinct flange and normal-sized aperture. Cauda with 5-7 hairs 3

186

3. R IV+V 1.08-1.25 times longer than HT II, and bearing 2-3 accessory hairs ....
.... ***intermedia*** Hille Ris Lambers, 1969

- R IV+V 0.7-1.0 times longer than HT II, and often without any accessory hairs 4

4. Length of siphunculi 0.65-0.75 of head width across (and including) eyes. Tergum often strongly pigmented. First tarsal segments all with only two hairs (lacking median sense peg; Fig. 187) .... *saxifragae* Remaudière, 1959

187

- Length of siphunculi 0.74-1.15 of head width across eyes. Tergum pale. First tarsal segments of fore and mid tarsi with 3 hairs (including median sense peg; Fig. 188) .... *aegopodii* (Scopoli, 1763)

188

5. Siphunculi cylindrical, slightly tapered, with no distal swelling (Fig. 189) .... *theobaldi* (Gillette & Bragg, 1918)

- Siphunculi swollen on distal half (e.g. Figs 190, 191) 6

189

6. PT 2.6-4.0 times longer than base of last antennal segment .... *pastinacae* (Linnaeus, 1758)

- PT 1.4-2.0 times longer than base of last antennal segment 7

190

7. Length of supracaudal process at least 1.6 times the maximum width of swollen part of siphunculi. Siphunculi 0.98-1.1 times longer than head width across (and including) eyes, and 6.7-8.7 times the maximum width of their swollen part (Fig. 190) .... *archangelicae* (Scopoli, 1763)

- Length of supracaudal process less than 1.5 times the maximum width of swollen part of siphunculi. Siphunculi 0.8-1.01 (-1.07) times longer than head width across eyes, and 5.0-7.3 times the maximum width of their swollen part (Fig. 191) .... *konoi* Takahashi, 1939

191

Key to alate viviparae of British *Cavariella*

1. PT less than 1.5 times longer than base of ANT VI. ANT III with 9-34 rhinaria 2

- PT more than 1.5 times longer than base of ANT VI. ANT III with 29-97 rhinaria 5

2. Siphunculi flangeless, with a small aperture. Cauda with 7-9 hairs .... *aquatica*

- Siphunculi with a distinct flange and normal-sized aperture. Cauda with 5-7 hairs 3

3. R IV+V 1.08-1.25 times longer than HT II, and bearing 2-3 accessory hairs. ANT IV with 2-9 rhinaria. Dorsal abdominal markings often pale and indistinct (sometimes darker cross-bands are visible in specimens developing at low temperatures) .... *intermedia*

- R IV+V 0.7-1.0 times longer than HT II, and without any accessory hairs. ANT IV with 0-2 rhinaria. Dorsal abdominal markings usually dark and distinctly defined 4

4. First tarsal segments all with only two hairs (lacking median sense peg, as in Fig. 187) .... *saxifragae*

- First tarsal segments usually all with 3 hairs (including median sense peg, as in Fig. 188) .... *aegopodii*

5. Siphunculi cylindrical, slightly tapered, with no distal swelling .... *theobaldi*

- Siphunculi swollen on distal half 6

6. PT 3.6-5.1 times longer than base of ANT VI. ANT IV usually without rhinaria, rarely with 1-3 .... *pastinacae*

- PT 1.5-2.8 times longer than base of ANT VI. ANT IV rarely without rhinaria, usually with at least 2 7

7. ABD TERG 6 with a dark cross-band, forming a continuation of the central sclerite formed by the partially fused bands on tergites 3-5 (Fig. 194). ANT III with 39-97 rhinaria, and IV with (0-) 2-19 .... *archangelicae*

- ABD TERG 6 with a pair of dark spots (Fig. 195). ANT III with 29-56 rhinaria, and IV with 1-8 .... *konoi*

Key to alate males of British *Cavariella*

1. PT less than 1.5 times longer than base of ANT VI. ANT III with 20-44 rhinaria 2

- PT more than 1.5 times longer than base of ANT VI. ANT III with 44-88 rhinaria 3

2. Siphunculi flangeless, with a small aperture, less than 0.08 of body length. R IV+V with 2 accessory hairs .... *aquatica*

- Siphunculi with a distinct flange and normal-sized aperture, more than 0.12 of body length. R IV+V without accessory hairs .... *aegopodii*

3. Siphunculi not clavate .... *theobaldi*

- Siphunculi distinctly clavate (swollen on distal half, with a narrower stem) 4

4. PT 2.9-3.4 times longer than base of ANT VI .... *pastinacae*

- PT 1.5-2.2 times longer than base of ANT VI 5

5. ABD TERG 6 with a dark cross-band (Fig. 194). Secondary rhinaria distributed ANT III 65-88, IV 14-19, V 8-11, VI base 0-3 .... *archangelicae*

- ABD TERG 6 with only a pair of dark spots, occasionally linked across midline (Fig. 195). Secondary rhinaria distributed ANT III 44-69, IV 10-16, V 4-8, VI base 0 .... *konoi*

Cavariella aegopodii (Scopoli, 1763) **Willow-Carrot Aphid** Figs 73, 188, 192

Fundatrices developing on young leaves and catkins of *Salix* spp. (especially *S. alba* and *S. fragilis*) in spring are rusty red-brown, and the second generation apterae are pale green, greenish yellow or yellowish white; BL 1.5-2.8 mm. Alatae (with secondary rhinaria distributed ANT III 14-32, IV 0, V 0) migrate in May-June to found colonies on leaves and umbels of numerous genera and species of Umbelliferae, although colonies can be found on new willow growth into July and August (Dunn, 1965). Apterae on secondary hosts are usually green or yellowish green, sometimes reddish; BL 1.0-2.6 mm. The return migration to *Salix* occurs in September to early November. Oviparae are rusty brown, BL 1.0-1.7 mm, with very swollen hind tibiae bearing numerous scent glands. Males are dusky yellow-brown with secondary rhinaria distributed III 36-44, IV 4-7, V 4-7, VI base 0-4. This common cosmopolitan aphid is a major pest of cultivated Umbelliferae (Blackman & Eastop, 2000). In warm climates it can live all-year-round on Umbelliferae.

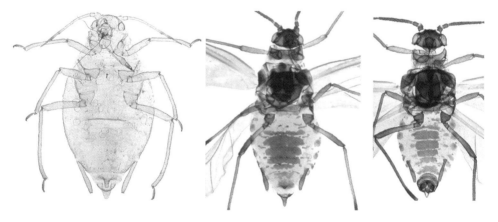

Figure 192. Aptera, alata and male of *Cavariella aegopodii*.

Cavariella (Cavaraiellia) aquatica (Gillette & Bragg, 1916) Figs 62, 63, 186, 193

Apterae in spring colonies on *Salix* spp. (*nigricans, purpurea*) are narrow-bodied, green, BL 1.4-2.0 mm. Fundatrices are larger (2.0-2.7 mm), and remarkable for the genus in that they completely lack siphunculi (Stroyan, 1969a, as *C. hillerislambersi*). Migration occurs to various species of Gramineae, Juncaceae and Cyperaceae, and occasionally to dicotyledons, growing in water or in marshy situations. Alatae have secondary rhinaria distributed III 9-20, IV 0-14, V 0-4. Apterae on secondary hosts are pale yellowish green, wax-dusted underneath; BL 1.3-2.6 mm. The return migration to *Salix* occurs in September. In Britain *C. aquatica* is only known from a population in July 1959 on *Salix nigricans* in Scotland (Stroyan, 1964, as *C. hillerislambersi*); it occurs through most of Europe, across Asia, and also in North America. Remaudière (1970) gave a full account of this species.

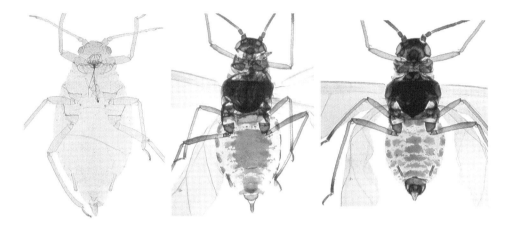

Figure 193. Aptera, alata and male of *Cavariella aquatica*.

Cavariella archangelicae (Scopoli, 1763) Figs 190, 194

Apterae in spring colonies on *Salix* spp. are pale yellow-green to straw-coloured, those on secondary hosts are green or yellowish; BL 1.5-2.6 mm. The siphuncular wax (discharged by prodding abdomen) is colourless to slightly greenish (cf. *konoi*). Migration occurs from late May to July, mostly to *Angelica* spp., sometimes to certain other Umbelliferae (*Apium*, *Heracleum*, *Myrrhis*, *Peucedanum*, *Pimpinella*). Sexual morphs can be found on *Salix* in October; males are reddish. In England, Scotland, Wales, Ireland, rest of Europe (including Iceland), and also recorded from western North America (Utah, Alaska).

Figure 194. Aptera, alata and male of *Cavariella archangelicae*.

Cavariella intermedia Hille Ris Lambers, (1969) 1970

Apterae are evenly light green, rather broadly spindle-shaped, BL 1.4-2.3 mm. Colonies developing on *Salix* spp. (*aurita*, *arbuscula*, *phylicifolia*) produce abundant alatae in late spring (with secondary rhinaria distributed III 18-34, IV 2-7, V 0-2), but persist on willows throughout the summer, and Hille Ris Lambers (1970) found apterae producing oviparae and alatoid nymphs (presumed males) on *Salix* in September, which seems to rule out host alternation. Oviparae are yellowish green, BL c.1.8 mm, with dark, strongly swollen hind tibiae bearing numerous scent glands; adult males are undescribed. In Britain it is only known from single specimens collected in England and Scotland (Stroyan, 1972); elsewhere known from Netherlands, Belgium and Switzerland.

Cavariella konoi Takahashi, 1939 Figs 191, 195

Apterae are green or yellow-green, often with two rather faint darker green longitudinal stripes, and with siphuncular wax distinctly yellow (cf. *archangelicae*); BL 1.6-2.9 mm. In spring colonies occur on *Salix* spp., producing alatae which migrate to *Angelica sylvestris*. This is the only recorded British host, although elsewhere it has been recorded from other genera of Umbelliferae Males flying back to *Salix* in October have the abdomen ochre-yellow with green pleural stripes, and oviparae are yellowish green, partly with a darker green, reddish or brownish tint (Heie, 1992). In England, Scotland, Wales, Europe (including Iceland, where it is very common), Asia, North America, and Mexico.

Figure 195. Aptera, alata and male of *Cavariella konoi*.

Cavariella pastinacae (Linnaeus, 1758) Fig. 196

Apterae in spring colonies on young leaves and new growth of *Salix* spp. are pale green, rather shiny; BL 1.6-2.2 mm. Alatae (with secondary rhinaria distributed III 43-59, IV 0-3, V 0) migrate to *Heracleum*, less commonly to *Pastinaca* and other genera of Umbelliferae. Apterae on the secondary host are pale green, BL 1.8-2.9 mm. Colonies can also persist on *Salix* into summer. Oviparae and alate males are found on *Salix* in October. In England, Scotland, Wales, Ireland; throughout Europe, and also in North America.

Figure 196. Aptera, alata and male of *Cavariella pastinacae*.

Cavariella saxifragae Remaudière, 1959 Fig. 187

Apterae are blackish in life; BL 1.2-1.8 mm. Alatae have secondary rhinaria distributed III 13-24, IV 0-2, V 0. Feeding is restricted to *Saxifraga aizoides*, on which the pale pink oviparae (with weakly swollen hind tibiae) and small (1.1-1.3 mm) apterous (alatiform) males are produced in late August to September. Only known from France (Pyrenees) and Scotland (Stroyan, 1964).

Cavariella theobaldi (Gillette & Bragg, 1918) Figs 189, 197

Apterae on both primary and secondary hosts are rather bright yellowish green to green, with dusky or dark-tipped, tapering siphunculi; BL 1.8-2.8 mm. On leaves and new growth of *Salix* spp. in spring, migrating in April-June to *Heracleum*, *Pastinaca* and sometimes other genera of Umbelliferae (e.g. *Aegopodium*, *Angelica*, *Chaerophyllum*), but colonies also persist on *Salix* throughout the summer. Alatae have secondary rhinaria distributed III 34-59, IV 0-3, V 0. Oviparae and males are found on Salix in October-November. There is possibly more than one species under this name in Britain; a colony found in Cornwall in March 1974 (BMNH collection, leg. J.H. Martin) had an abnormal karyotype and longer siphunculi (1.40-1.65 times longer than ANT III, compared with 0.94-1.46). In England, Scotland, Wales, throughout Europe, west Siberia, Turkey and north-eastern North America.

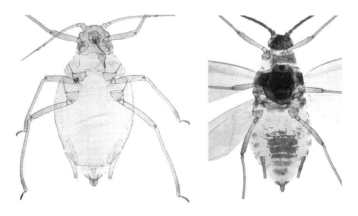

Figure 197. Aptera and alata of *Cavariella theobaldi*.

Ceruraphis Börner, 1926

Medium-sized shiny black oval aphids with short appendages and distinctive jet-black siphunculi. They have a broad head lacking antennal or median tubercles, so that the outline of the front of the head is straight or slightly convex. Antennae of apterae have a few small rhinaria on segment III; those of alatae have numerous rhinaria on III and some also on IV and V. Antennae of apterae are 5- or 6-segmented, only about half of length of body, but with a long PT. Hairs on dorsal body and appendages are rather long and pointed. First tarsal segments have 3-3-2 hairs. The dorsal abdomen is sclerotic and dark in both apterae and alatae, and has a reticulate pattern formed by small spinules. Spiracular apertures on the abdomen are small and reniform, but those on thorax are larger and more open. The jet-black siphunculi are very scabrous and often somewhat swollen in middle, with a very well-developed flange. The cauda is short, tongue-shaped to triangular, usually with 5 hairs. They are visited by ants.

Ceruraphis eriophori (Walker, 1848) Fig. 198

There are 3 species in the world, of which only one, *Ceruraphis eriophori*, occurs in Britain. This has a sexual phase on *Viburnum* spp. (*opulus, lantana*) and migrates to various monocotyledonous plants such as *Eriophorum, Carex, Typha* and *Luzula*.

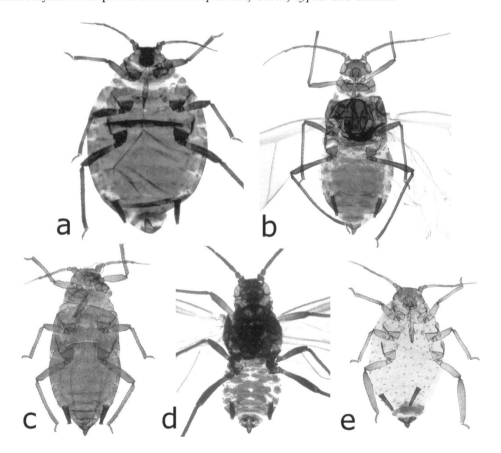

Figure 198. *Ceruraphis eriophori:* (a) fundatrix on *Viburnum,* (b) spring migrant alata, (c) aptera on *Carex,* (d) male, (e) ovipara on *Viburnum.*

The large plump fundatrices (BL 2.5-3.0 mm) roll and curl the leaves of *Viburnum* in April-May, producing exclusively emigrant alatae. Apterae on the secondary hosts are elongate oval, BL 2.0-2.8 mm, usually with a tuft of wax at the end of the body. The return migration occurs in September-October; the alate males have a reddish abdomen, and the small oviparae are yellowish green to dirty whitish, with strongly swollen hind tibiae bearing numerous scent glands. *C. eriophori* is recorded from England, Scotland, Wales and Ireland, most of the rest of Europe, west Siberia, India and North America.

Chaetosiphon Mordvilko, 1914

Rather small, pale yellow to green, broadly spindle-shaped aphids related to *Capitophorus*. The head has well-developed, angular antennal tubercles, and the median tubercle is also quite large. Antennae are usually 6-segmented (sometimes there are 5 segments in small summer apterae), with PT usually quite long. Antennae of apterae lack secondary rhinaria, those of alatae have numerous prominent rhinaria on ANT III, and sometimes a few on IV-V. Males have many rhinaria on ANT III-V. Dorsal hairs of apterae (and immatures) are thick and conspicuously capitate, and they usually arise from tuberculate bases. Capitate hairs also occur on the basal antennal segments, including ANT III, and on the legs. Alatae have mostly much shorter, non-capitate hairs. The rostrum is rather long, reaching to the hind coxae, and R IV+V is always longer than HT II. First tarsal segments have 5-5-5 hairs (a defining feature of this genus). The dorsal cuticle of apterae is pale and densely covered with small warts. Alatae have dark head and thorax, a large dark dorsal abdominal patch, and dark wing veins. Siphunculi are pale, cylindrical, sometimes quite thin, with a well-developed flange. The cauda is elongate triangular, often slightly constricted at base, and much shorter than the siphunculi.

There are 17 species in the world, mostly living without host alternation on Rosaceae of the *Rosa-Fragaria-Potentilla* group. Males may be apterous or alate. Colonies are not visited by ants. There are 3 British species, all in the subgenus *Pentatrichopus* (which is distinguished from *Chaetosiphon* s.str. by the absence of any hairs on the siphunculi).

Key to apterous viviparae of British *Chaetosiphon* (*Pentatrichopus*)

1. Head smooth or only very sparsely spiculose (Fig. 199). Antenna length only 0.6-0.8 of BL. Siphunculi 1.1-2.5 times longer than cauda which bears 6-9 (usually 7) hairs. R IV bears 9-16 accessory hairs .... ***tetrarhodum*** (Walker, 1849)

- Head spiculose (Fig. 200). Antenna length 0.9-1.1 of BL. Siphunculi 2.2-3.3 times longer than cauda which bears 5-7 (usually 5) hairs. R IV bears 3-8 accessory hairs 2

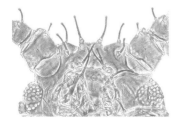
199

200

2. ANT III with 2-7 thick capitate hairs. ABD TERG 1-4 each with 6-8 hairs (Fig. 201) .... *fragaefolii* (Cockerell, 1901)

- ANT III with 8-12 thick capitate hairs, and often some on ANT IV. ABD TERG 1-4 each with 10 hairs (an additional hair on each side between the pleural and marginal hairs; arrowed in Fig. 202) .... *potentillae* (Walker, 1850)

 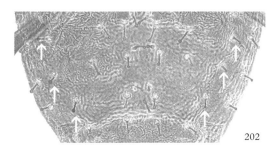

201   202

Key to alate viviparae of British *Chaetosiphon* (*Pentatrichopus*)

1. ANT III longer than IV and V together and bearing 37-74 rhinaria, IV usually having no rhinaria (rarely 1 or 2). Siphunculi 1.5-2.4 times longer than cauda which bears 5-8, usually 7, hairs. R IV bears 9-13 accessory hairs .... **tetrarhodum**

- ANT III shorter than IV and V together and bearing 20-38 rhinaria, IV having 0-10. Siphunculi 2.1-3.0 times longer than cauda which bears 5 (-6) hairs. R IV bears 3-8 accessory hairs 2

2. ANT IV with 2-10 secondary rhinaria, and V with 0-1. PT (3.7-) 4.0-5.0 times longer than base of ANT VI. Siphunculi 2.1-2.5 times longer than cauda .... *fragaefolii*

- ANT IV and V usually without secondary rhinaria, IV rarely with 1-4. PT 2.9-3.9 times longer than base of ANT VI. Siphunculi 2.3-3.0 times longer than cauda ...... *potentillae*

Chaetosiphon (*Pentatrichopus*) *fragaefolii* (Cockerell, 1905) **Strawberry Aphid** Figs 200, 201, 203

Apterae are translucent yellowish white to pale greenish yellow; BL 0.9-1.8 mm. It feeds on *Fragaria* spp., especially colonising cultivated varieties, and is an important cosmopolitan vector of strawberry viruses (Blackman & Eastop, 2000). It is apparently of nearctic origin, occurring frequently on *F. chiloensis* in America, but very rarely on wild *F. vesca* in Britain. It is also sometimes found on *Potentilla anserina*. Overwintering mainly occurs in the parthenogenetic phase; oviparae and both apterous and alate males have been produced in laboratory cultures, but are rare in the field.

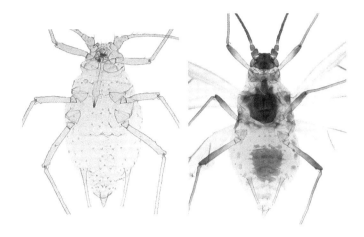

Figure 203. Aptera and alata of *Chaetosiphon fragaefolii*.

Chaetosiphon (*Pentatrichopus*) *potentillae* (Walker, 1850) Figs 202, 204

Apterae are yellowish or whitish; BL 1.4-2.1 mm. It lives all-year-round on cinquefoils, *Potentilla* ssp. (*anserina*, *sterilis*), and is usually found feeding singly or in small numbers on young leaves. Fundatrices mature in April-May. Yellowish oviparae, with hind tibiae not noticeably swollen and bearing only a few large scent glands on the distal half, and slender-bodied brown apterous males are produced in September-October. In England, Scotland, Wales, Ireland, most of Europe, and North America.

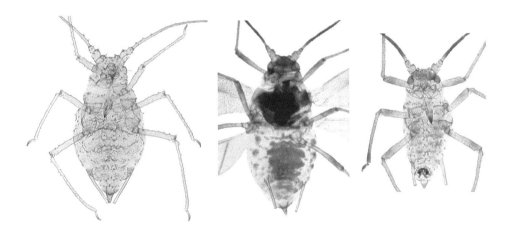

Figure 204. Aptera, alata and male of *Chaetosiphon potentillae*.

Chaetosiphon (*Pentatrichopus*) *tetrarhodum* (Walker, 1849) Figs 71, 72, 199, 205

Apterae are pale green to yellow-green, occasionally reddish; BL 1.0-2.6 mm. On both wild and cultivated *Rosa* spp., colonising shoot tips in spring, and later much smaller individuals live dispersed on the undersides of mature leaves. Fundatrices can be found in young folded leaves in late April. Dark olive-green oviparae with slightly to moderately swollen hind tibiae and small dark apterous males are produced in September-October. Distribution is almost world-wide.

Figure 205. Aptera, alata and male of *Chaetosiphon tetrarhodum*.

Clypeoaphis Soliman, 1937

Small pale olive-green aphids, in life covered in mealy wax. The head lacks antennal tubercles, and the front of the head is convex in outline. The clypeus is dark and bulbous (Fig. 89), a feature found in certain aphids that specialise on Chenopodiaceae. Antennae are usually 6-segmented, much shorter than the body, with PT slightly shorter than base of ANT VI. Antennae of apterae lack secondary rhinaria, alatae have 4-7 on ANT III only. The siphunculi are short, swollen, with a slight subapical constriction and a weak flange. The cauda is thumb-shaped, longer than the siphunculi, and bears 4-9 hairs.

Clypeoaphis suaedae (Mimeur, 1934) Figs 89, 206

There is only one species, *Clypeoaphis suaedae*, occurring in Europe, North Africa and Asia. In Britain it is found in estuarine saltmarsh localities of England and Wales, living without host alternation on *Suaeda maritima*. In other countries it has been found on *S. fruticosa*. Apterae (BL 1.2-1.6 mm) occur singly or in small dispersed groups, difficult to find and not easily dislodged (Gimingham, 1942). Alatae are rare. Oviparae with very slightly to moderately swollen hind tibiae and small apterous males occur in September.

Figure 206. Aptera, alata and male of *Clypeoaphis suedae*.

Coloradoa Wilson, 1910

Small, green or reddish oval aphids. Head lacks antennal tubercles, and the front of the head is convex in outline. Antennae are usually 6-segmented, always shorter than body in apterae, with PT varying in length between species, but always longer than base of last segment. Antennae of apterae lack secondary rhinaria, those of alatae have rhinaria on segments III-IV or III-V. The ocular tubercles (triommatidia) are displaced ventrally so, unusually for aphids, they do not project at the back of the compound eyes. The expanded dorsal body hairs are another characteristic feature of the genus; either capitate, spatulate, fan-shaped or rod-shaped, and usually short. R IV+V is usually stiletto-shaped (i.e. acutely pointed, with concave sides), as in many other aphids that feed on Anthemideae, and has a few short inconspicuous accessory hairs. Alatae have brown-bordered wing-veins. First tarsal segments have 3-3-2 hairs. The dorsal cuticle of the apterae is often wrinkled or granulate, without dark pigment except for intersegmental muscle plates. Alatae also have little or no dorsal abdominal pigmentation, except sometimes for marginal and antesiphuncular sclerites, and transverse bars on posterior tergites. The siphunculi are cylindrical or slightly swollen, often strongly imbricated, generally with a weak flange. The cauda is broadly tongue-shaped or triangular, with 4-9 (often 5) hairs.

There are 29 species in the world, most of them in the palaearctic region. They live without host alternation on composite plants belonging to Anthemideae, usually feeding on edges of leaves or at shoot apices. Males are usually small and apterous. Colonies are not visited by ants. There are 9 British species.

Key to apterous viviparae of British *Coloradoa*

1. Siphunculi more than 4 times longer than their maximum width, 1.3-2.2 times longer than cauda 2

- Siphunculi 2-3 times longer than their maximum width, 0.6-0.8 times longer than cauda 8

207

2. PT 2.2-2.6 times longer than base of ANT VI. Siphunculi swollen over most of length, with transverse rows of fine spinules (Fig. 207). R IV+V 0.7-0.85 times longer than HT II ....
.... *absinthii* (Lichtenstein,1885)

- PT 1.1-2.0 times longer than base of ANT VI. Siphunculi cylindrical or swollen on distal 0.3-0.7, smooth or with normal imbrication. R IV+V 0.9-1.52 times longer than HT II 3

208

3. Siphunculi moderately clavate and curved outwards towards apices, with the swelling asymmetrical and greatest on inner side (Fig. 208). R IV+V 1.25-1.52 times longer than HT II ....
.... *bournieri* Remaudière and Leclant, 1969

a   b

- Siphunculi cylindrical or only weakly and more symmetrically clavate (e.g. Fig. 209). R IV+V 0.9-1.4 times longer than HT II ... 4

209

4. PT 1.1-1.4 times longer than base of ANT VI. Tibial apices pale, contrasting with dark tarsi .... ***achilleae*** Hille Ris Lambers, 1939

- PT 1.4-2.0 times longer than base of ANT VI. Tibiae darkening towards their apices, so that they do not contrast with tarsi 5

5. R IV+V 0.9-1.0 times length of HT II. Longest hairs on ABD TERG 8 only 14-24 µm long, rod- or club-shaped (Fig. 210) .... ***tanacetina*** (Walker, 1850)

- R IV+V 1.0-1.4 times longer than HT II. Longest hairs on ABD TERG 8 are 20-40 µm long, and typically resemble partly opened fans (e.g. Fig. 211) 6

210

211

6. Siphunculi 2.3-3.5 times longer than R IV+V, with distal part slightly but distinctly swollen, at their widest part 1.5-2 times their apical diameters (Fig. 209a) ....
.... ***angelicae*** (del Guercio, 1911)

- Siphunculi 2.1-2.8 times longer than R IV+V, with distal part cylindrical or slightly swollen but not to more than 1.3 times their apical diameters (e.g. Fig. 209b) 7

7. Cauda tongue-shaped, with a rounded apex (Fig. 212). Hairs on front of head rod-shaped or pointed, the longest 16-22 µm, as long as or longer than diameter of basal articulation of ANT III (Fig. 213a) .... ***artemisiae*** (del Guercio, 1913)

- Cauda more triangular, with sides tapering to a more pointed apex (Fig. 214). Hairs on front of head usually shaped like a partially opened fan, the longest 10-18 µm, shorter than diameter of basal articulation of ANT III (Fig. 213b) ....
.... ***rufomaculata*** (Wilson, 1908)

212

a

b

213

214

8. R IV+V 1.2-1.5 times longer than HT II, and 0.75-1.0 of length of cauda. Subgenital plate pale, and siphunculi only dark at their apices. Longest hairs on ABD TERG 3 are 20-31 µm .... ***heinzei*** (Börner, 1952)

- R IV+V 0.9-1.1 times longer than HT II, and 0.5-0.7 times longer than cauda. Subgenital plate and siphunculi dark. Longest hairs on ABD TERG 3 are 43-51 µm ....
.... ***submissa*** Doncaster, 1961

Key to alate viviparae of British *Coloradoa*

1. Siphunculi longer than cauda. ANT III with 6-22 secondary rhinaria, IV with 4-16 and V with 0-9 2

- Siphunculi shorter than cauda. ANT III with 3-9 secondary rhinaria, IV with 1-5 and V with 0-1 8

2. PT 2.3-2.9 times longer than base of ANT VI. Siphunculi swollen over most of length, with transverse rows of small spicules. R IV+V 0.7-0.85 times longer than HT II ..... *absinthii*

- PT 1.1-2.0 times longer than base of ANT VI. Siphunculi cylindrical or swollen on distal half, smooth or with normal imbrication. R IV+V 0.9-1.4 times longer than HT II 3

3. Siphunculi longer than ANT III; moderately clavate and curved outwards towards apices, with the swelling distinctly asymmetrical and greatest on inner side. R IV+V 1.20-1.33 times longer than HT II .... *bournieri*

- Siphunculi shorter than ANT III, cylindrical or only weakly and more symmetrically clavate. R IV+V 0.9-1.4 times longer than HT II 4

4. PT 1.1-1.3 times longer than base of ANT VI, which is 1.1-1.7 times longer than cauda .... *achilleae*

- PT 1.4-2.0 times longer than base of ANT VI, which is 0.7-1.2 times longer than cauda 5

5. R IV+V 0.8-1.0 times length of HT II. Siphunculi 0.11-0.13 of body length ... *tanacetina*

- R IV+V 1.0-1.4 times length of HT II. Siphunculi 0.13-0.20 of body length 6

6. Siphunculi 1.75-1.9 times longer than cauda, with distal part slightly but distinctly swollen .... *angelicae*

- Siphunculi 1.35-1.75 times longer than cauda, with distal part cylindrical or hardly swollen 7

7. Secondary rhinaria distributed ANT III 7-19, IV 3-10, V 0-4 .... *rufomaculata*

- Secondary rhinaria distributed ANT III 14-22, IV 11-14, V 2-9 .... *artemisiae*

8. R IV+V 1.2-1.3 times longer than HT II .... *heinzei*

- R IV+V 0.9-1.1 times longer than HT II .... *submissa**

* Alatae of *submissa* are undescribed, but would be expected to differ from those of *heinzei* in at least this respect.

Coloradoa absinthii (Lichtenstein, 1885) Figs 207, 215

Apterae are greenish with tips of antennae, tibiae and tarsi black; BL 1.7-2.0 mm. Alatae have secondary rhinaria distributed ANT III 9-17, IV 7-10, V 3-6. On undersides of lower leaves of wormwood, *Artemisia absinthium*. Oviparae and small apterous orange-yellow males occur in October (Hille Ris Lambers, 1939b). In England, Scotland, Wales, widely distributed in continental Europe, eastward to Armenia, and introduced to North America.

Figure 215. Aptera and alata of *Coloradoa absinthii*.

Coloradoa achilleae Hille Ris Lambers, 1939 Fig. 216

Apterae are squat-bodied, pale green to greyish green or reddish, with tips of antennae and tarsi dark; BL 1.1-1.6 mm. Alatae have secondary rhinaria distributed ANT III 6-14, IV 2-10, V 0-3. On yarrow, *Achillea millefolium*, feeding mainly on the radical leaves and therefore easily overlooked. Sexuales occur in late September to October; males are very small (0.8-1.0 mm), apterous, orange yellow with black antennae, and oviparae are greyish green or yellow with a greenish or orange tint. In England, Scotland, Wales, throughout Europe, eastward to Russia and Turkey, and introduced to USA.

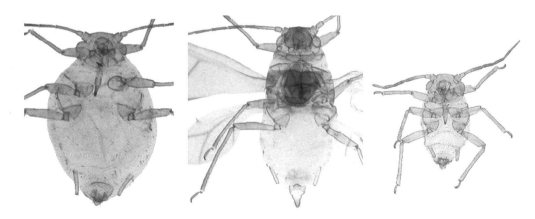

Figure 216. Aptera, alata and male of *Coloradoa achilleae*.

Coloradoa angelicae (del Guercio, 1911) Figs. 209a, 211

Apterae are green, with tips of antennae, legs and siphunculi and entire cauda brownish; BL 1.2-1.8 mm. Alatae have secondary rhinaria distributed ANT III 18-22, IV 8-16, V 3-6. On wormwood, *Artemisia absinthium* (the original host plant was probably misidentified). There are only single records from England and Wales; more common and widely distributed in continental Europe where it often occurs with *C. absinthii*, eastward to Iran, and introduced to North America.

Colorodoa artemisiae (del Guercio, 1913) Figs 98, 209b, 212, 213a, 217

Apterae are dirty green or reddish, with black tips to antennae and tarsi; BL 1.3-1.8. Alatae have secondary rhinaria distributed ANT III 14-22, IV 11-14, V 2-9. On *Artemisia* spp., most usually on mugwort, *A. vulgaris*, on the upper parts of the plant. Oviparae are green and occur in September (Heie, 1992); males are undescribed but like those of *C. absinthii* according to Hille Ris Lambers (1939b). In England and Wales, most of Europe, across Asia to eastern Himalayas, and introduced to USA and Canada.

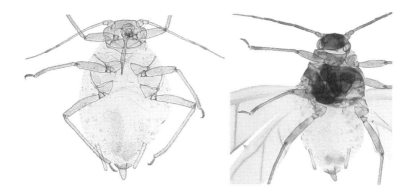

Figure 217. Aptera and alata of *Coloradoa artemisiae.*

Coloradoa bournieri Remaudière & Leclant, 1969 Fig. 208

Apterae are pale green, with dark apices to appendages; BL 1.1-1.5 mm. Alatae have secondary rhinaria distributed ANT III 8-14, IV 4-8, V 0-4. The only hosts are *Santolina* spp. (*chamaecyparissius, viridis*) not native (although widely planted) in Britain, and the only British records are from Kew Gardens (coll. V.F. Eastop, 21.ix.1960) and Cardiff Bay (Baker, 2009). Elsewhere it is recorded from France, Spain, Italy and the Middle East. No sexuales are known, and it is apparently parthenogenetic throughout the year.

Coloradoa heinzei (Börner, 1952) Figs 93, 218

Apterae are pale reddish brown or dull green, with apical parts of antennae, legs and siphunculi dark; BL 1.0-1.6 mm. Alatae have secondary rhinaria distributed ANT III 3-9, IV 2-5, V 0-1. On upper parts of sea wormwood, *Seriphidium maritimum*, and also recorded elsewhere from *S. tauricum*. In England, throughout Europe, and eastward to Pakistan. Stroyan (1979) gave a full redescription based on the British material including oviparae. and apterous males collected in Norfolk in September.

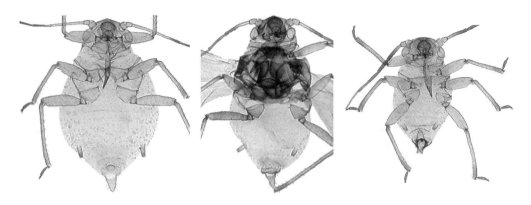

Figure 218. Aptera, alata and male of *Coloradoa heinzei*.

Coloradoa rufomaculata (Wilson, 1908) **Green Chrysanthemum Aphid**
Figs 20a, 213b, 214

Apterae are pale green, often with yellow spots at bases of siphunculi; BL 1.0-1.7 mm. Alatae with secondary rhinaria distributed ANT III 7-19, IV 3-10, V 0-4. On stems and undersides of leaves of cultivated chrysanthemums (*Dendranthema*), *Chrysanthemum coronarium*, and sometimes on other Compositae (*Artemisia, Pentzia, Siegesbeckia, Tanacetum*). Throughout the world, occurring mainly in glasshouses in cold temperate regions. It reproduces parthenogenetically throughout the year, although oviparae are known from Australia and New Zealand.

Coloradoa submissa Doncaster, 1961

Apterae in life are clothed in fine whitish wax powder; BL 1.6-2.0 mm. Alatae are still unknown. On undersides of leaves and stems of sea wormwood, *Seriphidium maritimum*, the wax covering making them difficult to see. Sexuales occur in September-October; males are alate, oviparae are dirty yellowish or greenish brown, wax powdered, with head, pronotum, siphunculi and cauda brown-black (Heie, 1992). In eastern England (Kent, Norfolk) and continental Europe (Denmark, France).

Coloradoa tanacetina (Walker, 1850) Figs 210, 219

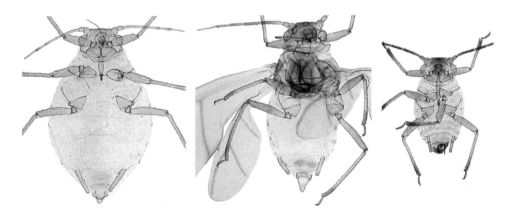

Figure 219. Aptera, alata and male of *Coloradoa tanacetina*.

Apterae are yellowish green or greenish yellow-brown, with tips of antennae and tarsi dark; BL 1.1-2.0 mm. Alatae have secondary rhinaria distributed ANT III 9-15, IV 5-11, V 1-9. On tansy, *Tanacetum vulgare*, feeding on the incisions at the margins of the leaves. There are also records from *Dendranthema* spp. and *Leucanthemum vulgare*. Pale green oviparae and very small orange-yellow apterous males occur in September and October. In southern England, across northern Europe, and introduced to USA.

Corylobium Mordvilko, 1914

Medium-sized broadly spindle-shaped *Macrosiphum*-like aphids with long appendages like *Macrosiphum*, but the apterae have long, thick, capitate dorsal hairs arising from tuberculate bases. Alatae have shorter, non-capitate hairs. The antennae are 6-segmented and very long, with a very long PT. Antennae of apterae have 1-3 small rhinaria near base of ANT III, and alatae have 11-25 on ANT III, none on IV or V. The rostrum is rather long, reaching beyond hind coxae, and R IV+V is long and rather slender, with many accessory hairs. First tarsal segments have 3-3-3 hairs. The dorsal cuticle of apterae is pale and densely covered with small warts, in addition to the large hair-bearing tubercles. Alatae have an abdomen with only dark marginal sclerites and intersegmental muscle plates. Siphunculi are pale with dark apices, long and tapering, with a subapical zone of polygonal reticulation and a well-developed flange. The cauda is very short and triangular, with 6-8 hairs.

Corylobium avellanae (Schrank, 1801) Figs 14, 15, 220

The genus has only one species in the world, *Corylobium avellanae*, common throughout the British Isles, living without host alternation on hazel, *Corylus avellana*. Apterae are yellowish green, or sometimes reddish, BL 1.7-2.7 mm, and feed on the shoots in spring, especially on the bark of young twigs and the petioles and undersides of very young leaves. Dense colonies may later occur on suckers growing up through the bush. It is not visited by ants. Sexuales occur in October; the pinkish oviparae have hind tibiae swollen along their whole length and bearing hundreds of scent glands, and the dark alate males have numerous secondary rhinaria on ANT III-V.

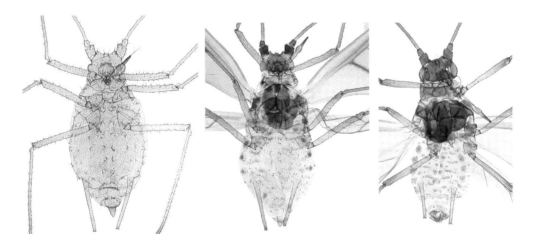

Figure 220. Aptera, alata and male of *Corylobium avellanae*.

Cryptaphis Hille Ris Lambers, 1947

Small grass-feeding aphids with long appendages, closely related to *Metopolophium* but having long, capitate dorsal body hairs in both apterous and alate morphs, apterae also having such hairs on antennae and legs. The head has well-developed antennal tubercles with divergent inner faces. Antennae are 6-segmented, longer than body, with a long PT. Both apterae and alatae have secondary rhinaria only on ANT III. First tarsal segments have 3-3-3 hairs. The dorsal cuticle of apterae is sclerotic, but smooth. Siphunculi are cylindrical with a large flange. The cauda is narrowly triangular, with few hairs.

Cryptaphis poae (Hardy) Figs 23, 221

There is only one British species, *Cryptaphis poae*, living without host alternation on various grasses growing in shady or humid places, such as *Festuca ovina* and *Holcus mollis*. It forms small colonies on the stem bases at or below soil level, or under stones. Apterae are shiny, green mottled with red, yellowish with brown markings or brownish black, BL 1.3-2.0 mm. Alatae are brownish with broad dusky sclerotic dorsal abdominal cross-bands, and 4-8 secondary rhinaria on ANT III. This aphid is easily overlooked as it is not visited by ants and tends to disperse rapidly when disturbed. Sexuales occur in October; oviparae have basal part of hind tibia swollen with 30-50 scent glands, and males are small, dark and apterous, with numerous small rhinaria on ANT III-V. In England, Scotland, Wales, Ireland, and northern and central Europe.

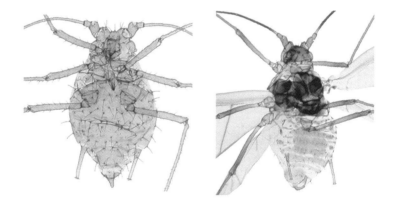

Figure 221. Aptera and alata of *Cryptaphis poae*.

Cryptomyzus Oestlund, 1922

Small to medium-sized, pale, broadly spindle-shaped aphids related to *Capitophorus*, the apterae having similar long, capitate dorsal body hairs, typically arising from tuberculate bases. Such hairs also often occur on the antennae and legs. Adult alatae usually have much shorter, non-capitate hairs. The head has rather low, divergent, smooth antennal tubercles. Antennae are 6-segmented, often much longer than body, with a very long PT. Antennae of apterae usually have secondary rhinaria on ANT III, and those of alatae have them on III-IV or III-V. Males have many rhinaria on ANT III-V. First tarsal segments have 3-3-3 or 3-3-2 hairs. Alatae have dark head and thorax and a large dark dorsal abdominal patch. Siphunculi are pale in apterae, usually darker in alatae; cylindrical, or more often somewhat swollen distally, with a small flange. The cauda varies from triangular to tongue- or finger-shaped.

180

There are 13 species in the world, all palaearctic in origin. Typically they host alternate between *Ribes* and Labiatae, or have lost this alternation and live all-year-round on one or other of these hosts, in which case the males may be apterous.

There are six British species, but a seventh species (*C. ulmeri*) has been included in the key as it is found in Belgium and the Netherlands and may occur in Britain but be as yet unrecognised.

Key to apterous viviparae of British *Cryptomyzus* (+ *C. ulmeri*)

1. R IV+V 1.2-1.75 times longer than HT II, with 5-18 accessory hairs. Longest hair on ANT III shorter than or only a little longer than (0.5-1.3 times) BD III, usually shorter than longest hair on ANT I, or if similar in length then R IV+V more than 1.4 times longer than HT II and bearing 7-18 accessory hairs. Siphunculi 2.4-4.4 times longer than cauda 2

- R IV+V 0.95-1.35 times longer than HT II, with 2-7 accessory hairs. Longest hair on ANT III usually distinctly longer than (1.2-2.1 times) BD III, similar in length to longest hair on ANT I (Fig. 222). Siphunculi 1.0-2.5 times longer than cauda 5

222

2. ABD TERG 1-4 with long thick capitate hairs very irregularly present, so that each has at most 4-6 (exceptionally up to 8) long thick capitate hairs (0-1 spinal, 0-1 pleural and 0-2 marginal hairs on each side), plus some much smaller hairs (Fig. 223a). R IV+V with 11-18 accessory hairs .... ***korschelti*** Börner, 1938 (part, on primary host)

- ABD TERG 1-4 each with (8-)10-18 long thick capitate hairs (spinal hairs usually and pleural hairs sometimes duplicated, and 2-5 marginal hairs on each side (Figs 223b-e). R IV+V with 5-18 accessory hairs 3

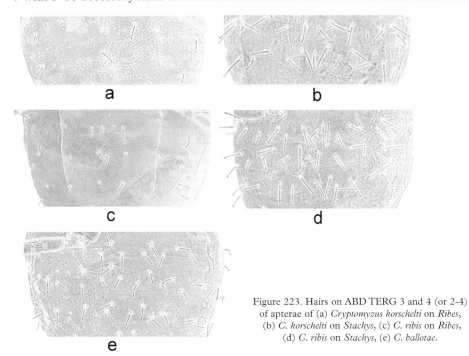

a

b

c

d

e

Figure 223. Hairs on ABD TERG 3 and 4 (or 2-4) of apterae of (a) *Cryptomyzus korschelti* on *Ribes*, (b) *C. korschelti* on *Stachys*, (c) *C. ribis* on *Ribes*, (d) *C. ribis* on *Stachys*, (e) *C. ballotae*.

3. ANT PT/BASE 5.9-9.0. Longest hair on ANT III similar in length to longest hair on inner side of ANT I, or only a little shorter (Fig. 224) .... ***ballotae*** Hille Ris Lambers, 1953

- ANT PT/BASE 9.0-11.5. Longest hair on ANT III much shorter than longest hair on inner side of ANT I (Fig. 225) 4

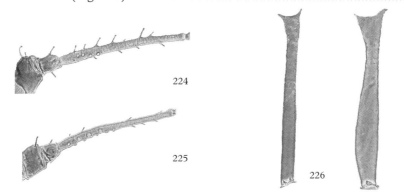

4. R IV+V 1.2 -1.5 times longer than HT II, with 5-10 accessory hairs. Siphunculi almost cylindrical or only slightly swollen on distal half (Fig. 226) .... ***ribis*** (Linnaeus, 1758)

- R IV+V 1.5-1.7 times longer than HT II, with 11-18 accessory hairs. Siphunculi with distinct swelling of distal half (Fig. 227) .... ***korschelti*** (part)

5. ABD TERG 1-5 each with 12-20 hairs (2 spinal, 1-2 pleural and 2-6 marginal hairs on each side; Fig. 228). Siphunculi only 0.09-0.13 of BL and 1.0-1.5 times longer than cauda... ***alboapicalis*** (Theobald, 1916)

- ABD TERG 1-5 each with 4-14 hairs (e.g. Fig. 229), but if with 12-14 hairs then siphunculi are more than 0.16 of BL and more than twice as long as cauda 6

6. Siphunculi only 0.10-0.23 mm long, 0.11-0.15 of BL and less than twice as long as cauda. R IV+V 1.2-1.35 times longer than HT II .... ***ulmeri*** (Börner, 1952)

- Siphunculi 0.17-0.42 mm long, 0.1-0.2 of BL and (1.1-) 1.3-2.5 times longer than cauda, but if less than twice as long as cauda then R IV I V is less than 1.2 times longer than HT II 7

7. PT 9-14 times longer than base of ANT VI. R IV+V 0.95-1.15 times longer than HT II. Siphunculi 1.1-2.1 times longer than cauda .... ***galeopsidis*** (Kaltenbach, 1843)

- PT 7.8-9.3 times longer than base of ANT VI. R IV+V 1.15-1.4 times longer than HT II. Siphunculi 2.1-2.5 times longer than cauda .... ***maudamanti*** Guldemond, 1990

Key to alate viviparae of British *Cryptomyzus* (+ *C. ulmeri*)

1. Siphunculi 2.3-4.0 times longer than cauda. R IV+V at least 1.35 times longer than HT II, with at least 6 accessory hairs 2

- Siphunculi 1.0-2.2 times longer than cauda. R IV+V less than 1.35 times longer than HT II, with 2-5(-6) accessory hairs 4

2. Siphunculi 2.3-3.0 times longer than cauda, cylindrical or with thinnest part in middle. Subapical hair on inner side of ANT I about twice as long as longest hair on ANT III (Fig. 230). Dorsal abdomen with central sclerite having deep marginal indentations, and postsiphuncular sclerites indistinct (Fig. 238). R IV+V with 6-9 accessory hairs ..... *ribis*

- Siphunculi 3.0-4.0 times longer than cauda, thinnest on basal half and slightly to distinctly swollen over distal 0.5-0.7. Subapical hair on inner side of ANT I only a little longer than longest hair on ANT III (Fig. 231). Dorsal abdomen with a large rectangular or trapezoid hardly indented central sclerite and distinct postsiphuncular sclerites (Figs. 235, 237). R IV+V with 9-18 accessory hairs 3

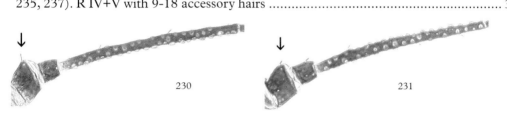

230   231

3. ANT V usually without secondary rhinaria, sometimes with 1-5 on one side. PT 2.0-2.5 times longer than siphunculi, and 6.5-9.1 times longer than base of ANT VI ..... *ballotae*

- ANT V usually with 6-14 secondary rhinaria, rarely with 1-5. PT 2.6-3.0 times longer than siphunculi, and 8.9-12.0 times longer than base of ANT VI .... *korschelti*

4. Siphunculi 1.0-1.25 times longer than cauda which is 0.15-0.20 mm long. ABD TERG 2-4 each with 14-20 hairs (including 3-6 marginal hairs on each side on or near marginal sclerite; Fig. 232) .... *alboapicalis*

- Siphunculi 1.0-2.3 times longer than cauda, but only ever less than 1.3 times in small specimens with cauda less than 0.14 mm long. ABD TERG 2-4 each with 6-14 hairs (including 1-4 marginal hairs on each side on or near marginal sclerite; Fig. 233) 5

232   233

5. Secondary rhinaria distributed ANT III 15-28, IV 4-11, V 0-5. Siphunculi 0.30-0.37 of length of ANT III .... *ulmeri*

- Secondary rhinaria distributed ANT III 25-66, IV 4-40, V 0-13. Siphunculi (0.31-)0.39-0.55 of length of ANT III 6

6. Siphunculi 0.31-0.47 of length of ANT III. R IV+V 0.95-1.15 times longer than HT II .... *galeopsidis*

- Siphunculi 0.47-0.55 of length of ANT III. R IV+V 1.15-1.40 times longer than HT II .... *maudamanti*

Key to alate males of British *Cryptomyzus*

1. Siphunculi less than twice as long as cauda, less than 0.4 of length of ANT III .... *galeopsidis*

- Siphunculi more than twice length of cauda, more than 0.4 of length of ANT III 2

2. Siphunculi cylindrical or with thinnest part in middle (Fig. 238d) .... *ribis*

- Siphunculi distinctly clavate, swollen on distal half with narrow basal stem (e.g. Fig. 237) ... 3

3. R IV+V c.1.2 times longer than HT II, and bearing 5-6 accessory hairs .... *maudamanti*

- R IV+V c.1.5 times longer than HT II and bearing 8-14 accessory hairs .... *korschelti*

Cryptomyzus alboapicalis (Theobald, 1916) Figs 222, 228, 232, 234

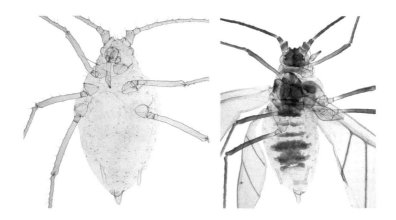

Figure 234. Aptera and alata of *Cryptomyzus alboapicalis.*

Apterae are pale greenish, with a green spinal stripe, or yellowish with faint greenish cross-bands; BL 1.6-2.9 mm. Alatae have a deeply indented dark brown dorsal abdomen patch and secondary rhinaria distributed III 22-38, IV 11-23, V 0-8. It is found on the undersides of the leaves of white dead-nettle, *Lamium album*, and occasionally on *Ballota nigra*, and it is able to reproduce in the laboratory on *L. amplexicaule* and *L. purpureum*, but not on *L. maculatum* (Guldemond, 1991a). There is no migration to *Ribes*. In autumn in the Netherlands it produces oviparae and apterous males on *L. album* (Hille Ris Lambers, 1953), but in Britain sexuales have not been recorded and it may overwinter mainly or exclusively in the parthenogenetic phase, viviparae having been found in December and February (BMNH colln). In England, Wales, and across northern and central Europe to western Siberia and the Caucasus.

Cryptomyzus ballotae Hille Ris Lambers, 1953 Figs 24a, 223e, 224, 231, 235

Apterae are green; BL 1.7-2.1 mm. Alatae have a trapezoid dark dorsal abdominal patch and secondary rhinaria distributed III 40-60, IV 6-26, V 0-5. It feeds on black horehound, *Ballota nigra*, with records also from *Lamium album*, *Leonurus* sp., *Marrubium vulgare* and *Melittis melissophyllum*. Specimens from *Leonurus* sp. in England (BMNH colln, leg. V.F.Eastop) have shorter antennal, femoral and rostral hairs and could be a distinct taxon. It probably overwinters exclusively in the parthenogenetic phase, although oviparae and alate males have been obtained after prolonged rearing in the laboratory (Guldemond, 1991b). In England, Scotland, and in most of western, central and southern Europe.

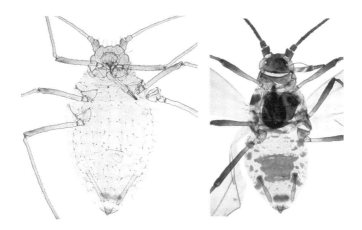

Figure 235. Aptera and alata of *Cryptomyzus ballotae*.

Cryptomyzus galeopsidis (Kaltenbach, 1843) **European Blackcurrant Aphid** Figs 229, 233, 236

Apterae are pale greenish white, often with a darker green spinal stripe; BL 1.3-2.6 mm. Alatae have the dorsal abdominal patch more-or-less divided intersegmentally into broad cross-bands, and secondary rhinaria distributed III 25-66, IV 11-35, V 0-5. It feeds on the undersides of the leaves of *Ribes* spp. in spring, the most common primary host being blackcurrant, *R. nigrum*. It migrates in June mainly to hemp-nettles, *Galeopsis* spp, where it causes curling and rolling of the edges of young leaves. It is also sometimes found on *Lamium purpureum* and *L. amplexicaule*, occasionally on other Labiatae, and also *Veronica* (Scrophulariaceae), living dispersed on undersides of the leaves. Migration back to *Ribes* occurs in late September to October; oviparae are yellowish without any green spinal stripe. However, not all populations migrate from *Ribes*, and the non-migrating populations in western Europe are currently regarded as subspecies, ***C. galeopsidis citrinus*** Hille Ris Lambers, 1953 which is lemon yellow and occurs on *R. rubrum*, and ***C. galeopsidis dickeri*** Hille Ris Lambers, 1953 which is found only on *R. nigrum*. Guldemond (1990, 1991a) studied the genetic relationships between life cycle category and host preferences in this species complex (see also discussion by Heie, 1994). *C. galeopsidis* s. lat. occurs in England, Scotland, Wales and Ireland, and throughout Europe (incl. Iceland and Faroes), also Russian Far East, and North America.

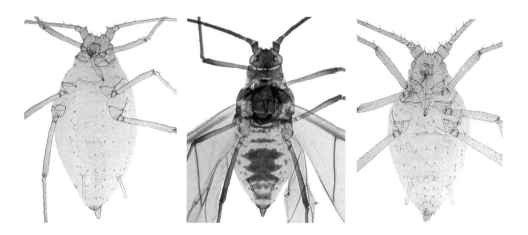

Figure 236. *Cryptomyzus galeopsidis* (left to right): aptera from *Ribes*, spring migrant alata, and aptera from *Galeopsis*.

Cryptomyzus korschelti Börner, 1938 Figs 223a,b, 225, 227, 237

Apterae are pale whitish green with some bright green mottling, or (on *Ribes*) rose pink to salmon red; BL 1.5-2.5 mm. Alatae have a large trapezoid dorsal abdominal patch and secondary rhinaria distributed III 38-57, IV 5-27, V 0-14. This species migrates from *Ribes alpinum* to the undersides of the leaves of *Stachys sylvatica*, and is also able to colonise certain *Lamium* spp. and *Galeopsis tetrahit*, although it may not occur naturally on these plants. On *Ribes* the aphids live in cavities beneath red or yellow leaf blister galls, which can persist until autumn, and may eventually produce small apterous males (Guldemond, 1990, 1991a). In England, Scotland, Wales, Isle of Man, widely distributed in Europe, and eastward at least to central Asia.

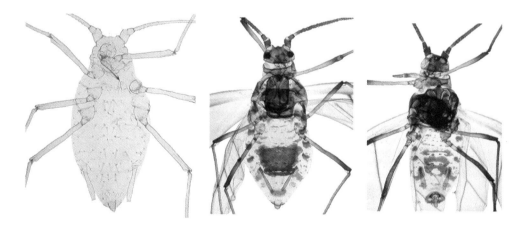

Figure 237. *Cryptomyzus korschelti* (left to right): aptera from *Stachys*, spring migrant alata, and alate male.

Cryptomyzus maudamanti Guldemond, 1990

Apterae are pale yellow to pale green, sometimes with a faint green spinal stripe; BL 1.1-2.3 mm. Alatae have dorsal abdominal markings like those of *C. galeopsidis* (with which species it was confused prior to 1990), and secondary rhinaria distributed III 26-45, IV 4-22, V 0-9. *C. maudamanti* migrates from redcurrant (*Ribes rubrum*) to yellow archangel, *Lamiastrum galeobdolon*, and is probably specific to this secondary host, as *Lamium* spp. and *Galeopsis tetrahit* were colonised with reduced fecundity in the laboratory (Guldemond, 1991a+b). In England, Netherlands, Germany, Czech Republic and Italy.

Cryptomyzus ribis (Linnaeus, 1758) **Redcurrant Blister Aphid** Figs 103b, 225c,d, 226, 230, 238

Apterae are very pale green to pale yellow or whitish, with a variably developed green longitudinal spinal stripe; BL 1.2-2.6 mm. Alatae have a marginally indented dorsal abdominal patch and secondary rhinaria distributed III 31-47, IV 11-27, V 1-10. In spring it occurs on redcurrant, *Ribes rubrum*, and occasionally on certain other *Ribes* spp. (but not blackcurrant), living in concavities on undersides of leaves that show on the uppersides as brownish or purplish red blister galls. Migration occurs in May-June to leaves and stems of woundworts (*Stachys* spp.), with occasional records from other Labiatae. The return to redcurrant is in September. Colonies also sometimes persist on redcurrant through the summer and may give rise to apterous males (Hille Ris Lambers, 1953). In England, Scotland, Wales and Ireland, and widely distributed through Europe, Asia and North America.

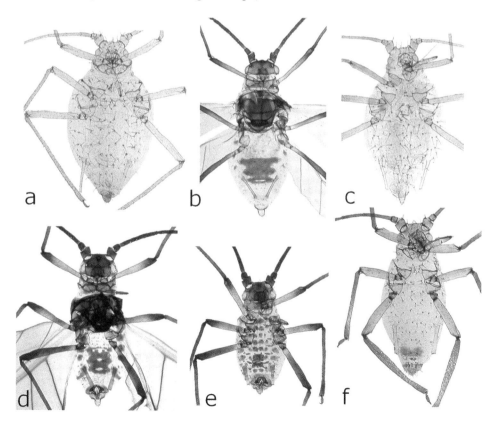

Figure 238. *Cryptomyzus ribis:* (a) aptera from *Ribes*, (b) spring migrant alata, (c) aptera from *Stachys*, (d) alate male, (e) apterous male on *Ribes*, (f) ovipara on *Ribes*.

Cryptomyzus ulmeri (Börner, 1952)

Apterae are mid to darkish green with faint cross-bands on dorsal abdomen; BL 1.0-1.5 mm. Alatae have a marginally indented dorsal abdominal patch and secondary rhinaria distributed III 15-28, IV 4-11, V 0-5. It feeds on the undersides of leaves of *Lamium maculatum*, and is probably specific to this plant, although it can feed on *L. amplexicaule* and *L. purpureum* in the laboratory (Guldemond, 1991b). For many years confused with *C. galeopsidis*, this species has not yet been recorded from Britain, but is found in the Netherlands, and Belgium as well as further east in Europe.

Cryptosiphum Buckton, (1875) 1879

Small, wax-powdered, very plump-bodied aphids with very short appendages. The head lacks antennal tubercles, and the front of the head is convex. Antennae are usually 6-segmented, sometimes 5-segmented, less than half of body length in apterae, with PT shorter than base of last segment. Antennae of apterae lack secondary rhinaria, those of alatae have rhinaria mostly on segment III. The ocular tubercles (triommatidia) are not distinct, being partly inserted into the compound eyes. Dorsal body hairs are very short. The rostrum is very short, and R IV+V is stiletto-shaped (i.e. acutely pointed, with concave sides). First tarsal segments have 3-2-2 or 3-3-2 hairs. The siphunculi are very small, raised pores, hardly visible. The cauda is broadly rounded.

There are 9 species in the world, most of them in the Eurasian steppes. They all live without host alternation on *Artemisia* spp., forming leaf galls. They are not visited by ants.

Because of its specialised morphology and lack of marginal tubercles it has been uncertain whether *Cryptosiphum* belongs in Aphidini or Macrosiphini, but recent molecular work has placed it firmly within the Macrosiphini (Kim & Lee, 2010).

Cryptosiphum artemisiae Buckton Figs 54, 239

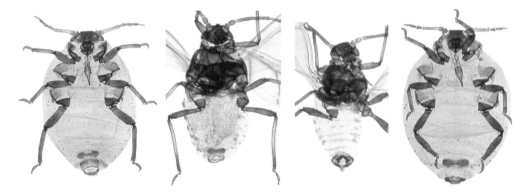

Figure 239. *Cryptosiphum artemisiae* (left to right) aptera, alata, male and ovipara.

The one British species, *Cryptosiphum artemisiae*, forms red leaf galls on mugwort, *Artemisia vulgaris*, and occasionally *A. campestris*. Apterae in the galls are small (BL 1.0-1.9 mm), almost globular, dark red, powdered with greyish wax. Alatae are also wax-powdered in life, BL 1.0-1.5 mm, and have secondary rhinaria distributed III 9-30, IV 0-5, V 0-2. Sexual morphs are produced in October; oviparae, BL 1.2-1.6 mm, have hind tibiae swollen with about 30-50 scent glands of varying size and shape distributed over most of their surface. Males are alate, BL 0.9-1.3 mm, and have secondary rhinaria distributed III 27-52, IV 3-8, V 1-10. It is the only widely distributed species in the genus, occurring throughout Europe and Asia.

Decorosiphon Börner, 1939

Small, oval moss-feeding aphids with long appendages, characterised particularly by the very long, erect, pointed hairs on the legs and antennae, and by their distinctive siphunculi. The head is broad with divergent, scabrous, antennal tubercles. The antennae are longer than the body. The rostrum is long, reaching beyond hind coxae, with R IV+V longer than HT II. First tarsal segments have 3-3-2 hairs. In apterae the metanotum and ABD TERG I-V are fused to form a sclerotic, lightly pigmented carapace, ornamented with rows of fine spinules. Alatae have a large dark dorsal abdominal patch. The siphunculi are much longer than the cauda and strongly swollen, their surface scabrous or squamous even on the swollen part, and constricted between the swelling and the large flange. The cauda is basally swollen and distally narrow, as in most moss-dwelling aphids, and bears 5 hairs.

Decorosiphon corynothrix Börner, 1939 Figs 37, 38, 240

There is only one species in the genus, *Decorosiphon corynothrix*, and it lives in damp, shady situations, well-concealed on the basal parts of the hair cap moss *Polytrichum commune*. It is also recorded from *Catharinea* (= *Atrichum*) *undulata*. Apterae are dirty brownish green to brownish yellow, BL 1.4-1.9 mm, and secondary rhinaria distributed III 0-1, IV 0-12, V 0. Alatae are usually larger (BL c. 2.4 mm) and have secondary rhinaria distributed III 36-61, IV 25-34, V 11-18. It overwinters parthenogenetically, and no males or oviparae have been described. It is not visited by ants. In England, Scotland and Wales; north-west, northern and central Europe, and eastern North America. Müller (1973) discussed its biology.

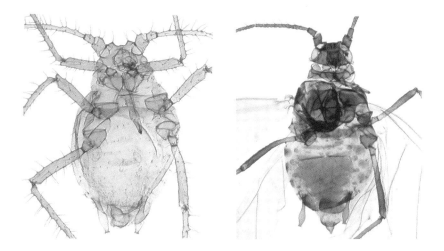

Figure 240. Aptera and alata of *Decorosiphon corynothrix*.

Delphiniobium Mordvilko, 1914

Large broadly spindle-shaped aphids with long, mainly dark appendages, related to *Macrosiphum* but with siphunculi somewhat swollen in middle and thoracic spiracles remarkably large and rounded. Antennae of both apterae and alatae have numerous secondary rhinaria on segment III, and an extremely long PT. First tarsal segments have 3-3-3 hairs. The dorsal cuticle of apterae is membranous, and the abdomen of the alatae has only pale marginal and intersegmental sclerites. Siphunculi are quite long, dark and slightly swollen, with subapical polygonal reticulation. The cauda is long, dark, finger-like and hairy.

Delphiniobium junackianum (Karsch, 1887) Figs 9, 241

There are 8 species in the world, only one of which, *Delphiniobium junackianum*, occurs in Britain. It lives without host alternation on *Aconitum* (monkshood) and *Delphinium* spp., feeding primarily on upper parts of stems and between the flowers. Apterae are bluish green, BL 2.9-4.7 mm. They have 20-65 protruberant rhinaria on ANT III (alatae have 40-72). Colonies are not attended by ants and seem to be avoided by natural enemies, possibly gaining defence from chemicals sequestered from the host plant. Oviparae with numerous scent glands on the swollen hind tibiae, and alate males with secondary rhinaria distributed III 40-60, IV 7-12, V 7-10, appear in late September and October. In England, Scotland and Wales; north-west and central Europe, and west Siberia.

Figure 241. Aptera, alata and male of *Delphiniobium junackianum*.

Diuraphis Aizenberg, 1935

Rather small, wax-dusted, narrowly oval grass-feeding aphids, related to *Brachycolus*. The head has undeveloped or very low antennal and median tubercles. Antennae are 5- or 6-segmented, much shorter than body, with the PT quite short but always longer than the base of the last segment. Antennae of apterae lack secondary rhinaria, those of alatae have a few rhinaria on segment III or III-IV. First tarsal segments have 3-3-2 hairs. The dorsum of the apterae is membranous, and alatae have only marginal sclerites and sometimes dark bands on posterior tergites. The siphunculi are very short, not longer than their basal widths, and sometimes little more than raised pores. ABD TERG 8 has a backwardly projecting process in *Diuraphis* s. str., but not in subgenus *Holcaphis*. The cauda is tongue-shaped, with 4-9 hairs.

There are 10 species in the world, living without host alternation on stems and leaves of Gramineae. Their feeding often causes discoloration and deformation of the plant tissues. They are not visited by ants. There are 4 British species, 3 of them in subgenus *Holcaphis*. The fourth species, *D. muehlei*, is closely related to a major cereal pest, the Russian Wheat Aphid *D. noxia*, and was synonymised with that species by Miller & Stoetzel (2005), but is morphologically and biologically distinct. *D. noxia* is not yet recorded from northern Europe, but has spread to most parts of the world in recent years, so it is included in the key.

Key to apterous and alate viviparae of British *Diuraphis* (+ *D. noxia*)

1. ABD TERG 8 with a backwardly-projecting spinal process above the cauda (Fig. 242). ABD TERG 2-6 mostly with small marginal tubercles 2

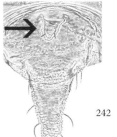

242

- ABD TERG 8 without a spinal process. Abdomen usually without marginal tubercles (subgenus *Holcaphis*) 3

2. Process on ABD TERG 8 in aptera 0.5-0.75 of length of cauda. ANT PT 1.4-2.6 times longer than base of last segment (but only less than 1.6 times in very small specimens with BL less than 1.1 mm) Alata with ANT PT 1.8-2.7 times longer than base of last segment .... ***noxia*** (Kurdjumov, 1913)

243

- Process on ABD TERG 8 in aptera 0.25-0.33 of length of cauda. ANT PT 1.0-1.65 times longer than base of last segment. Alata with ANT PT 1.2-1.8 (-1.9) times longer than base of last segment .... ***muehlei*** (Börner, 1950)

3. Siphunculi as short dark cylinders with apertures directed backwards, placed equidistantly from spiracles on abdominal segments 6 and 7 (Fig. 243). ABD TERG 6 without any dark spinal sclerotisation, and adjacent pleural muscle plates unpigmented .... ***frequens*** (Walker, 1848)

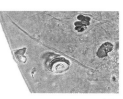

244

- Siphunculi as raised pores or shallow cones placed closer to spiracle on abdominal segment 6 than to that on 7 (Figs 244, 245). ABD TERG 6 often with a dark spinal sclerite, and pleural muscle plates usually somewhat pigmented 4

245

4. Siphuncular pores hardly raised above body surface and directed upward, with only a small area of pigmentation at their bases (Fig. 244). Pigmentation of pleural abdominal muscle plates and spinal sclerite on ABD TERG 6 well-developed. ANT III (in 6-segmented antennae) 0.65-1.0 of length of ANT IV+V together .... ***agrostidis*** (Muddathir, 1965)

- Siphunculi distinctly raised above body surface with aperture directed slightly backwards (Fig. 245). Pleural abdominal muscle plates only weakly pigmented and spinal sclerite on ABD TERG 6 variably developed, but if large then siphunculi have large pigmented areas around their bases. ANT III (in 6-segmented antennae) 1.0-1.2 times length of ANT IV+V together .... ***holci*** (Hille Ris Lambers, 1956)

Diuraphis (*Holcaphis*) *agrostidis* (Muddathir, 1965) Figs 244, 246

Apterae are yellowish green, densely wax powdered, with head and appendages blackish; BL 1.7-2.6 mm. They live in unfurled leaves of *Agrostis stolonifera*. Alatae have 1-6 rhinaria on ANT III and 0-1 on IV. Oviparae. and apterous males are produced in late September to October (Muddathir, 1965). In England, Scotland and northern Europe.

Figure 246. *Diuraphis agrostidis* (left to right); aptera, alata, male, ovipara.

Diuraphis (*Holcaphis*) *frequens* (Walker, 1848) Figs 243, 247

Apterae are pale green, wax-powdered, with head darker, and blackish appendages; BL 1.3-2.1 mm. They are usually found on *Elymus repens*, bunching the still unfurled leaves and stopping growth. Also recorded from *Hordeum*, *Leymus*, *Lolium* and *Triticum*. Alatae have 4-8 rhinaria on ANT III and 0-2 on IV. Oviparae and apterous males are produced on *Elymus* in October (Hille Ris Lambers, 1939b). In England, Scotland, Wales, Ireland, and widespread in Europe, Asia (Turkey, Mongolia) and also in North America.

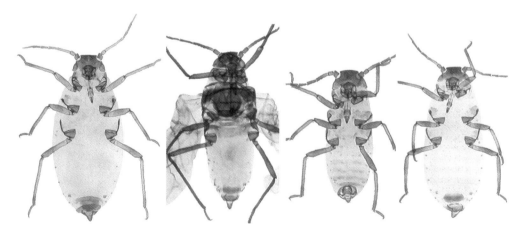

Figure 247. *Diuraphis frequens* (left to right); aptera, alata, male, ovipara.

Diuraphis (*Holcaphis*) *holci* (Hille Ris Lambers, 1956) Figs 245, 248

Apterae are green, wax-powdered, with dark green head and appendages; BL 1.3-2.1 mm. The usual hosts are *Holcus* spp., but there are also records from *Agropyron* and *Poa*. Alatae have 4-8 rhinaria on ANT III and 0-2 on IV. Oviparae are recorded from Denmark on *Holcus* in October (Heie, 1992). In England, Scotland, Wales, Ireland, throughout Europe, and also in North America.

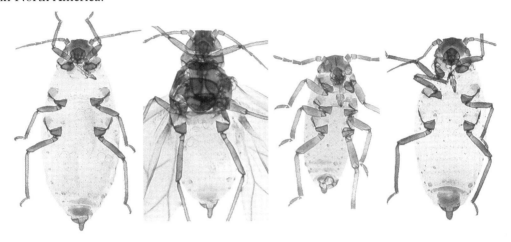

Figure 248. *Diuraphis holci* (left to right); aptera, alata, male, ovipara.

Diuraphis muehlei (Börner, 1950) Figs 58, 242, 249

Apterae are dirty yellowish, wax-powdered, with brownish head and appendages; BL 1.3-2.0 mm. It is found in rolled, yellowed leaves of *Phleum pratense*, and is apparently specific to this host. Alatae have (1-)3-8 rhinaria on ANT III and 1-3 on IV (or 6-15 on a fused III+IV when antennae are 5-segmented). Oviparae and apterous males occur in October in Germany (Börner, 1950), but have not yet been recorded in UK. In England, Scotland, Denmark, Netherlands, Sweden, Germany, Italy and European Russia.

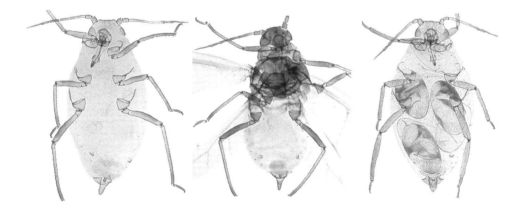

Figure 249. *Diuraphis muehlei*; aptera, alata and ovipara.

Dysaphis Börner, 1931

A large genus of small to medium-sized greenish, pinkish or bluish grey, wax-powdered, broadly oval aphids, usually with rather short appendages. Most consistent recognition features are the short usually helmet-shaped cauda and the paired spinal tubercles on the head and posterior abdomen. The head is broad, with median and antennal median tubercles only weakly developed (except in some species of subgenus *Pomaphis* on secondary hosts). Antennae are 5- or 6-segmented, with PT quite long (except in fundatrices). Antennae of fundatrices and normal apterae lack secondary rhinaria (but alatiform apterae are common in some species). Antennae of alatae have often numerous rhinaria on segments III-V. Hairs on the dorsal body and appendages vary greatly in length between species. First tarsal segments have 3-3-3 or 3-3-2 hairs (2-2-2 in fundatrices of some species). Apterae typically have dark transverse bars on posterior abdominal tergites, and often there are also small dark scleroites at bases of spinal hairs on more anterior tergites. Alatae typically have a large dark dorsal abdominal patch, formed by fusion of broad cross-bands on ABD TERG 3-5 or 3-6. Marginal tubercles are typically present on prothorax and most abdominal segments, and conspicuous paired spinal tubercles are almost always present on head and ABD TERG 8, often also on ABD TERG 7, and sometimes on other segments. Spiracular apertures are rather small, broadly reniform. Siphunculi are of short or moderate length, tapering, usually distinctly imbricated, with a fairly distinct flange. The cauda is short and usually helmet-shaped (pentangular), sometimes triangular, with 4-13 (commonly 5-7) hairs.

There are 87 species in the world, all of palaearctic origin. They typically distort and often discolour the leaves of Pyroidea (*Crataegus, Malus, Pyrus, Cotoneaster, Sorbus*) in spring before migrating to herbaceous plants in various families, most commonly Umbelliferae. Most species have specific associations with both primary and secondary hosts, and some have lost their host alternation and live only either on Pyroidea or herbaceous plants. In some apple-feeding species of subgenus *Dysaphis* the fundatrix develops to maturity in a small apical leaf gall from which its progeny migrate to induce a larger rolled or twisted gall affecting the whole leaf lamina. In host-alternating species of subgenus *Dysaphis* spring migrant alatae are produced in the second and/or third generation, and migration to secondary hosts therefore occurs several weeks earlier than in species of subgenus *Pomaphis*, which have more generations on the primary host.

Species of subgenus *Dysaphis* form rather dense colonies at stem or expanded leaf-petiole bases of the secondary hosts, usually well attended by ants which protect them with earth shelters. In subgenus *Pomaphis* more diffuse secondary host colonies are usually formed on the stems and undersides of leaves, and these are mostly ignored by ants. In *Pomaphis* both apterae and alatae produced on the secondary hosts can differ substantially in morphology from the primary host generations. Males and return migrant females (gynoparae) are typically produced from the end of August to late September in southern England. Mature oviparae are generally much smaller than parthenogenetic females and can be found on leaves of the primary host in October. After mating they move down to lay their eggs in bark crevices on the trunk and older branches.

There are 25 British species and subspecies. Species determination can be very difficult. In host-alternating species of subgenus *Pomaphis*, the forms developing on primary and secondary hosts may be very different in morphology. In *Dysaphis* s. str. there are groups of closely-related taxa with *Crataegus* and *Malus* as the present or original primary hosts, which cannot be reliably distinguished by morphological criteria alone, and are only recognised as distinct species because of their different biologies. Natural hybridisation between closely related taxa sharing the same primary host is also suspected to be blurring the distinction between some of these taxa (Stroyan, 1958). The keys below are based mainly on the data of Stroyan (1957, 1963, 1966), who made detailed studies of the British species of this genus, together with that of Heie (1992) and V.F. Eastop (unpublished). They cannot be expected to be more than 90-95% reliable, and may be less so if only single specimens are available such as trapped alatae. Information on host plant and colour in life will help to confirm identification. For more detailed information on morphology and biology of British species the reader should consult the detailed accounts by Stroyan (1957, 1963).

Key to apterous viviparae of British *Dysaphis* (not fundatrices)

1. Arms of mesothoracic furca joined together by a rigid sclerotic bridge to form a single, broadly Y-shaped structure (Fig. 250; subgenus *Pomaphis*) 2

- Arms of mesothoracic furca both free, separated by membranous cuticle, so that they can move independently of one another (Fig. 251; *Dysaphis* s.str.) 12

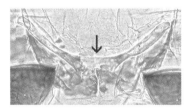

250

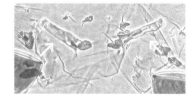

251

2. Abdomen with pairs of small dark spinal sclerites on ABD TERG 1-5 3

- ABD TERG 1-5 without pairs of spinal sclerites 4

3. Siphunculi more than twice as long as R IV+V ....
.... fundatrigeniae of ***aucupariae*** (Buckton, 1879) on *Sorbus*

- Siphunculi less than twice as long as R IV+V ....
.... fundatrigeniae of ***pyri*** (Boyer de Fonscolombe, 1841) on *Pyrus*

4. Longest hairs *either* on ANT III *or* on ABD TERG 3 more than 25 µm in length. Spinal and marginal tubercles protruberant, conspicuous 5

- Longest hairs on both ANT III and ABD TERG 3 less than 15 µm in length. Spinal and marginal tubercles flat if large, or small and inconspicuous 6

5. Head, antennal bases, siphunculi and femora pale (Fig. 286b). ABD TERG 7 with a pair of marginal tubercles. Longest hairs on ANT III 36-54 µm, much longer than those on ABD TERG 3 (11-36 µm) .... fundatrigeniae of ***sorbi*** (Kaktenbach, 1843) on *Sorbus*

- Head, antennae, siphunculi and femora dark or mainly dark (Fig. 282b). ABD TERG 7 without marginal tubercles. Longest hairs on ANT III 11-18 µm, much shorter than those on ABD TERG 3 (25-60 µm) .... fundatrigeniae of ***plantaginea*** (Passerini, 1860) on *Malus*

6. Spinal and marginal tubercles large and flat. R IV+V 1.4-1.6 times longer than HT II
.... exules of ***pyri*** (on Rubiaceae)

- Spinal and marginal tubercles small and inconspicuous, often less than twice diameter of adjacent hair-bases. R IV+V 1.0-1.4 (-1.5) times longer than HT II 7

7. Siphunculi slightly to distinctly swollen on distal 0.5-0.6 of length (Figs 252, 286d), or at least cylindrical with a subapical constriction (on Campanulaceae) 8

- Siphunculi tapering or cylindrical on distal half, or with slight asymmetric swelling (Fig. 253, 254), but without any subapical constriction (on other plants) 9

252

8. R IV+V 1.23-1.38 times longer than HT II. Hairs on ABD TERG 8 maximally 15-22 μm
.... exules of ***sorbi***

- R IV+V 1.04-1.19 times longer than HT II. Hairs on ABD TERG 8 maximally 10-15 μm
.... ***brevirostris*** (Börner, 1950)

9. ANT PT 3.4-4.6 times longer than base of ANT VI 10

- ANT PT 2.1-3.3 (-3.4) times longer than base of ANT VI 11

10. PT 4.0-4.6 times longer than base of ANT VI. Siphunculi (Fig. 253) mostly more than 8.1 times longer than their midlength width, or if 7.1-8.1 times longer then use the function ab/cd, which is more than 1.5 (where a is the maximum length of the outer apical hairs on the hind tibia, b is the siphuncular length, c is the length of R IV+V and d is the midlength siphuncular diameter) .... exules of ***plantaginea*** (on *Plantago*)

253

- PT 3.4-3.8 times longer than base of ANT VI. Siphunculi (Fig. 254) mostly less than 7.1 times longer than their midlength width, or if 7.1-8.1 times longer then use the function ab/cd, which is less than 1.4 .... ***gallica*** (Hille Ris Lambers, 1955)

254

11. Dorsal cuticle rather pale and not distinctly reticulate. Spinal and marginal tubercles if present not much larger than adjacent hair-bases .... exules of ***aucupariae*** (on *Plantago*)

- Dorsal cuticle usually smoky and distinctly reticulate. Spinal and marginal tubercles when present up to twice the diameter of adjacent hair-bases, the marginal tubercles often appearing smoky .... ***maritima*** (Hille Ris Lambers, 1955)

12. Pronotum with a pair of pleural hairs close to the posterior border (Fig. 255) 13

- Pronotum without a pair of pleural hairs close to posterior border (Fig. 256) 17

255

256

13. Hairs on ABD TERG 3 maximally 8-23 μm long, with blunt apices. Hairs on ANT III longer than those on ABD TERG 3, maximally 20-40 μm long ....
.... *radicola* (Mordvilko, 1897)

- Hairs on ABD TERG 3 maximally 35-93μm long, usually with rather acute and sometimes finely-pointed apices. Hairs on ANT III of similar length to those on ABD TERG 3, maximally (26-) 31-97 μm long 14

14. Dorsal hairs very numerous, densely and irregularly arranged on each tergite, long (on ABD TERG 3 maximally 54-93 μm), and very fine-pointed. Hairs on ANT III maximally 57-97μm long, 2.5-3.7 times basal diameter of segment (Fig. 257) ....
.... *hirsutissima* (Börner, 1940)

- Dorsal hairs less numerous, usually shorter (on ABD TERG 3 maximally 35-74 μm), acutely or finely pointed, and arranged in 1 or 2 more-or-less clearly defined rows. Longest hairs on ANT III 26-72 μm, 1.15-2.7 times basal diameter of segment (Figs 258, 259) 15

257   258   259

15. Cauda with 7-13 hairs, and ABD TERG 8 with 8-16 hairs. Longest hairs on ANT III finely pointed, 55-72 μm long, 1.9-2.7 times longer than basal diameter of segment (Fig. 258). Hairs on ABD TERG 3 maximally 52-74 μm ....
.... *chaerophylli* (Börner, 1940)

- Cauda with 4-6 hairs, and ABD TERG 8 with 4-10 hairs. Longest hairs on ANT III acutely pointed, 28-62 μm long, 1.15-2.0 times longer than basal diameter of segment (Fig. 259). Hairs on ABD TERG 3 maximally 32-68 μm 16

16. HT I almost always with only 2 hairs (no median sense peg). R IV+V 0.15-0.18 μm long, 1.1-1.6 times longer than HT II. Siphunculi 1.7-2.4 times longer than cauda. (Any alatiforms have head and thorax strongly alatiform but abdomen without increased dorsal sclerotisation) .... ***anthrisci*** (Börner, 1950)

- HT I with 3 hairs in at least 51% of individuals (a lateral pair plus a median sense peg, arrowed in Fig. 260). R IV+V 0.14-0.16 μm long, 1.0-1.15 times longer than HT II. Siphunculi 1.25-2.0 times longer than cauda. (Apterae are commonly alatiforms, with degree of alatiformity of head and thorax correlated with extent of dorsal abdominal sclerotisation) .... ***devecta*** (Walker, 1849)

260

17. Cauda with 6-12 hairs, but rarely less than 7. HT I usually with 3 hairs (median sense peg present – see Fig. 260), more rarely (in up to 15% of tarsi) with 2 hairs ....
.... ***brancoi*** (Börner, 1950) ssp. ***rogersoni*** (Stroyan, 1955)

- Cauda with 4-8 hairs, but rarely more than 6. HT I with 2 hairs (no median sense peg)
.... 18

18. Siphunculi 2.9-3.9 times longer than cauda (Fig. 266d). All antennal and dorsal body hairs very short; even those on ABD TERG 8 are maximally 6-12 μm long
.... ***bonomii*** (Hille Ris Lambers, 1935)

- Siphunculi 1.2-2.6 times longer than cauda. Longest hairs on ABD TERG 8 are at least 14 μm long, and usually much longer 19

19. Hairs on ANT III maximally 27-56 μm long, distinctly longer and more acute than those on ABD TERG 3 which are maximally 12-20 μm long. ABD TERG 7 almost always with a pair of marginal tubercles (arrowed in Fig. 261). Antennae always with secondary rhinaria (III 12-55, IV 0-20, V 0-3), even in true apterae without dark cross-bands on ABD TERG 1-4 ....
.... ***newskyi*** (Börner, 1940)

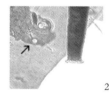

261

- Hairs on ANT III usually of about the same length as, or shorter than, those on ABD TERG 3, but if distinctly longer (some *ranunculi*) then ABD TERG 7 rarely has marginal tubercles, and secondary rhinaria (up to 26 on III and up to 13 on IV) are present only in alatiform apterae with dark cross-bands on ABD TERG 1-4 20

20. Head with spinal occipital hairs (Fig. 262) longer than diameter of adjacent spinal tubercles (which are sometimes absent). Antennae without secondary rhinaria except in some alatiform apterae. Antennal and dorsal body hairs with variable apices, from all acute or finely pointed to all or most slightly blunted 21

- Head with spinal occipital hairs shorter than diameter of adjacent spinal tubercles (Fig. 263a). Antennae with or without secondary rhinaria. Antennal hairs and those on ABD TERG 1-6 all slightly to distinctly blunted (e.g. Fig. 263b), at most those on ABD TERG 7-8 somewhat acute 24

262

b

263

a

21. Siphunculi 1.25-2.0 times longer than cauda *and* longest hairs on ANT III 10-27 µm, often somewhat blunt apically, 0.6-1.1 times longer than basal diameter of segment. Longest hairs on ABD TERG III 14-36 µm 22

- Siphunculi 1.4-2.6 times longer than cauda, but if less than 2.1 times longer then hairs on ANT III are maximally 22-63 µm, (0.8-) 1.1-2.4 times longer than basal diameter of segment, usually with rather acute or even finely-pointed apices, and longest hairs on ABD TERG 3 are 25-65 µm 23

22. Spinal tubercles normally present on head and ABD TERG 8, often also on ABD TERG 7 .... *tulipae* Boyer de Fonsclombe, 1841

- Spinal tubercles often completely absent, when present very small and only on head and/or ABD TERG 8, never more than 3 in total .... *crithmi* (Buckton, 1886)

23. Subgenital plate with 2-9 hairs on anterior half and 12-23 along posterior margin. (On *Angelica sylvestris*) .... *angelicae* (Koch, 1854)

- Subgenital plate with 5-20 hairs on anterior half and 17-38 along posterior margin. (On *Heracleum sphondylium* and other Umbelliferae) .... *lauberti* (Börner, 1940)

24. Most individuals alatiform to a varying degree, having at least a broad dark band across ABD TERG 5 and usually more extensive dorsal sclerotisation of anterior tergites (Fig. 285c,d), the more heavily sclerotised individuals usually having some secondary rhinaria on ANT III-V, but rarely more than 20 on III (distributed III 0-26, IV 0-13, V 0-5) ....
.... *ranunculi* (Kaltenbach, 1843)

- Most individuals are normal apterae, only the occasional individual alatiform, and these have more than 20 secondary rhinaria on ANT III 25

25. Total number of spinal tubercles on head and body segments 8-20, but rarely less than 10 (i.e. irregularly present on other thoracic and abdominal segments besides head and ABD TERG 7 and 8, and sometimes duplicated). Hairs on ABD TERG 8 maximally 17-33 μm long .... *lappae* (Koch, 1854), including **ssp. *cirsii*** (Börner, 1950)

- Total number of spinal tubercles on head and body segments 9 or less (i.e. on head, ABD TERG 8, usually on 7, occasionally on pro- and mesothorax). Hairs on ABD TERG 8 maximally 11-80 μm long 26

26. Posterior hair on hind trochanter 0.24-0.56 (but rarely more than 0.5) times as long as diameter of trochantro-femoral suture (Fig. 264). Hairs on ABD TERG 8 maximally 11-36 μm long (only ever more than 30 μm in large individuals with BL more than 2 mm) .... *apiifolia* (Theobald, 1923)

- Posterior hair on hind trochanter 0.42-1.00 (but rarely less than 0.5) times as long as diameter of trochantro-femoral suture (Fig. 265). Hairs on ABD TERG 8 maximally 25-80 μm long (usually only less than 30 μm in small individuals with BL less than 2 mm) 27

264

265

27. Subgenital plate with 2-9 hairs on anterior half, but usually only 2-3 .... *crataegi* (Kaltenbach, 1843) **s. str.**

- Subgenital plate with 2-15 hairs on anterior half, but rarely less than 4 28

28. Subgenital plate usually with 4-7 hairs on anterior half .... *crataegi* **ssp. *aethusae*** (Börner, 1950)

- Subgenital plate usually with 7-11 hairs on anterior half .... *crataegi* **ssp. *kunzei*** (Börner, 1950)

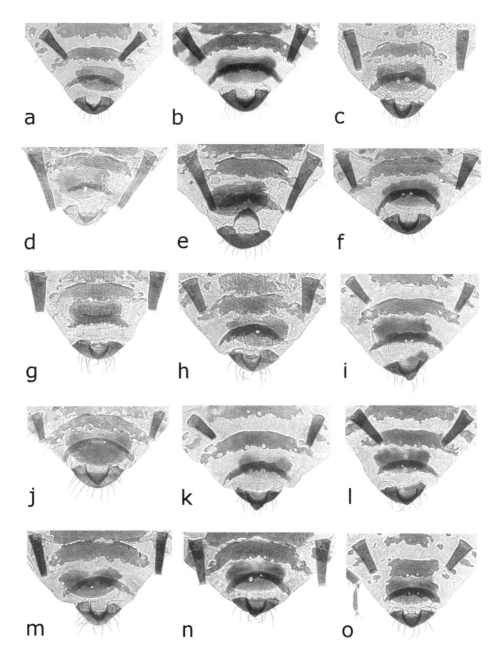

Figure 266. Posterior abdominal segments of apterae of *Dysaphis* s. str. (a) *angelicae*, (b) *anthrisci*, (c) *apiifolia*, (d) *bonomii*, (e) *brancoi rogersoni*, (f) *chaerophylli*, (g) *crataegi*, (h) *crithmi*, (i) *devecta*, (j) *hirsutissima*, (k) *lappae cirsii*, (l) *lauberti*, (m) *newskyi*, (n) *ranunculi*, (o) *tulipae*.

Key to alate viviparae of British *Dysaphis*

N.B. In cases where hair lengths are borderline, an arbitrary choice can be made, as species with borderline values are taken out in both parts of the key.

1. Siphunculi 1.85-3.75 times longer than HT II, but *if* 1.85-2.30 times longer *then* ABD TERG 7 is without any marginal tubercles 2

- Siphunculi 0.87-2.30 times longer than HT II, but *if* 1.85-2.30 times longer *then* ABD TERG 7 has a pair of marginal tubercles (rarely on one side only) 10

2. ABD TERG 7 usually with marginal tubercles, at least on one side. ABD TERG 8 with 6-11 hairs and cauda with 6-10 hairs 3

- ABD TERG 7 usually without marginal tubercles. ABD TERG 8 and cauda with 4-7(-8) hairs, but usually with 5 hairs 4

3. Siphunculi tapering/cylindrical (Fig. 286c), 2.35-2.92 times HT II. Hairs on ANT III maximally 14-25 μm .... *sorbi* (spring migrants)

- Siphunculi slightly to distinctly swollen on about distal 0.7 of length (Fig. 286e), and 2.90-3.75 times HT II. Hairs on ANT III maximally 7-16 μm .... *sorbi* (return migrants)

4. Siphunculi distinctly swollen over distal 0.7 of length. Hairs on ABD TERG 8 maximally 10-22 μm. ANT III with 30-40 secondary rhinaria .... *brevirostris*

- Siphunculi tapering/cylindrical. Hairs on ABD TERG 8 maximally 16-64 μm, but if less than 23 μm then ANT III has more than 40 secondary rhinaria 5

5. ANT PT (3.9) 4.0-5.1 times longer than base of ANT VI (only ever less than 4.0 in early spring) 6

- ANT PT 2.3-3.9 times longer than base of ANT VI 8

6. Siphunculi 2.9-3.4 times longer than HT II .... *plantaginea* (return migrants)

- Siphunculi 2.1-2.8 times longer than HT II 7

7. R IV+V 1.0-1.2 times longer than HT II. Siphunculi 2.1-2.5 times HT II and 2.1-2.7 times cauda. Hairs on ANT III maximally 11-14 μm and on ABD TERG 3 maximally 14-25 μm .... *plantaginea* (spring migrants)

- R IV+V 1.3-1.55 times longer than HT II. Siphunculi 2.4-2.8 times HT II and 2.67-3.0 times cauda. Hairs on ANT III maximally 6-9 μm and on ABD TERG 3 maximally 8-13 μm .... *gallica*

8. Siphunculi 1.86-2.23 times longer than HT II. Hairs on ANT III maximally 14-18 μm and on ABD TERG 3 maximally 20-36 μm. Secondary rhinaria distributed ANT III 62-79, IV 24-33, V 1-7 .... *aucupariae* (spring migrants)

- Siphunculi 2.33-3.0 times longer than HT II. Hairs on ANT III maximally 7-11 μm and on ABD TERG 3 maximally 9-14 μm. Secondary rhinaria distributed ANT III 25-68, IV 5-28, V 0-9 9

9. Secondary rhinaria distributed ANT III 42-68, IV 10-28, V 0-9; those on III at a mean density of 104 per mm ±13. PT 2.7-3.9 times longer than base of VI .... *aucupariae* produced on secondary host (exules and return migrants)

- Secondary rhinaria distributed ANT III 25-49, IV 5-12, V 0-3; those on III at a mean density of 63 per mm ±12. PT 2.2-3.1 times longer than base of VI .... *maritima*

10. Longest hair on ABD TERG 3 exceeds 40 μm in length 11

- Longest hair on ABD TERG 3 is 40 μm long or shorter 17

11. Siphunculi 1.1-1.4 times longer than cauda and 0.87-1.08 times longer than HT II. ABD TERG 8 with 8-11 hairs that are maximally 86-107 μm long. Hairs on ANT III very long, fine and erect, maximally 56-79 μm, and those on ABD TERG 3 are maximally 72-97 μm .... *hirsutissima*

- Siphunculi 1.4-2.3 times longer than cauda and 1.14-2.0 times longer than HT II. Longest hairs usually shorter 12

12. Siphunculi 0.11-0.12 of BL. ANT III with 77-129 secondary rhinaria, IV with 36-67 and V with 5-21 .... spring migrants of *brancoi* ssp. *rogersoni* (part)

- Siphunculi 0.07-0.105 of BL. Antennae usually with fewer secondary rhinaria (never more than 90 on III, and never more than 37 on IV) 13

13. ABD TERG 8 with 6-12 hairs, and cauda with 5-11 hairs (usually 8-10). Longest hairs on ANT III are 36-71 μm, with apices fine and difficult to resolve 14

- ABD TERG 8 with 3-7 hairs, and cauda with 4-8 hairs (usually 5-6). Longest hairs on ANT III are 13-37 μm, with acute or blunt apices 15

14. Siphunculi 1.5-1.8 times longer than cauda. Secondary rhinaria distributed ANT III 35-55, IV 5-20, V 0-1 .... *chaerophylli* (spring migrants)

- Siphunculi 1.8-2.0 times longer than cauda. Secondary rhinaria distributed ANT III 47-73, IV 15-25, V 0-4 .... *chaerophylli* produced on secondary host (exules and return migrants)

15. ABD TERG 7 almost always with a pair of marginal tubercles, rarely with a tubercle on one side only, never with none. Secondary rhinaria distributed ANT III 32-67, IV 4-26, V 0-7 .... *anthrisci* (part)

- ABD TERG 7 usually without marginal tubercles, sometimes (4-25% of specimens) with a tubercle on one side only, never with a pair. Secondary rhinaria distributed ANT III 46-89, IV 11-37, V 0-17 16

16. Total number of secondary rhinaria on ANT V (adding both sides together) is 0-3 in more than 80% of individuals, and never exceeds 9 .... *lauberti* (part)

- Total number of secondary rhinaria on ANT V (adding both sides together) is 0-31, but is never less than 6 in spring migrants, and in most individuals exceeds 9 .... *angelicae* (part)

17. Siphunculi 5.6-7.5 times longer than their width at midlength. Hairs on ABD TERG 8 very short and blunt, maximally 6-11 μm. Dorsal abdomen with separate cross-bands, not fused into a solid patch (Fig. 273) .... *bonomii*

- Siphunculi 2.5-5.7 times longer than their midlength width, if more than 5.3 times then longest hairs on ABD TERG 8 are more than 11 μm long (and often much longer). Dorsal abdomen usually with bands fused intersegmentally to form a solid patch 18

18. Longest hairs on ABD TERG 8 only 7-20 μm. ANT PT 2.6-3.3 times base of ANT VI .... *lappae* (including ssp. *cirsii*)

- Longest hairs on ABD TERG 8 are 7-87 μm, but *if* less than 24 μm *then* ANT PT is more than 3.3 times longer than base of ANT VI 19

19. Hairs on ABD TERG 3 maximally 16 μm 20

- Longest hairs on ABD TERG 3 exceed 16 μm 25

20. Longest hairs on ANT III 24-32 μm. ANT PT 2.4-3.2 times longer than base of ANT VI .... *newskyi* (part)

- Longest hairs on ANT III 6-32 μm, but if more than 20 μm then ANT PT is more than 3.5 times longer than base of ANT VI 21

21. Hairs on ABD TERG 8 usually short and blunt, the longest 10-36 μm long but rarely more than 30 μm in spring migrants, and not more than 26 μm in summer and autumn. Most individuals (100% in summer and autumn) with paired or unpaired marginal tubercles on ABD TERG 7 .... *apiifolia*

- Longest hairs on ABD TERG 8 are 18-87 μm, but only less than 30μm in summer and autumn alatae of *crataegi*, which never have paired marginal tubercles on ABD TERG 7 (but up to 33% have a tubercle on one side of ABD TERG 7) 22

22. ABD TERG 7 always with marginal tubercles; usually (93%) with a pair. (Secondary rhinaria distributed ANT III 31-53, IV 7-16, V 0-1) .... *radicola* (part)

- ABD TERG 7 usually without marginal tubercles, or with up to 33% having a tubercle on one side only, a pair being rare (only found in a few spring migrants of *crataegi*). ANT III-V often with more rhinaria 23

23. Subgenital plate with 0-3 hairs on the anterior half of the disc, and 8-12 on the posterior margin (Fig. 267). Dorsal patch well separated from marginal sclerites. ABD TERG 7 always without marginal tubercles. (Secondary rhinaria distributed III 15-60, IV 6-23, V 0-8) .... return migrants of *pyri* (part)

- Subgenital plate with 2-14 hairs on the anterior half of the disc, and 10-25 on the posterrior margin (e.g. Fig. 268). Dorsal patch with lateral extensions closing space between it and marginal sclerites. ABD TERG 7 sometimes with marginal tubercles ... 24

24. Total number of secondary rhinaria on ANT V (adding both sides together) is 0-5 (usually 0-1) .... *crataegi* (part)

- Total number of secondary rhinaria on ANT V (adding both sides together) is 1-22 (usually 9 or more) .... exules and return migrants of *ranunculi* (part)

25. Siphunculi only 2.68-2.86 times longer than their width at midlength. ABD TERG 7 without marginal tubercles .... *crithmi*

- Siphunculi 2.5-5.7 times longer than their midlength width, but *if* less than 3 times longer *then* ABD TERG 7 has marginal tubercles 26

26. ANT III with 70-129 secondary rhinaria, IV with 28-67 and V with 2-21. ABD TERG 7 almost always with a pair of marginal tubercles .... ***brancoi* ssp. *rogersoni*** (part)

- ANT III-V usually with less secondary rhinaria; if ANT III has more than 69 rhinaria, and/or IV has more than 27, then marginal tubercles are either absent from ABD TERG 7 or, in a minority of individuals, unpaired 27

27. Longest hairs on ANT III 20 µm or less 28

- Longest hairs on ANT III exceed 20 µm 36

28. ABD TERG 7 always with marginal tubercles; usually (93-100%) with a pair 29

- ABD TERG 7 usually without marginal tubercles, or with up to 33% having a tubercle on one side only, a pair being rare (only found in a few spring migrants) 30

29. Siphunculi 0.08-0.09 of BL, and 1.4-1.8 times longer than cauda. R IV+V 1.1-1.4 times HT II. ANT V with up to 7 secondary rhinaria ....
.... exules and return migrants of ***anthrisci*** (part)

- Siphunculi 0.10-0.11 of BL and 1.8-2.3 times longer than cauda. R IV+V 1.2-1.6 times HT II. ANT V with 0-1 rhinaria .... ***radicola*** (part)

30. Dorsal abdominal patch without any significant lateral extensions so that there is a wide gap between it and the marginal sclerites. Anterior half of subgenital plate with 0-6 hairs
.... 31

- Dorsal patch with lateral extensions closing space between it and marginal sclerites. Anterior half of subgenital plate with 2-14 hairs 32

31. Siphunculi 1.19-1.62 times longer than HT II. Subgenital plate with 0-6 hairs on anterior part and 12-20 on posterior margin (Fig. 269) .... spring migrants of ***pyri***

- Siphunculi 1.6-2.1 times longer than HT II. Subgenital plate with 0-3 hairs on anterior part and 8-12 on posterior margin (Fig. 267) .... return migrants of ***pyri*** (part)

32. Siphunculi 0.06-0.08 of BL, 1.08-1.29 times longer than HT II and 1.4-1.5 times longer than cauda. Secondary rhinaria distributed ANT III 24-55, IV 3-14, V 0 .... ***tulipae***

- Siphunculi 0.08-0.12 of BL, 1.14-2.0 times longer than HT II and 1.5-2.3 times longer than cauda. Secondary rhinaria distributed 31-89, IV 4-37, V 0-13 33

33. Total number of secondary rhinaria on ANT V (adding both sides together) is 0-3 in more than 80% of individuals, and never exceeds 9 34

-   Total number of secondary rhinaria on ANT V (adding both sides together) is 0-31, but is never less than 6 in spring migrants, and in most individuals exceeds 9 35

34. Longest hairs on ABD TERG 3 are 20-40(-61) µm. Longest hairs on ANT III are 14-35 µm .... *lauberti* (part)

-   Longest hairs on ABD TERG 3 are 17-24 µm (less than 20 µm in exules and return migrants). Longest hairs on ANT III are 6-19 µm .... *crataegi* (part)

35. ABD TERG 2 with a cross-band (Fig. 285b,e) sometimes thin and fragmented or divided in the middle in return migrants), separate from the large central sclerite covering ABD TERG 3-5 .... *ranunculi* (part)

-   ABD TERG 2 without a cross-band, at most with small sclerotic spots (Fig. 270) .... *angelicae* (part)

36. Siphunculi 0.07-0.08 of BL and 1.4-1.6 times longer than cauda and 1.1-1.4 times longer than HT II. Secondary rhinaria distributed ANT III 27-45, IV 6-23, V 0-4 .... *devecta*

-   Siphunculi 0.08-0.12 of BL and 1.6-2.3 times longer than cauda and 1.1-2.1 times longer than HT II. Secondary rhinaria distributed ANT III 31-89, IV 4-37, V 0-17 37

37. ABD TERG 7 always with marginal tubercles; usually (93-100%) with a pair 38

-   ABD TERG 7 usually without marginal tubercles, or with up to 25% having a tubercle on one side only, a pair being rare (only found in a few spring migrants) 40

38. Longest hairs on ABD TERG 3 exceed 30 µm in length. Siphunculi 1.5-1.8 times longer than cauda. Anterior part of subgenital plate with 5-15 hairs .... spring migrants of *anthrisci* (part)

-   Hairs on ABD TERG 3 maximally 12-22 µm. Siphunculi 1.8-2.3 times longer than cauda. Anterior part of subgenital plate with 2-8 hairs 39

39. Secondary rhinaria distributed ANT III 52-69, IV 11-24, V 0-5. R IV+V 1.1-1.4 times longer than HT II and bearing 2-5 accessory hairs .... *newskyi* (part)

-   Secondary rhinaria distributed ANT III 31-53, IV 7-16, V 0-1. R IV+V 1.2-1.6 times longer than HT II and bearing 4-8 accessory hairs .... *radicola* (part)

40. Total number of secondary rhinaria on ANT V (adding both sides together) is 0-3 in more than 80% of individuals, and never exceeds 9 .... *lauberti* (part)

- Total number of secondary rhinaria on ANT V (adding both sides together) is 0-31, but is never less than 6 in spring migrants, and in most individuals exceeds 9 41

41. ABD TERG 2 with a cross-band, separate from the large central sclerite covering ABD TERG 3-5 (Fig. 285b) .... spring migrants of *ranunculi* (part)

- ABD TERG 2 without a cross-band, at most with small sclerotic spots (Fig.270) ....
.... *angelicae* (part)

Key to alate males of British *Dysaphis*

(The ranges of measurements and ratios given in this key should be taken as only an approximate guide, as in in several cases they are based on very few specimens)

1. Siphunculi 2.4-3.6 times longer than HT II and 2.4-3.7 times longer than cauda 2

- Siphunculi 1.0-2.0 times longer than HT II and 1.5-2.4 times longer than cauda 5

2. Siphunculi tapering/cylindrical. ABD TERG 7 without marginal tubercles. ANT PT 2.3-2.6 or 4.5-5.9 times longer than base of ANT VI 3

- Siphunculi slightly or distinctly swollen over distal about 0.7 (Fig. 286f). ABD TERG 7 often with marginal tubercles. PT 3.1-4.0 times longer than base of ANT VI 4

3. ANT PT 4.5-5.9 times longer than base of ANT VI. Secondary rhinaria distributed III 71-85, IV 22-35, V 4-13 .... *plantaginea*

- ANT PT 2.3-2.6 times longer than base of ANT VI. Secondary rhinaria distributed III 38-41, IV 8-11, V 5-6 .... *maritima*

4. Secondary rhinaria distributed III 54-102, IV 17-30, V 4-13. R IV+V (1.1-)1.2-1.4 times longer than HT II .... *sorbi*

- Secondary rhinaria distributed III 41-47, IV 12-13, V 5-6. R IV+V c.1.1 times longer than HT II .... *brevirostris*

5. Longest hair on ABD TERG 2 or 3 is less than 20 μm 6

- Longest hair on ABD TERG 2 or 3 is 20 μm in length or longer 13

6. Longest hair on ABD TERG 8 is less than 30 μm long 7

\- Longest hair on ABD TERG 8 is more than 30 μm long 8

7. Marginal tubercles usually present at least on one side of ABD TERG 7. R IV+V 1.2-1.5 times longer than HT II. ANT PT 3.2-4.6 times longer than base of ANT VI .... ***apiifolia***

\- Marginal tubercles usually absent from ABD TERG 7. R IV+V 1.0-1.2 times longer than HT II. ANT PT 4.3-5.3 times longer than base of ANT VI .... ***crataegi*** **s.str.**

8. ABD TERG 7 with a pair of marginal tubercles 9

\- ABD TERG 7 without marginal tubercles, or a tubercle on one side only 11

9. ANT PT 3.0-3.6 times longer than base of ANT VI. Siphunculi 1.1-1.3 times longer than HT II, and 1.5-1.75 times longer than cauda .... ***anthrisci*** (part)

\- ANT PT 4.3-5.7 times longer than base of ANT VI. Siphunculi 1.33-1.9 times longer than HT II, and 2.0-2.3 times longer than cauda 10

10. R IV+V 1.4-1.75 times longer than HT II. ABD TERG 7 always with a pair of marginal tubercles. ANT III with 70-104 rhinaria .... ***brancoi*** **ssp.** ***rogersoni*** (part)

\- R IV+V 1.2-1.5 times longer than HT II. ABD TERG 7 usually with a marginal tubercle on one side only. ANT III with 66-91 rhinaria .... ***crataegi*** **ssp.***kunzei* (part)

11. ABD TERG 5 with spinal sclerite not extending laterally to link with postsiphuncular sclerites (Fig. 283f). ANT PT 2.9-3.9 times longer than base on ANT VI .... ***pyri***

\- ABD TERG 5 with spinal sclerite forming a broad transverse band extending laterally as far as the postsiphuncular sclerites. ANT PT 3.6-5.1 times longer than base on ANT VI 12

12. ANT PT 3.6-4.6 times longer than base on ANT VI. Siphunculi 1.08-1.31 times longer than HT II. ABD TERG 7 always without any marginal tubercles .... ***ranunculi*** (part)

\- ANT PT 4.7-5.1 times longer than base on ANT VI. Siphunculi 1.33-1.50 times longer than HT II. ABD TERG 7 often with a marginal tubercle on at least one side .... ***crataegi*** **ssp.** ***kunzei*** (part)

13. ABD TERG 7 with a pair of marginal tubercle(s) 14

\- ABD TERG 7 without marginal tubercles, or a tubercle on one side only 16

14. ANT III with 25-55 secondary rhinaria, and IV with 3-26. R IV+V 1.0-1.2 times longer than HT II .... *devecta* (part)

- ANT III with 62-104 secondary rhinaria, and IV with 22-38. R IV+V 1.2-1.7 times longer than HT II 15

15. Siphunculi 1.33-1.91 times longer than HT II, and 2.0-2.3 times longer than cauda. R IV+V 1.4-1.7 times longer than HT II. ANT III with 70-104 rhinaria .... *brancoi* ssp. *rogersoni* (part)

- Siphunculi 1.09-1.27 times longer than HT II, and 1.5-1.75 times longer than cauda. R IV+V 1.2-1.4 times longer than HT II. ANT III with 62-85 rhinaria .... *anthrisci* (part)

16. R IV+V 1.0-1.2 times longer than HT II. Siphunculi 0.87-1.1 times longer than HT II. ANT III with 25-55 secondary rhinaria, and IV with 3-26 .... *devecta* (part)

- R IV+V 1.2-1.6 times longer than HT II. Siphunculi 1.08-1.45 times longer than HT II. ANT III with 47-82 secondary rhinaria, and IV with 15-36 17

17. Longest hairs on ABD TERG 2 or 3 are 20-24 μm long .... *ranunculi* (part)

- Longest hairs on ABD TERG 2 or 3 are 25-50 μm long .... *angelicae* or *lauberti*

Dysaphis angelicae (Koch, 1854) Figs 251, 256, 266a, 270

Cherry-red to crimson curled-leaf galls are formed in spring on hawthorn, like those of *D. apiifolia*, *D. crataegi* and *D. lauberti*. The fundatrix is greenish-grey, powdered with wax. All or nearly all the second generation are alatae (greyish pink with black dorsal markings and secondary rhinaria distributed III 58-79, IV 19-32, V 2-17), which migrate to wild angelica, *Angelica sylvestris*, forming colonies with wax-powdered yellowish grey or greenish grey apterae (BL 1.7-2.2 mm) on lower leaf bases attended by *Lasius* and *Myrmus* spp. Return migration to *Crataegus* occurs from mid-August to late September (Stroyan 1963); return migrants have secondary rhinaria distributed III 46-87, IV 15-37, V 0-13. Oviparae are small (BL 1.0-1.2 mm) and reddish brown with strongly swollen hind tibiae; males are reddish with black dorsal abdominal cross-bands. In England and Wales, and continental Europe (France, Germany, Hungary, Netherlands, Sweden).

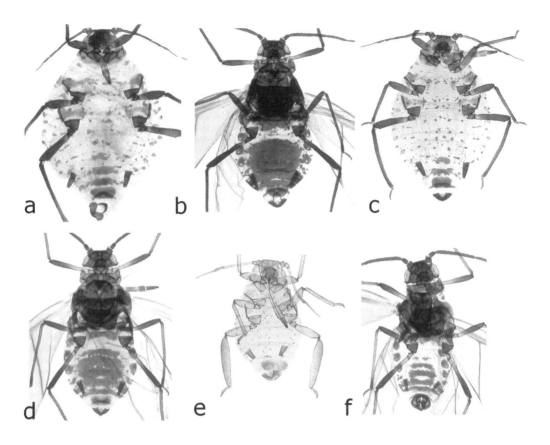

Figure 270. *Dysaphis angelicae* (representative of the *crataegi* group): (a) fundatrix on hawthorn, (b) spring migrant, (c) apterous exule on *Angelica*, (d) autumn migrant, (e) ovipara on hawthorn, (f) male.

Dysaphis anthrisci Börner, 1950 **Apple-Cow Parsley Aphid** Figs 7c, 84b, 255, 259, 266b, 271

Fundatrices are large, plump, bluish grey, wax-powdered, and induce yellow to red leaf-roll galls on apple that are indistinguishable from those of other closely-related species (*chaerophylli*, *devecta*). Their progeny are almost all alatae (with secondary rhinaria distributed III 32-61, IV 4-23, V 0-5), the few apterae being mostly alatiform (but without the dark dorsal abdominal markings exhibited by the alatiforms of *devecta*). Migration occurs to lower leaf-bases of cow parsley, *Anthriscus sylvestris*. Apterae on *Anthriscus* are bluish grey coated with wax powder, BL 1.9-2.3 mm, with very variable dorsal sclerotisation (e.g. Figs 271d, e). Colonies are usually ant-attended. Alatae produced on *Anthriscus* (exules and return migrants) have secondary rhinaria distributed III 42-67, IV 13-26, V 0-7. Sexuales can be found on *Malus* in September and October. Oviparae are small (1.1-1.6 mm), plump-bodied, mottled grey-green with reddish internal pigmentation and a slight wax bloom. In England, Wales, and through most of Europe.

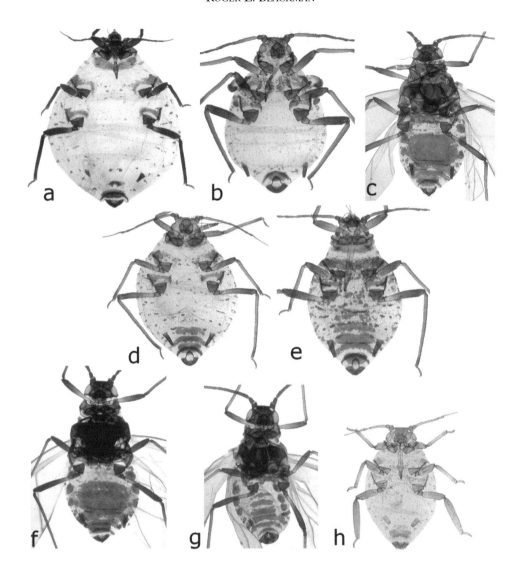

Figure 271. *Dysaphis anthrisci*: (a) fundatrix on apple, (b) fundatrigenia on apple, (c) spring migrant, (d) and (e) apterous exules on *Anthriscus*, (f) autumn migrant, (g) male, (h) ovipara on apple.

Dysaphis apiifolia (Theobald, 1923) **Hawthorn-Parsley Aphid** (Figs 6b, 264, 266c)

Fundatrices are greenish-grey and induce cherry-red to crimson curled-leaf galls on hawthorn like those of *angelicae, crataegi* and *lauberti*. The second generation are all alatae (with secondary rhinaria distributed III 58-96, IV 19-42, V 0-13), and migrate to form dense ant-sheltered colonies at leaf bases of various Umbelliferae, especially *Petroselinum* (parsley) but also sometimes on *Conium, Apium, Foeniculum, Smyrnium*, etc. (see Stroyan 1963). Apterae on Umbelliferae are yellowish to greenish grey, wax-powdered; BL 1.6-2.4 mm. Alatae produced on secondary hosts have secondary rhinaria distributed III 52-82, IV 16-34, V 0-7. Return migrants (with a reddish tinge) are produced in late September to early November. In England, Channel Isles, most of Europe, and widely distributed in other parts of the world as permanently parthenogenetic populations on Umbelliferae. Host-alternating populations in north and central Europe have been regarded as a subspecies (*petroselini* Börner, 1950), but there are many examples of life cycle variation within aphid species, and no reliable morphological discriminants nor experimental evidence to justify any particular taxonomic distinction in this case.

Dysaphis (Pomaphis) aucupariae (Buckton, 1879) Fig. 250, 272

Spring generations live in conspicuous rolled or twisted-leaf galls on the wild service tree, *Sorbus torminalis*, which are initially pale yellow-green, becoming tinged with red and later golden yellow. Despite its name this aphid is not found on *S. aucuparia*. Fundatrices (BL 2.7-3.1 mm) and their apterous progeny (2.2-2.5 mm) are mottled greyish and blue-green underneath a thick coat of mealy white wax. Spring migrants, with secondary rhinaria distributed III 62-79, IV 24-33, V 1-7, are produced in the third and subsequent generations. They migrate in late May and June to produce colonies on undersides of leaves of plantains, *Plantago* spp., especially *P. lanceolata*, in grooves between the veins. Contrary to Blackman & Eastop (2006), colonies are not ant-attended. Apterous exules (BL 1.1-2.0 mm) strongly resemble those of *D. plantaginea*, and are almost indistinguishable from *D. maritima*. Alatae produced on the secondary host have secondary rhinaria distributed III 42-68, IV 10-28, V 0-9. The return migration occurs in late September, but the sexual morphs on *Sorbus* have apparently not been described. In England (only three records, from Cambridge, Sussex and Kent), Wales (Cardiff; E. Baker, pers. comm. 2007); northern, central and eastern Europe, the Azores, and (on *Plantago* only) in Australia and New Zealand.

Figure 272. *Dysaphis aucupariae* (left to right): aptera of second generation (fundatrigenia) on *Sorbus torminalis*, spring migrant alata, and apterous exule on *Plantago*.

Dysaphis bonomii (Hille Ris Lambers, 1935) **Permanent Parsnip Aphid** Figs 266d, 273

Apterae are pale to dull greyish green with dark dorsal bands or patches, wax-dusted; BL 1.2-2.5 mm. Secondary. rhinaria in apterae (usually alatiform) distributed III 0-33, IV 1-12, V 0-1, in alatae III 27-43, IV 6-13, V 0-3 (III and IV sometimes fused in both morphs), mostly strongly tuberculate. Living all-year-round on basal parts of wild parsnip, *Pastinaca sativa*, attended by ants (*Lasius* and *Mymica* spp., *L. flavus* giving nest care to the eggs). Alatae produced in July and August migrate to young first-year parsnip plants where oviparae and apterous males are produced in October. In England south of the Wash, and also recorded from Sweden, Germany, Austria and Italy.

Figure 273. Aptera, alata and male of *Dysaphis bonomii.*

Dysaphis brancoi (Börner, 1950) **Apple-Valerian Aphid** Figs 266e, 274

Spring generations form deep purplish-red leaf-roll galls on apple trees (*Malus* spp.). The plump bluish-grey fundatrix lives enclosed in a separate small pouch-shaped gall formed by pushing up the central part of the leaf lamina, its progeny moving to feed at the leaf edge which is rolled downward, distortion and discoloration usually spreading eventually to the whole leaf. Apterae produced in the second generation are all to some degree alatiform with a varying degree of dorsal sclerotisation. Spring migrants produced in the second and third generations migrate to common valerian, *Valeriana officinalis*, where colonies are formed at stem-bases and on fleshy roots near the soil surface, attended by ants. Apterous exules are dark grey or yellowish-greenish grey dusted with wax powder, BL 1.9-2.5 mm, and they also tend to be alatiform with variable dorsal sclerotisation and numbers of secondary rhinaria sometimes approaching those found in alatae. Migration back to apple occurs in September to October. Oviparae are small (BL 1.0-1.5 mm), dull brownish with yellow eggs visible through cuticle. *D. brancoi* s. lat. occurs throughout Europe (except Iberian peninsula), and across Asia. Populations in Britain (so far only found in Cumbria, England and Cardigan, Wales) tend to be longer-haired and have been separated as a subspecies (***D. brancoi rogersoni*** Stroyan, 1955), and this form is also reported from Sweden (Heie, 1992).

Figure 274. *Dysaphis brancoi* ssp. *rogersoni* (left to right): aptera of second generation (fundatrigenia) on apple, spring migrant alata, and apterous exule on *Valeriana.*

Dysaphis (Pomaphis) brevirostris (Börner, 1950) Figs 252, 275

Apterae are pale brown, with brown siphunculi; BL 1.2-1.6 mm. This species is closely related to *D. sorbi* and has been confused with that species, but lives all-year-round on Campanulaceae (harebell, *Campanula rotundifolia* and sheep's bit, *Jasione montana*), usually in moist situations such as the rocky or shingly banks of streams (Stroyan, 1966), but on *Jasione* it may occur in drier situations. Oviparae and alate males are produced in September. However, Prior (1971) found that a population from *Jasione* in Devon was anholocyclic. In England, Scotland, Wales, Channel Isles, and originally described from Germany.

Figure 275. Aptera, alata and male of *Dysaphis brevirostris.*

Dysaphis chaerophylli (Börner, 1940) **Apple-Chervil Aphid** Figs 258, 266f

Fundatrices and their progeny cause leaf-roll galls on apple (*Malus* spp.) in spring similar to those of *D. devecta* and *D. anthrisci*, to which it is closely related. The second generation consists almost entirely of alatae (purplish grey in life, with secondary rhinaria distributed III 35-55, IV 5-20, V 0-1), migrating to stem-bases of rough chervil, *Chaerophyllum temulum*, where dull greyish pink wax-coated apterae, BL 1.5-2.6 mm, with very variable dorsal sclerotisation, live just below the soil surface, attended by ants (Stroyan 1963). In England this species has so far only been collected on its secondary host, and from only one locality near Cambridge; elsewhere recorded from Austria, Czechoslovakia, Germany and Switzerland.

Dysaphis crataegi (Kaltenbach, 1843) **Hawthorn-Carrot Aphid** Figs 263, 265, 266g and for general morphology see Fig. 270

The deep cherry-red curled-leaf galls produced on hawthorn in spring are indistinguishable from those of *D. angelicae*, *D. apiifolia* and *D. lauberti*, and the life cycle, appearance in life and general morphology of the different morphs are as in those species (see *angelicae*). Nearly all the second generation are alatae (with secondary rhinaria distributed III 48-87, IV 12-31, V 0-6), and they migrate to ground level parts of Umbelliferae. Apterae on secondary hosts are.yellowish grey or greenish grey, wax-powdered; BL 1.4-2.5 mm, and form dense ant-attended colonies. Alatae produced on the secondary hosts have secondary rhinaria distributed III 31-89, IV 4-30, V 0-4. The name *crataegi* is applied to a complex of closely related forms with different secondary host plant relationships which are classified as subspecies. Three of these occur in Britain: (1) **D. crataegi** ssp. **crataegi** is recorded from England, Wales, Ireland, through Europe to the Middle East and Central Asia, as well as introduced to North America, and preferentially colonises carrots (*Daucus carota*) but is also sometimes found on cow parsley, *Anthriscus sylvestris* and sweet cicely, *Myrrhis odorata*; (2) **D. crataegi** ssp. **kunzei** (Börner, 1950), the **Hawthorn-Parsnip Aphid,** is known from England, Germany, Greece and Slovenia, and migrates to wild parsnip, *Pastinaca sativa*; and (3) **D. crataegi** ssp. **aethusae** (Börner, 1950) is recorded from England, Netherlands, Belgium and Germany and migrates to fool's parsley, *Aethusa cynapium* and upright hedge-parsley, *Torilis japonica*. These taxa are all part of a larger group of closely-related *Crataegus*-feeding and host-alternating species that includes *angelicae, apiifolia, lauberti*, and possibly also *ranunculi*. Stroyan (1958, as *Sappaphis*) studied relationships within the group, and suggested that occasional hybridisation between species may be occurring.

Dysaphis crithmi (Buckton, 1886) Figs 266h, 276

Apterae are grey to greenish grey, wax-powdered; BL 1.7-2.2 mm. They inhabit the sheathing leaf-bases of rock samphire (*Crithmum maritimum*) growing in sheltered situations such as rock clefts, crevices in sea-walls, etc. (Stroyan, 1963). Alatae have secondary rhinaria distributed III 37-46. IV 4-11, V 0. On coasts of England, Wales, Ireland, Channel Isles, and western and southern Europe, including Iberian peninsula and Mediterranean islands. This species is closely related to *D. tulipae*, and like that species seems to be completely parthenogenetic.

Figure 276. Aptera and alata of *Dysaphis crithmi*.

Dysaphis devecta (Walker, 1849) **Rosy Leaf-curling Apple Aphid** Figs 260, 266i, 277

Spring colonies of this species roll and redden the edges of the leaves of apple in spring. The galls contain a mixture of normal bluish-grey wax-powdered apterae and dark green to reddish alatiform apterae with different degrees of pigmentation and sclerotisation of head and thorax (Fig. 277). True alatae produced in the second and third generations have secondary rhinaria distributed III 27-45, IV 6-23, V 0-4. This aphid does not host-alternate, and has an abbreviated life cycle of only three or four generations; oviparae and alate males being produced within the galls (Forrest, 1970; Forrest & Dixon, 1975). Despite its unusual biology, comparable morphs are very similar to those of *D. anthrisci* and its relatives, and indicate a close relationship to that group. In England and Wales, and also recorded from Netherlands, France, Germany, Rumania, western Russia and China.

Figure 277. Second generation aptera (fundatrigenia), alatiform aptera and alata of *Dysaphis devecta*.

Dysaphis (Pomaphis) gallica (Hille Ris Lambers, 1955) Figs 254, 278

Apterae are dark mottled blackish green, usually with a reddish tinge at the bases of the siphunculi; BL 1.2-1.6 mm. Alatae have secondary rhinaria distributed III 54-92, IV 16-35, V 0-8. It lives on ivy-leaved toadflax, *Cymbalaria muralis* (not *Linaria vulgaris*, as stated erroneously in Blackman & Eastop, 2006), usually feeding singly on stems and leaf petioles. In Sicily it has been found on water speedwell, *Veronica anagallis-aquatica*, and it was originally described from snapdragons (*Antirrhinum majus*). In Britain *D. gallica* lives through the winter parthenogenetically on *Cymbalaria*, but in northern Germany it host-alternates; the primary host is unconfirmed, but in experimental transfers numerous oviparae were produced on *Cotoneaster tomentosus* (Müller, 1968). In England and Wales, with records also from France, Germany, Switzerland, Italy, Israel and Turkey.

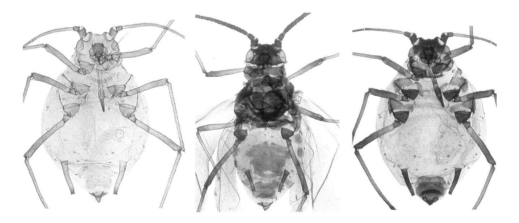

Figure 278. Aptera, alata, and more deeply pigmented overwintering aptera, of *Dysaphis gallica*.

Dysaphis hirsutissima (Börner, 1940) Figs 257, 266j, 279

Apterae are bluish green with a dark dorsal pattern of paired sclerites and cross-bands; BL 1.5-2.3 mm. Alatae have secondary rhinaria distributed III 33-74, IV 19-36, V 1-11. On stem bases and in leaf sheaths of cow parsley (*Anthriscus sylvestris*) growing in dry situations, attended by ants, and also found on *A. caucalis*. There is no host alternation, oviparae being produced in late September (Stroyan, 1963). A single apterous male was collected in the Netherlands in early October (BMNH collection, V. F. Eastop). In England and Scotland, with records also from Denmark, the Netherlands, Sweden, Switzerland and Italy.

Figure 279. Aptera, alata and male of *Dysaphis hirsutissima*.

Dysaphis lappae (Koch, 1854) Figs 266k, 280

Figure 280. Aptera and alata of *Dysaphis lappae* ssp. *cirsii*.

Apterae are dirty olive greenish to brownish, sometimes with a purple tinge, and older adults may have yellowish margins to abdomen; BL 1.7-2.5 mm. Alatae have secondary rhinaria distributed III 37-55, IV 9-19, V 0-1. *D. lappae* s.str. lives without host alternation at stem bases, and on root collars and roots of burdocks (*Arctium* spp.), usually attended by ants. The only British records are those of Theobald (1927), from Berkshire and Surrey, both collections in May, and there is also a record from southern Ireland (Carter *et al.*, 1987). Oviparae and alate males are recorded from mid-September in the Netherlands. Very similar aphids at stem bases and on roots of creeping thistle (*Cirsium arvense*) are regarded as a subspecies, *D. lappae* ssp. *cirsii* (Börner, 1950), and this form is also hardly known in

Britain, the only record being from Godalming, Surrey in 1916. Populations of *D. lappae* s. lat. occur throughout Europe; in Transcaucasia, central Asia and west Siberia; also in North Africa (Egypt, Eritrea), and have been introduced to South America (Brazil).

Dysaphis lauberti (Börner, 1940) Fig. 266*l*, and for general morphology see Fig. 270

Deep red curled-leaf galls like those of other members of the *crataegi* group (*angelicae*, *apiifolia*, *crataegi*) are formed on hawthorn leaves in spring. The second generation are almost all alatae (with secondary rhinaria distributed III 63-85, IV 16-36, V 0-7), migrating to form ant-attended summer colonies on lower leaf bases and root collar of hogweed, *Heracleum sphondylium*, with sporadic records from some other Umbelliferae (Stroyan 1963). Mixed colonies may occur on *Heracleum* with *D. newskyi* (distinguishable by its shorter dorsal body hairs and presence of marginal tubercles on ABD TERG 7), and *Anuraphis subterranea*. Apterae of *D. lauberti* on *Heracleum* are pinkish to greenish grey, wax-powdered; BL 1.7-2.6 mm. Alatae produced on the secondary host have secondary rhinaria distributed III 46-93, IV 11-40, V 0(-5). Return migration to hawthorn occurs in September. Some samples from *Pastinaca* in Britain have shorter, blunter antennal hairs and could be hybrids between *lauberti* and *crataegi* (Stroyan, 1963). In England, Scotland, Wales and Channel Isles; other records are from Netherlands, Germany, Spain, Turkey and Tajikistan.

Dysaphis (Pomaphis) maritima (Hille Ris Lambers, 1955)

Apterae are brownish or staw-coloured to pinkish yellow or pinkish red, with dark tips to appendages; BL 1.8-2.1 mm. Alatae have secondary rhinaria distributed III 25-49, IV 5-12, V 0-4. *D. maritima* lives without host alternation on aerial parts of *Plantago* spp.(*maritima*, *coronopus*) in coastal areas, and is not usually ant-attended. Apterae lie still when beaten from the plant and are easily mistaken for sand particles. On slides they cannot be reliably distinguished from apterous exules of *D. aucupariae*. Oviparae and alate males were collected in late September/ early October in the Netherlands. In England, Scotland, Ireland, Isle of Man, Channel Isles, coasts of north-west Europe, and Iceland.

Dysaphis newskyi (Börner, 1940) Figs 261, 266m, 281

Figure 281. Aptera, alata and male of *Dysaphis newskyi*.

Fundatrices in May are dull purplish grey, powdered with wax. Apterae of the following generations are pinkish to lilac grey, wax-dusted; BL 1.5-2.7 mm. They live without host alternation as ant-attended colonies in basal leaf sheaths and on root collars of hogweed,

Heracleum sphondylium, sometimes mixed with *D. lauberti* (q.v.). Oviparae and apterous males may be found in September to November. In Scotland, north-east England, south Wales (Baker, 2009) and also recorded from Austria and Italy.

Dysaphis (Pomaphis) plantaginea (Passerini, 1860) **Rosy Apple Aphid**
Figs 253, 282

Fundatrices and their progeny curl and then crumple the leaves of apple trees in spring, the leaves turning yellowish as the colonies develop. They are visited by ants, especially *Lasius niger* (L.). The apterae on apple are dull reddish to pinkish grey with a grey or off-white wax bloom, BL 2.1-2.6 mm. The common name 'rosy apple aphid' in this case refers to the colour of the aphids, sometimes confused with the "rosy leaf-curling aphid" (*Brachycaudus helichrysi*, q.v.), where the name refers to the colour of the distorted apple leaves. Spring migrant alatae, with secondary rhinaria distributed III 52-81, IV 13-41, V 0-10, are produced in the third and subsequent generations, and migrate to form colonies along veins on undersides of leaves of plantains, *Plantago* spp., especially *P. lanceolata* Contrary to Blackman & Eastop (2006), these colonies seem to be ignored by ants. Apterae on plantains are pinkish or reddish yellow, BL 1.4-1.7 mm, with brownish patches around the bases of the dark-tipped siphunculi, and strongly resemble apterous exules of *D. aucupariae*. The migration back to apple occurs from mid- September to mid-October, return migrant alatae having secondary rhinaria distributed III 50-92, IV 16-40, V 1-11. Oviparae are small (BL 1.0-1.4 mm), reddish yellow to greenish yellow, nearly without wax. In England, Scotland, Wales, Ireland, throughout Europe, North Africa, and also widely distributed in Asia and North America.

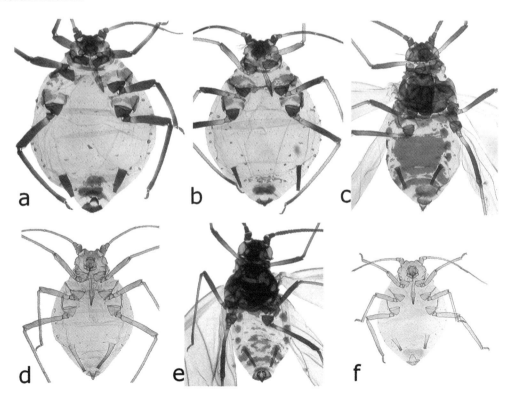

Figure 282. *Dysaphis plantaginea:* (a) fundatrix on apple, (b) second generation aptera (fundatrigenia) on apple, (c) spring migrant, (d) apterous exule on *Plantago*, (e) male, (f) ovipara on apple.

Dysaphis (Pomaphis) pyri (Boyer de Fonscolombe, 1841) **Pear-Bedstraw Aphid**
Figs 267, 269, 283

Fundatrices are large (BL 2.6-3.2 mm), brown, and plump-bodied, forming colonies which distort and yellow the leaves of pear trees in spring and often last into summer. Their apterous progeny are brownish-red to dark brown, rather thickly coated with wax meal, BL 2.1-3.1 mm. After about 3 generations on pear, which in some years can result in heavy attacks, alatae (with secondary rhinaria distributed III 27-64, IV 8-27, V 0-7) migrate to bedstraws, *Galium* spp, and sometimes woodruff, *Asperula cynanchica*, giving rise to colonies on the roots and prostrate stems below the soil surface, sometimes attended by ants. The apterous exules are small, pinkish to reddish brown with a grey wax bloom, BL 1.0-1.4 mm. The return migration to pear is in October. In Britain it is only common on pears in certain years. It occurs in England, Scotland, through most of Europe, in north Africa, and across Asia to Nepal.

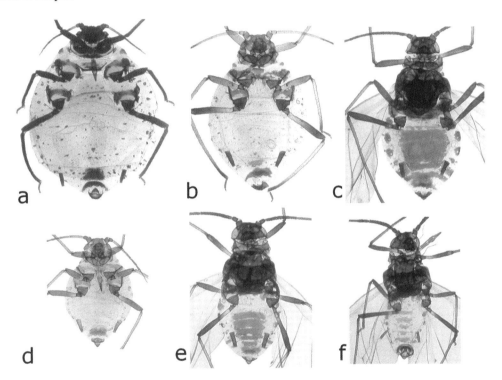

Figure 283. *Dysaphis pyri;* (a) fundatrix on pear, (b) second generation aptera (fundatrigenia) on pear, (c) spring migrant, (d) apterous exule on *Galium*, (e) return migrant, (f) male.

Dysaphis radicola (Mordvilko, 1897) **Apple-Dock Aphid** Fig. 284

Apterae are greenish grey to leaden grey, wax-powdered, BL 1.5-2.6 mm. They live all year round below soil level on the roots of docks (*Rumex* spp.), attended in summer by ants. No sexuales have been recorded in Britain; partial host alternation to apple possibly occurs in continental Europe, but needs to be confirmed. In England, Scotland, Wales, Channel Isles, through most of Europe, and introduced to Australia and USA.

Figure 284. Aptera and alata of *Dysaphis radicola.*

Dysaphis ranunculi (Kaltenbach, 1843 Figs. 266n, 268, 285

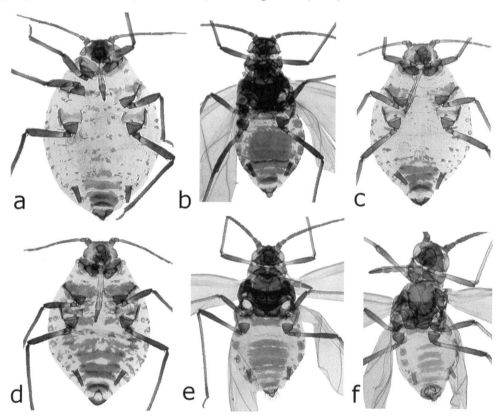

Figure 285. *Dysaphis ranunculi:* (a) fundatrix on hawthorn, (b) spring migrant, (c) and (d) apterae on buttercup, (e) return migrant, (f) male.

Pale yellowish-green curled-leaf galls, often suffused with rosy pink are produced in spring on hawthorn. These do not have the sharp demarcation line between red of gall and green of leaf lamina found in *D. crataegi* and its close relatives. Fundatrices are deep blue-grey, with a grape-like bloom, producing immature alatae that are brownish grey to grey. Migration occurs in the second generation to basal parts of buttercups, *Ranunculus repens* and *R. bulbosus*. The spring migrant alatae have secondary rhinaria distributed III 39-79, IV 13-41, V 0-10. Apterous exules in the ant-attended colonies on *Ranunculus* are mottled grey-green, brownish around bases of siphunculi, wax-dusted, with variable dark sclerotisation; BL 1.7-2.3 mm. The return migration to hawthorn occurs in September (Stroyan 1963). In England, Scotland, Wales, Ireland, Channel Isles, throughout Europe and in Central Asia.

Dysaphis (Pomaphis) sorbi (Kaltenbach, 1843) Fig. 286

The large plump pale green fundatrices (BL 2.4-3.4 mm) give rise to crumpled-leaf galls in spring on rowan, *Sorbus aucuparia*. Mid-rib and leaflets curl into tight bunches, with only slight discoloration, and the colonies therein are assiduously attended by ants. Apterous progeny of the fundatrix are dull green or olive-brown or reddish, BL 2.1-3.1 mm. Alatae are not produced in significant numbers until the fourth generation on *Sorbus* in June. They have secondary rhinaria distributed III 52-83, IV 14-38, V 5-18, and migrate to form colonies of small (BL 1.3-1.7 mm) dull yellow apterae on basal parts of harebells (*Campanula* spp.) and sheep's bit, *Jasione montana*. The return to *Sorbus* occurs in September and October. Host alternation seems to be facultative; colonies often persist on *Sorbus* into late summer, and can apparently give rise to sexuales without leaving the primary host (see Stroyan 1963, pp 54-55). In England, Scotland, Wales and Ireland, throughout Europe except the Iberian peninsula, and east to Turkey and the Caucasus.

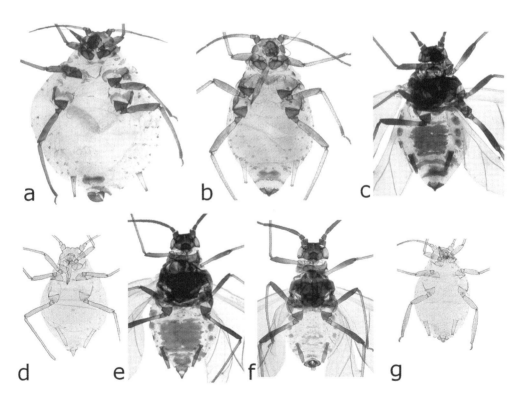

Figure 286. *Dysaphis sorbi:* (a) fundatrix on *Sorbus aucuparia*, (b) fundatrigenia on *Sorbus*, (c) spring migrant, (d) aptera on *Jasione*, (e) return migrant, (f) male, (g) ovipara.

Dysaphis tulipae (Boyer de Fonscolombe, 1841) **Tulip Bulb Aphid** Fig. 266o

Apterae are whitish, wax-powdered; BL 1.7-2.3 mm. They colonise the shoots and leaves not only of tulips but of many monocotyledonous plants in families Liliaceae, Iridaceae, Araceae and Musaceae including *Arum, Chionodoxia, Crocus, Freesia, Gladiolus, Iris, Lilium, Moraea, Musa, Scilla,* and *Strelitzia.* This species is apparently entirely parthenogenetic, overwintering on rhizomes or in crevices of bulbs or corms. Alatae have secondary rhinaria distributed III 24-55, IV 3-14, V 0. Colonies are sometimes but not always ant-attended. In England, Scotland, Wales, and almost cosmopolitan. See also Blackman and Eastop (2000).

Elatobium Mordvilko, 1914

Pale-coloured, broadly spindle-shaped conifer-feeding aphids with rather short appendages. The head has low antennal tubercles, with the median frontal tubercle similarly developed. Antennae are 6-segmented, shorter than the body. Antennae of apterae lack secondary rhinaria; those of alatae have rhinaria spaced out along ANT III , and sometimes also on IV and V. Dorsal body hairs are short, blunt or rod-shaped. First tarsal segments have 3-3-3 hairs. The dorsal cuticle of apterae is rather rugose, especially on posterior abdominal tergites. Neither apterae not alatae have any dark dorsal abdominal markings. Siphunculi are rather long, cylindrical, often slightly curved outward distally. The cauda is finger-shaped, with a slight midway constriction.

Elatobium abietinum (Walker) **Green Spruce Aphid** Figs 92, 287

There are 8 species in the world, 5 of which are in eastern Asia. The single British species is the *Elatobium abietinum,* an important and widely distributed pest of conifers. Apterae of *E. abietinum* are green, with two darker green longitudinal stripes, and feed on two-year-old needles of spruce trees (*Picea* spp.), on which they are well-camouflaged. Spring colonies on *P. sitchensis* in particular can be very damaging, causing discoloration and loss of one-year-old needles, and sometimes leading to serious defoliation. Oviparae and alate males occur in September-October in central and northern Europe, but overwintering is predominantly by parthenogenetic females wherever the winter is mild enough, including Britain (Powell and Parry, 1976). In England, Scotland, Wales, Ireland, Europe, and introduced to Australia, New Zealand, and North and South America.

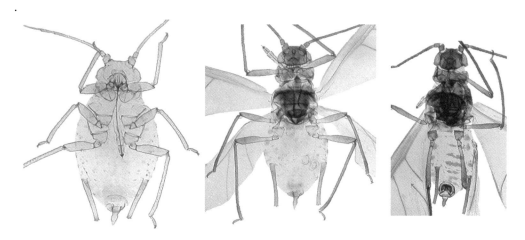

Figure 287. Aptera, alata and male of *Elatobium abietinum.*

Ericaphis Börner, 1939

Pale green or brown, often shiny, oval to broadly spindle-shaped aphids. The head has antennal and median frontal tubercles rather variably developed, and somewhat spinulose or scabrous. Antennae are 6-segmented, shorter than body. Antennae of apterae lack secondary rhinaria; those of alatae have rather few (4-12) rhinaria spaced out along segment III only. The rims of the secondary rhinaria have a fine cilia-like fimbriation or striation, although this can sometimes be difficult to resolve. Dorsal body hairs are usually short and blunt. First tarsal segments have 3-3-3 or 5-5-5 hairs. The dorsal cuticle of apterae tends to be wrinkled or rugose. Apterae lack dark dorsal markings, alatae have a dark dorsal abdominal patch, which can be quite large but usually has clear areas within it. Siphunculi are of moderate length, cylindrical or tapering, and often slightly curved outward distally, with a well-developed flange. The cauda is finger- or tongue-shaped, often slightly constricted on the basal part, with 5-6 hairs.

There are 9 species in the world, 6 nearctic and 3 native to northern Europe, living without host alternation on Ericaceae (4 species), Rosaceae (3) and Liliaceae (2). They are not visited by ants.

There are 4 species in Britain, two of which were introduced rather recently from North America.

Key to apterous viviparae of British *Ericaphis*

1. Antennae as long as or longer than body. Antennal tubercles well-developed, projecting forward much further than middle part of front of head (Fig. 295). Siphunculi 1.9-2.8 times longer than cauda. Dorsum usually with variably developed dark pigmentation ......
   .... ***wakibae*** (Hottes, 1934)

- Antennae shorter than body. Antennal tubercles rather low, and median frontal tubercle as prominent, so that front of head has sinuate or w-shaped outline in dorsal view (Figs. 292-294). Siphunculi 1.4-1.9 times longer than cauda. Dorsum pale 2

288

2. ANT PT 2.3-3.8 times longer than base of ANT VI. Siphunculi with a small flange (Fig. 288) .... ***scammelli*** (Mason, 1940)

- ANT PT 1.6-2.2 times longer than base of ANT VI. Siphunculi with a large flange (Fig. 289) 3

289

3. R IV+V 1.3-1.7 times longer than HT II. First tarsal segments usually with 5 hairs (3 subapical and 2 lateral; Fig. 290). Hairs on ANT III conspicuous, the longest of them 0.6-1.0 times basal diameter of segment .... ***ericae*** (Börner, 1933)

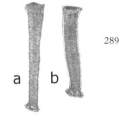

a b

- R IV+V 0.8-1.2 times longer than HT II. First tarsal segments with 3 hairs (no lateral pair). Hairs on ANT III inconspicuous, the longest of them 0.3-0.6 times basal diameter of segment ....
  .... ***latifrons*** (Börner, 1942)

290

Key to alate viviparae of British *Ericaphis*

1. ANT PT 3.7-4.6 times longer than base of ANT VI. Siphunculi 1.8-2.8 times longer than cauda, with (sometimes rather indistinct) subapical polygonal reticulation (Fig. 291) ... ***wakibae***

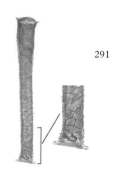

291

- ANT PT 1.5-3.6 times longer than base of ANT VI. Siphunculi 1.3-2.0 times longer than cauda, without any subapical polygonal reticulation 2

2. R IV+V 1.3-1.5 times longer than HT II. First tarsal segments with 5 hairs (Fig. 290). ANT PT 1.5-2.4 times longer than base of ANT VI. ANT hairs conspicuous, those on ANT III maximally 0.6-0.9 times basal diameter of segment .... ***ericae***

- R IV+V 0.9-1.2 times longer than HT II. First tarsal segments with 3 hairs. ANT PT 2.3-3.6 times longer than base of ANT VI. ANT hairs inconspicuous, those on ANT III maximally 0.3-0.5 times basal diameter of segment 3

3. Siphunculi 0.15-0.17 of body length, c.1.33 times longer than cauda, with aperture often turned outwards, and a large flange. R IV+V with 4-6 accessory hairs, cauda with 5 hairs .... ***latifrons***

- Siphunculi 0.18-0.21 of body length, 1.4-2.0 times longer than cauda, with aperture not turned outwards, and a moderate flange. R IV+V with 6-10 accessory hairs, cauda with 6-7 hairs .... ***scammelli***

Key to alate males of British *Ericaphis*

- Secondary rhinaria distributed III 20-31, IV 0, V 6-13. Siphunculi with a few rows of (sometimes rather indistinct) subapical polygonal reticulation .... ***wakibae***

- Secondary rhinaria distributed III 34-48, IV 15-24, V 10-19. Siphunculi without subapical polygonal reticulation .... ***scammelli***

Ericaphis ericae (Börner, 1933) Figs 289a, 290, 292

Apterae are green or brownish green, with tips of antennae and legs black; BL 1.1-1.7 mm. Alatae have a dark dorsal abdominal patch with clear windows. *E. ericae* lives without host alternation on *Erica* spp., especially cross-leaved heath (*E. tetralix*), feeding on flowers and in shoot apices, where it is often overlooked because of its small size and cryptic colouration. There are also records from heather, *Calluna vulgaris*, and from *Daboecia cantabrica*. Oviparae and apterous males are produced in September and October. In England, Scotland, Wales, north and west Europe, east to Poland and south to the Iberian peninsula.

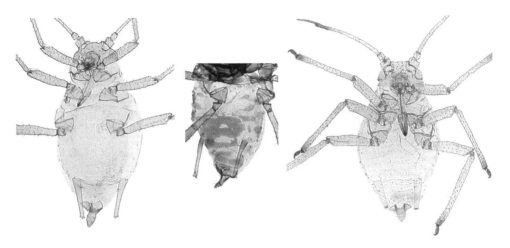

Figure 292. Aptera, (abdomen of) alata and ovipara of *Ericaphis ericae.*

Ericaphis latifrons (Börner, 1942) Figs 289b, 293

Apterae are yellow-green, with tips of antennae and legs black; BL 1.3-1.9 mm. Alatae have broad dark cross-bands more-or-less fused into a patch, and seem very rare. It lives without host alternation on various moorland Ericaceae, most usually crowberry (*Empetrum nigrum*) but also recorded from *Calluna vulgaris*, *Erica umbellata* and *Vaccinium uliginosum*. Oviparae and apterous males occur in Britain from mid-August to September. In England, Scotland, Wales, north and west Europe, including Iceland, east to Poland and the Kola peninsula, and south to the Iberian peninsula.

Figure 293. *Ericaphis latifrons* (left to right): aptera, alata, male and ovipara.

Ericaphis scammelli (Mason, 1940) Figs 288, 294

Apterae are pale yellow-green; BL 1.5-2.4 mm. Alatae have dark brown dorsal abdominal markings partly fused into a central patch, with a conspicuous pale window between the siphunculi. It lives without host alternation on young shoots of various Ericaceae (*Vaccinium* spp., *Andromeda polifolia*, *Empetrum nigrum*, *Gaultheria mucronata*). Prior (1971) obtained oviparae and alate males in culture in October and November, and a fundatrix in early May (Prior, 1971, as *Fimbriaphis fimbriata* ssp, *pernettyae*). A native of North America, introduced to Europe (southern England, Sweden, Netherlands, northern Italy). In England, apart from the original record from Kew Gardens, it has been found on blueberry seedlings at Jealott's Hill (1977) and Reading (1989), and there are recent (June-July 2009) findings on cultivated blueberry and imported plants in Kent nurseries (S. Reid, personal communication).

Figure 294. Aptera, alata and male of *Ericaphis scammelli*.

Ericaphis wakibae (Hottes, 1934) Figs 53a, 291, 295

Apterae are pale brownish green or greenish yellow, with dorsal abdomen somewhat sclerotic and variably tanned, often with darker brown spinal and marginal regions, and siphunculi pale brown with pale areas around their bases; BL 1.6-2.8 mm. Alatae usually have an extensive dark dorsal abdominal patch with a clear window between the siphunculi. In England, *E. wakibae* lives without host alternation on wild strawberry, *Fragaria vesca*, producing oviparae and alate males October, with fundatrices hatching in late February to March (Prior,1971); but in its native North America there may be at least a partial migration to Ericaceae (see Blackman & Eastop, 2006). Not known elsewhere in Europe and only so far found in two localities in England; Malham Tarn, Yorkshire (Prior, 1971, as *Fimbriaphis*), and near Froghall Wharf , Staffordshire (BMNH collection, coll. J.H. Martin); and one in Wales (Michaelston-Le-Pit, E. Baker, pers.comm. 2007). The generic placement of this species is uncertain.

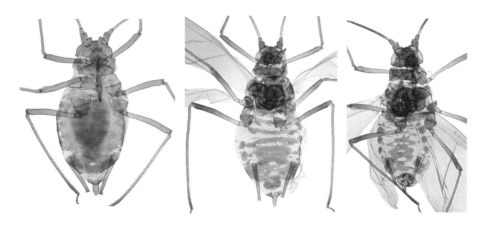

Figure 295. Aptera, alata and male of *Ericaphis wakibae*.

Eucarazzia del Guercio, 1921

Rather small, broadly oval, green aphids with distinctive large swollen siphunculi. The head has broadly divergent antennal tubercles, the median tubercle is undeveloped. Antennae are 6-segmented, with a long PT. Antennae of apterae have a few rhinaria on segment III; those of alatae have rhinaria on III and IV. The dorsum is pale and membranous in apterae, but alatae have distinctive black dorsal abdominal markings, comprising a large transverse patch across tergites IV and V linking with large marginal sclerites on V and VI, and also black triangular spots at the ends of all the wing veins. Siphunculi of apterae are entirely pale, whereas those of alatae have the swollen part dark and the thinner basal part much paler. The cauda is short and bluntly triangular.

Eucarazzia elegans (Ferrari, 1872) Fig. 296

There are 2-3 species in the world, associated with Labiatae. One of these, *Eucarazzia elegans*, has become widely distributed outside its native area (Mediterranean, Middle East). Alatae of this species have recently been trapped in Britain, and it is possible that it will eventually become established in this country. It feeds on the undersides of leaves of *Mentha* spp. and various other Labiatae (*Salvia, Coleus, Lavandula, Melissa, Nepeta*, etc). Sexual morphs have been found on *Nepeta* in Iran.

Figure 296. Alata of *Eucarazzia elegans*.

Hayhurstia del Guercio, 1917

Pale, wax-powdered aphids with rather short appendages, related to *Brachycolus*. The head has antennal tubercles undeveloped, so that the outline of the front of the head is almost straight. Antennae are 6-segmented, shorter than body, with PT more than twice length of base of segment VI. Antennae of apterae lack secondary rhinaria; those of alatae have 8-20 slightly protruberant rhinaria in an irregular row on segment III, and 0-2 (usually 0) on IV. Dorsal body hairs are short and blunt, sometimes slightly spatulate on posterior abdominal tergites in apterae. First tarsal segments have 3-3-3 hairs. The dorsal cuticle of apterae is membranous and smooth. Alatae have dark marginal sclerites and dorsal cross-bands at least on posterior tergites. Siphunculi are short or very short, and usually slightly swollen. The cauda is finger-shaped, or elongate triangular, with 5-7 hairs.

Hayhurstia atriplicis (del Guercio, 1917) Figs 94, 297

The genus has only one species, *Hayhurstia atriplicis*, which lives without host alternation on Chenopodiaceae, usually *Atriplex* and *Chenopodium* spp., inside pod-like yellowish leaf-galls formed by rolling the leaves upwards. It is not visited by ants. Sexual morphs occur in late September to October; males may be apterous or alate (Heie, 1992). In England, Scotland, Wales, Ireland, Isle of Man, widespread in Europe and Asia, and also in North Africa, and North and Central America.

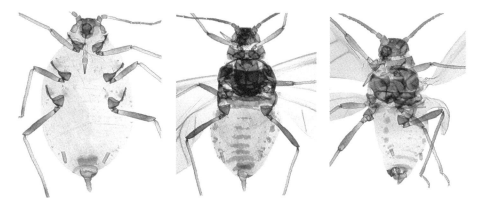

Figure 297. Aptera, alata and alate male of *Hayhurstia atriplicis.*

Hyadaphis Kirkaldy, 1904

Pale aphids with rather short, often dark, appendages, and the body usually dusted with greyish wax. The head has antennal tubercles undeveloped, so that the outline of the front of the head is almost straight, or convex. Antennae are 6-segmented or, more rarely, 5-segmented, shorter than body, with an often very narrow PT that is more than twice the length of the base of the last segment. Antennae of apterae lack secondary rhinaria; those of alatae have numerous somewhat protruberant rhinaria distributed over the whole of ANT III, usually some also on IV, and sometimes on V. First tarsal segments usually all have 3 hairs. The dorsal cuticle of apterae is membranous. Alatae have dark marginal sclerites, and dorsal cross-bands that are often only on posterior tergites. Siphunculi are short, swollen, smooth or only weakly imbricated, with a slight constriction below the flange. The cauda is finger- or tongue-shaped, or triangular.

There are about 15 species in the world, which typically host-alternate between *Lonicera* spp. as primary hosts and Umbelliferae as secondary hosts. They are not visited by ants. There are two species in Britain, preferring different *Lonicera* spp. as primary hosts but morphologically so similar that there are no absolute discriminants, and some individuals of both apterae and alatae cannot be definitively assigned to species. The keys below are largely based on unpublished work by V.F. Eastop.

Key to apterous viviparae of British *Hyadaphis*

- Prosternal sclerite 1.36-2.6 times wider than long, and often with posterior margin convex (Fig. 298). Siphunculi 1.05-1.45 times longer than cauda. R IV+V (0.093-) 0.110-0.137 mm long .... *foeniculi* (Passerini, 1860)

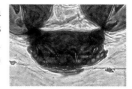

298

- Prosternal sclerite 2.2-3.6 times wider than long, and usually with posterior margin rather straight (Fig. 299). Siphunculi 0.85-1.15 times longer than cauda. R IV+V 0.082-0.114 (-0.122) mm long .... *passerinii* (del Guercio, 1911)

299

Key to alate viviparae of British *Hyadaphis*

- Siphunculi 1.2-1.6 times longer than cauda, 0.55-0.85 of length of ANT III and 2.4-3.1 times longer than R IV+V. Secondary rhinaria distributed ANT III 36-71, IV 6-28, V 0-2(-5) .... *foeniculi*

- Siphunculi 0.9-1.3 times longer than cauda, 0.45-0.65 of length of ANT III and 1.7-2.5 times longer than R IV+V. Secondary rhinaria distributed ANT III 23-45, IV 3-18, V 0 (rarely 1-2) .... *passerinii*

Hyadaphis foeniculi (Passerini, 1860) Figs 1j, 298, 300

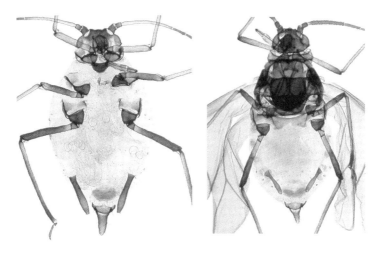

Figure 300. Aptera and alata of *Hyadaphis foeniculi*.

Apterae are greyish green or light green with dark appendages (generally smaller and paler on secondary hosts); BL 1.3-2.6 mm on primary hosts, 1.4-2.0 mm on secondary hosts. Spring colonies occur on *Lonicera* spp., especially *L. xylosteum*, and sometimes *Symphoricarpos*, curling leaves upwards, migrating to various Umbelliferae, where they colonise stems, leaves and flowerheads. Common secondary hosts are *Angelica*, *Apium*,

Conium, *Foeniculum*, *Pastinaca*, *Peucedanum* and *Pimpinella*, but apparently not *Daucus*, which is a preferred host of *H. passerinii* (see below). Oviparae have been found on *L. xylosteum* in October in Germany (BMNH collection), and in North America, but there are no records of sexual morphs on honeysuckle in autumn in Britain, making the life cycle here something of a mystery. Apterous viviparae (not fundatrices) have been collected on *Lonicera* in February (BMNH collection, leg. J.H. Martin), indicating that overwintering may be in the parthenogenetic phase, despite the apparent host alternation. In England and Wales, widespread in Europe, especially in the north, eastward to Turkey and Iraq, and in North America.

Hyadaphis passerinii (del Guercio, 1911) Figs 97, 299

Apterae are greyish green or light green with dark appendages (smaller and paler on secondary hosts); BL 1.2-2.4 mm on primary hosts, 1.0-1.9 mm on secondary hosts. It forms spring colonies on honeysuckles, especially *Lonicera caprifolium* and *L. periclymenum*, curling leaves upwards, migrating to various Umbelliferae, particularly carrots (*Daucus*), but also on *Conium*, *Foeniculum* and *Pastinaca*, colonising stems, leaves and flowerheads. As in the case of *H. foeniculi*, the sexual morphs are not known to occur in Britain, but oviparae have been recorded on *L. caprifolium* in Germany. In England, Scotland, Wales, Ireland, Isle of Man, rest of Europe, especially the south, Mediterranean region, Middle East, Pakistan, India, and introduced to southern Africa, Australia, New Zealand, North and South America. *H. passerinii* is confused in the literature with *H. foeniculi* (q.v.).

Hyalopteroides Theobald, 1916

Medium-sized, pale, narrow-bodied aphids, probably related to *Metopolophium* but with morphology more specialised for living on grasses. The head has well-developed, but rather low, antennal tubercles, their inner faces divergent but each bearing a small, forwardly-directed process, surmounted by a small hair. Antennae are 6-segmented, shorter than body, with PT 2.5 or more times longer than base of segment VI. Antennae of apterae have 1-7 secondary rhinaria, and those of alatae have 11-20, on segment III only. Males have secondary rhinaria on segments III-V. Hairs on the dorsal body and antennae are short and blunt. R IV+V is very short as is typical for a grass-feeder; only about half of the length of HT II. First tarsal segments have 3-3-3 hairs. The dorsal cuticle of apterae is membranous, and the dorsal abdomen of alatae has only pale marginal sclerites and pale transverse sclerites on posterior tergites. Siphunculi are very small, flangeless, less than half the length of the cauda, which is long and tongue-shaped.

Hyalopteroides humilis (Walker, 1852) Figs 56, 301

There is only one species in the genus, *Hyalopteroides humilis*, living without host alternation on cocksfoot grass, *Dactylis glomerata* (with a very few records from other grasses). It is pale yellowish with pale appendages, and feeds on the upper sides of the leaves, which it may turn brown. Alate males have been trapped in July and November in England, but oviparae have not been found, and the presence of apterous viviparae in March and November indicates overwintering in the parthenogenetic phase. Oviparae have been found in Denmark in October (Heie, 1994). This aphid is not visited by ants. In England, Scotland, Wales, Ireland, Isle of Man, Channel Isles, widespread in Europe, and in North America.

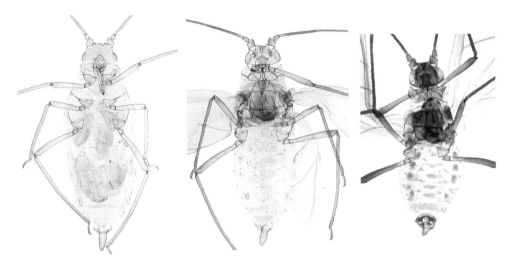

Figure 301. Aptera and alata of *Hyadaphis humilis.*

Hydaphias Börner, 1930

Pale, greenish or yellowish aphids with rather short, mainly dark, appendages. The cuticle of the head is scabrous, with antennal tubercles undeveloped, so that the outline of the front of the head is almost straight. Antennae are 6-segmented, much shorter than the body, with PT 1.7-3 times length of base of ANT VI. Antennae of apterae have 2-9 secondary rhinaria on distal part of segment III, and those of alatae have 10-18 distributed over the length of segment III, and 0-4 on IV. Dorsal body hairs are short and blunt, rod-shaped or sometimes with expanded apices. First tarsal segments all have 2 hairs. The dorsal cuticle of the apterae is membranous, but rather rugose, wrinkled or reticulate, and there may be dark tranverse sclerites on ABD TERG 7 and 8. Alatae have the dorsal abdomen mainly membranous with small marginal sclerites, and sometimes dorsal cross-bands on posterior tergites. Marginal tubercles are often present on prothorax, and ABD TERG I-V (but never on VII as in *Aphis*, to which *Hydaphias* has a superficial resemblance). Siphunculi are tapered or slightly expanded distally, and often curved inwards, rounded and flangeless at apex, with a small terminal aperture. The cauda is finger- or tongue-shaped, as long as the siphunculi or longer, with at least 12 hairs.

There are 4 species in the world, all living without host alternation on *Galium* and visited by ants. Males where known are apterous.

There are two species recorded from Britain, both rarely collected.

Key to apterous viviparae of British *Hydaphias*

- Hairs on anterior abdominal sternites often blunt-tipped, with the longest of them 0.7-1.4 of length of basal diameter of ANT III, and 0.15-0.28 of length of R IV+V (Fig. 302). Marginal tubercles (arrowed) distinctly larger than spiracular apertures on same segments (Fig. 303). R IV+V 0.9-1.1 times longer than HT II. Siphunculi 0.07-0.09 of body length. Cauda with 15-22 hairs .... *mosana* Hille Ris Lambers, 1956

- Hairs on anterior abdominal sternites mostly fine-pointed, the longest of them more than 1.5 times as long as ANT BD III, and 0.3-0.5 of length of R IV+V (Fig. 304). Marginal tubercles (when present) similar in size to spiracular apertures on same segments (Fig. 305). R IV+V 0.7-0.9 of length of HT II. Siphunculi 0.10-0.11 of body length. Cauda with 12-16 hairs .... *hofmanni* Börner, 1950

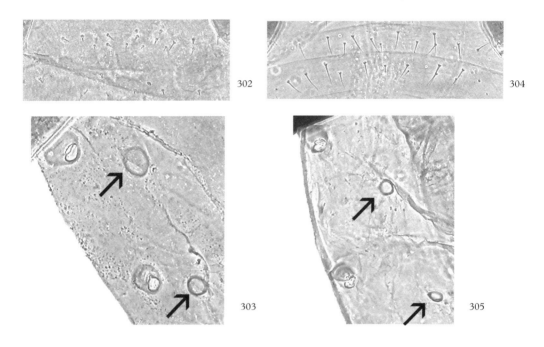

Key to alate viviparae of British *Hydaphias*

- ABD TERG 7 and 8 with dark cross-bands (Fig. 306). Siphunculi 0.09-0.10 and cauda 0.10-0.12 of body length .... *hofmanni*

- ABD TERG 7 and 8 without dark cross-bands (Fig. 307). Siphunculi and cauda both 0.06-0.08 of body length .... *mosana*

Hydaphias hofmanni Börner, 1950 Figs 66, 67, 304, 305, 306

Apterae are small, dirty green to greenish yellow, with dark head, siphunculi and cauda, and mainly dark antennae and legs; BL 1.3-2.0 mm. They live all year around on lady's bedstraw (*Galium verum*), feeding on stems near ground level, and closely attended by ants. The growth of the plant is strongly affected by the aphids, resulting in deformation of shoots and flowerheads. Small oviparae with black, strongly swollen hind tibiae bearing numerous scent glands appear in autumn. Males are apparently as yet undescribed. In England (only one record, from Bristol, 28.vi.1947), and widely distributed in the rest of Europe. [Very similar aphids on *Galium mollugo* in Europe not yet recognised to occur in Britain are regarded as a separate species, *H. molluginis* Börner, 1939.]

Figure 306. Aptera and alata of *Hydaphias hofmanni*.

Hydaphias mosana Hille Ris Lambers, 1956 Figs 302, 303, 307

Apterae are dull, pale yellowish green to dark green with dusky appendages; BL 1.0-2.0 mm. They colonise subterranean parts of the bedstraws *Galium mollugo* and *G. verum*, attended by ants. Oviparae, with hind tibiae only slightly swollen and bearing few scent glands, and small apterous (alatiform) males, occur in September. In England (Hertfordshire, Cambridge) and through most of Europe, eastward to Turkey.

Figure 307. *Hydaphias mosana* (left to right); aptera, alata, male, ovipara.

Hyperomyzus Börner, 1933

Medium-sized to rather large broadly spindle-shaped to oval aphids related to *Nasonovia* but with markedly clavate siphunculi. The head is smooth with low divergent, rather rounded antennal tubercles. Antennae of apterae as well as alatae have many small rhinaria on ANT III. Males have numerous rhinaria on ANT III -V. The ANT PT is long to very long. Hairs on dorsal body and antennae are usually short with blunt or slightly expanded apices (longer in subgenus *Hyperomyzella*). First tarsal segments have 3-3-3, 3-3-2 or 4-4-4 hairs (the latter in subgenus *Hyperomyzella*). The dorsal abdomen of apterae is either membranous (*Hyperomyzus* s. str.) or sclerotic with a varying degree of dark pigmentation (subgenera *Neonasonovia* and *Hyperomyzella*). Alatae usually have black dorsal abdominal markings, varying according to subgenus; *Hyperomyzus* s.str. have a central patch but *Neonasonovia* and *Hyperomyzella* have separate segmental cross-bands. Spiracular apertures are usually rounded and rather large, especially those on the thorax. Siphunculi are rather long and markedly inflated over distal two-thirds of length. The cauda is finger-shaped, and always shorter than siphunculi.

The genus is holarctic, with 18 species. They typically have host alternation between *Ribes* as primary hosts and secondary hosts among the liguliflorous Compositae and Scrophulariaceae. Some species live without host alternation on Compositae or Scrophulariaceae. Except for the swollen siphunculi they resemble *Nasonovia*, which have a similar biology. They are not visited by ants.

There are 7 British species, with all three subgenera represented.

Key to apterous viviparae of British *Hyperomyzus*

1. Tergum entirely membranous, lacking any dark pigmentation. R IV+V 0.8-1.3 times longer than HT II 2

- Tergum partly sclerotic and pigmented, at least having dark intersegmental markings and/or with small sclerites (scleroites) at base of dorsal hairs, if not more extensively pigmented. R IV+V 1.1-1.7 times longer than HT II 5

308

2. Sensoriated part of ANT III infuscated. Cauda tapering from base to apex without any constriction (Fig. 308) ....
.... *thorsteinni* Stroyan, 1960

- ANT III mainly pale, only dark at apex. Cauda at least slightly constricted on basal half (e.g. Fig. 309) 3

309

3. ANT 1.2-1.4 times BL, with PT 7.75-10.20 times longer than base of ANT VI. R IV+V 1.1-1.3 times longer than HT II. Apices of femora often markedly dark brown/black (Fig. 314) .... *lampsanae* (Börner, 1932)

- ANT 0.8-1.05 times BL, with PT 4.6-8.0 times longer than base of ANT VI. R IV+V 0.82-1.12 times longer than HT II. Apices of femora pale or dusky (Figs 313, 315) 4

4. Siphunculi 3-5 times longer than the maximum width of their swollen part, which is 1.6-2.4 times the minimum width on basal part. R IV+V 0.9-1.12 times (mostly 0.95-1.1 times) longer than HT II .... ***pallidus*** Hille Ris Lambers, 1935

- Siphunculi 4-7 times longer than the maximum width of their swollen part, which is 1.3-2.0 times the minimum width on basal part. R IV+V 0.82-1.07 times (mostly 0.9-1.0 times) longer than HT II .... ***lactucae*** (Linnaeus, 1758)

5. Dorsal abdomen with cross-bands at least partially separated between segments and in midline, or with only dark intersegmental sclerites (Fig. 316). R IV+V 1.45-1.8 times longer than HT II. Siphunculi 1.5-1.6 times longer than the long slender cauda (Fig. 310) .... ***picridis*** (Börner and Blunck, 1916)

- Dorsal abdomen with an extensive solid dark central sclerite extending over at least ABD TERG 2-4 (Figs 312, 317). R IV+V 1.05-1.5 times longer than HT II. Siphunculi 1.6-2.0 times longer than the rather thick cauda 6

310

6. Tibiae entirely dark. R IV+V 1.05-1.2 times longer than HT II. First tarsal segments all with 4 hairs (Fig. 311) .... ***rhinanthi*** (Schouteden, 1903)

- Tibiae only dark distally. R IV+V 1.3-1.5 times longer than HT II. First tarsal segments with 3 hairs .... ***hieracii*** (Börner, 1939)

311

Key to alate viviparae of British *Hyperomyzus*

1. Dorsal abdomen with a dark central patch, frequently with marginal incisions and lacunae but at least partially fused across ABD TERG 3-5 (Figs 313-315) 2

- Dorsal abdomen either pale or with segmentally divided dark bands (Figs 312, 316-318) 4

2. Dorsal patch very irregular in outline and with large lacunae (Fig. 313). R IV+V 0.90-1.03 times longer than HT II .... ***lactucae***

- Dorsal patch without any large lacunae. R IV+V 0.96-1.26 times longer than HT II ... 3

3. Dorsal patch almost straight-sided (Fig. 314). ANT PT 8.5-11.0 times longer than base of ANT VI. R IV+V 1.14-1.26 times longer than HT II .... ***lampsanae***

- Dorsal patch with lateral indentations (Fig. 315). ANT PT 6.1-8.4 times longer than base of ANT VI. R IV+V 0.96-1.13 times longer than HT II .... ***pallidus***

4. Tibiae entirely dark. First tarsal segments all with 4 hairs (Fig. 311) .... *rhinanthi*

- Tibiae mainly pale, darker distally. First tarsal segments with 3 hairs 5

5. Dorsal abdomen pale with only small intersegmental sclerites and dusky marginal sclerites (Fig. 318). R IV+V 1.1-1.2 times longer than HT II .... *thorsteinni*

- Dorsal abdomen with a well-developed pattern of dark cross bands, large intersegmental sclerites and conspicuous marginal sclerites (Figs 312, 316). R IV+V 1.3-1.7 times longer than HT II 6

6. ANT III with 55-95 rhinaria and ANT IV with 12-34. ANT PT 5.5-7.3 times longer than base of ANT VI. R IV+V 1.5-1.7 times longer than HT II .... *picridis*

- ANT III with 26-33 rhinaria and ANT IV with 6-12. ANT PT 7.5-9.2 times longer than base of ANT VI. R IV+V 1.3-1.4 times longer than HT II .... *hieracii*

Key to alate males of British *Hyperomyzus*

1. Dorsal abdomen with central dark patch having a large central lacuna but with at least partial fusion in pleural regions across ABD TERG 4 and 5 (Figs 313, 315) 2

- Dorsal abdomen either pale or with segmentally divided dark bands or paired segmental sclerites (Figs 316-318) 4

2. ANT PT more than 9.5 times longer than base of ANT VI. R IV+V 1.2-1.3 times longer than HT II .... *lampsanae*

- ANT PT less than 9.5 times longer than base of ANT VI. R IV+V 0.9-1.1 times longer than HT II 3

3. Cauda dusky .... *lactucae*

- Cauda very pale, almost colourless .... *pallidus**

4. ANT III with 60-94 rhinaria. R IV+V 1.0-1.2 times longer than HT II. First tarsal segments with 4 hairs (as in Fig. 311) .... *rhinanthi*

- ANT III with 29-55 rhinaria. R IV+V 1.1-1.6 times longer than HT II. First tarsal segments with 3 hairs 5

5. Dorsal abdomen with dark cross bands or paired pleural patches (Fig. 316). ANT III with 38-55 strongly tuberculate rhinaria .... ***picridis***

-   Dorsal abdomen with only intersegmental sclerites (Fig. 318). ANT III with 29-39 rhinaria .... ***thorsteinni***

*The male of *pallidus* has not yet been recorded from Britain.

Hyperomyzus (*Neonasonovia*) *hieracii* (Börner, 1939) Fig. 312

Apterae are shining brownish black, with black antennae, siphunculi and cauda; BL 1.7-2.0 mm. Alatae have dark dorsal abdominal cross-bands. Apterae have secondary rhinaria distributed III 14-23, IV 0-6 and alatae have III 26-33, IV 6-12, V 0-1. This species lives all year around on hawkweeds (*Hieracium* spp.), in summer colonising upper parts of stems and inflorescences. Oviparae and males have not hitherto been recorded in the literature, but the BMNH collection contains these morphs reared in culture from a sample collected on Mull, 14.x.57, leg. H.L.G. Stroyan. Oviparae (BL 1.8-2.1mm) have an extensive solid black dorsal patch like that of apterous viviparae and hind tibiae hardly at all swollen, bearing 20-40 rather sparsely scattered scent glands. Males are apterous, BL 1.27-1.36 mm, with broad dark dorsal abdominal cross-bands often partially fused between segments, and antennae c.1.25 times longer than body with secondary rhinaria distributed III 13-18, IV 3-6, V 1-4. In England, Scotland and Wales, and also recorded from Denmark, Germany, Austria, Switzerland and Italy.

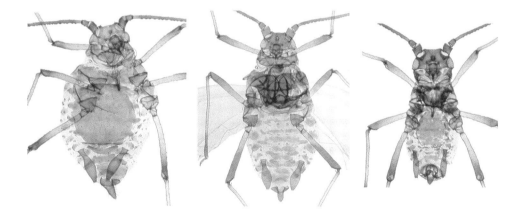

Figure 312. Aptera, alata and male of *Hyperomyzus hieracii*.

Hyperomyzus lactucae (Linnaeus, 1758) **Blackcurrant-Sowthistle Aphid**
Figs 309, 313

Apterae are opaque green with pale appendages; BL 2.0-3.2 mm. Alatae are green with a rather fragmented dark dorsal abdominal patch, pale brownish to dark olive siphunculi, and secondary rhinaria distributed III 30-62, IV 4-22, V 0-8. Spring colonies are found on *Ribes* spp., especially blackcurrant (*R. nigrum*), feeding on undersides of young leaves which curl slightly and acquire yellow spots. Migration occurs in late May-June to form colonies on upper parts of stems and flowerheads of sow-thistles (*Sonchus* spp.), and occasionally other related Compositae (but not *Lactuca sativa*). Migration back to *Ribes* occurs in mid-September. The pale yellow oviparae on blackcurrant have brown markedly swollen hind tibiae with numerous scent glands The males developing on *Sonchus* are reddish. A common species in England, Scotland, Wales and Ireland, and widely distributed in temperate parts of the world.

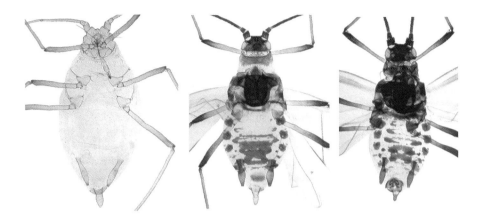

Figure 313. Aptera (from *Sonchus*), alata and male of *Hyperomyzus lactucae*.

Hyperomyzus lampsanae (Börner, 1932) Fig. 314

Apterae are ivory white, with dark apices to segments of antennae and legs; BL 2.3-3.0 mm. Alatae have a dark trapezoid central abdominal patch and secondary rhinaria distributed III 45-75, IV 18-32, V 3-12. It passes its entire life cycle on the undersides of radical leaves of nipplewort, *Lapsana communis*. Oviparae and alate males were recorded in October 1929 in Germany, but have not yet been collected in Britain. In England, Scotland, Wales, and northern and central Europe.

Figure 314. Aptera and alata of *Hyperomyzus lampsanae*.

Hyperomyzus pallidus Hille Ris Lambers, 1935 **Gooseberry-Sowthistle Aphid** Fig. 315

Apterae are opaque yellowish white, sometimes tinged with green, the appendages pale with dark apices to segments, the siphunculi dark-tipped ; BL 2.3-3.5 mm. Alatae have a more-

or-less solid black dorsal abdominal patch, blackish siphunculi (cf. *lactucae*), and secondary rhinaria distributed III 50-75, IV 15-28, V 1-9. Spring colonies occur at shoot tips and on undersides of young curled leaves of gooseberry, *Ribes uva-crispa*. Migration occurs in the second generation to sow-thistles, *Sonchus* spp., usually *S. arvensis*, where it is found on the undersides of lower leaves, sometimes in mixed colonies with *H. lactucae* (Hille Ris Lambers, 1953). The return migration to gooseberry occurs in late September-October. The sexual morphs have not been recorded in Britain, and have not been properly described. In England, Scotland, Wales, Ireland, probably widely distributed in Europe, west Siberia, and (introduced to) North America.

Figure 315. Aptera (from *Sonchus*), alata and male of *Hyperomyzus pallidus*.

Hyperomyzus (Neonasonovia) picridis (Börner and Blunck, 1916) Figs 310, 316

Small colonies of this species may be found in summer on *Picris hieracioides* and *P. echioides* just beneath the inflorescences. The apterae are shining pale yellow-green to dark green, with variably developed brownish dorsal intersegmental markings, and have dusky siphunculi and cauda; BL 2.0-2.8 mm. *Crepis* spp. are also occasionally colonised. Alatae are dark green with a blackish pattern of dorsal sclerotisation, and have numerous tuberculate secondary

Figure 316. Aptera (from *Picris*), alata (autumn migrant) and male of *Hyperomyzus picridis*.

rhinaria distributed III 55-95, IV 12-34, V 0-6. *H. picridis* is a host-alternating species, with *Ribes alpinum* as the only known primary host. Fundatrices in late April-May on *R. alpinum* are shining bright green and cause slight leaf curl. Migration to *Picris* occurs in the second and third generations. The only UK record of sexuales is of a male trapped in Essex in late October (pictured in Fig. 316). In England, Scotland, south Wales (Baker, 2009), and widespread in continental Europe, east to Lebanon and Turkey.

Hyperomyzus (*Hyperomyzella*) *rhinanthi* (Schouteden, 1903) **Currant-Yellow Rattle Aphid** Figs 311, 317

Apterae are yellowish green, green or dark green with extensive shiny black dorsal sclerotisation includng a large ovoid central abdominal patch, antennae and legs mainly black, siphunculi and cauda black; BL 2.4-3.0 mm. Spring colonies feed on young growth of redcurrant (*Ribes rubrum*), curling and distorting leaves into leaf-nests. Alatae are dark green with appendages and sclerotic parts black; spring migrants have secondary rhinaria distributed III 36-48, IV 12-22, V 0-3, but these are much more numerous on ANT III of autumn return migrants (III 65-95, IV 12-24, V 0-6). Migration occurs in the second and third generations to flower-stems and flowers of yellow rattles (*Rhinanthus* spp.), and eyebrights (*Euphrasia* spp.), plants in cool moist habitats being preferred. On *Rhinanthus* they feed mainly on the inner sides of the calyces, and can often be found only by opening the flowers. The return migration starts in late August. In England, Scotland, Wales, Ireland, and widely distributed in Europe, including Iceland and the Faroes. In Britain it is more common in the north of England and Scotland than in the south.

Figure 317. Aptera (from *Rhinanthus*), alata and male of *Hyperomyzus rhinanthi*.

Hyperomyzus (*Neonasonovia*) *thorsteinni* Stroyan Figs 308, 318

Apterae are shining bright yellow-green; BL 1.5-2.0 mm. Alatae have not hitherto been described; one specimen in BMNH collection (from Malham Tarn, Yorks. has only faint dorsal abdominal markings, and secondary rhinaria distributed III 32-36, IV 9, V 0. This species passes its entire life cycle on *Euphrasia* spp., living on young growth and in inflorescences, which become slightly curved and stunted. Alate males, and oviparae with hind tibiae swollen on basal two-thirds bearing numerous scent glands, were collected at Malham Tarn in early September, and on Rhum, Scotland in late August (BMNH collection, leg. H.L.G. Stroyan). In England, Scotland, Iceland (where it was originally described) and Norway.

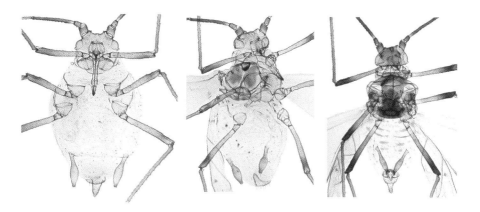

Figure 318. Aptera, alata and male of *Hyperomyzus thorsteinni*.

Idiopterus Davis, 1909

Small, oval, black aphids with distinctive black-and-white antennae and siphunculi. The head is spiculose with well-developed, steep-sided antennal tubercles. Antennae are 6-segmented, longer than body, with a long PT; they are mainly white, except for segments I and II and apices of other segments, which are contrastingly black. Antennae of apterae have a few rhinaria on segment III near base; those of alatae have rhinaria on III-IV or III-V. Hairs on antennae are very short, but those on dorsal body are long and very pale, expanded at their apices and arising from tuberculate bases. First tarsal segments have 3-3-3 hairs. The dorsal cuticle is wrinkled, with minute spinules forming a reticulation. Alatae have very distinctive forewings with radial sector and media touching, a conspicuous white spot in the black pterostigma, and all veins thickly bordered with black. Dorsal abdominal hairs of alatae arise from small scleroites. Siphunculi of apterae are tapering or cylindrical and have the basal part black and the distal part contrastingly white, with a large flange. The cauda is black and tongue-shaped.

Idiopterus nephrelepidis Davis, 1909 Figs 1t, 21, 101a, 319

The genus has only one species, *Idiopterus nephrelepidis*, which feeds on various species of ferns (e.g. *Asplenium*, *Pteridium*, *Polypodium*). It is almost cosmopolitan in distribution, but in Britain, Ireland and the rest of northern Europe it is found only in glasshouses or other indoor situations. It is not visited by ants, and reproduces entirely parthenogenetically. No sexual morphs have yet been found.

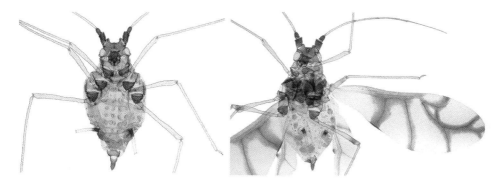

Figure 319. Aptera and alata of *Idiopterus nephrelepidis*.

243

Illinoia Wilson, 1910

Pale spindle-shaped aphids with long appendages. The head has well-developed antennal tubercles, with inner faces smooth and divergent, and the median tubercle is also frequently apparent. Antennae are 6-segmented, longer than body; those of apterae have a few secondary rhinaria on basal part of segment III, and alatae usually have them on segment III only. Hairs on dorsal body and antennae are short and blunt. First tarsal segments can have 3, 4 or 5 hairs. The dorsal abdomen is membranous both in apterae and alatae. Siphunculi are long, broad-based with a narrow cylindrical basal part, then slightly to moderately swollen on distal two-thirds, and then with a more constricted subapical region with polygonal reticulation before a well-developed flange. Cauda is slender, finger-shaped, often with 7 hairs.

There are about 45 species in the world, all except one nearctic. They mostly live without host alternation on plants in many families, and are generally monophagous or oligophagous, with some pattern to their host relationships at subgeneric level. They are not visited by ants.

The five species in Britain are all introduced from North America.

Key to apterous and alate viviparae of British *Illinoia*

1. R IV+V 1.38-1.88 times longer than HT II and bearing 15-23 accessory hairs. Second tarsal segments with minute spinules on the imbrications (Fig. 320; needs high magnification). First tarsal segments mostly with 5 hairs (3 subapical and 2 lateral), occasionally with 4. ANT III of alata with 21-30 rhinaria ....
.... *lambersi* (MacGillvray, 1960)

- R IV+V 0.75-1.45 times longer than HT II and bearing 5-12 accessory hairs. Second tarsal segments without spinules on the imbrications (Fig. 321). First tarsal segments with 3, 4 or 5 hairs. ANT III of alata with 7-21 rhinaria 2

320   321

2. First tarsal segments usually with 5 hairs (Fig. 321; 3 subapical and 2 lateral), occasional individuals having 4 on one or two tarsi. R IV+V 1.10-1.45 longer than HT II (usually more than 1.20) .... *azaleae* (Mason, 1925)

- First tarsal segments usually with 3 hairs (all subapical), rarely with one or two tarsi having 4 hairs. R IV+V 0.75-1.20 times longer than HT II 3

3. ANT PT 3.6-4.7 times longer than base of ANT VI. ANT III of aptera with 0-1 rhinaria (rarely more in alatiform apterae), and ANT III of alata with 7-11 rhinaria. Siphunculi distinctly clavate (Fig. 322) .... ***morrisoni*** (Swain, 1918)

- ANT PT 4.8-7.5 times longer than base of ANT VI. ANT III of aptera with 0-7 rhinaria (rarely 0), and alata with 13-20 rhinaria. Siphunculi only slightly swollen on distal half 4

4. R IV+V 0.96-1.20 times longer than HT II (rarely less than 1.0), with 7-10 accesory hairs. Siphunculi pale or with dusky/dark apices (Fig. 323), 1.8-2.4 times longer than cauda .... ***goldamaryae*** (Knowlton, 1938)

- R IV+V 0.75-0.93 times longer than HT II, with 5-7 accessory hairs. Siphunculi dark except at bases (Fig. 324), 2.3-2.9 times longer than cauda .... ***liriodendri*** (Monell, 1879)

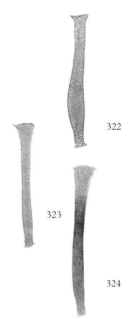

322

323

324

Illinoia azaleae (Mason, 1925) Figs 1r, 10, 321, 325

Apterae are rather shiny deep green, with appendages usually dark towards apices of segments and siphunculi darker distally; BL 1.9-2.7 mm. Immatures are grey-green. Alatae have darker appendages, rather dark wing-veins, and 10-21 secondary rhinaria on ANT III. *I. azaleae* lives on young stems and leaves of *Rhododendron* spp., especially azaleas. It can be a troublesome pest of potted azaleas grown indoors, causing defoliation. It also sometimes occurs on other Ericaceae (*Andromeda, Leucothoe, Pieris, Vaccinium*) and occasionally some other plants (*Myrica, Viola, Tulipa*). The specimens from *Andromeda glaucophylla* collected at Kew in 1960 and provisionally assigned to *I. andromedae* MacGillivray, 1958 (Stroyan, 1964) are this species. Native to eastern North America, it has been introduced to Europe, South Africa, Hawaii, Australia, New Zealand, and most recently Argentina. The earliest British record is 1936, but it is only so far recorded from England. In protected environments it reproduces parthenogenetically throughout the year. Oviparae sometimes occur, but males have not so far been recorded.

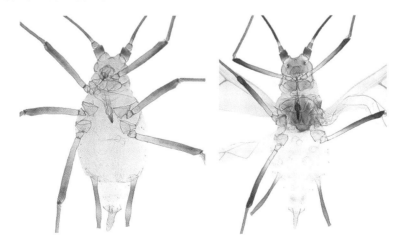

Figure 325. Aptera and alata of *Illinoia azaleae*.

Illinoia goldamaryae (Knowlton, 1938) Fig. 323

Apterae are green with antennae and legs mainly pale but darker towards apices; BL 1.8-2.9 mm. Alatae have darker appendages and 14-20 rhinaria on ANT III. This species forms dense colonies on young growth of species of *Aster*, *Conyza*, *Erigeron* and *Solidago*. Introduced to England from North America (Stroyan, 1964), it was common in the southeast (Surrey, Herts) on cultivated Michaelmas daisies and golden rods in 1960-62 (BMNH collection), and has since been caught regularly in suction traps (Mark S. Taylor, pers. comm., 2009). Sexual morphs and life cycle are unknown, and the population introduced to England appears to have been permanently parthenogenetic.

Illinoia (Masonaphis) lambersi (MacGillivray, 1960) Fig. 320

Apterae are green, pink or yellow, often mixed in same colony, with apices of antennal segments, apices of tibiae and tarsi dark, and siphunculi usually darker distally; BL 2.2-3.3 mm. Alatae have darker appendages and 21-30 rhinaria on ANT III. On young leaves, shoots and flowers of *Rhododendron* spp., including deciduous varieties. Heavy infestations halt development of leaves and production of flower-buds. Colonies can sometimes also occur on holly (*Ilex aquifolium*). Native to western North America, it was introduced to Europe (England, Denmark, Netherlands, Germany) in about 1970 (Stroyan, 1972; Hille Ris Lambers, 1973), and subsequently to South America (Chile) and Japan. Occasional males have been recorded, but oviparae are unknown and parthenogenetic reproduction seems to occur all year around in Europe. *I. lambersi* is recorded from England, Scotland, Wales, Isle of Man, and Ireland.

Illinoia liriodendri (Monell, 1879) Fig. 324

Apterae are pale green or reddish, lightly dusted with wax, with antennae and siphunculi black except at bases, and legs pale green except for black tibial apices and tarsi; BL 1.7-2.5 mm. Alatae have legs black except for bases of femora, and 13-20 rhinaria on ANT III. It lives all year around on the tulip-tree, *Liriodendron tulipifera*, feeding on the undersides of the leaves. A native of North America, it was introduced to Japan in about 1997, and to Europe in about 2002. Oviparae and alate males occur in Japan in September, and in California in October, but there is no information yet about the life cycle in Europe. Baker (2009) recorded attack on populations in South Wales by predators, parasitoids and a fungal pathogen. In England (Surrey, Somerset) and South Wales, and in Europe it is now also recorded from France, Germany, Greece, Italy and Slovenia.

Illinoia morrisoni (Swain, 1918) Fig. 322

Apterae are rather dark apple green, with antennae dusky to dark beyond the base of ANT III, and legs and siphunculi tipped with black; BL 1.5-2.3 mm. They feed on terminal leaves and shoots of numerous conifers, mainly Cupressaceae (e.g. *Chamaecyparis*, *Cupressocyparis*, *Cupressus*, *Juniperus*, *Thuja*, *Widdringtonia*) and Taxodiaceae (*Metasequoia*, *Sequoia*, *Taxodium*). There is only one record from Pinaceae (*Cedrus deodora*). In western North America, and introduced into south-east England in about 1960 (Stroyan, 1964), and France in 1995 (Rabasse *et al.*, 2005). More recently it has been reported from Scotland (trap catches since 2001) and SouthWales (Baker, 2009). In Britain it has been collected on *Cupressus macrocarpa*, *Sequoia sempervirens* and *Taxodium distichum*. No sexual morphs have been described and it apparently has all-year-round parthenogenesis.

Impatientinum Mordvilko, 1914

Shiny black pear-shaped aphids with rather long appendages. The head is smooth and dark with well-developed, steep-sided antennal tubercles. Antennae are 6-segmented, with secondary rhinaria on segment III or III to V of both apterae and alatae. First tarsal segments have 3-3-3 hairs. Dorsal cuticle of apterae is typically almost entirely black and strongly sclerotised, and alatae have extensive black dorsal markings. Siphunculi are black, tapering, heavily imbricated, with a rather narrow subapical zone of polygonal reticulation. The cauda is pale and tongue-shaped.

There are six species in the world, four palaearctic, one nearctic and one neotropical. The palaearctic species typically have host alternation from primary hosts *Smilax* spp. to *Impatiens* spp. in Asia, but the two species introduced to Britain and Europe live all year around on different *Impatiens* spp. They are not visited by ants.

Key to apterous viviparae of British *Impatientinum*

- Apices of tibiae dark or black, distal parts of femora black. ANT III with 1-11 secondary rhinaria, IV and V with 0. R IV+V 0.84-1.0 times longer than HT II. Siphunculi 0.63-0.81 times longer than ANT III. Height of ANT tubercles about half of length of ANT I along inner side .... *asiaticum* Nevsky, 1929

- Apices of tibiae pale, and apices of femora pale or dusky. ANT III with 4-17 secondary rhinaria, IV with 1-7 and V with 0-7. R IV+V 0.64-0.77 times longer than HT II. Siphunculi 0.57-0.66 times longer than ANT III. Height of ANT tubercles much less than half length of ANT I along inner side .... *balsamines* (Kaltenbach, 1862)

Key to alate viviparae of British *Impatientinium*

- Siphunculi 0.59-0.75 times longer than ANT III. R IV+V 0.84-0.99 times longer than HT II. Secondary rhinaria distributed ANT III 9-23, IV 0(-2), V 0 .... *asiaticum*

- Siphunculi 0.49-0.56 times longer than ANT III. R IV+V 0.65-0.77 times longer than HT II. Secondary rhinaria distributed ANT III 9-23, IV 4-12, V 3-9 .... *balsamines*

Impatientinum asiaticum Nevsky, 1929

Adult apterae are shiny black due to the extensive dorsal shield, with bright green, pink or red unsclerotised parts of body, black siphunculi and a yellow to whitish cauda; BL 2.1-3.1 mm. Immatures are green or pale pink. In spring it may be found on the undersides of leaves along the main veins, and later forms dense colonies on flowerstalks, of the naturalised Asian balsams *Impatiens parviflora* and *I. glandulifera*, but not *I. noli-tangere*. Probably originating from central Asia, it is now widely distributed in Europe, and reached England in about 1982 (Blackman, 1984). *I. asiaticum* lives all year around on *Impatiens* in Europe, producing oviparae and alate males in autumn on the continent, but these have so far not been recorded in Britain, where it is so far only known from south-east England (Middlesex, Surrey).

Impatientinum balsamines (Kaltenbach, 1862) Fig. 326

Apterae have an extensive shiny black dorsal shield, brownish green unsclerotised parts, black siphunculi and a pale cauda; BL 2.0-2.7 mm. Immatures are brownish. This species occurs singly or in small colonies on undersides of leaves of touch-me-not balsam, *Impatiens noli-tangere*, living all year around on this plant and producing oviparae and alate males in September-October. It is probably east Asian in origin, but now widely distributed in Europe and Asia. In Britain it is only recorded from where its host grows naturally in the north-west of England (Shropshire, Lancs, Cumbria) and North Wales (Flint).

Figure 326. Aptera, alata and male of *Impatientinum balsamines*.

Jacksonia Theobald, 1923

Rather small broadly oval, *Myzus*-like aphids with characteristically-shaped siphunculi. The cuticle of the head is scabrous with well-developed antennal tubercles, their inner faces converging apically. Antennae 6-segmented, much shorter than body. Antennae of apterae lack secondary rhinaria, those of alatae have large, protruberant rhinaria on ANT III-V. Hairs on the dorsal body and antennae are very short and blunt. First tarsal segments have 3-3-2 hairs. The dorsal cuticle of apterae is rugose, strongly wrinkled or scabrous. Alatae have a dark dorsal abdominal patch on tergites III-VI, and transverse sclerites on other tergites. Spiracular apertures are narrowly reniform. Siphunculi are scabrous, dusky, darker towards apex; swollen at base, very thin in middle and slightly flared at apex, with a small terminal aperture and no flange. The cauda is dark and tongue-shaped, with a slight constriction at the base.

Jacksonia papillata Theobald, 1923 Figs 49, 327

There are 3 species in the world, one of which, *Jacksonia papillata* is widely distributed and occurs in Britain and Ireland. Apterae in life are brownish or olive-green, sometimes dull greenish yellow or reddish, lightly dusted with wax on the underside; BL 1.5-1.9 mm. They live concealed on the colourless basal parts of the stems of grasses such as *Poa* spp., *Festuca rubra*, *Dactylis glomerata* and *Deschampsia flexuosa*. It may also sometimes feed on the tissues of other plants in similar concealed situations, including mosses. Alatae are dark green with an extensive dark dorsal sclerotic pattern and secondary rhinaria distributed ANT III 20-32, IV 7-18, V 1-6. No oviparae have been found, although males that are possibly of this species (but might be of another, undescribed species of *Jacksonia*) are rather regularly caught in suction traps during mild spells in English winters. It is not visited by ants.

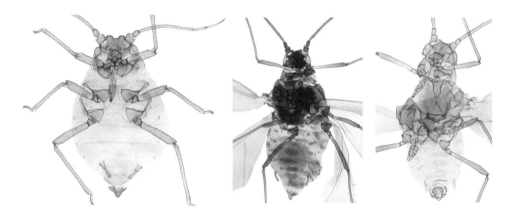

Figure 327. Aptera and alata of *Jacksonia papillata*, and male of *Jacksonia* sp. from suction trap.

Linosiphon Börner, 1950

Shiny green spindle-shaped aphids with rather long appendages, related to *Macrosiphum*. The head is smooth with well-developed, divergent antennal tubercles. Antennae are 6-segmented, longer than body, without secondary rhinaria on segment III in apterae, and with only a few rhinaria on III in alatae. First tarsal segments have 3-3-3 hairs. The dorsal cuticle of apterae is smooth and slightly sclerotic, and alatae have an abdomen with only dark marginal sclerites and small intersegmental sclerites. Siphunculi are pale/dusky at base, and darker towards apex, tapering or cylindrical, with a *Macrosiphum*-like zone of polygonal reticulation on the distal 0.10-0.15 of length. The cauda is pale and finger-shaped. There are 4 species in the world, living without host alternation on Rubiaceae. They are not visited by ants.

Linosiphon galiophagum (Wimshurst, 1923) Fig. 328

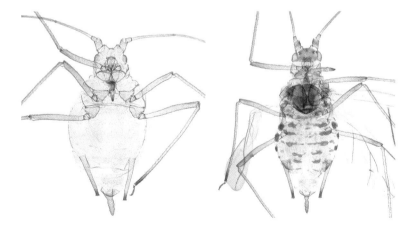

Figure 328. Aptera and alata of *Linosiphon galiophagum*.

There is only one British species, *Linosiphon galiophagum*. Apterae are medium-sized, shining green with dark apices to antennae, legs and siphunculi; BL 1.7-2.5 mm. They live on *Galium mollugo* and other *Galium* spp., feeding usually along the veins on the undersides of the leaves. Alatae have dark intersegmental markings and only 3-6 rhinaria on ANT III. Oviparae have been found in October in Germany, but a population in southern England was still reproducing parthenogenetically in October. Males are apparently undescribed. In England, Scotland, Ireland, continental Europe south to Corsica, and west Siberia.

Liosomaphis Walker, 1868

Rather small, variably-coloured, broadly spindle-shaped aphids with rather short appendages, the body lightly dusted with wax. They resemble and seem closely related to *Cavariella*, but lack the supracaudal process found in that genus. The head is smooth and has antennal tubercles weakly developed, lower than the well-developed, rounded median tubercle. Antennae of apterae are 5- or 6-segmented, much shorter than body, with PT hardly longer than base of last segment. Antennae of apterae lack secondary rhinaria; those of alatae have secondary rhinaria on segment III-V. Dorsal body and antennal hairs are very short and sparse. First tarsal segments have 3-3-3 hairs. The dorsal cuticle of apterae is unpigmented, but somewhat wrinkled. Alatae also have little or no dorsal abdominal pigmentation. Siphunculi are well developed and markedly swollen on distal two-thirds, constricted at apex and with a rather small flange. The cauda is tongue-shaped with 5-6 hairs.

There are 5 species in the world, typically living without host alternation on Berberidaceae. They are not visited by ants.

Liosomaphis berberidis (Kaltenbach) Figs 90, 329

The single British species is the widely distributed *Liosomaphis berberidis*. Apterae are small to medium-sized and either greenish yellow or orangy red (the two colour forms usually occurring as a mixture in colonies); BL 1.1-2.3 mm. They live along the veins on the undersides of leaves of *Berberis* and *Mahonia*, and occur commonly on cultivated plants in parks and gardens. Alatae are similarly pigmented except for a somewhat darker head, thorax and appendages; they have secondary rhinaria distributed III 19-31, IV 4-10, V 1-6. Oviparae with strongly swollen hind tibiae and an extensive pattern of dorsal sclerotic markings, and alate males with black dorsal cross-bars and secondary rhinaria distributed III 19-29, IV 5-10, V 5-7, are produced in early November, but are seldom collected. In England, Scotland, Wales, Isle of Man, and in Europe, Asia, North America and Australasia.

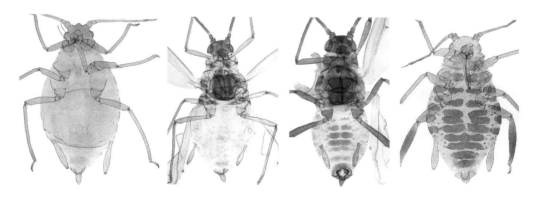

Figure 329. *Liosomaphis berberidis* (left to right): aptera, alata, male, ovipara.

Lipamyzodes Heinze, 1960

Small to medium-sized mid to dark greyish or bluish green oval aphids, with rather short appendages, the body lightly dusted with wax. They superficially resemble *Lipaphis*, but are probably more closely related to *Myzus*. The head is spinulose with quite well-developed, steep-sided, antennal tubercles, and an almost equally developed (but more ventral), angular, median tubercle bearing two rather thick and slightly capitate hairs. Antennae are 6-segmented, shorter than the body, without secondary rhinaria in apterae; those of alatae have rhinaria on ANT III or III and IV. Antennal and dorsal body hairs are short (longer on head and posterior abdomen) with expanded apices. First tarsal segments have 3-3-2 hairs. The dorsal cuticle of apterae is somewhat sclerotic, but unpigmented. Alatae have a rather regular dark central dorsal patch on ABD TERG 3-6. Siphunculi are similar to those of *Lipaphis*; of moderate length, rather narrow-based, cylindrical over most of length or with slightly swollen distal part, and constricted just proximal to the flange; they are pale to dusky in apterae, but in alatae they are dark, and more distinctly swollen . The cauda is broad-based, bluntly triangular, often with a slight constriction near middle, and bearing 5 hairs.

Lipamyzodes matthiolae Doncaster, 1954 Figs 88, 330

There is one species in the world, *Lipamyzodes matthiolae*, originally described from *Matthiola* sp. under glass in northern England, and also collected from *Arabis alba* and *A. caucasica* in North Wales, and from *Galium* sp. in southern England. Apterae are mid- to dark green, with the head pale grey and pulverulent; BL 1.9-2.5 mm. The distinctive alatae occur fairly regularly in suction traps in England and Scotland, and there are single alate specimens in the BMNH collection from *Glaucium grandiflorum* in Lebanon and from *Lepidium draba* in Washington, USA. There were no records of colonies on host plants outside Britain until it was found in Iran in 2009 on an *Achillea* sp. (M. Mehrparvar, pers. comm., 2009). The apparently remarkable host range needs confirmation. The sexual morphs and life cycle are unknown.

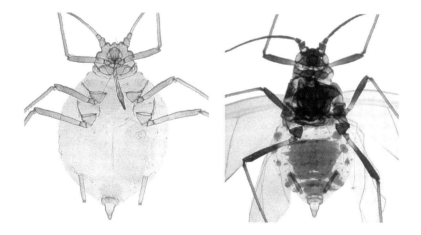

Figure 330. Aptera and alata of *Lipamyzodes matthiolae.*

Lipaphis Mordvilko, 1928

Small to medium-sized usually dark greyish or brownish green oval aphids, with rather short appendages, the body sometimes powdered with wax. The head is spinulose with variably developed, scabrous, divergent antennal tubercles, and the median tubercle is similarly developed. Antennae are 6-segmented (5-segmented in fundatrices), shorter than the body, without secondary rhinaria in apterae; those of alatae have rhinaria on ANT III-IV or III-V. Dorsal body hairs are very short. First tarsal segments have 3-3-2 or 3-3-3 hairs. The dorsum of apterae is sclerotic, often wrinkled or reticulate, pale or with varying degrees of pigmentation; some species have a complete pattern of dark cross-bands. Alatae may also have a complete series of dorsal abdominal cross-bands, or such bands only on the posterior tergites. Siphunculi are of moderate length, rather narrow-based, cylindrical over most of length or with slightly swollen distal part, and constricted just proximal to the flange. The cauda is broad-based, tongue-shaped or elongate triangular, often with a slight constriction near middle, with 4-6 hairs.

There are 11 species in the world, living without host alternation on Cruciferae. They are not visited by ants. Males are apterous.

Four species have been found in Britain.

Key to apterae viviparae of British *Lipaphis*

1. Dorsal abdomen without dark sclerites except on ABD TERG 7 and 8. Siphunculi in most specimens paler than cauda, or darker only towards apices ..... ***erysimi*** (Kaltenbach, 1843)

- Dorsal abdomen with dark cross-bands or paired dark pleural and marginal sclerites on more anterior tergites. Siphunculi uniformly dusky to dark like cauda 2

2. Dorsal abdomen with variably developed paired dark pleural sclerites not fused across midline on anterior tergites. Antennal and median frontal tubercles rather well developed, so that outline in dorsal view is strongly sinuous (Fig. 331). Siphunculi 1.1-1.4 (-1.5) times longer than cauda .... ***cochleariae*** Jacob, 1956

- Dorsal abdomen with broad dark cross-bands across all tergites. Antennal and median frontal tubercles weakly developed. Siphunculi 1.3-1.9 times longer than cauda 3

3. R IV+V 0.10-0.13 mm long .... ***rossi*** Börner, 1939

- R IV+V 0.135-0.16 mm long .... ***turritella*** (Wahlgren, 1938)

Key to alate viviparae of British *Lipaphis*

1. Dorsal abdomen without extensive dark spinopleural sclerotisation anterior to siphunculi, at most with narrow cross-bands or scattered small sclerites. Secondary rhinaria distributed ANT III 9-32, IV 2-11, V 0-4. R IV+V 0.6-0.9 times longer than HT II 2

- Dorsal abdomen anterior to siphunculi with extensive dark spinopleural sclerotisation, comprising broad dark cross-bands sometimes partially fused between tergites. Secondary rhinaria distributed ANT III 27-53, IV 10-24, V 2-12. R IV+V 1.0-1.2 times longer than HT II 3

2. ANT III 1.5-2.0 times longer than siphunculi, which are 0.18-0.26 mm long .... *erysimi*

- ANT III 2.1-2.8 times longer than siphunculi, which are 0.15-0.175 mm long .... *cochleariae*

3. R IV+V 0.10-0.12 mm long .... *rossi*

- R IV+V 0.13-0.15 mm long .... *turritella*

Lipaphis cochleariae Jacob, 1956 Fig. 331

Apterae are dull olive green with variably-developed brown patches; BL 1.2-2.1 mm. Alatae (not yet formally described) have secondary rhinaria distributed III 19-30, IV 5-11, V 0-4. *L. cochleariae* lives all-year-round on common scurvygrass, *Cochlearia officinalis*, just above or within the intertidal zone, on rosettes of young plants, or in flower-heads. Fundatrices and sexual morphs were collected in Northumbria in October (Stroyan, 1957b); oviparae have conspicuously swollen hind tibiae with about 50-70 scent glands, males are small, dark and apterous, BL 1.0-1.3 mm. It has been collected in northern England (Northumbria), Scotland (Argyll), and Wales (Anglesey, Pembrokeshire), but is not known outside Britain.

Figure 331. Aptera, alata and male of *Lipaphis cochleariae*.

Lipaphis erysimi (Kaltenbach, 1843) Fig. 100a, 332

Apterae are yellowish green, dirty green or brownish; BL 1.5-2.3 mm. Alate have secondary rhinaria distributed III 9-32, IV 2-10, V 0-3. *L. erysimi* lives all-year-round on various Cruciferae (*Arabis, Capsella, Coronopus, Erysimum, Isatis, Lepidium, Matthiola, Sinapis, Sisymbrium, Thlaspi*), but not usually on field *Brassica* crops. Oviparae have been collected in early October. Males are apterous but are not recorded in Britain. In England, Scotland, Wales, Ireland, and northern continental Europe. This species has been commonly confused with the world-wide crucifer pest, *L. pseudobrassicae* (Davis, 1914), which is not found in Britain. (Note also that in continental Europe, but not yet recorded from Britain, there is a form specific to *Alliaria petiolata, L. alliariae* Müller, 1955.)

Figure 332. Aptera and alata of *Lipaphis erysimi*.

Lipaphis rossi Börner, 1939 Fig. 333

Apterae are dark grey green with a slight waxy bloom, with a dark grey-brown head, broad dark grey-brown bars across the dorsum, and large marginal sclerites; BL 1.2-1.6 mm. Alate have dark dorsal cross-bands and secondary rhinaria distributed III 27-53, IV 10-26, V 2-12. This species lives all-year-round on hairy rock-cress, *Arabis hirsuta*, stunting flower stems and deforming the inflorescences. Fundatrices were found in late April, and sexual morphs in October (Prior, 1971). Oviparae have hind tibiae only slightly swollen with a few scent glands (9-26), and males are very small (BL 0.8-0.9 mm), brown and apterous. In Britain it is only recorded from one site in south Wales (Whiteford Burrows, Gower); elsewhere in Europe there are records from Netherlands, Denmark, Sweden and Germany (the latter on thale cress, *Arabidopsis thaliana*).

Figure 333. Aptera, alata and male of *Lipaphis rossi*.

Lipaphis turritella (Wahlgren, 1938) Fig. 100b

Apterae are greenish yellow to yellowish brown, dusted with white wax, and a dark sclerotic pattern like that of *L. rossi*; BL 1.5-2.3 mm. Alate have broad dark dorsal cross-bands and secondary rhinaria distributed III 40-53, IV 10-24, V 2-12. It lives all-year-round on tower mustard, *Arabis* (=*Turritis*) *glabra*, causing deformation of the inflorescences, and has also been found on treacle-mustard, *Erysimum cheiranthoides*. The only British record is from Surrey (no locality details) in August, 1924 (BMNH, Theobald Colln, nos 984 and 985, under the manuscript name "Aphis arabis"). Widely distributed (but rarely collected) elsewhere in Europe, eastward to west Siberia and Ukraine.

Longicaudus van der Goot, 1913

Medium-sized spindle-shaped pale aphids, lightly wax-dusted, with rather short appendages and the unusual combination of very short siphunculi and a long hairy cauda. The head lacks antennal or median tubercles. Antennae are 6-segmented, shorter than the body, with an unusually long ANT III and a short PT. Antennae of apterae lack secondary rhinaria, those of alatae and males have very numerous rhinaria distributed all over segment III, but none at all on IV or V. Dorsal body hairs are of moderate length, blunt. First tarsal segments have 6-6-6 hairs. The dorsum of apterae is pale and membranous, whereas alatae have broad dark transverse sclerites on ABD TERG 3-6, more or less fused into an irregular-shaped quadrate patch. Spiracular apertures are narrow, more-or-less covered by opercula. Siphunculi are very short, truncate, with a small flange (fundatrices completely lack siphunculi). The cauda is long and finger-shaped, with numerous hairs.

Longicaudus trirhodus (Walker, 1849) Figs 1d, 91, 334

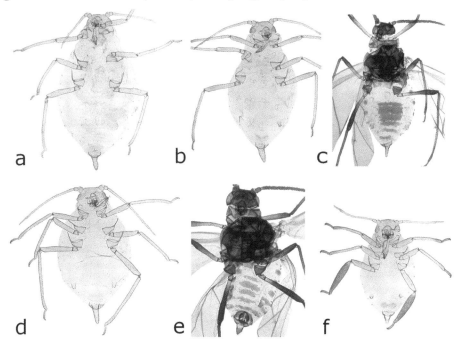

Figure 334. *Longicaudus trirhodus*: (a) fundatrix on rose. (b) second generation aptera (fundatrigenia) on rose, (c) spring migrant alata, (d) aptera on *Aquilegia*, (e) male, (f) ovipara on rose.

There are six species in the world, of which only one is in Britain, *Longicaudus trirhodus*. Fundatrices hatch in March and give rise to small colonies on young leaves and flower-buds of roses in April, from which alate migrate in late May and June to the secondary hosts, *Aquilegia* and *Thalictrum* (Ranunculaceae) where colonies can be found on stems and undersides of the leaves. Apterae on roses are pale apple green, lightly wax-dusted, BL 2.0-2.7 mm, those on secondary hosts are more yellowish in colour, and generally smaller, down to BL 1.3 mm. Alatae have an irregular-shaped dorsal abdominal central patch and 45-100+ rhinaria covering the entire surface of ANT III. The colonies are not visited by ants. The return to roses occurs in October; oviparae are small (BL 1.0-1.3 mm) with inflated dark hind tibiae bearing numerous scent glands. Unusually, the alate males are much larger (BL 1.8-2.1 mm) with short broad abdominal cross-bars. In England, Scotland, Wales and Ireland, and throughout Europe, Asia and North America.

Macrosiphoniella del Guercio, 1911

Green or brown, red-eyed, broadly oval to spindle-shaped aphids, frequently with a thin layer of wax powder but leaving some areas of dorsum, such as intersegmental boundaries and a spinal stripe, devoid of wax. The head is smooth with usually well-developed, divergent antennal tubercles. Antennae are 6-segmented, longer than the body except in fundatrices, with secondary rhinaria on ANT III in apterae, and on III or III-IV in alatae. Males are apterous or alate, often slender-bodied, and have secondary rhinaria on segments III-V. The PT is often long, never less than twice base of ANT VI. Antennal hairs are rather long and often have slightly expanded apices. R IV+V usually has 6 accessory hairs and is often stiletto-shaped (in species feeding on Anthemideae). First tarsal segments have 3-3-3 hairs. Dorsal body hairs are of variable length, often rather long, and often placed on dark scleroites. The dorsum is pale or has dark sclerotic markings in both apterae and alatae that are variably developed according to species; these frequently include crescent-shaped antesiphuncular sclerites, but very rarely are there postsiphuncular sclerites. Siphunculi are cylindrical or tapering, varying in length, but in most species they are rather short and of similar length to cauda, with an extensive distal zone of reticulation comprising numerous small closed polygonal cells. They may be expanded or even flared at the apex, but lack a distinct, differentiated flange. The cauda is long, finger-shaped, and often rather hairy.

There are 115 species in the world, mostly palaearctic, all living without host alternation on Compositae, and mostly specialising on Anthemideae. Most show host specificity at least at the generic level. Most of them are not visited by ants. For additional information see Heie (1995).

There are 15 British species.

Key to apterous viviparae of British *Macrosiphoniella*

1. Siphunculi pale at least basally, although often dark towards their apices 2

- Siphunculi entirely dark to black 8

2 Siphunculi 1.5-2.3 times longer than cauda 3

- Siphunculi 0.7-1.4 times longer than cauda 5

3. Siphunculi with reticulation only on distal 12-26% of length, and usually on less than 20% (Fig. 335) .... *tapuskae* (Hottes and Frison, 1931)

- Siphunculi with reticulation extending over distal 32-69% of length 4

4. Siphunculi with reticulation extending over distal 32-42% of length (Fig. 336). Base of ANT VI 1.7-1.9 times longer than R IV+V which is 0.7-0.8 of length of HT II. Cauda with 18-30 hairs. BL more than 3.5 mm .... *persequens* (Walker, 1852)

- Siphunculi with reticulation extending over distal 48-69% of length (Fig. 337). Base of ANT VI 0.9-1.2 times longer than R IV+V which is 1.1-1.3 times longer than HT II. Cauda with 9-15 hairs. BL less than 3.5 mm .... *sejuncta* (Walker, 1848)

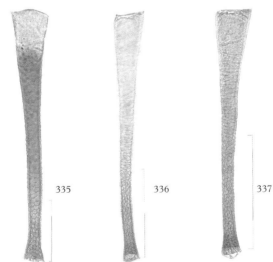

5. Large, rather elongate-bodied aphid (BL more than 3.2 mm). Siphunculi 0.45-0.76 mm long, 1.0-1.4 times longer than cauda which bears 22-30 hairs ....
.... *oblonga* (Mordvilko, 1901)

- Oval-bodied aphid, BL usually less than 3.2 mm. Siphunculi 0.26-0.44 mm long, 0.7-1.0 of length of cauda which bears 13-34 hairs 6

6. ANT III with 8-34 rhinaria. Cauda with 22-34 hairs ....
.... *ptarmicae* Hille Ris Lambers, 1956 (part)

- ANT III with 2-7 (or rarely up to 13) rhinaria. Cauda with 13-25 hairs 7

7. Base of ANT VI 1.4-1.5 times longer than R IV+V, which is 0.6-0.8 of length of HT II. Longest hair on ANT III 1.1-1.8 times basal diameter of segment .... ***abrotani*** (Walker, 1852)

- Base of ANT VI 1.1-1.3 times longer than R IV+V, which is 0.9-1.2 of length of HT II. Longest hair on ANT III 0.7-1.0 of basal diameter of segment .... ***pulvera*** (Walker, 1848)

8. R IV+V with accessory hairs on basal part all shorter than the longest pair of subapical hairs (Fig. 338). Dark spots (scleroites) at bases of dorsal abdominal hairs and conspicuous black crescent-shaped antesiphuncular sclerites present 9

- R IV+V with 1-2 pairs of accessory hairs on basal part longer than the longest pair of subapical hairs (Fig. 339). Dark spots (scleroites) and antesiphuncular sclerites present or absent 10

9. R IV+V rather short, 0.7-0.8 of length of HT II and 0.75-0.85 of length of base of ANT VI (Fig. 338a). Dorsal hairs and their basal scleroites not numerous, mainly in longitudinal rows (Fig. 343). ANT III with 4-12 rhinaria. Siphunculi usually a little longer than (1.0-1.2 times) cauda, which is rather paler than siphunculi .... ***asteris*** (Walker, 1849)

- R IV+V long and slender, 1.0-1.2 times longer than HT II and 0.9-1.1 times length of base of ANT VI (Fig. 338b). Dorsal hairs and sclerites numerous, not in longitudinal rows (Fig. 344). ANT III with 8-28 rhinaria. Siphunculi usually shorter than (0.7-1.0 times) cauda, which is black .... ***millefolii*** (De Geer, 1773)

10. ABD TERG 1-5 each with dark sclerites encompassing bases of spinal hairs to form a series of paired patches or short cross-bands (Fig. 341). ANT III with 29-55 rhinaria (many of them very small) .... ***absinthii*** (Linnaeus, 1758)

- ABD TERG 1-5 without sclerites or with only small scleroites at bases of dorsal hairs, not joined between hair bases. ANT III with 3-45 rhinaria 11

11. Base of ANT VI 0.7-0.9 of length of R IV+V. ANT III with 5-28 rhinaria usually distributed over its entire length .... *sanborni* (Gillette, 1908)

\- Base of ANT VI 1.0-1.9 times longer than R IV+V. ANT III with 2-45 rhinaria restricted to basal half 12

12. Antennae black or only paler on basal half or less of ANT III 13

\- Antennae with at least most of ANT III pale 15

13. ANT III paler on about basal third, and bearing 3-14 rhinaria. Cauda 1.9-3.2 times longer than R IV+V .... *artemisiae* (Boyer de Fonscolombe, 1841)

\- ANT III black almost to base, and bearing 8-34 rhinaria. Cauda 3.2-4.2 times longer than R IV+V 14

14. Longest hairs on ANT III 0.8-1.2 times basal diameter of segment, and longest hairs on outer side of hind tibiae are 0.9-1.3 times its midlength width. Tibiae entirely black .... *tanacetaria* (Kaltenbach, 1843)

\- Longest hairs on ANT III are 1.1-1.7 times basal diameter of base of segment, and longest hairs on outer side of hind tibiae are 1.5-2.0 times its midlength width. Tibiae sometimes with paler middle section .... *ptarmicae* (part)

15. ANT III with 10-22 rhinaria. Siphunculi more than 0.5 mm long, usually longer than (0.9-1.15 times) cauda .... *subterranea* (Koch, 1855)

\- ANT III with 2-11 rhinaria. Siphunculi usually less than 0.5 mm long and shorter than (0.8-1.0 times) cauda .... *usquertensis* Hille Ris Lambers 1935

Key to alate viviparae of British *Macrosiphoniella*

1. ANT IV with 3-12 rhinaria (and siphunculi shorter than cauda) .... *sanborni*

\- ANT IV without rhinaria (except rarely one or more in *tapuskae*, which has siphunculi much longer than cauda) 2

2. ABD TERG 2-4 each with dark sclerites encompassing bases of spinal hairs to form paired patches or short cross-bands (Figs 341, 343) 3

\- ABD TERG 2-4 without sclerites or with only small scleroites at bases of dorsal hairs, only rarely joined between hair bases 4

3. Cauda dark like siphunculi. R IV+V stiletto-shaped, with concave sides and some of accessory hairs very long, much longer than any of subapical ones. ANT III very numerous (85-150+) small rhinaria .... *absinthii*

- Cauda much paler than siphunculi. R IV+V not stiletto-shaped, with short accessory hairs. ANT III with 20-30 rhinaria .... *asteris*

4. Siphunculi pale at least basally, although often dark over most of length 5

- Siphunculi entirely dark to black 11

5. Siphunculi 1.5-2.6 times longer than cauda 6

- Siphunculi 0.7-1.3 times longer than cauda 8

6. Siphunculi with reticulation only on distal 18-28% of length .... *tapuskae*

- Siphunculi with reticulation extending over distal 33-67% of length 7

7. Dorsal abdomen with small scleroites at bases of dorsal hairs. R IV+V 1.0-1.25 times longer than HT II. Cauda with 9-15 hairs .... *sejuncta*

- Dorsal hairs without basal scleroites. R IV+V 0.7-0.9 of length of HT II. Cauda with 17-25 hairs .... *persequens*

8. Large, elongate-bodied aphid, with siphunculi more than 0.45 mm long, longer than cauda .... *oblonga*

- Oval-bodied aphid with siphunculi less than 0.4 mm long, shorter than cauda 9

9. ANT III with 42-65 rather small rhinaria. Cauda with 20-30 hairs ...... *ptarmicae* (part)

- ANT III with 11-35 rhinaria. Cauda with 12-19 hairs 10

10. R IV+V 0.7-0.8 of length of HT II. ANT III with 21-35 rhinaria, and with longest hair 1.0-1.5 times basal diameter of segment .... *abrotani*

- R IV+V 0.9-1.1 of length of HT II. ANT III with 11-23 rhinaria, and with longest hair 0.7-1.0 of basal diameter of segment .... *pulvera*

11. Tibiae with pale middle section 12

- At least the hind tibiae entirely black 13

12. ANT III with 35-55 rhinaria. Siphunculi more than 0.45 mm long, usually longer than cauda .... ***subterranea***

- ANT III with 20-35 rhinaria. Siphunculi usually less than 0.45 mm long, similar in length to or a little shorter than cauda .... ***usquertensis***

13. R IV+V long and narrow, usually more than 3.5 times longer than its basal width, gradually tapering to a rather blunt apex, with accessory hairs not longer than subapical ones (as in Fig. 338b) .... ***millefolii***

- R IV+V usually less than 3 times longer than its basal width, if rather long then stiletto-shaped with concave sides, and with at least one pair of accessory hairs longer than the subapical ones 14

14. ANT III with 22-36 rhinaria. Base of ANT VI 1.2-1.4 times longer than R IV+V ....
.... ***artemisiae***

- ANT III with 40-65 rhinaria. Base of ANT VI 1.5-1.9 times longer than R IV+V 15

15. Longest hairs on ANT III are 1.1-1.7 times basal diameter of base of segment, and longest hairs on outer side of hind tibiae are 1.4-2.0 times its midlength width, with fine-pointed apices .... ***ptarmicae***

- Longest hairs on ANT III are 0.8-1.2 times basal diameter of segment, and longest hairs on outer side of hind tibiae are 0.9-1.3 times its midlength width, with acute apices ......
.... ***tanacetaria***

Key to alate males of British *Macrosiphoniella*

Eight of the British species have alate males. The following key may help to discriminate trapped specimens, although it may not be wholly reliable as it is based on only a few specimens. Information on *ptarmicae* and *subterranea* is taken from the literature, and couplet 7 is based on the assumption that males of *ptarmicae* have tibial hairs like those of alate females:

1. Hind tibiae mainly pale or with pale middle section 2

- Hind tibiae entirely dark 4

2. Siphunculi pale to dusky. ANT III with more than 80 rhinaria, and ANT IV with more than 30 (based on 1 specimen with rhinaria distributed III 88-89, IV 33-44, V 18-19) ....
.... ***abrotani***

- Siphunculi mainly or wholly dark. ANT III with 30-66 rhinaria, IV with 1-23 and V with 5-20 3

3. Siphunculi with reticulation on more than half of length. R IV+V more than 0.9 of length of HT II (based on 1 specimen with R IV+V 0.97 times longer than HT II) .... *sanborni*

- Siphunculi with reticulation on distal third or less of length. R IV+V 0.8-0.9 of length of HT II .... *usquertensis*

4. R IV+V 0.15-0.17 mm long, with accessory hairs not longer than subapical ones (as in Fig. 338b). ANT IV with only 1-9 rhinaria (III 29-49, IV 1-9, V 5-10) .... *millefolii*

- R IV+V 0.10-0.14 mm long, with at least one pair of very long accessory hairs, longer than the longest subapical hairs. ANT IV with 8-23 rhinaria (III 34-70, IV 8-23, V 5-20) 5

5. ANT III with 34-41 rhinaria (IV 12-20, V 8-13). Siphunculi 0.07-0.08 of body length .... *artemisiae*

- ANT III with 45-70 rhinaria (IV 8-23, V 8-20). Siphunculi 0.08-0.11 of body length 6

6. Siphunculi with only a few subapical rows of polygonal cells .... *subterranea*

- Siphunculi with polygonal reticulation extending over at least distal 0.25 of length 7

7. Longest hairs on ANT III are 1.1-1.7 times basal diameter of base of segment, and longest hairs on outer side of hind tibiae are 1.4-2.0 times its midlength width, with fine-pointed apices .... *ptarmicae*

- Longest hairs on ANT III are 0.8-1.2 times basal diameter of segment, and longest hairs on outer side of hind tibiae are 0.9-1.3 times its midlength width, with acute apices .... *tanacetaria*

Macrosiphoniella abrotani (Walker, 1852) Fig. 340

Apterae are greyish green or dull grass green, wax-dusted, with a darker green spinal stripe, with legs and antennae mainly pale, and siphunculi pale brown with darker apices; BL 2.4-3.1 mm. Alatae are without dark dorsal markings. Colonies are usually found on young stems of southernwood, *Artemisia abrotanum*, with occasional records from other *Artemisia* spp., and from *Matricaria discoidea*, *Tripleurospermum inodorum*, *Anthemis cotula* and (once) *Achillea millefolium*. Oviparae and alate males occur on *A. abrotanum* in September and October. In England, Scotland, Wales, continental Europe, and now with an almost worldwide distribution.

Figure 340. Aptera, alata and male of *Macrosiphoniella abrotani*.

Macrosiphoniella absinthii (Linnaeus, 1758) Fig. 341

Apterae are reddish brown, wax-powdered, with black head, antennae, prothorax, legs, siphunculi and cauda, and a distinctive black spot in the centre of the abdomen; BL 1.7-2.5 mm. Alatae are similarly pigmented. It occurs commonly on the upper parts of stems of wormwood, *Artemisia absinthium*. Apterous males and oviparae occur in October in England, (but alate males have been recorded from Latvia). In England, Scotland and Wales; also in northern and central Europe, eastward to Siberia, North Africa and the Mediterranean area, and introduced to USA and Canada.

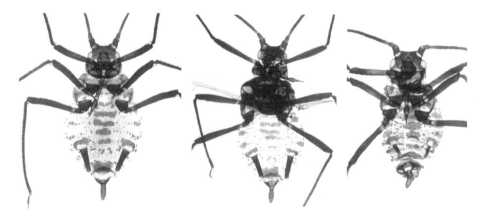

Figure 341. Aptera, alata and male of *Macrosiphoniella absinthii*.

Macrosiphoniella artemisiae (Boyer de Fonscolombe, 1841) Figs 16a, 17a, 342

Apterae are greyish green, wax dusted, with appendages mainly black, but basal parts of ANT III and femora are yellowish; BL 2.3-3.6 mm. Alatae are similarly pigmented. A yellow mutant form has been found in Kent (Blackman, 2006). *M. artemisiae* occurs commonly on upper parts of mugwort, *Artemisia vulgaris*, especially between the inflorescences, and frequently forms large colonies. Several other species of *Artemisia* including *A. absinthium* are recorded as occasional hosts, and there are also records from *Leucanthemum vulgare* and *Tanacetum parthenium*. Oviparae and alate males occur on *A. vulgaris* in September and October. In England, Scotland, Wales and Ireland, throughout Europe, eastward to Siberia, Mongolia and China, and introduced to North America.

Figure 342. Aptera, alata and male of *Macrosiphoniella artemisiae*.

Macrosiphoniella (*Asterobium*) *asteris* (Walker, 1849) Figs 338a, 343

Apterae are brownish green with longitudinal rows of small black dorsal spots, body somewhat wax-powdered, and appendages mainly dark, but cauda noticeably paler than siphunculi; BL 2.3-3.2 mm. Alatae have broken dark dorsal abdominal cross-bands. It feeds on sea aster, *Aster tripolium*, in small colonies on upper parts of stems and in the inflorescences. Oviparae and small dark apterous males occur in late September to October. In coastal areas of England, Wales and Ireland, and continental Europe.

Figure 343. Aptera, alata and male of *Macrosiphoniella asteris*.

Macrosiphoniella millefolii (De Geer, 1773) Figs 8b, 338b, 344

Apterae are yellowish green, powdered with pale grey wax except for a green spinal stripe on abdomen and presiphuncular spots, and with antennae and legs mainly black except for yellowish brown basal halves of fore femora; BL 2.1-3.6 mm. Alatae are similarly pigmented. It feeds on yarrow, *Achillea millefolium*, forming colonies especially in the inflorescences. It is also sometimes found on other *Achillea* spp., including *A. ptarmica*, and on plants in related genera (*Leucanthemum, Tanacetum, Tripleurospermum*). Oviparae and alate males (often reddish in colour) occur in September and October. Sobhani (1970) studied the biology, life cycle and morphology of *M. millefolii* in Germany. In England, Scotland, Wales, common throughout most of Europe, and introduced to North America.

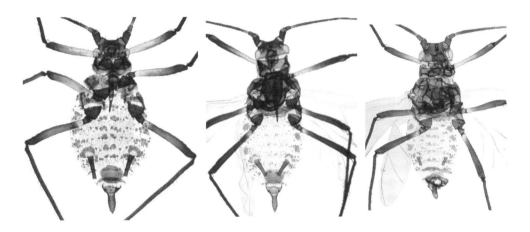

Figure 344. Aptera, alata and male of *Macrosiphoniella millefolii*.

Macrosiphoniella (*Phalangomyzus*) *oblonga* (Mordvilko, 1901) Fig. 345

Apterae are long-bodied, pale green or apple green, with a darker green spinal stripe, and mostly pale appendages; BL 3.0-5.1 mm. This species is usually found dispersed on undersides of lower leaves of mugwort, *Artemisia vulgaris*, also sometimes on other *Artemisia* spp., on cultivated florists' chrysanthemum (*Dendranthema indicum, morifolium, frutescens*), and occasionally on plants in other related genera (*Leucanthemum, Tanacetum, Tripleurospermum*). Oviparae with variably swollen hind tibiae and small slender apterous males occur in September and October. In England, Scotland (one trap record) and Wales, and throughout Europe and Asia.

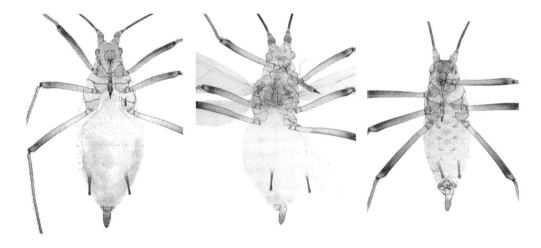

Figure 345. Aptera, alata and male of *Macrosiphoniella oblonga*.

Macrosiphoniella (Phalangomyzus) persequens (Walker, 1852) Figs 336, 346

Apterae are green, with a darker green spinal stripe, dark apices to segments of antennae and legs, and dark-tipped siphunculi; BL 4.2-5.2 mm. It feeds on the undersides of the lower leaves of tansy, *Tanacetum vulgare*. Yellowish green oviparae and dark green apterous males are produced in September and October. Eggs are deposited on fallen leaves and mosses between the plants (Hille Ris Lambers, 1938, as *pseudolineata*). In England, Scotland and continental Europe.

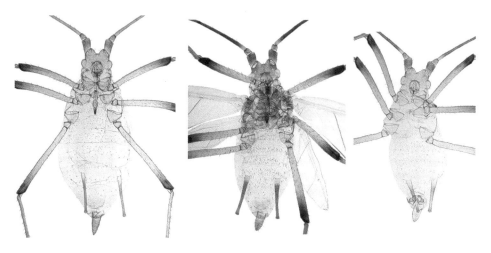

Figure 346. Aptera, alata and male of *Macrosiphoniella persequens*.

Macrosiphoniella ptarmicae Hille Ris Lambers, 1956 Fig. 347

Apterae are green, wax-powdered, with antennae and legs rather variably pigmented, dark bluish grey head, and olive patches at the bases of the siphunculi, which may be either entirely black or pale basally; BL 2.2-3.3 mm. It feeds only on sneezewort, *Achillea ptarmica*. Reddish brown oviparae and alate males occur in September and October. Sobhani (1970) studied its biology, life cycle and morphology in Germany. In northern England, Scotland and Wales, across Europe and eastward to Central Asia.

Figure 347. *Macrosiphoniella ptarmicae* (left to right): aptera, darker aptera, and alata.

Macrosiphoniella pulvera (Walker, 1848) Fig. 348

Apterae are greyish green or greyish white, heavily wax-powdered, with antennae pale on base of III and darkening distally, legs with femora black distally and tibiae mainly pale but with black apices, siphunculi pale basally but black on about distal half, and cauda dusky; BL 1.9-2.9 mm. They feed on the undersides of leaves of sea wormwood, *Seriphidium maritimum*, on which they are well camouflaged, and have also been recorded from *Artemisia* spp. Oviparae, with numerous scent glands on dark swollen basal half of hind tibia, and small (BL 1.3-1.4 mm), apterous males are produced on *S. maritimum* in September. Found on east coast of England south of the Wash, west coast of Ireland (Galway), and widely distributed in Europe (not Italy or Iberian Peninsula), eastward across Asia to Mongolia.

Figure 348. Aptera, alata and male of *Macrosiphoniella pulvera*.

Macrosiphoniella sanborni (Gillette, 1908) **Chrysanthemum Aphid** Figs 339, 349

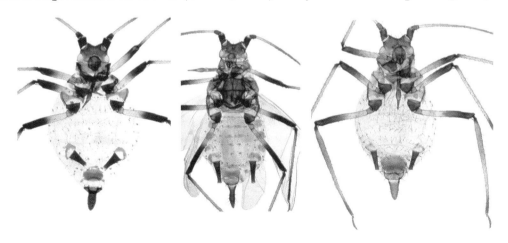

Figure 349. Aptera, alata and ovipara of *Macrosiphoniella sanborni*.

Apterae are shiny, dark red-brown to blackish brown, without wax powder, antennae dark except for base of III, black-banded legs and black, relatively short and thick siphunculi, shorter than the black cauda; BL 1.0-2.3 mm. *M. sanborni* is a widespread pest on cultivated florists' chrysanthemum (*Dendranthema indicum, morifolium, frutescens*) living on the undersides of the leaves, and overwintering in the parthenogenetic phase in protected environments. Contrary to previous reports, sexual morphs are sometimes produced, although still undescribed; in the BMNH collection there are oviparae from chrysanthemums imported to Essex from Malta in November 1973, and oviparae plus one alate male from chrysanthemums at Littlehampton, Sussex in November 1986 (leg. N. Halyer). Probably of East Asian origin, it occurs in England, Scotland, Wales and Ireland, and throughout the world.

Macrosiphoniella sejuncta (Walker, 1848) Figs 337, 350

Apterae variable in colour, often green mottled with brownish red, or dark green, never with any trace of wax powder; antennae dark except for base of III, legs greenish brown with dark apices to femora and tibiae, siphunculi greenish brown with tips darker, cauda greenish brown; BL 2.5-3.1 mm. It lives on yarrow, *Achillea millefolium*, on leaves close to ground level, and is therefore usually overlooked. Oviparae and smaller apterous males (BL 1.6-2.2 mm) are produced in October. In England, Scotland, Wales, Ireland, and across Europe to western Siberia.

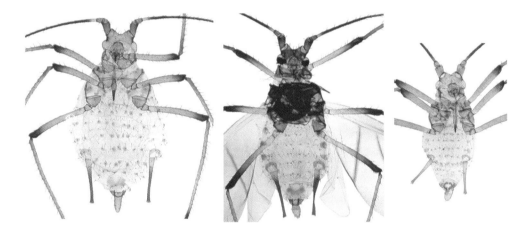

Figure 350. Aptera, alata and male of *Macrosiphoniella sejuncta*.

Macrosiphoniella subterranea (Koch, 1855) Fig. 351

Apterae are reddish brown dusted with greyish wax except on mid-dorsum and around bases of siphunculi, appendages have contrasting pale and black sections, and the siphunculi and cauda are black; BL 2.6-3.5 mm. It feeds on the undersides of the leaves of ox-eye daisy (*Leucanthemum vulgare*) and also cultivated *Leucanthemum* (shasta daisy), causing yellow spots. Oviparae and alate males are produced in October and November in the Netherlands (Hille Ris Lambers, 1938, as *trimaculata*), but are not yet recorded from Britain, where it has only been collected twice (Cumbria, Herts); widely distributed in continental Europe, and also in North America.

Figure 351. Aptera and alata of *Macrosiphoniella subterranea*.

Macrosiphoniella tanacetaria (Kaltenbach) Figs 17b, 352

Apterae are pale grey-green, dusted with fine wax powder, with black antennae, legs, siphunculi and cauda; BL 3.2-4.1 mm. *M. tanacetaria* is most commonly found in summer colonising the flowers and flowers stems of tansy, *Tanacetum vulgare*, but it seems to be able to feed on a much wider range of plants than most other *Macrosiphoniella*, including not only other *Tanacetum* spp., but species of *Achillea*, *Anthemis*, *Artemisia*, *Aster*, *Bidens*, *Chamaemelum*, *Chrysanthemum*, *Dendranthema* and *Tripleurospermum*, and has even been found on *Salvia officinalis* (Labiatae). Massonet *et al.* (2002) and Massonet & Weisser (2004) studied genetic variation in French and German populations. Oviparae (usually flesh-coloured) and alate males may be found on the lower leaves of *Tanacetum* in September to November, and eggs are laid on withered leaves and moss at the base of the plants (Hille Ris Lambers, 1938). In England, Scotland, Wales and continental Europe, Asia, North Africa, and introduced to North and South America.

Figure 352. Aptera, alata and male of *Macrosiphoniella tanacetaria*.

Macrosiphoniella tapuskae (Hottes & Frison, 1931) Figs 16b, 335, 353

Apterae are pale to dark green, not wax-powdered, if pale then with a darker green area on the dorsal abdomen between the siphunculi, and in life there is a dark spot in front of each siphuncular base; BL 2.5-3.3 mm. *M. tapuskae* colonises the lower leaves of its hosts, usually yarrow (*Achillea millefolium*), wild chamomile (*Matricaria chamomilla*), pineappleweed (*M. discoides*) or scentless mayweed (*Tripleurospermum inodorum*), but it has also been found on plants in various other anthemid genera (*Anacyclus, Anthemis, Argyranthemum, Artemisia, Chrysanthemum, Tanacetum*). On *Achillea* it seems to prefer poorly growing plants in dry sandy habitats, whereas *M. sejuncta* favours lusher growth (Hille Ris Lambers, 1938). Yellowish oviparae and slender apterous males occur in September to November. In England, Scotland (one trap record), Wales, continental Europe, eastward to Central Asia, North Africa and North America.

Figure 353. Aptera, alata and ovipara of *Macrosiphoniella tapuskae*.

Macrosiphoniella usquertensis Hille Ris Lambers, 1935 Fig. 354

Figure 354. Aptera, alata and male of *Macrosiphoniella usquertensis*.

Apterae are brownish, powdered with greyish wax, with antennae and legs banded yellow and black, siphunculi and cauda black; BL 2.4-3.2 mm. Its principal host plant is *Achillea millefolium*, but it is also occasionally found on *Artemisia campestris*. It lives on the lower leaves, particularly near the tips, which eventually turn brownish and wither. Reddish oviparae and alate males have been collected in England from mid-September to November. Sobhani (1970) studied the biology, life cycle and morphology of *M. usquertensis* in Germany, and Sobhani & Iglisch (1972) compared the morphology of males with that of *M. ptarmicae*. In England, Scotland, and throughout most of Europe.

Macrosiphum Passerini, 1860

Medium-sized to large spindle-shaped aphids, usually green and/or red, with long appendages. Immatures often have a thin layer of wax powder. The head is smooth with well-developed, divergent antennal tubercles, the median tubercle being undeveloped. Antennae are 6-segmented, as long as or longer than body, with secondary rhinaria on ANT III in both apterae and alatae. Males have secondary rhinaria on ANT III and V, and only sometimes also on IV. The PT is long, always more than three times longer than the base of ANT VI. Antennal hairs are long enough to be conspicuous. First tarsal segments have 3-3-3 hairs. Dorsal body hairs are of variable length, in some species very short, never placed on dark scleroites. The dorsum is pale, usually without any dark sclerotic markings in apterae, and alate females usually only have marginal and intersegmental sclerites, although males have more dark markings. The siphunculi are long, tapering from a rather broad base, usually almost cylindrical on distal part, with a well-developed flange. There is a subapical zone of reticulation that is often somewhat constricted and comprises relatively few, large polygonal cells, and in apterae occupies rarely more than 0.2 of the total length of the siphunculus. The cauda is finger-shaped, pale or dusky (never black), and has 7-20 hairs.

There are about 120 species in the world, nearctic and palaearctic, mostly living without host alternation on a wide variety of herbs and shrubs, often with specific host associations. A few species have host alternation between *Rosa* as primary host and various herbaceous plants, and this is thought to be the ancestral condition. They are not usually visited by ants (except for *M. weberi*). Further information on European *Macrosiphum* can be found in Meier (1961), Watson (1982) and Heie (1994).

There are 16 species recorded from Britain, including three introduced from North America (one of these is a member of a fern-feeding group that should possibly be in a separate genus). The keys below owe much to the work of Watson (1982).

Key to apterous viviparae of British *Macrosiphum*

Apterae of the "*euphorbiae* group" (couplets 6 onward) are difficult to separate and it is advisable to examine as many specimens as possible to assess individual variation. The separation on the basis of femoral pigmentation at couplet 6 may sometimes break down, particularly for pale individuals collected in mid-summer. Most species are host-specific so that the host plant can provide additional confirmation of correct identity.

1. Siphunculi 2.7-3.5 times longer than cauda. Hairs on ANT III short and blunt, the longest 0.2-0.5 times basal diameter of segment .... ***ptericolens*** (Patch, 1919)

-   Siphunculi 1.4-2.2 (-2.8) times longer than cauda. Longest hairs on ANT III more than 0.5 times basal diameter of segment 2

2. R IV+V 1.2-1.5 times longer than HT II, with 14-21 accessory hairs as well as the 3 subapical pairs. Siphunculi mainly very dark but usually paler basally ....
.... *funestum* (Macchiati, 1885)

- R IV+V 0.7-1.2 times longer than HT II, with 4-12 accessory hairs. Siphunculi either entirely dark, or mainly pale/dusky and only very dark towards apices 3

3. Siphunculi entirely dark, with a dark crescent-shaped antesiphuncular sclerite. Front of head and ANT I and II also dark 4

- Siphunculi pale at least on basal part, although often darker towards apices, and ante-siphuncular sclerite absent or weakly developed. Front of head and ANT I-II not dark 5

4. Body spindle-shaped. Siphunculi thicker than hind tibiae at their respective midlengths, and 1.8-2.2 times longer than head width across (and including) eyes ....
.... *rosae* (Linnaeus, 1758)

- Body oval. Siphunculi about equal in thickness to hind tibiae at midlength, and 1.1-1.5 times longer than head width across eyes .... *weberi* Börner, 1933

5. ANT III with 17-40 rhinaria. Body plump, oval .... *albifrons* Essig, 1911

- ANT III with 1-14 rhinaria. Body spindle-shaped 6

6. Femora entirely pale, or slightly dusky distally, but without any definite apical or subapical dark patch or smudge. Longest hairs on ABD TERG 3 are usually less than 38 µm 7

- Femora with dark apices or with a dusky/dark apical or subapical smudge. Longest hairs on ABD TERG 3 are usually more than 38 µm 10

7. Longest hairs on ABD TERG 3 are 41-72 µm .... *daphnidis* Börner, 1940 (part)

- Longest hairs on ABD TERG 3 are 16-38 µm 8

8. Siphunculi 0.21- 0.29 of body length. ANT PT 3.1-4.7 times longer than base of ANT VI .... *penfroense* Stroyan, 1979 (part)

- Siphunculi 0.30-0.37 of body length. ANT PT 4.6-7.1 times longer than base of ANT VI 9

9. R IV+V 0.98-1.11 times longer than HT II. Dark apical sections of tibiae usually markedly swollen, to 1.5 or more times the least more proximal diameter (Fig. 355a). Posterior part of head (between eyes) usually with one or a pair of small spinal tubercles (Fig. 356), and similar, often paired, tubercles common also on ABD TERG 8, or 7 and 8 .... *tinctum* (Walker, 1849)

-   R IV+V 0.83-1.02 times longer than HT II. Apices of tibiae not so distinctly swollen (Fig. 355b). Spinal tubercles absent or only irregularly present, rarely on head and rarely paired on ABD TERG 7-8 .... *euphorbiae* (Thomas, 1878)

355 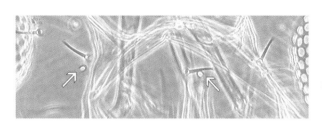356

a   b

10. Siphunculi 0.21- 0.29 of body length. ANT PT 3.1-4.7 times longer than base of ANT VI. Longest hairs on ABD TERG 3 are 18-34 μm ...... *penfroense* Stroyan, 1979 (part)

-   Siphunculi 0.26-0.40 of body length. ANT PT 4.1-7.6 times longer than base of ANT VI. Longest hairs on ABD TERG 3 are 26-84 μm, but if less than 35 μm then either the siphunculi or the ANT PT are relatively longer 11

11. R IV+V similar in length to or longer than (0.95-1.15 times) hind tarsus II. Longest hair on ABD TERG 3 usually more than 55 μm (except in *stellariae*) 12

-   R IV+V shorter than (0.75-0.95 of length of) hind tarsus II (if close to 0.95 then measure several specimens). Longest hair on ABD TERG 3 usually less than 55 μm (except in *daphinidis* and *melampyri*) 15

12. Siphunculi (2.0-) 2.2-2.8 times longer than cauda. ANT PT 6.4-7.9 times longer than base of ANT VI .... *hellebori* Theobald & Walton, 1923 (part)

-   Siphunculi 1.7-2.1 (-2.3) times longer than cauda. ANT PT 4.0-6.7 times longer than base of ANT VI 13

13. R IV+V is 0.85-0.98 of length of HT II. Longest hair on ABD TERG 3 is 26-56 μm (mean 46 μm) .... *stellariae* Theobald, 1913 (part)

-   R IV+V is 0.95-1.18 of length of HT II. Longest hair on ABD TERG 3 is 43-84 μm (means 57 and 63 μm) 14

14. Longest hair on outer side of hind tibia is 82-126 µm. Anterior part (disc) of subgenital plate with (2-) 5-12 hairs .... ***gei*** (Koch, 1855)

\- Longest hair on outer side of hind tibia is 50-96 µm. Anterior part of subgenital plate with 2-5(-7) hairs .... ***cholodkovskyi*** (Mordvilko, 1909)

15. Siphunculi 1.6-1.8 times cauda and 0.28-0.33 of body length. Longest hair on ABD TERG 3 is 43-71 µm .... ***daphnidis*** Börner, 1940 (part)

\- Siphunculi 1.7-2.8 times cauda, if less than 1.8 times (some *centranthi*) then they are 0.33-0.40 of body length. Longest hair on ABD TERG 3 is 26-72 µm (in *centranthi* 33-49 µm) 16

16. ANT PT 4.2-5.2 times longer than base of ANT VI .... ***euphorbiellum*** Theobald, 1917

\- ANT PT (4.0-) 5.5-7.7 times longer than base of ANT VI (only less than 5.5 times longer in some large *stellariae* with body length more than 3.3 mm) 17

17. Longest hair on ABD TERG 3 is 51-69 µm, and on ABD TERG 8 is 70-90 µm. ANT III with 1-6 rhinaria .... ***melampyri*** Mordvilko, 1919

\- Longest hair on ABD TERG 3 is 26-59 µm, and on ABD TERG 8 is 37-86 µm. ANT III with 1-13 rhinaria 18

18. ANT PT 6.4-7.6 times longer than base of ANT VI. Siphunculi (2.0-) 2.2-2.8 times longer than cauda .... ***hellebori*** Theobald & Walton, 1923 (part)

\- ANT PT 4.0-6.35 (-6.7) times longer than base of ANT VI. Siphunculi 1.7-2.3 times longer than cauda 19

19. Antennae 1.55-1.73 times longer than body .... ***centranthi*** Theobald, 1915

\- Antennae 1.08-1.42 times longer than body .... ***stellariae*** Theobald, 1913 (part)

Key to alate viviparae of British *Macrosiphum*

Note: Only very few specimens were available for some species, which will affect the key's reliability in the case of more difficult separations (couplet 6 onwards), and it will not always be possible to assign individual specimens to species. *M. melampyri* could not be included due to lack of specimens.

1. Hairs on ANT III very short and blunt, the longest 0.2-0.5 times basal diameter of segment .... ***ptericolens***

- Longest hairs on ANT III more than 0.5 times basal diameter of segment 2

2. Siphunculi entirely black. Head black. Marginal sclerites and crescent-shaped antesiphuncular sclerites dark and conspicuous. ANT III with 32-66 rhinaria 3

- Siphunculi mainly pale or sometimes dark over most of length but at least somewhat paler at base. Head pale, dusky or dark. Marginal sclerites pale, dusky or dark. ANT III usually with less than 32 rhinaria 4

3. Hind tibiae 0.79-0.95 of body length. Siphunculi 4.8-7.0 times longer than R IV+V ... ***rosae***

- Hind tibiae 0.65-0.71 of body length. Siphunculi 3.5-4.5 times longer than R IV+V ......
.... ***weberi***

4. R IV+V 1.3-1.6 times longer than HT II, with 16-22 accessory hairs as well as the 3 subapical pairs. Siphunculi rather dark except at bases .... ***funestum***

- R IV+V 0.8-1.2 times longer than HT II, with 7-12 accessory hairs. Siphunculi mainly pale or dusky, only ever really dark towards apices 5

5. ANT III with 30-56 rhinaria .... ***albifrons***

- ANT III with 6-28 rhinaria (except 33 in one specimen of *stellariae*, and 34-47 reported to occur in *daphnidis* in Switzerland – Meier, 1961) 6

6. Siphunculi 0.19-0.23 of body length and 2.5-3.2 times longer than base of ANT VI. ANT PT 3.9-4.6 times longer than base of ANT VI .... ***penfroense***

- Siphunculi 0.22-0.40 of body length and 3.25-5.5 times longer than base of ANT VI. ANT PT 4.6-8.0 times longer than base of ANT VI 7

7. HT II 4.3-6.7 times longer than longest hair on ABD TERG 3, which is 19-39 µm ... 8

- HT II 2.1-4.2 times longer than longest hair on ABD TERG 3, which is 40-75 µm ... 13

8. R IV+V 1.0-1.1 times longer than HT II, and bearing 9-12 accessory hairs (normally 10). Dark apical sections of tibiae often markedly swollen, to 1.5 or more times the least more proximal diameter .... ***tinctum***

- R IV+V 0.8-1.0 times longer than HT II and bearing 7-11 accessory hairs (normally 8). Apices of tibiae not so distinctly swollen 9

9. Siphunculi 2.2-2.9 times longer than cauda. ANT PT 5.9-8.0 times longer than base of NT VI .... *hellebori* (part)

- Siphunculi 1.7-2.3 times longer than cauda. ANT PT 4.6-7.1 times longer than base of ANT VI 10

10. ANT PT 4.6-5.2 times longer than base of ANT VI .... *euphorbiellum* (part)

- ANT PT 5.2-7.1 times longer than base of ANT VI 11

11. Subgenital plate with 3-13 hairs on anterior part and 12-23 on posterior edge. Hind tibia 0.66-0.87 of body length .... *stellariae* (part)

- Subgenital plate with 2-6 (often 2-3) hairs on anterior part and 7-16 on posterior edge. Hind tibia 0.78-1.03 of body length 12

12. Longest hair on ABD TERG 3 is 33-39(-44) μm, and on ABD TERG 8 is 54-72 μm. Mesothoracic sclerites often rather dark, and femora dark on distal 0.33 .... *centranthi* (part)

- Longest hair on ABD TERG 3 is 19-35 μm, and on ABD TERG 8 is 36-55(-61) μm. Mesothoracic sclerites usually rather pale/dusky, and femora dark on only about distal 0.25 .... *euphorbiae*

13. R IV+V 0.96-1.15 times longer than HT II. Longest hair on ABD TERG 3 is 43-75 μm 14

- R IV+V 0.80-0.96 (-0.99) times as long as HT II. Longest hair on ABD TERG 3 is 40-63 μm 15

14. Siphunculi 4.7-5.3 times longer than base of ANT VI. ANT PT 1.9-2.3 times longer than cauda which is usually thick and blunt and with a midway constriction. Siphunculi thicker than hind tibia at their respective midlengths .... *cholodkovskyi*

- Siphunculi 3.3-4.65 times longer than base of ANT VI. ANT PT 2.35-4.0 times longer than cauda which usually tapers almost to a point. Siphunculi not thicker than hind tibia at their respective midlengths .... *gei*

15. Siphunculi 2.2-2.9 times longer than cauda. ANT PT 5.9-8.0 times longer than base of ANT VI .... *hellebori* (part)

- Siphunculi 1.6-2.2 times longer than cauda. ANT PT 4.3-7.1 times longer than base of ANT VI 16

16. ANT PT 4.3-5.7 times longer than base of ANT VI. R IV+V 0.80-0.91 of length of HT II 17

- ANT PT 5.2-7.1 times longer than base of ANT VI. R IV+V 0.83-0.99 of length of HT II 18

17. Longest hair on outer side of hind tibia is 75-108 µm, on ABD TERG 3 is 42-56 µm, and on ABD TERG 8 is 72-96 µm .... ***daphnidis***

- Longest hair on outer side of hind tibia is 62-84 µm, on ABD TERG 3 is 28-51 µm, and on ABD TERG 8 is 48-82 µm .... ***euphorbiellum*** (part)

18. Subgenital plate with 3-13 hairs on anterior part and 12-23 on posterior edge. Antenna length 1.0-1.35 times body length .... ***stellariae*** (part)

- Subgenital plate with 2-6 (often 2-3) hairs on anterior part and 10-16 on posterior edge. Antenna length 1.2-1.6 times body length .... ***centranthi*** (part)

Key to alate males of British *Macrosiphum*

Identification of males of *Macrosiphum* is only possible for the more distinctive species. Males of most species are rare or unrecorded in Britain. Authenticated males of *centranthi*, *gei*, and *melampyri* were not available, and males of *penfroense* are unknown. The key is based partly on data of Meier (1961) and Watson (1982).

1. Longest hairs on ANT III 0.2-0.5 times basal diameter of segment .... ***ptericolens***

- Longest hairs on ANT III more than 0.5 times basal diameter of segment 2

2. Siphunculi entirely black. Femora dark for more than half of length. Dorsal abdominal sclerotisation well-developed 3

- Siphunculi paler at least basally. Femora dark for less than half of length. Dorsal scelrotisation variably developed 4

3. Longest hair on ABD TERG 3 is 38-44 µm, and on ABD TERG 8 is 51-60 µm ... ***rosae***

- Longest hair on ABD TERG 3 is 52-67 µm, and on ABD TERG 8 is 66-78 µm ... ***weberi***

4. R IV+V 1.3-1.6 times longer than HT II and bearing with 16-19 accessory hairs as well as the 3 subapical pairs .... ***funestum***

- R IV+V 0.8-1.2 times longer than HT II, with 7-12 accessory hairs 5

5. Siphunculi 0.17-0.19 of BL. Secondary rhinaria distributed ANT III 50-70, IV 0(-9), V 14-19 .... *albifrons*

- Siphunculi 0.21-0.41 of BL. Secondary rhinaria distributed ANT III 26-64, IV 0(-4), V 8-23 6

6. Longest hair on ABD TERG 3 is 34-42 μm, and on ABD TERG 8 is 44-62 μm 7

- Longest hair on ABD TERG 3 is 37-68 μm, and on ABD TERG 8 is 49-84 μm 8

7. R IV+V 0.78-0.93 times longer than HT II .... *euphorbiae*

- R IV+V 1.04-1.15 times longer than HT II .... *tinctum*

8. R IV+V longer than (1.08-1.09 times) HT II .... *cholodkovskyi, gei*

- R IV+V shorter than (0.78-0.98 times) HT II .... *centranthi, daphnidis, euphorbiellum, hellebori*

Macrosiphum albifrons Essig, 1911 **Lupin Aphid** Fig. 357

Apterae are large pale bluish-grey-green aphids, dusted with white wax; BL 3.2-5.1 mm. Adults have brownish, dark-tipped siphunculi, whereas the siphunculi of immatures are uniformly dark. They form large damaging colonies on the leaves, stems and flowers of *Lupinus* spp. In Britain this species seems to overwinter mainly or entirely in the parthenogenetic phase (Carter and Nichols, 1989), but a sexual phase with alate males occurs in North America and Germany. In England, Scotland, Ireland, Isle of Man, and now widely distributed in Europe since its introduction from North America in the 1970s. See also Blackman and Eastop (2000).

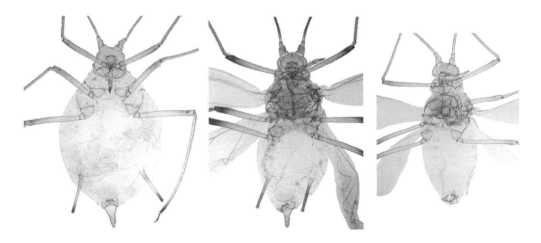

Figure 357. Aptera, alata and male of *Macrosiphum albifrons*.

Macrosiphum centranthi Theobald, 1915 Fig. 358

Apterae are whitish green, yellowish green or green with darker green spinal stripe, with dark brown eyes (not red as in *euphorbiae*), and femora and siphunculi darker towards apices; BL 2.0-3.6 mm. It feeds on leaves and stems of Valerianaceae (*Centranthus*, *Valeriana*), sometimes in mixed colonies with *M. rosae*, and colonies also occur sporadically on various other plants. Greenish oviparae and alate males occur in October-November in Switzerland, but are not recorded from Britain where it possibly overwinters in the parthenogenetic phase. In England, Wales, Ireland, and also recorded from Italy, Switzerland, Russia, India, and Africa.

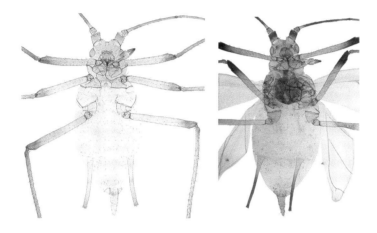

Figure 358. Aptera and alata of *Macrosiphum centranthi.*

Macrosiphum cholodkovsyi (Mordvilko, 1909) Fig. 359

Apterae are yellow-green to dark blue-green or vivid coral-pink to red, with femora and siphunculi dark distally; BL 3.1-5.1 mm. It is found on the upper leaves, stems and inflorescences of meadowsweet, *Filipendula ulmaria*, and occasionally on *Valeriana* spp. Pink or greenish yellow oviparae and dirty reddish or brownish green alate males occur on *Filipendula* in October-November. In England, Scotland, Wales, Ireland, and widely distributed in Europe including Iceland.

Figure 359. Aptera, alata and male of *Macrosiphum cholodkovskyi.*

Macrosiphum daphnidis Börner, 1940

Apterae are pale yellowish or whitish green with slightly darker spinal stripe, with dark brown eyes (cf. *euphorbiae*), entirely pale femora, and siphunculi only slightly darker at apices; BL 2.4-4.2 mm. It specialises on mezereon, *Daphne mezereum*, with occasional records from other *Daphne* spp. including *D. laureolum*, forming small, rather loose colonies on growing buds and shoots, and scattered on undersides of leaves (Watson, 1982). Oviparae and alate males are recorded from continental Europe (Heie, 1994), but not yet from Britain. In southern England, across Europe, and introduced to western North America.

Macrosiphum euphorbiae (Thomas, 1878) **Potato Aphid** Figs 8a, 355b, 360

Apterae are usually green, sometimes yellowish, pink or magenta, with red eyes, and femora and siphunculi pale or only slightly darker towards apices; BL 1.7-3.6 mm. Immatures are paler than adults but with a dark spinal stripe, and dusted with greyish wax. Alatae have a pale greenish to yellow-brown thorax. *M. euphorbiae* is highly polyphagous, having been recorded from more than 200 plant species in more than 20 families. In Britain and Europe it overwinters mainly in the parthenogenetic phase, although sexual morphs and eggs have been found in continental Europe on plants in several families (Heie, 1994). In north-eastern USA there is host alternation with *Rosa* spp. as primary hosts, but spring populations on roses in Britain have probably overwintered parthenogenetically. Of North American origin, *M. euphorbiae* was introduced to Europe early in the last century and now has an almost world-wide distribution. See also Blackman & Eastop (2000).

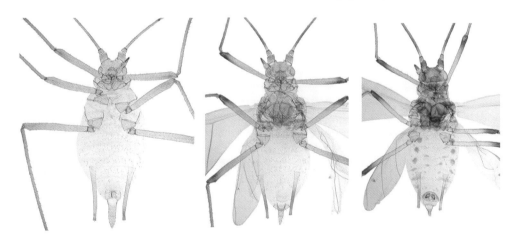

Figure 360. Aptera, alata and male of *Macrosiphum euphorbiae*.

Macrosiphum euphorbiellum Theobald, 1917 (= *M. amygdaloides* Theobald, 1925)

Apterae are very variable in colour, yellow-green, mid green, pink, magenta or wine red, with black apices to antennae, femora, tibiae and siphunculi; BL 1.5-3.7 mm. It lives on wood spurge, *Euphorbia amygdaloides*, feeding on the stems and in the flowerheads. There are a few records from other *Euphorbia* spp., including *E. esula* (on which the type specimen was collected). Red oviparae and red alate males occur in late September to October in Switzerland (Meier, 1961), but are not yet recorded from Britain. In southern England, southern Ireland, and central and southern Europe (Germany, Austria, Switzerland, Corsica, Italy).

Macrosiphum funestum (Macchiati, 1885) Fig. 361

Apterae are rather dull mid- to dark green, or magenta to reddish brown, with mainly dark antennae and siphunculi; BL 1.9-4.0 mm. They feed on young shoots and leaves of *Rubus* spp., especially blackberry, *R. fruticosus* s. lat. Oviparae and alate males are produced in October. In England, Scotland, Wales, Ireland, Channel Isles, throughout Europe, and also recorded from Canada.

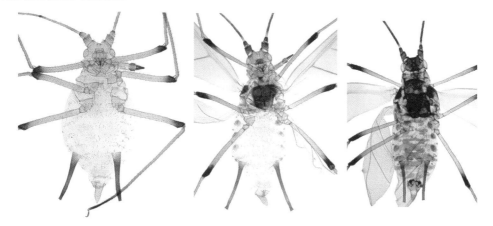

Figure 361. Aptera, alata and male of *Macrosiphum funestum.*

Macrosiphum gei (Koch, 1855) Fig. 362

Apterae are spindle-shaped, mid-green to bluish green, or mauve with green mottlings to wine red, with femora and siphunculi dark towards apices; BL 1.9-5.4 mm. It feeds on *Geum* spp., especially wood avens (*G. urbanum*), where it forms dense colonies on upper parts of stems during flowering. It can also occur on certain Umbelliferae (*Aethusa, Anthriscus, Chaerophyllum, Conium, Myrrhis, Torilis*), and occasionally on Caryophyllaceae, usually scattered or in small colonies on the undersides of the leaves. In continental Europe oviparae and dirty greenish red alate males are produced on *G. urbanum* in late September to October, but males are so far unrecorded in Britain, and overwintering in the parthenogenetic phase may be common. In England, Scotland, Wales, Ireland, Channel Isles, across Europe, and introduced to North America.

Figure 362. Aptera and alata of *Macrosiphum gei.*

Macrosiphum hellebori Theobald & Walton, 1923

Apterae are yellow-green with darker marbling, with dark apices to antennal segments, femora, tibiae and siphunculi; BL 1.7-4.3 mm. On undersides of leaves of hellebores, *Helleborus* spp. (*foetidus, viridis*). Oviparae and alate males occur in September in continental Europe, but in Britain it may overwinter mainly or entirely in the parthenogenetic phase, although Watson (1982) obtained oviparae and males by exposing British clones to artificial short days. Badmin (1991) studied the population ecology of this species in south-east England. In England, Scotland, Wales, northern and central parts of Europe, and introduced to New Zealand.

Macrosiphum melampyri Mordvilko,1919

Apterae are green with dark distal parts of antennae, femora, tibiae and siphunculi; BL 3.2-4.0 mm. It feeds on cow-wheats (*Melampyrum pratense, sylvaticum*). In continental Europe it is also recorded from *M. nemorosum* and *Digitalis ambigua* (not *D. purpurea*, contrary to Blackman and Eastop, 2006). Oviparae and alate males were found on *Melampyrum pratense* in Sweden in late August (BMNH colln, leg. F. Ossiannilsson), but are not recorded from Britain. In northern England (Stroyan, 1964), Scotland and northern Europe.

Macrosiphum penfroense Stroyan, 1979

Apterae are bright apple green, immatures having a wax bloom; BL 1.9-3.4 mm. It specifically colonises *Silene uniflora* (= *maritima*), feeding in small groups in flowers, or singly on buds or on upper surfaces of leaves. Overwintering occurs in the parthenogenetic phase, although oviparae have been reared in the laboratory. Only known from coastal areas of south-west England and Wales (Stroyan, 1979, as *M. sileneum* ssp. *penfroense*) and on the Isle of Man.

Macrosiphum ptericolens Patch,1919 Fig. 363

Apterae are pale yellowish green to darker shiny green; BL 2.3-3.3 mm. Apterae have 3-35 rhinaria on ANT III, alatae have 27-66. It colonises the fronds of the bracken fern, *Pteridium aquilinum*. Oviparae and alate males have been collected in October (BMNH collection, leg. J.H.Martin). Introduced in the 1970s to England from North America (Lawton & Eastop, 1975), and now also in South Wales (Baker, 2009).

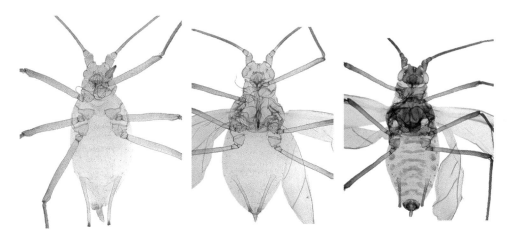

Figure 363. Aptera, alata and male of *Macrosiphum ptericolens.*

Macrosiphum rosae (Linnaeus, 1758) **Rose Aphid** Fig. 364

Apterae are green or deep pink to red-brown or magenta, with shiny black head and prothorax, bicoloured yellow and black antennae and legs, black siphunculi with variably pigmented antesiphuncular sclerites, and a pale yellow cauda; BL 1.7-4.2 mm. A common sight on young growth of wild and cultivated roses in spring, *M. rosae* migrates in April, May and June to form summer colonies on Dipsacaceae (*Dipsacus, Knautia, Succisa*), Valerianaceae (*Centranthus, Valeriana*), and other Rosaceae (*Fragaria, Geum, Pyrus, Malus, Rubus*). Certain other plants, notably holly (*Ilex aquifolium*), may also be colonised. Host alternation is facultative; colonies can remain on *Rosa* through the summer, producing some sexuales in autumn, and in mild winters some may overwinter in the parthenogenetic phase. *M. rosae* has an almost world-wide distribution. See also Blackman and Eastop (2000).

Figure 364. Aptera, alata and male of *Macrosiphum rosae*.

Macrosiphum stellariae Theobald, 1913 Fig. 365

Figure 365. Aptera, alata and male of *Macrosiphum stellariae*.

Apterae are yellowish green, green or red, all segments of appendages, including femora and siphunculi, having blackish apices; BL 1.8-4.4 mm. It forms small, loose colonies on young shoots of various Caryophyllaceae (*Dianthus, Gypsophila, Moehringia, Silene, Stellaria*), and apparently sometimes on certain other plants (*Papaver*, *Ranunculus*, *Valeriana*), although pale specimens may easily be confused with *M. euphorbiae*. Sexual morphs have not been collected in the field, but red alate males have been reared in the laboratory (BMNH colln, leg. G.W. Watson). In England, Wales, Isle of Man, Ireland, northern and central Europe, and introduced to Canada and New Zealand.

Macrosiphum tinctum (Walker, 1849) Fig. 355a, 356

Apterae are mid- to blue green with a darker spinal stripe (a red form is recorded from Switzerland), with femora entirely pale and siphunculi only dusky at apices; BL 2.0-4.0 mm. It restricts its feeding to willow-herbs, *Epilobium* spp., especially broad-leaved willow-herb *E. montanum*, feeding in small numbers on stems, flower-buds and seed-cases. Yellowish green oviparae and reddish alate males occur in late August- September in continental Europe, and oviparae have been reared in the laboratory in Britain (BMNH colln, leg. G.W. Watson), but not so far collected in the field. In England, Wales, and widely distributed through continental Europe.

Macrosiphum weberi Börner, 1933 Fig. 366

Apterae are usually dark red or dark violet, with black siphunculi; BL 1.8-3.0 mm. They form small, frequently ant-attended colonies on stems of devil's bit scabious, *Succisa pratensis*, and sometimes also on *Scabiosa* spp. Oviparae and alate males occur in September-October. In England, Scotland, Wales and parts of continental Europe. A green colour variant has been collected in Scotland (BMNH colln, leg. H.L.G. Stroyan).

Figure 366. Aptera, alata and male of *Macrosiphum weberi*.

Megoura Buckton, 1876

Rather large broadly spindle-shaped legume-feeding aphids, usually green with dark appendages. The head is smooth, often dark, with well-developed, divergent antennal tubercles. Antennae are 6-segmented, about as long as body, with secondary rhinaria on ANT III in apterae, and III-IV in alatae. Males have secondary rhinaria on ANT III-V. Antennal and dorsal body hairs are fairly long. First tarsal segments have 3-3-3 hairs. The dorsum of apterae is mainly unmarked except that there are often dark antesiphuncular sclerites. Alatae have large marginal, antesiphuncular and postsiphuncular sclerites, and cross-bands on ABD TERG 7 and

8. Siphunculi are usually dark, shorter than cauda or only a little longer, and somewhat swollen in middle (cigar-shaped), with a small flange. The cauda is long, finger-shaped, and rather hairy. There are 6 species in the world, all living without host alternation on Leguminosae. They are not visited by ants.

Megoura viciae Buckton, 1876 **Vetch Aphid** (Figs 29a, 31, 367).

The one British species, *Megoura viciae*, lives all year around on legumes, especially vetches, *Vicia* spp. (*cracca, sativa, sepium*) and meadow vetchling *Lathyrus pratensis*, mainly feeding at the stem apices. It is toxic to certain species of ladybirds (Blackman, 1967). Apterae have BL 3-5 mm and are apple green to dark bluish green with black head, prothorax, antennae, legs, siphunculi and cauda; there are 5-26 secondary rhinaria on ANT III. Fundatrices are found in April and are plumper with lower antennal tubercles and ANT PT only about 2 times longer than base of ANT VI (about 4 times longer in apterae of later generations). Alatae have black head and thorax and green abdomen with black marginal and antesiphuncular sclerites, and dorsal cross-bands on ABD TERG 7 and 8; they have 20-40 secondary rhinaria on ANT III and 1-11 on IV. The production of sexual morphs in this species was famously studied in classic research on aphid photoperiodism by Lees (1973). Oviparae with strongly swollen hind tibiae bearing numerous scent glands, and very dark alate males (BL about 2.5mm, with secondary rhinaria distributed III 28-40, IV 7-15, V 3-10) can be found from August to October. *M. viciae* is recorded from England, Scotland, Wales, Isle of Man and Ireland, as well as throughout Europe and in the Middle East, northern and central Asia and North Africa.

Figure 367. Aptera, alata and male of *Megoura viciae*.

Megourella Hille Ris Lambers, 1949

These are rather large oval aphids with mainly dark appendages and black slightly swollen siphunculi, similar to *Megoura* but both apterae and alatae have a pattern of dark dorsal spots. The head is smooth and dark, with well-developed, divergent antennal tubercles. Antennae are 6-segmented, about as long as the body, with rather protruberant secondary rhinaria on ANT III (rarely also on IV) in apterae, and III-IV in alatae. Males are apterous and have secondary rhinaria on ANT III-V. The PT is 3.8-4.6 times longer than base of ANT VI. First tarsal segments have 3-3-3 hairs. Both apterae and alatae have longitudinal rows of dark spinal, marginal and (usually) pleural sclerites, bearing hairs with slightly expanded apices, often arising from somewhat tuberculate bases. Large antesiphuncular sclerites are also present, and cross-bands on the posterior tergites. Siphunculi are black, 1.5 or more times longer than cauda, slightly swollen on distal two-thirds, with a small flange. The cauda is shorter than in *Megoura*, triangular or tapering, and bears less than 10 hairs.

There are two species in the world, both European, living monophagously and without host alternation on the basal parts of two species of vetches. They are difficult to find because of their feeding position and their habit of falling from the plant and lying still when disturbed. They are not visited by ants. Both species occur in Britain. Both apterous and alate morphs can be separated by the following key:

- Basal parts of tibiae (the 'knuckles' immediately below the femoro-tibial joints) pale, distinctly paler than the more distal parts .... ***purpurea*** Hille Ris Lambers, 1949

- Basal parts of tibiae dark .... ***tribulis*** (Walker, 1849)

Megourella purpurea Hille Ris Lambers, 1949 Figs 29b, 30, 368

Apterae are dull reddish violet, pink or dirty yellow-green, with black dorsal spots, and have antennae black except for base of ANT III, legs black except for bases of femora and tibiae, black siphunculi and a yellowish cauda; BL 2.1-2.9 mm. Alatae have a purple abdomen and antennae with rather large protruberant secondary rhinaria distributed III 26-35, IV 8-16. *M. purpurea* feeds specifically on meadow vetchling, *Lathyrus pratensis*, and may be collected by sharp thrashing of well-grown bushy parts of its host. Oviparae and and small dark apterous males have been reared in October in the Netherlands (Hille Ris Lambers, 1949) but have not yet been collected in Britain. Recorded from England, Scotland, Wales and countries in western, central and southern Europe.

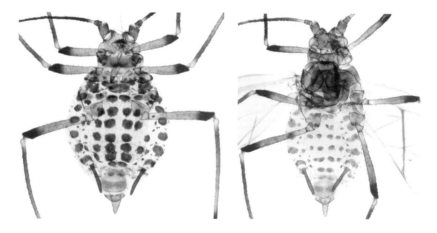

Figure 368. Aptera and alata of *Megourella purpurea*.

Megourella tribulis (Walker, 1849) Fig. 369

Apterae are dark green to black with black antennae, legs except bases of femora, black siphunculi and a dusky cauda; BL 2.4-3.0 mm. Alatae are black with secondary rhinaria distributed III 26-38, IV 3-18. *M. tribulis* lives specifically on bush vetch, *Vicia sepium*, feeding at the base of the stem at or near ground level. Sexual morphs were found in late September to October in the Netherlands (Hille Ris Lambers, 1949), and have been obtained in culture in England (BMNH colln, leg. H.L.G. Stroyan). Males are small and apterous (BL 1.4-1.8 mm). Recorded from England and Scotland, and countries in north-western, northern and central Europe.

Figure 369. Aptera, alata and male of *Megourella tribulis.*

Metopeurum Mordvilko, 1914

Medium-sized to rather large, oval aphids with dark head and prothorax, and dark appendages, related to *Macrosiphoniella* but with morphology adapted for ant attendance. The head is broad with very low divergent antennal tubercles, and the median tubercle undeveloped, so that the front of the head is almost straight or shallowly concave in dorsal view. Antennae are 6-segmented, about as long as body, with numerous protruberant secondary rhinaria on segment III or III-IV in apterae, and on III-IV or III-V in alatae. Males have secondary rhinaria on ANT III-V. Antennal hairs are rather short. First tarsal segments have 3-3-3 hairs. Dorsal body hairs are short and do not arise from scleroites, and there are no antesiphuncular sclerites. Alatae have dorsal abdomen with marginal sclerites only. Spiracular apertures are partially or wholly covered by opercula. Siphunculi are black, rather thin, and cylindrical on distal part which is extensively reticulated, the reticulation comprising numerous small closed polygonal cells. They lack a distinct flange. The cauda is rather short; triangular or finger-shaped, and hairy. The anal plate forms a dark conical protrusion below the cauda.

There are 8 species in the world, all living without host alternation on *Tanacetum* spp. All are attended by ants.

Metopeurum fuscoviride Stroyan, 1950 Figs 1k, 11, 12, 370

The single British species, *Metopeurum fuscoviride*, has apterae (BL 2.2-2.9 mm) with a dark brown head and thorax, and a greenish or reddish abdomen which in life carries a large dark central dorsal spot (this disappears after preservation and mounting). Antennae, legs, siphunculi and cauda are all dark. It lives all-year-round on tansy, *Tanacetum vulgare* (including cultivated varieties), in colonies that are heavily ant-attended but may nevertheless be decimated by hymenopterous parasitoids in late summer. There are some (non-British) records from other *Tanacetum* spp. (but not *T. parthenium*), as well as from

Achillea millefolium and *Leucanthemum vulgare*. Oviparae and small, narrow-bodied, rather pale apterous males (BL only about 1.5-1.6 mm) occur from late August to November. In England and Wales, throughout most of Europe, and in west Siberia and Central Asia.

Figure 370. Aptera, alata and male of *Metopeurum fuscoviride*.

Metopolophium Mordvilko, 1914

Medium-sized to rather large spindle-shaped aphids with both biological and morphological similarities to *Sitobion*, but without the reticulate siphunculi. The head has rather low, divergent antennal tubercles, and the median tubercle is also developed, but to a lesser extent, so that the front of the head has a W-shaped outline in dorsal view. Antennae of apterae are shorter than or about as long as body, and most often have 1-4 small rhinaria on ANT III near base. Alatae have secondary rhinaria only on ANT III, and males have them on III and V, or in some species III-V. Antennal and dorsal body hairs are very short, and blunt or expanded distally. The rostrum is short, with R IV+V usually short and blunt. First tarsal segments have 3-3-3 or 3-3-2 hairs. The dorsal cuticle of apterae is sclerotic, pale or smoky, and smooth or slightly wrinkled, or faintly warty. Alatae have dorsal markings varying between species, sometimes including dorsal cross-bands. Small marginal tubercles are often present on ABD TERG 2-5, and there are usually small spinal tubercles on the head and ABD TERG 8, and sometimes on other segments. Siphunculi are broad-based, tapering or cylindrical, usually pale, with a small but distinct flange, and without subapical polygonal reticulation (sometimes with a few narrow transverse cells). The cauda is pale, tongue- or finger-shaped, or triangular.

There are about 20 species in the world, mostly palaearctic. They typically resemble *Sitobion* in having host alternation between primary hosts in the Rosaceae and various grasses, but many live all-year-round on grasses. They are not visited by ants.

There are seven British species, accounts of which have been provided by Prior (1976) and Stroyan (1982). The keys are based mainly on those of Stroyan (1982).

Key to apterous viviparae of British *Metopolophium*

Preferably identifications should be based on examination of several specimens, to get a range of values for each of the required parameters. Some species may be difficult to identify with certainty using morphological characters alone, but the subsequent information on host plant and appearance in life can often provide useful confirmation.

1. R IV+V usually with only 0-2 accessory hairs, rarely with 3 (plus the normal 3 subapical pairs). Siphunculi 1.95-2.80 times longer than cauda. Dorsum usually dusky brown, darker than venter, with dark intersegmental muscle sclerites (Fig. 374) ....
   .... ***frisicum*** Hille Ris Lambers, 1947

- R IV+V with 4-10 accessory hairs, exceptionally with 3. Siphunculi 1.09-2.37 times longer than cauda. Dorsum usually rather pale (except *tenerum*) 2

2. Siphunculi 1.09-1.35 times longer than cauda (usually less than 1.3 times longer). R IV+V 0.86-1.14 times longer than HT II. Hind tibiae less than 0.9 µm long ....
   .... ***sabihae*** Prior, 1976

- Siphunculi 1.3-2.4 times longer than cauda, but *if* less than 1.36 times *then* R IV+V is only 0.62-0.71 of length of HT II, and/*or* hind tibiae more than 0.9 µm long 3

3. R IV+V 0.92-1.10 times longer than HT II. ANT PT 1.8-2.9 times longer than base of ANT VI .... ***tenerum*** Hille Ris Lambers, 1947

- R IV+V 0.60-0.98 times longer than HT II; *if* more than 0.91 times longer (some *festucae*) *then* ANT PT is normally 2.9-4.2 times longer than base of ANT VI (although individuals developing in cold conditions may have values of this ratio down to 2.1) 4

4. Length of siphunculus is 0.25-0.36 of length of hind tibia. HT II 0.128-0.183 mm (only less than 0.146 mm if BL is less than 2 mm and ANT PT 3-4 times longer than base VI) 5

- Length of siphunculus is 0.34-0.52 of length of hind tibia, but if this ratio is less than 0.36 then HT II is 0.096-0.146 mm long (only more than 0.128 mm if BL is more than 2 mm *and/or* ANT PT is less than 3 times longer than base VI) 6

5. Siphunculi 1.7-2.0 times longer than cauda. ANT V 1.2-1.7 times longer than cauda. ANT PT 3.3-4.4 times longer than HT II. R IV+V 0.65-0.78 of length of HT II. If still inconclusive, the function (length of ANT PT x length of siphunculus)/ (length of cauda x length of HT II) is in the range 6.0-8.6 .... ***fasciatum*** Stroyan, 1982

- SIPH 1.3-1.9 times longer than cauda. ANT V 0.9-1.4 times longer than cauda. ANT PT 2.6-4.1 times longer than HT II. R IV+V 0.61-0.72 of length of HT II. If still inconclusive, the function (length of ANT PT x length of siphunculus)/ (length of cauda x HT II) is in range 3.6-6.5 .... ***dirhodum*** (Walker, 1848)

6. Hind tibia 11.3-16.7 times longer than R IV+V (only ever less than 12 times longer when BL is less than 2.2 mm). Base of ANT VI 1.20-1.62 times longer than HT II (only less than 1.3 times longer when *either* BL is less than 2 mm *or* base of ANT VI is 0.36-0.42 of length of ANT IV) .... ***albidum*** Hille Ris Lambers, 1947

- Hind tibia 7.1-12.0 times longer than R IV+V (only more than 11.3 times longer when BL is 2.2-2.7 mm). Base of ANT VI 0.95-1.29 times longer than HT II (only more than 1.2 times longer when *both* BL is more than 2 mm *and* base of ANT VI is 0.43-0.53 of length of ANT IV) 7

7. Hind tibia 0.87-1.71 mm long, 0.53-0.69 of BL. HT II 0.116-0.164 mm long. R IV+V 0.67-0.87 of length of HT II, and bearing 5-10 accessory hairs. ANT PT 3.0-5.0 times longer than base of ANT VI. If inconclusive then function (A x B x C) / (D x E x F) is 6.5-12.7, where A = length of antennal flagellum (III+IV+V+VI incl. PT), B = length of hind tibia, C = HT II, D = body length (in this case including cauda), E = base of ANT VI, and F = R IV+V ....***festucae*** ssp. ***cerealium*** Stroyan, 1982

- Hind tibia 0.75-1.22 mm long, 0.41-0.53 of BL. HT II 0.096-0.133 mm long. R IV+V 0.72-0.98 of length of HT II, and bearing 3-8 accessory hairs. ANT PT 2.1-4.2 times longer than base of ANT VI. If inconclusive then function (A x B x C) / (D x E x F) is 3.9-8.1 .... ***festucae*** (Theobald, 1917) **s. str.**

Key to alate viviparae of British *Metopolophium*

(Specimens of *festucae* s. str. with borderline values in couplet 5 can be taken either way.)

1. Dorsal abdomen without any clearly defined pattern of dark sclerotisation, the marginal and intersegmental sclerites and any segmental cross-bands being weakly pigmented ... 2

- Dorsal abdomen with a distinct pattern of dark marginal and intersegmental sclerites, and often also with entire or fragmented segmental cross-bands (e.g. Figs 373, 374, 375) 4

2. Base of ANT VI 1.2-1.6 times longer than HT II. ANT III with 3-18 rhinaria. Maximum diameter of marginal tubercle on ABD TERG 5 (adjacent to base of siphunculus) is 7-12 µm. Siphunculi thin, imbricated, about 12-18 times longer than their width at midlength .... ***albidum***

- Base of ANT VI 0.8-1.3 times longer than HT II; *if* 1.2 –1.3 times longer then ANT III has 17-30 rhinaria and maximum diameter of marginal tubercle on ABD TERG 5 is 17-35 µm. Siphunculi thicker, about 8-13.5 times longer than their width at midlength ... 3

3. Function (ANT V + PT) divided by HT II in range 4.8-6.6 (exceptionally more than 6.6 in autumn migrants, but then siphunculi are less than 1.8 times cauda). Siphunculi 1.4-2.0 times longer than cauda. ANT V 1.1-2.0 times longer than cauda and 1.9-2.8 times longer than HT II .... *dirhodum*

- (ANT V + PT) divided by HT II is in range 6.7-7.9 (although might be lower in spring migrants, as yet unknown). Siphunculi 1.8-2.3 times longer than cauda. ANT V 1.8-2.5 times longer than cauda and 2.5-3.4 times longer than HT II .... *fasciatum* (part)

4. R IV+V usually with only 0-2 accessory hairs, rarely with 3 (plus the normal 3 subapical pairs). HT I often with only 2 hairs (i.e., without a medial sense peg). Siphunculi 2.2-2.7 times longer than cauda .... *frisicum*

- R IV+V with 4-8 accessory hairs, exceptionally with 3. HT I almost always with 3 hairs, including a medial sense peg. Siphunculi 1.1-2.5 times longer than cauda 5

5. R IV+V 0.87-1.10 of length of HT II 6

- R IV+V 0.60-0.86 of length of HT II 8

6. Siphunculi 1.09-1.35 times longer than cauda, and 0.23-0.28 of length of hind tibia ......
.... *sabihae*

- Siphunculi 1.38-2.46 times longer than cauda, and 0.28-0.38 of length of hind tibia ... 7

7. Base of ANT VI 0.86-1.52 times longer than cauda. Function (base of ANT VI x R IV+V) divided by (length of cauda x HT II) is in range 0.8-1.4 .... *tenerum*

- Base of ANT VI 0.50-0.84 times longer than cauda. Function (base of ANT VI x R IV+V) divided by (length of cauda x HT II) is in range 0.5-0.8 .... *festucae* s.str. (part)

8. Siphunculi a little darkened just before their apices, this darker zone often somewhat constricted and with some polygonal reticulation (Fig. 372). Maximum diameter of marginal tubercles on ABD TERG 5 (adjacent to bases of siphunculi) is 20-41 µm. Cauda with 8-14 hairs .... *fasciatum* (autumn migrants)

- Siphunculi usually not darker at apices, and without any subapical constriction or polygonal reticulation. Maximum diameter of marginal tubercles on ABD TERG 5 if present (adjacent to bases of siphunculi) is rarely more than 19 µm. Cauda with 5-8, or exceptionally 9, hairs 9

9. Typical specimens (BL 2 mm or more) have dark cross-bands that are especially thick on ABD TERG 4-5, where they are linked to intersegmental muscle sclerites (Fig. 373). ANT PT 3.2-4.9 times longer than base of ANT VI. Hind tibiae 1.04-1.80 mm long, 0.55-0.69 of BL. Siphunculi 0.19-0.24 (usually more than 0.20) of BL and 12-15 times longer than their midlength width. Function (A x B x C) / (D x E x F) is 7.4-13.0, where A = length of antennal flagellum (III+IV+V+VI incl. PT), B = length of hind tibia, C = HT II, D = body length (in this case incl. cauda), E = base of ANT VI, and F = R IV+V .... *festucae* ssp. **cerealium**

- Dorsal abdomen with variably developed, narrow and often fragmented cross bands, always separate from intersegmental muscle sclerites (Fig. 373). ANT PT 2.2-4.3 times longer than base of ANT VI. Hind tibiae 0.95-1.45 mm long, 0.47-0.61 of BL. Siphunculi 0.16-0.21 (usually less than 0.20) of BL and 8-12 times longer than their midlength width. Function (A x B x C) / (D x E x F) is 5.4-9.1 ......*festucae* **s. str.** (part)

Key to alate males of British *Metopolophium*

This is a tentative key based on only a few specimens, and the ranges of some of the discriminating characters used are likely to show overlap when more males are examined. It does not include *albidum* due to lack of material. Alate males of *sabihae* are included although in this species the males may be more often without wings, and their restricted habitat makes them unlikely to be encountered in traps (see Prior, 1976).

1. Secondary rhinaria distributed ANT III 20-30, IV 1-10, V 4-12 .... *tenerum*

- Secondary rhinaria distributed ANT III 29-77, IV 0(-4), V 5-21 (if 29-30 on III then there are 0 on IV) 2

2. Siphunculi 1.40-1.65 times longer than cauda. R IV+V 0.92-1.04 times longer than HT II .... *sabihae*

- Siphunculi 1.7-2.9 times longer than cauda. R IV+V 0.56-0.92 times longer than HT II ... 3

3. Secondary rhinaria distributed ANT III 46-74, IV 0-4, V 6-21 4

- Secondary rhinaria distributed ANT III 29-44, IV 0, V 6-13 5

4. Siphunculi 2.2-2.9 times longer than cauda. ANT flagellum (III-VI including PT) 17.8-20.5 times longer than HT II. R IV+V 0.69-0.78 of length of HT II ....*fasciatum*

- Siphunculi 1.7-2.3 times longer than cauda. ANT flagellum 13.0-17.7 times longer than HT II. R IV+V 0.56-0.69 of length of HT II .... *dirhodum*

5. Siphunculi 2.25 -2.75 times longer than cauda. R IV+V 0.65-0.75 of length of HT II ....
....*festucae* ssp. *cerealium*

- Siphunculi 1.7-2.15 times longer than cauda. R IV+V 0.76-0.92 of length of HT II ......
....*festucae* **s.str.**

Metopolophium albidum Hille Ris Lambers, 1947 Fig. 35a

Apterae are pale straw yellow to (in autumn) pale yellowish green, without a green spinal stripe, but sometimes with green spots at bases of siphunculi; antennae have dark apices to segments with terminal process wholly dark, and tarsi are black; BL 1.9-2.7 mm. Alatae have a pale greenish yellow abdomen and pale golden yellow to brownish orange head and mesonotal lobes and a pale greenish yellow abdomen with pale marginal and intersegmental sclerites, and sometimes vaguely discernible cross-bands. *M. albidum* lives all-year-round on false oat, *Arrhenatherum elatius*, sometimes in large numbers causing red and yellow discoloration of grass blades (Stroyan, 1950). It may occur on other wild grasses occasionally, but only temporarily. Oviparae and alate males occur in November in the Netherlands; immature males are conspicuous by their pale red colour (Hille Ris Lambers, 1947a). They have not yet been found in Britain, and overwintering seems to be mostly in the parthenogenetic phase, although sexual reproduction must also occur because fundatrices have been found in southern England in April-May of some years (Stroyan, 1979). In England, Scotland, Wales and throughout Europe.

Metopolophium dirhodum (Walker, 1848) **Rose-Grain Aphid** Figs 33, 371

Apterae are green or yellowish green with a brighter green spinal stripe, and antennae with dark apices to each segment; BL 1.6-2.9 mm. Alatae have a rather pale abdomen, sometimes (particularly in autumn) with indistinct brownish cross-bars on anterior tergites. *M. dirhodum* has host alternation between *Rosa*, both wild and cultivated, and Gramineae, where it is well-known to economic entomologists as an important cereal pest (see Blackman & Eastop, 2000). The migration from rose occurs in the second and third generations in May-June. Numerous species of grasses and cereals are colonised, and occasionally other monocots such as irises and sedges. The return migration to roses occurs in October-November, the oviparae on rose being whitish, pale yellow or pink. However, in recent times overwintering in the parthenogenetic phase on grasses seems to have become common in the UK (Prior, 1976). In all parts of UK and Ireland, and widely distributed in all temperate parts of world.

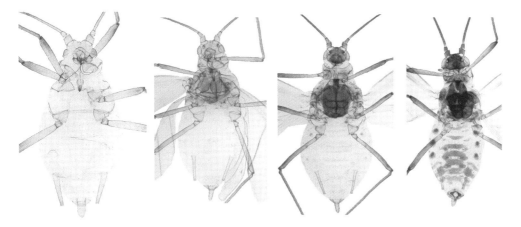

Figure 371. *Metopolophium dirhodum* (left to right): aptera (on cereals), summer alata, return migrant alata (gynopara), male.

Metopolophium fasciatum Stroyan, 1982 Fig. 372

Apterae are pale green with a darker green spinal stripe, and frequently with yellow spots at the bases of the siphunculi; BL 1.7-3.4 mm. Alatae are easily confused with those of *M. dirhodum* but have relatively longer antennae and siphunculi, and those produced in autumn have generally darker pigmentation. It lives on wild grasses, especially *Arrhenatherum elatius*. The life cycle is still unclear, as in some years there is an autumn migration to and production of oviparae on *Rosa canina*, but males are rare compared with those of *M. dirhodum* and spring populations on rose have not been identified (see Stroyan, 1982). Probably most of the population overwinters parthenogenetically on grasses. In England, Scotland, Wales, and Iceland (one aptera, coll. R.N.B. Prior, 27.viii.58); not known from continental Europe.

Figure 372. Aptera (on *Arrhenatherum*), return migrant alata (gynopara) and male of *Metopolophium fasciatum*.

Metopolophium festucae (Theobald, 1917) **Fescue Aphid** (Fig. 373)

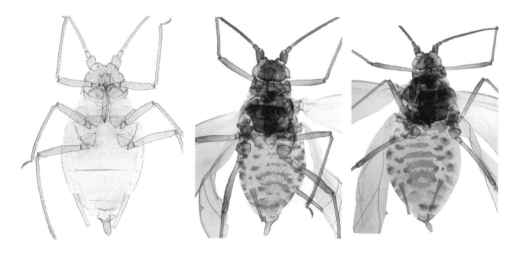

Figure 373. Aptera and alata of *Metopolophium festucae*, and alata of *M. festucae* ssp. *cerealium*.

Apterae are rather shiny, evenly yellowish green to green or salmon pink, with antennae progressivly darker from III to VI; BL 1.4-2.2 mm. Alatae have a conspicuous dark dorsal sclerotic abdominal pattern including segmental cross-bands. *M. festucae* feeds all-year-round on many genera and species of grasses. Populations on cereal crops, especially those colonising winter-sown oats and barley in spring, and producing large numbers of alatae in June-July, are longer-legged and have more heavily banded alate, and are distinguished as a subspecies, ***M. festucae* ssp. *cerealium*** Stroyan, 1982. Both forms overwinter mostly in the parthenogenetic phase, autumn production of sexual morphs being rare, although males have been caught in spring in suction traps. See also Blackman & Eastop (2000). *M. festucae* s.str. occurs in all parts of UK and Ireland, and throughout Europe (including Iceland), and there are also probable records of it from Argentina, Bolivia, and western USA. *M. festucae cerealium* is recorded from England, Scotland, Wales, most of continental Europe, and Saudi Arabia.

Metopolophium frisicum Hille Ris Lambers, 1947 Fig. 374

Apterae are shining green, with an ill-defined olive or brownish green dorsal abdominal shield, dark antennae, dusky siphunculi and a rather dark cauda; BL 1.3-2.4 mm. Alatae have a dark green abdomen with conspicuous dark intersegmental sclerites and variably developed cross-bands. This species feeds specifically on grasses of the genus *Poa*, especially *P. trivialis*, feeding on the upper sides of the leaf-blades in shady, damp situations. Oviparae and very dark apterous males are produced in late October in the Netherlands (Hille Ris Lambers, 1947a), but British populations may overwinter parthenogenetically (Stroyan, 1950). In England, Scotland, Shetland Isles, Wales, north-west and central Europe, and possibly North America (Börner, 1952).

Figure 374. Aptera and alata of *Metopolophium frisicum*.

Metopolophium sabihae Prior, 1976

Apterae are yellow-green, apple green or blue-green; BL 1.3-2.1 mm. Alatae have a bright green to yellow-green abdomen dark brown marginal and pleural (intersegmental) sclerites. *M. sabihae* feeds on *Festuca rubra* and *Vulpia membranacea* growing in sand dunes. Overwintering is probably mostly in the parthenogenetic phase, although a few oviparae and alate and brachypterous males have been reared in culture in November (Prior, 1976). In England, Scotland, Wales and France.

Metopolophium tenerum Hille Ris Lambers Fig. 375

Apterae are dirty pale green or reddish, semi-translucent and rather shiny, appearing almost as if parasitised; BL 1.3-2.2 mm. Alatae have a pale green to reddish abdomen with very distinct dark brown intersegmental sclerites and irregularly present, often faint or fragmented cross-bands. *M. tenerum* is found only on the narrow-leaved grasses *Festuca ovina*, *F. rubra* and *Deschampsia flexuosa*, growing in dryish but shady situations, such as under pine trees. Oviparae and alate males were produced in October in the Netherlands (Hille Ris Lambers, 1947a), but are not yet known in Britain. In England, Scotland, Wales, and northern and central Europe.

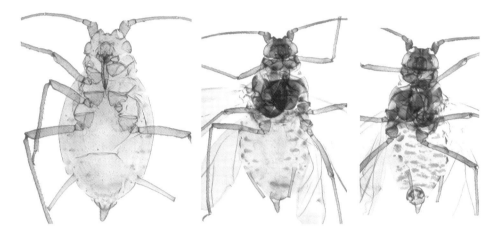

Figure 375. Aptera, alata and male of *Metopolophium tenerum*.

Microlophium Mordvilko, 1914

Rather large, pale brownish green or reddish, spindle-shaped aphids with long appendages, with affinities to both *Acyrthosiphon* and *Aulacorthum*. Immatures are slightly wax-powdered. The head is smooth with very well-developed, divergent antennal tubercles. Antennae of apterae are longer than body, with a few small rhinaria on ANT III near its base, and a long PT. Alatae have secondary rhinaria only on ANT III, and males have them on III and V, or III, IV and V. Antennal and dorsal body hairs are mostly rather short and blunt. First tarsal segments have 3-3-3 hairs. The dorsal cuticle of apterae is lightly sclerotised but pale, and smooth or slightly wrinkled. Dorsal markings of alatae vary between species. The siphunculi are long, broad-based, cylindrical over most of their length, without subapical polygonal reticulation (except sometimes for a few narrow transverse cells), ending in a very well-developed, almost trumpet-like flange. The cauda is tongue-shaped or triangular.

There are 4 or 5 species in the world, mostly living without host alternation on *Urtica*. They are not visited by ants.

There are two British species, with apterous viviparae separable by the following couplet (alatae of the second species are unknown, but probably have similar differences):

- ANT I with 7-12 hairs. R IV+V with 7-13 accessory hairs. Anterior part of subgenital plate with 2-9 hairs. Siphunculi 0.27-0.36 of BL .... ***carnosum*** (Buckton, 1876)

- ANT I with 13-18 hairs. R IV+V with 13-19 accessory hairs. Anterior part of subgenital plate with 10-15 hairs. Siphunculi 0.35-0.45 of BL .... ***Microlophium*** sp.

Microlophium carnosum (Buckton, 1876) Figs 32, 376

Apterae are various shades of green, pink or reddish purple; BL 2.7-4.3 mm. Alatae have dark marginal sclerites but only faint spino-pleural markings. Dense colonies are commonly found on the undersides of the leaves and up the stems of *Urtica* spp., especially *U. dioica*. Oviparae with weakly swollen hind tibiae and alate males are produced in October, but parthenogenetic overwintering seems also to be common. Perrin (1976) has studied the population ecology and natural enemies of *M. carnosum* in England. *M. carnosum* occurs throughout Europe, across Asia to Mongolia, in Africa, and in North and South America.

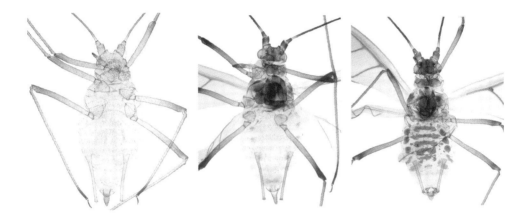

Figure 376. Aptera, alata and male of *Microlophium carnosum*.

Microlophium sp.

In England another, apparently much rarer, species was collected several times on *Urtica dioica* in west London in 1977-78 (Kew, Chiswick; coll. V. F. Eastop, M.A. Beach). No differences from *M. carnosum* in its biology, host preferences or appearance in life were noted, but it can be distinguished morphologically by the characters given in the key, and also by its chromosome number (2n=16 whereas *M. carnosum* has 2n=20) as well as by differences in esterase electrophoretic mobility (M.A. Beach, unpublished work, 1978).

Microsiphum Cholodkovsy, 1902

Medium-sized oval aphids, with dark head and long dark antennae and legs, related to *Macrosiphoniella* but with greatly reduced siphunculi and a short cauda, which are probably adaptations for myrmecophily. The head is smooth with very low divergent antennal tubercles. The antennae are 6-segmented, as long as or longer than the body with a long PT except in fundatrices, and with secondary rhinaria on ANT III or III and IV in both apterae and alatae. Males are apterous and have secondary rhinaria on ANT III-V. R IV+V has 6-8 long accessory hairs and is straight-sided and pointed. First tarsal segments have 3-3-3 hairs. The dorsum is membranous with sparse, short, blunt hairs, but the hairs on ANT III may be longer, and those on the venter are numerous, long and fine. The siphunculi are very small, short cylinders, about as broad as long, with 1-3 rows of polygonal reticulation distally, and no flange. In fundatrices they are almost indiscernible. The cauda is triangular and rather hairy. The anal plate has a dark rounded conical protrusion as in *Metopeurum*.

There are 8 species in the world, all living without host alternation on Compositae (mostly Anthemideae), with a high degree of host specificity.

Microsiphum millefolii Wahlgren, 1940 Figs 18, 377

There is only one British species, *Microsiphum millefolii*, and it has only been found in Scotland, although widely distributed in other parts of Europe. Apterae are yellowish or greyish red to dark brown or dirty dark green, with brown-black head, antennae, legs, siphunculi and cauda; BL 1.8-2.5 mm. Immatures are translucent greyish green to pale grey, and very shiny. Colonies occur on *Achillea millefolium*, feeding at the stem bases in ant shelters, or on runners below ground level. Oviparae and small green apterous males were obtained from Scottish colonies in mid- to late August (Stroyan, 1964).

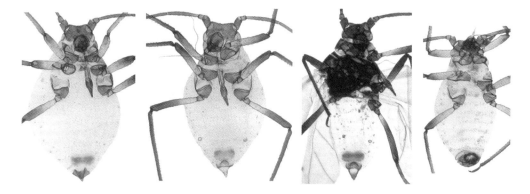

Figure 377. *Microsiphum millefolii* (left to right): fundatrix, aptera, alata and male.

Muscaphis Börner, 1933

Very small, oval, shiny brown or green aphids living on mosses. The head is broad without evident antennal or median tubercles, so that the outline of the front of the head is slightly convex or almost straight. The antennae of apterae are short, 5- or (rarely) 6-segmented, with a rather pointed PT that is as long as or longer than the base of the last segment, and without rhinaria on ANT III. Hairs on dorsal body are short and sparse. First tarsal segments have 2 or 3 hairs. The dorsum is sclerotic, with granulate and/or papillate sculpturing. Spiracular apertures are covered by opercula. Siphunculi are scabrous, tapering from a somewhat swollen base, flangeless, and the aperture is sometimes subapical, in which case they taper to a narrow, rounded apex. The cauda is short, with a broad basal part and a narrow apical part, and bears about 4 short hairs. Alatae look very different from the apterae; their antennae are longer and usually 6-segmented with numerous protruding or tuberculate rhinaria on III-V, their dorsal cuticle is unsculptured with dusky/dark often fragmented abdominal cross-bands, and their siphunculi are smoother and more cylindrical.

There are 8 species in the world, mostly nearctic. Possibly they all have host alternation somewhere in the world, with a sexual phase on Pyroidea, but this has so far only been established for two species, one in Europe and the other in Mexico. The fundatrices that hatch from eggs of these species on Pyroidea are quite different insects; large, plump and hairy. Three species have been found in Britain, and only their moss-feeding generations:

Key to apterous viviparae of British *Muscaphis*

1. Siphunculi with a terminal pore (Fig. 378). ANT PT 2.0-3.3 times longer than base of last segment .... *musci* Börner, 1933

- Siphunculi tapering to a rounded apex, with pore placed subapically. ANT PT 0.6-1.5 times as long as base of last segment 2

378

2. ANT PT 0.6-1.16 times as long as base of last segment. R IV+V 1.2-1.5 times longer than HT II. Siphunculi more than twice as long as their basal widths, more than 0.15 of BL (Fig. 379, 2 views) .... *escherichi* Börner, 1939

379

- ANT PT 1.2-1.5 times longer than base of last segment. R IV+V 0.9-1.15 times longer than HT II. Siphunculi less than twice as long as their basal widths, less than 0.15 of BL (Fig. 380) .... *cuspidati* (Stroyan, 1955)

380

Key to alate viviparae of British *Muscaphis*

1. ANT PT 2.4-3.1 times longer than base of last segment. Siphuncular pore not directed outwards (Fig. 381) .... *musci*

- ANT PT 1.0-2.2 times longer than base of last segment. Siphuncular pore directed outwards (Figs 382, 383) 2

381

2. Siphunculi (Fig. 382) more than 1.8 times longer than cauda. R IV+V 1.2-1.4 times longer than HT II. ANT PT 1.0-1.6 times as long as base of last segment .... *escherichi*

382

- Siphunculi (Fig. 383) less than 1.8 times longer than cauda. R IV+V 0.9-1.15 times as long as HT II. ANT PT 1.6-2.2 times as long as base of last segment .... *cuspidati*

383

Muscaphis cuspidati (Stroyan, 1955) Figs 380, 383, 384

Apterae are dark greenish brown with brown antennae and legs and shiny black dorsum and siphunculi, ; BL 0.9-1.3 mm. They are found on mosses, usually *Calliergon cuspidatum* or *Drepanocladus aduncus* (Amblystegiaceae), close to or below water-level. They can live submerged, apparently because the papillate sculpturing of the cuticle is able to trap a layer of air around the body (Stroyan, 1955 and Müller, 1975b, as *Aspidaphium*). Alatae have protruberant transversely oval secondary rhinaria distributed ANT III 15-24, IV 4-13, V 4-7. Only parthenogenetic generations are known, passing the winter in a specialised, strongly sclerotised, hibernating fourth instar stage (Müller, 1973). In England, and also recorded from Germany and the Czech Republic.

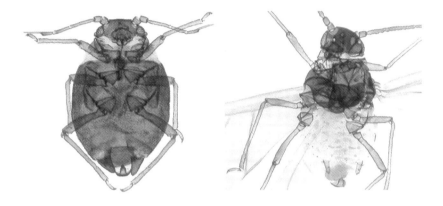

Figure 384. Aptera and alata of *Muscaphis cuspidata.*

Muscaphis escherichi (Börner, 1939) Figs 65, 379, 382, 385

Figure 385. Aptera and alata of *Muscaphis escherichi.*

Apterae are shiny pale brown to ochreous brown or greenish, with brown antennae and legs and dark reddish brown to black siphunculi; BL 0.9-1.1 mm. They feed on a wide variety of mosses; collections in Britain have been mainly from *Eurhynchium* and *Hypnum*. Alatae have markedly protruberant transversely oval secondary rhinaria distributed ANT III 15-20, IV 7-11, V 5-6. Overwintering in the parthenogenetic phase on mosses is common. In northern continental Europe and Canada a sexual phase occurs on *Sorbus*, but this has not been found in Britain. The fundatrices hatching in spring on *Sorbus* are very different morphologically, and were originally described as *Toxopterella drepanosiphoides* MacGillivray and Bradley, 1961, later becoming *Muscaphis drepanosiphoides* (e.g. in Blackman and Eastop, 1994). In England, Scotland, widely distributed in continental Europe, and also in North America and Korea.

Muscaphis musci Börner, 1933 Figs 378, 381, 386

Apterae are greyish yellow, pale brown, or shiny dark olive-green, with reddish brown siphunculi ; BL 0.5-1.0 mm. They feed on mosses in the genera *Acrocladium, Amblystegia* (Amblystegiaceae); *Barbula, Tortula* (Pottiaceae); *Brachythecium, Eurhynchium, Pseudoscleropodium* (Brachytheciaceae); *Bryum* (Bryaceae); *Catharinaea, Polytrichum* (Polytrichaceae); *Hylocomium* (Hylocomiaceae); and *Mnium* (Mniaceae). Alatae are larger (BL 1.1-1.5 mm), and have protruding, transversely oval secondary rhinaria distributed ANT III 18-24, IV 10-16, V 6-11. The life cycle is uncertain; alate males have been collected in Germany, but overwintering in the parthenogenetic phase is probably common. The first British record was from the vesicula seminalis of a slug, presumably picked up during copulation (Stroyan, 1964, as *M. stammeri*). In England, Scotland, northern and central Europe, and North America.

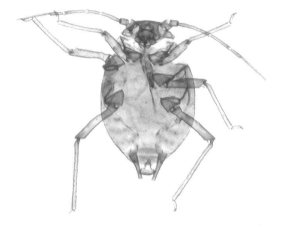

Figure 386. Aptera of *Muscaphis musci*.

Myzaphis van der Goot, 1913

Small spindle-shaped aphids with rather short appendages. The head has low antennal tubercles, but a characteristic feature of the genus is a strongly projecting quadrate or rounded median tubercle. Antennae are 5- or 6-segmented, only about half of body length, without secondary rhinaria in apterae. Alatae have secondary rhinaria on III only, or on III-IV. Dorsal body hairs are blunt or somewhat capitate. First tarsal segments all have 5 hairs. The dorsum of the aptera is sclerotic, and wrinkled or ornamented with numerous small rounded depressions. Alatae have dusky or dark sclerotic markings, often forming a central dorsal abdominal patch. Spiracular apertures are partly covered by opercula. Siphunculi are rather long, cylindrical for much of their length with the distal part often curved outwards and slightly swollen, and with a small but distinct flange. The cauda is tongue-shaped or elongate triangular.

There are 6 species in the world, living without host alternation on Rosaceae. In Britain there are two species.

Key to apterous viviparae of British *Myzaphis*

- Median frontal tubercle rounded, and usually bearing four hairs as long as or longer than the basal diameter of ANT III (Fig. 387). Dorsum with a pair of broad dark stripes converging at about the level of the siphunculi (Fig. 389) .... ***bucktoni*** Jacob, 1946

387

- Median frontal tubercle approximately quadrate, with two hairs that are shorter than the basal diameter of ANT III (Fig. 388). Dorsum without dark pleural stripes ....
.... ***rosarum*** (Kaltenbach, 1843)

388

Key to alate viviparae of British *Myzaphis*

- Dorsal abdominal pigmentation weak, variable and usually divided intersegmentally in the midline, but with large marginal sclerites on ABD TERG 2-4 (Fig. 389). Hairs on front of head conspicuous. ANT PT 1.3-1.4 times longer than base of last segment. Secondary rhinaria distributed ANT III 10-14, IV 0-3 .... ***bucktoni***

- Dorsal abdominal sclerites fused across ABD TERG 2-5 to form a large almost rectangular patch, whereas marginal sclerites are rather small and widely separated (Fig. 390). Hairs on front of head inconspicuous. ANT PT 1.4-1.9 times longer than base of last segment. Secondary rhinaria distributed ANT III 14-32, IV 0 .... ***rosarum***

Myzaphis bucktoni Jacob, 1946 Figs 387, 389

Apterae are pale yellow to pale green with brown dorsal markings consisting of a brown head, two large brown patches on pronotum, and paired broad stripes extending from mesothorax to base of cauda, converging between siphunculi; BL 1.0-1.9 mm. *M. bucktoni* lives all-year-around on *Rosa* spp. (*canina*, *tomentosa*), with apterae feeding usually dispersed along the mid-ribs on the upper sides of the leaves. The sexual morphs are present in November; males are apterous, small, dark and very active, and the oviparae are pale dusky olive green and differ from those of *M. rosarum* in having much more strongly swollen hind tibiae bearing numerous scent glands. In England, Scotland, Wales, continental Europe, Asia and North America.

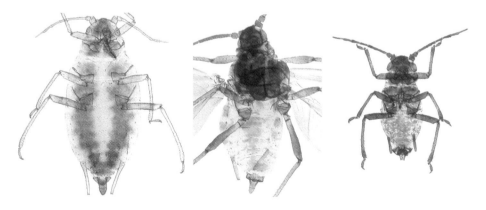

Figure 389. Aptera, alata and male of *Myzaphis bucktoni*.

Myzaphis rosarum (Kaltenbach, 1843) **Lesser Rose Aphid** Figs 388, 390

Apterae are yellow-green to green; BL 1.2-2.4 mm. They live all-year-around on wild and cultivated *Rosa* (especially rambler roses) and frequently also on shrubby *Potentilla* spp. such as *fruticosa*. They feed mainly along the mid-ribs on both the upper and undersides of young leaves. Sexual morphs occur in October to November; males are small, dark and apterous, and oviparae differ from those of *M. bucktoni* in having only slightly swollen hind tibiae and large dark marginal patches on ABD TERG 5 and 6. In England, Scotland, Wales, Ireland, Europe, and introduced to most other parts of the world.

Figure 390. Aptera, alata, male and ovipara of *Myzaphis rosarum*.

Myzodium Börner, 1949

Small, broadly oval brown aphids. The head is broad, dark and nodulose with low, rounded antennal and median tubercles. The antennae are shorter than the body, 5- or 6-segmented in apterae, 6-segmented in alatae, with a rather pointed PT that is much longer than the base of segment VI. Secondary rhinaria are absent in apterae, present on III-IV or III-V in alatae. Alatae have variable wing venation; the forewings sometimes have a once-branched media, and hind wings occasionally have only one oblique vein. The dorsum of the aptera is sclerotic and mostly dark, with wrinkles or granulate sculpturing. Alatae have an extensive dark dorsal shield. Hairs on the dorsal body and appendages are short and blunt. First tarsal segments have 3-3-2 hairs. Spiracular apertures are broadly open and conspicuous. Siphunculi are dark, cylindrical, with a slight S-curve, strongly imbricated to scabrous, constricted just below a large flange. The cauda is short and tongue-shaped with a papillate apical part, and bears 4 hairs.

There are four species in the world, at least two of which live without host alternation on mosses.

Myzodium modestum (Hottes) Figs 74a, 76, 391

The one species in Britain, *Myzodium modestum*, has small, shiny, reddish brown to dark olive brown apterae with dark brown legs and antennae, and black siphunculi; BL 1.2-1.9 mm. Alatae have secondary rhinaria distributed ANT III 21-45, IV 7-13, V 0-4. It is found on various mosses, and is the only aphid recorded from *Sphagnum*; in Britain *Polytrichum commune* seems to be a common host. It is not attended by ants. No sexual morphs are known. In England, Scotland, continental Europe, Iceland, Jan Mayen Island, Greenland, and North America.

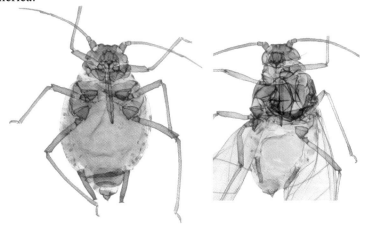

Figure 391. Aptera and alata of *Myzodium modestum*..

Myzotoxoptera Theobald, 1927

Broadly oval dark-coloured aphids with rather long appendages, closely related to *Rhopalosiphoninus*. The head is blackish and strongly spinulose, with rather well-developed antennal tubercles, having divergent inner faces, the median tubercle being undeveloped. Antennae of apterae have a few secondary rhinaria on the basal part of segment III, and alatae have them distributed along III and IV. The hairs on the dorsal body and antennae are very short, sparse and blunt. R IV+V has only 2 accessory hairs (sometimes 3 in fundatrices). The first tarsal segments all have 3 hairs. The dorsal cuticle of apterae has reticulate sculpturing, which traps an air film when the aphid becomes submerged in water. (Prior, 1971). Alatae have a very dark head and thorax and well-developed dark cross-bands on ABD TERG 3-8, with those on 7 and 8 often fragmented. Spiracular apertures are covered by opercula. The siphunculi are much +longer than the cauda, cylindrical, dark, imbricated, with a large flange. The cauda is short, dark and helmet-shaped, with 4 hairs.

Myzotoxoptera wimshurstae Theobald, 1927 Figs 36, 392

There is only a single species in the genus, *Myzotoxoptera wimshurstae*, living all-year-around on basal parts of *Cardamine* spp. in damp situations. Apterae are shining dark olive green, with head blackish; BL 1.5-1.9 mm. They feed at stem-bases and on roots of cuckooflower or lady's smock (*Cardamine pratensis*), and certain other *Cardamine* spp. (*flexuosa, hirsuta*) growing in bogs and other wet situations, and are therefore difficult to collect. Prior (1971) obtained sexual morphs in an insectary culture in September to October, and fundatrices the following April, with alate viviparae in May-June. Males are small (1.0-1.3 mm), apterous and dark blue-green with reddish brown legs, oviparae have hardly swollen hind tibiae with very small scent glands. In England (known from Northumbria, Yorkshire and Kent), Scotland (one alata trapped near Edinburgh) and Czech Republic (although presumably it has a wider European distribution).

Figure 392. Aptera and alata of *Myzotoxoptera wimshurstae*.

Myzus Passerini, 1860

Medium-sized oval aphids, characterised by the morphology of the head which is spiculose with well-developed antennal tubercles, their inner faces spiculose to scabrous and converging apically. Antennae are usually 6-segmented, often shorter than the body in apterae, with PT much longer than the base of ANT VI. Antennae of apterae lack secondary rhinaria, those of alatae have a row of secondary rhinaria on segment III, more rarely on III-IV, or III-V. The hairs on the dorsal body and antennae are short and blunt or slightly expanded apically. First tarsal segments have 3-3-3 or 3-3-2 hairs (except 2-2-2 in subgenus *Galiobium*). The dorsal cuticle of apterae is sclerotic (except in subgenus *Prunomyzus*), and often rather wrinkled or warty, sometimes very dark but more often unpigmented. Alatae have dark marginal abdominal sclerites, and usually there is a dark dorsal abdominal patch on tergites 3-5 or 3-6, and transverse sclerites on other tergites. Siphunculi are tapering, cylindrical or somewhat clavate (with swelling usually asymmetrical); imbricated or rather scabrous, usually with a well-developed flange. The cauda is usually rather short, tongue-shaped or triangular, with less than 10 hairs.

Myzus is a palaearctic genus of about 64 species, mostly of east Asian origin, several of which are now widely distributed. Biology and host associations vary; some have host alternation from *Prunus* to herbaceous plants in many different families, but the majority live all-year-around on either a woody or a herbaceous plant and have a high degree of host specificity. However, the genus also contains some of the most polyphagous aphid species.

There are 15 British species.

Key to apterous viviparae of British *Myzus* (not fundatrices)

(Identification of members of the subgenus *Nectarosiphon* (couplets 8-14) may require examination of several specimens to assess the range of variation. All measurements are in mm.)

1. ANT PT less than 1.5 times longer than base of ANT VI. Siphunculi very rugose, with ventral surfaces warty and dorsal surfaces corrugated; swollen over most of length, narrowing abruptly and turned outwards at apices (Fig. 393). ABD TERG 7 with a rugose posterior projection (Fig. 394). First tarsal segments all with 2 hairs .... *langei* (Börner, 1942)

- ANT PT more than 1.6 times longer than base of ANT VI. Siphunculi not as above. No projection on ABD TERG 7. First tarsal segments with 3-3-2 or 3-3-3 hairs 2

393

394

2. Siphunculi tapering or cylindrical (*Myzus* s. str. and subgenus *Prunomyzus*) 3

- Siphunculi slightly to moderately clavate, i.e. with narrower part proximal to a distal swollen part (subgenera *Nectarosiphon* and *Sciamyzus*) 7

3. Dorsum completely dark brown or black (Fig. 408). Siphunculi black. Cauda with 6-9 hairs .... *cerasi* (Fabricius,1775)

- Dorsum mainly pale, sometimes with dark head and/or intersegmental markings. Siphunculi pale or dark. Cauda with 4-6 hairs 4

4. Siphunculi with black distal part contrasting with pale basal part (Fig. 395). ANT PT 3.9-5.5 times longer than base of ANT VI .... *varians* Davidson, 1912

- Siphunculi pale or uniformly dark. ANT PT 1.7-3.5 times longer than base of ANT VI 5

395

5. Siphunculi dark. Tergum membranous .... *padellus* Hille Ris Lambers and Rogerson, 1946

- Siphunculi pale/dusky. Tergum sclerotic 6

6. Dorsum with dark intersegmental markings (Fig. 415) .... *ornatus* Laing, 1932

- Dorsum without dark intersegmental markings .... *lythri* (Schrank, 1801)

7. Siphunculi 0.82-1.34 times longer than ANT III 8

-   Siphunculi 0.54-0.81 times longer than ANT III 15

8. Siphunculi (Fig. 396a) blackish on distal 0.3-0.5, contrasting with pale basal 0.5-0.7, and 2.6-3.2 times longer than the cauda, which is triangular and only a little longer than its basal width (Fig. 396b) .... *ligustri* (Mosley, 1841)

-   Siphunculi entirely pale or dusky, or only darker at apices, and 1.7-3.0 times longer than cauda, which is tongue-shaped and at least 1.3 times longer than its basal width 9

a   b

396

9. Hairs on inner sides of antennal tubercles mostly pointed with at least one of them 0.75 or more times longer than basal diameter of ANT III (Fig. 397). Siphunculi 0.84-1.02 of length of ANT III and 0.17-0.20 of BL .... *myosotidis* (Börner, 1950)

-   Hairs on inner sides of antennal tubercles short and blunt, all less than 0.75 of basal diameter of ANT III (e.g. Fig. 398). Siphunculi 0.99-1.34 of length of ANT III and 0.18-0.30 of BL 10

397   398

10. Siphunculi 2.5-3.0 times longer than cauda, which is 0.37-0.49 of length of ANT III. Value of function (HTII x cauda) ÷ (R IV+V x ANT III) is in range 0.33-0.44 .... *ajugae* Schouteden, 1903

-   Siphunculi 1.7-2.5 times longer than cauda, which is 0.45-0.67 of length of ANT III. Value of function (HTII x cauda) ÷ (R IV+V x ANT III) is in range 0.44-0.89 11

11. ANT PT 0.44-1.16 times as long as (usually shorter than) ANT III. Value of function cauda length ÷(ANT III x PT) in the range 1.20-2.70, but rarely less than 1.26 12

-   ANT PT 0.90-1.49 times as long as (usually longer than) ANT III. Value of function cauda length ÷(ANT III x PT) in the range 0.87-1.52, but rarely more than 1.25 (except in small specimens with ANT III less than 0.32 mm) 13

12. ANT PT 2.1-3.7 (mostly less than 3.25) times longer than base of ANT VI. R IV+V 0.87-1.28 (rarely less than 0.9) times longer than HT II. Value of function (306 x R IV+V) *minus* (127 x HT II) is more than 17 .... ***certus*** (Walker, 1849)

- ANT PT 2.5-4.0 (mostly more than 3.25) times longer than base of ANT VI. R IV+V 0.78-0.98 (rarely more than 0.9) times longer than HT II. Value of function (306 x R IV+V) *minus* (127 x HT II) is less than 17 .... ***dianthicola*** Hille Ris Lambers, 1966

13. R IV+V 0.113-0.139 mm long. Value of function (204 x R IV+V) *minus* (53 x HT II) more than 18, and that of function (185 x R IV+V) *minus* (37 x base of ANT VI) more than 17. In borderline cases, value of function (208 x R IV+V) *plus* (7 x caudal length) *minus* (6 x hind femur length) *minus* (117 x maximum width of swollen part of siphunculus) greater than 16.7, *or* maximum width of swollen part of siphunculus less than 0.11 of its length .... ***persicae*** **spp.** ***nicotianae*** Blackman, 1987

- R IV+V 0.090-0.128 mm long. Value of function (204 x R IV+V) *minus* (53 x HT II) less than 18, and that of function (185 x R IV+V) *minus* (37 x base of ANT VI) less than 17. In borderline cases, value of function (208 x R IV+V) *plus* (7 x caudal length) *minus* (6 x hind femur length) *minus* (117 x maximum width of swollen part of siphunculus) less than 16.7, *or* maximum width of swollen part of siphunculus more than 0.11 of its length 14

14. R IV+V 0.102-0.128 mm long. Siphunculi usually dusky over entire length with maximum width of swollen part more than 0.11 of its length (Fig. 399). Value of function (138 x ANT PT) *plus* (708 x R IV+V) *minus* (53 x ANT III) *minus* (500 x base of ANT VI) usually greater than 58 .... ***antirrhinii*** (Macchiati, 1883)

- R IV+V 0.090-0.122 mm long. Siphunculi variably pigmented but usually pale except at apices, with maximum width of swollen part less than 0.11 of its length (Fig. 400). Value of function (138 x ANT PT) *plus* (708 x R IV+V) *minus* (53 x ANT III) *minus* (500 x base of ANT VI) usually less than 58 .... ***persicae*** (Sulzer, 1776) **s.str.**

399   400

15. Siphunculi weakly imbricated with a narrow basal stem, its narrowest part thinner than, or as thin as, the hind tibia at midlength (Fig. 401). R IV+V 0.114-0.144 mm long with 7-15 accessory hairs. Antennal tubercles with inner faces approximately parallel in dorsal view (Fig. 402). Dorsal cuticle not scaly .... *ascalonicus* Doncaster, 1946

- Siphunculi coarsely imbricated with the narrowest part of the stem slightly thicker than the hind tibia at midlength (Fig. 403). R IV+V 0.101-0.120 mm long with 4-8 accessory hairs. Antennal tubercles with inner faces apically convergent in dorsal view (Fig. 404). Dorsal cuticle scaly .... *cymbalariae* Stroyan, 1954

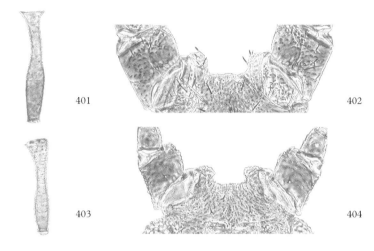

401   402

403   404

Key to alate viviparae of British *Myzus*

1. Siphunculi tapering or cylindrical 2

- Siphunculi slightly to moderately clavate (with narrower part proximal to a distal swollen part) 7

2. Secondary rhinaria distributed ANT III 17-33, IV 6-14, V 0-4. Dorsal abdomen with a rather small irregular-shaped dark central sclerotic patch (Fig. 416) .... *padellus*

- Secondary rhinaria distributedANT III 4-21, IV 0(-3),V 0. Dorsal abdomen usually with a large central patch, although this is sometimes partially fragmented or has large 'windows' 3

3. ANT PT less than 1.6 times longer than base of ANT VI. Sclerite on ABD TERG 7 with a broad, rugose conical or domed posterior projection (Fig. 405) .... *langei*

- ANT PT more than 1.7 times longer than base of ANT VI. No projection on ABD TERG 7 4

405

4. ANT PT 1.8-2.7 times longer than base of ANT VI. Siphunculi pale/dusky, 0.45-0.6 of length of ANT III and 1.6-2.2 times longer than base of ANT VI. Dorsal abdominal patch variably developed, sometimes rather pale and fragmented, always with a large window between ABD TERG 5 and 6 (Fig. 415) .... *ornatus*

- ANT PT 2.7-6.3 times longer than base of ANT VI. Siphunculi dark, 0.6-1.0 of length of ANT III and 2.0-3.6 times longer than base of ANT VI. Dorsal sclerite solid or with only narrow windows (Figs 408, 413, 418) 5

5. ANT PT 4.3-6.3 times longer than base of ANT VI .... *varians*

- ANT PT 2.4-4.1 (-4.4) times longer than base of ANT VI 6

6. R IV+V 0.48-0.60 of length of ANT V, which is 0.19-0.26 mm .... *cerasi*

- R IV+V 0.65-0.83 of length of ANT V, which is 0.165-0.195 mm .... *lythri*

7. Dorsal abdominal sclerotisation at least partly divided into separate segmental cross-bands (Fig. 410). Siphunculi only 0.17-0.24 mm long. Secondary rhinaria distributed ANT III 26-42, IV 3-10, V 0 .... *cymbalariae*

- Dorsal abdominal pigmentation mainly consisting of a large central dark patch extending over at least central areas of ABD TERG 3-6 or 4-6, often with 'windows' between segments but not divided transversely (e.g. Figs 407, 412, 417). Siphunculi longer than 0.24 mm. If there are more than 25 rhinaria on ANT III then there are also some on V as well as IV 8

8. Siphunculi 0.34-0.52 of length of ANT III. Secondary rhinaria distributed *either* 6-25 on ANT III, 0-6 on IV and 0-3 on V, *or* 30-56 on III, 13-36 on IV and 4-19 on V (both types of antennae can occur in one individual). R IV+V with 7-15 accessory hairs ....
.... *ascalonicus*

- Siphunculi 0.60-0.84 of length of ANT III. Secondary rhinaria distributed ANT III 6-19, IV 0(-6), V 0(-2). R IV+V with 2-7 accessory hairs 9

9. Dorsal abdominal patch usually restricted to ABD TERG 4-6, with large windows, and a separate cross-band on ABD TERG 3 that is frequently interrupted medially (Fig. 412). Siphunculi very distinctly clavate .... *ligustri*

- Dorsal abdominal patch usually extending solidly over ABD TERG 3-6, or with a large window only between 5 and 6 (e.g. Fig. 417). Siphunculi slightly to distinctly clavate .....
.... 10

10. ANT IV rarely without secondary rhinaria, usually with 2-5, and V with 0-2. Siphunculi 0.14-0.16 of BL and 1.50-1.74 times longer than cauda .... *myosotidis*

-    ANT IV and V almost always without secondary rhinaria; rarely with 1-2 on IV. Siphunculi 0.15-0.22 of BL and 1.65-2.40 times longer than cauda 11

11. Dorsal abdominal patch with a narrowly transverse window between ABD TERG 5 and 6 (Figs 406, 409). ANT PT 0.36-0.49 mm long, but if more than 0.45 mm long then shorter than ANT III 12

-    Dorsal abdominal patch with an irregularly oval window between ABD TERG 5 and 6 (Fig. 417). ANT PT 0.38-0.69 mm long, but if less than 0.45 mm long then longer than ANT III 14

12. R IV+V 0.7-0.9 of length of HT II .... *dianthicola*

-    R IV+V 0.9-1.2 of length of HT II 13

13. Siphunculi 2.1-2.4 times longer than cauda .... *ajugae*

-    Siphunculi 1.7-2.0 times longer than cauda .... *certus*

14. R IV+V 0.099-0.128 mm long, but only more than 0.113 mm in larger specimens (ANT III more than 0.45 mm long). Value of function (197 x R IV+V) *minus* (16 x base of ANT VI) less than 21. In borderline cases, value of function (220 x R IV+V) *plus* (9 x ANT PT) *minus* (4 x ANT III) *minus* (23 x base of ANT VI) less than 25 .... *persicae* **s.str.**

-    R IV+V 0.113-0.143 mm long. Value of function (197 x R IV+V) *minus* (16 x base of ANT VI) greater than 21. In borderline cases, value of function (220 x R IV+V) *plus* (9 x ANT PT) *minus* (4 x ANT III) *minus* (23 x base of ANT VI) greater than 25 15

15. Value of function (168 x R IV+V) *plus* (34 x cauda length) *minus* (16 x hind femur length) *minus* (140 x maximum width of swollen part of siphunculus) greater than 9 .... *persicae* **ssp. nicotianae**

-    Value of function (168 x R IV+V) *plus* (34 x cauda length) *minus* (16 x hind femur length) *minus* (140 x maximum width of swollen part of siphunculus) less than 9 .... *antirrhinii*

Key to alate males of British *Myzus*

1. Siphunculi tapering or cylindrical 2

-    Siphunculi slightly to moderately clavate (with narrower part proximal to a distal swollen part) 3

2. Siphunculi 0.11-0.31 mm long, 0.5-0. 7 of length of ANT III .... *cerasi*

- Siphunculi 0.33-0.41 mm long, 0.9-1.1 of length of ANT III .... *varians*

3. Siphunculi 0.17-0.22 mm long, 0.39-0.48 of length of ANT III .... *cymbalariae*

- Siphunculi 0.25-0.35 mm long, 0.53-0.72 of length of ANT III 4

4. Siphunculi with minimum diameter greater than diameter of hind tibia at midlength. Secondary rhinaria distributed ANT III 34-43, IV 8-17, V 6-14. R IV+V 1.0-1.2 times longer than HT II .... *ligustri*

- Siphunculi with minimum diameter less than diameter of hind tibia at midlength. Secondary rhinaria distributed ANT III 15-51, IV 5-34, V 4-20 (but rarely less than 17 on IV, or less than 14 on V) . R IV+V 0.90-1.05 of length of HT II .... *persicae*

Myzus (Nectarosiphon) ajugae Schouteden, 1903 Fig. 406

Apterae are rather small, brownish to dirty yellowish green, BL 1.4-2.0 mm. Alatae have a black dorsal abdominal patch and secondary rhinaria distributed ANT III 7-12, IV 0(-3). *M. ajugae* lives all-year-round on bugle, *Ajuga* spp. (*reptans*, *genevensis*), usually growing in deep shade. It feeds on the upper sides of the leaves, which become tightly curled upwards. Oviparae and apterous males are found in October. In England, Scotland, and widely distributed in continental Europe. For a detailed account of this species see Meier (1954).

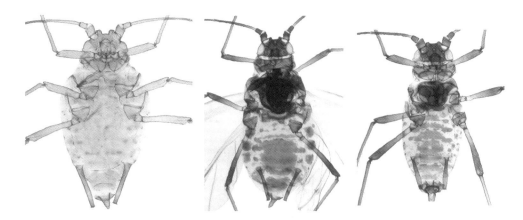

Figure 406. Aptera, alata and male of *Myzus ajugae*.

Myzus (Nectarosiphon) antirrhinii (Macchiati, 1883)

Apterae are mid grey-green to dark green (darker at low temperatures), occasionally dark red; BL 1.4-2.2 mm. On leaves and young growth of numerous plants, on which it may be confused with *M. persicae* (Blackman & Paterson, 1986). Unlike *M. persicae*, it often forms large, dense colonies, and only produces alatae rather sporadically. It is permanently parthenogenetic, and therefore most frequently found on perennial herbs and shrubs. In England, Scotland, Wales, Ireland, continental Europe, East Asia, Australia and western North America.

Myzus (*Sciamyzus*) *ascalonicus* Doncaster, 1946 **Shallot Aphid** Figs 401, 402, 407

Apterae are shining pale brownish green, straw-coloured or dirty yellow, with tips of antennae and legs black; BL 1.1-2.3 mm. It is an extremely polyphagous aphid, with hosts in more than 20 families, but particularly Alliaceae, Caryophyllaceae, Compositae, Cruciferae, Liliaceae and Rosaceae (see also Blackman & Eastop, 2000). It apparently reproduces entirely by parthenogenesis, no sexual morphs having ever been found or reared. *M. ascalonicus* has a world-wide ditribution, although it was unknown before 1940. Thereafter it seems to have spread very rapidly, and was first found in England in 1941, on stored shallots in Lincolnshire (Doncaster, 1946). It is possibly of hybrid origin (which might explain the peculiar bimodal distribution of rhinarial numbers on the antennae), but its parentage is unclear. It is often placed in subgenus *Nectarosiphon*, but it clearly does not belong there, and is closer to *M. cymbalariae*.

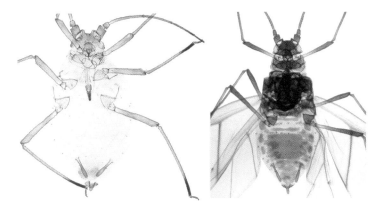

Figure 407. Aptera and alata of *Myzus ascalonicus*.

Myzus cerasi (Fabricius, 1775) **Cherry Blackfly** Fig. 408

Apterae on *Prunus* trees in spring and summer are shining, very dark brown to black, with antennae and legs bicoloured yellow and black, and siphunculi and cauda wholly black; BL 1.5-2.6 mm. They form dense, usually ant-attended colonies at shoot tips of cherry trees (*Prunus avium*), curling leaves into "nests" and often causing severe damage. Sour cherries (*P. cerasus*) are also colonised but with less effect on growth. Migration occurs in June-July to secondary hosts mainly in Rubiaceae (*Galium, Asperula, Sherardia*) and Scrophulariaceae (*Euphrasia, Rhinanthus, Veronica*), where apterae are smaller (BL 1.1-1.7 mm), shiny dark brown to yellowish brown or olive green, and form colonies mainly on the stems. In other parts of the world (North America, New Zealand) populations are common on Cruciferae. The return migration to cherries occurs in September-October. However, in northern Europe some populations remain on secondary host plants and reproduce sexually, giving rise in spring to fundatrices that differ morphologically from those on cherry (Dahl, 1968), indicating that there is a non-host-alternating form that should be regarded as at least a separate subspecies, to which the name *M. cerasi veronicae* (Walker, 1848) may be applicable. There is also evidence from electrophoretic studies in Germany that the primary host populations on *P. avium* may differ from those on *P. cerasus* (Gruppe, 1988). *M. cerasi* occurs throughout the British Isles and in Europe, Asia, Australia, New Zealand and North America.

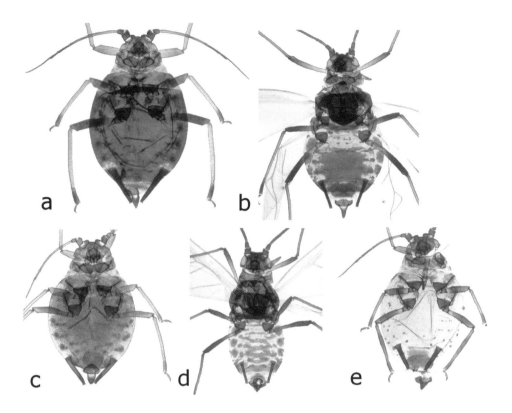

Figure 408. *Myzus cerasi*: (a) aptera on cherry, (b) spring migrant alata, (c) aptera on *Galium*, (d) male, (e) ovipara.

Myzus (*Nectarosiphon*) *certus* (Walker, 1849) Fig. 409

Apterae are pink to dark reddish-brown; BL 1.2-2.0 mm. Alatae have secondary rhinaria distributed ANT III 8-20, IV 0(-4). *M. certus* lives all-year-round on Caryophyllaceae (*Cerastium*, *Dianthus*, *Stellaria*) causing spotting and curling of leaves. It is also often found on Violaceae (*Viola tricolor*), and occasionally on certain other plants. Oviparae and apterous (alatiform) males are produced in October, but parthenogenetic overwintering is also common. In England, Scotland, Wales, continental Europe, Iran, and North America. For a detailed account see Meier (1954).

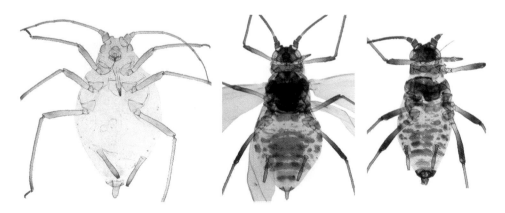

Figure 409. Aptera, alata and male of *Myzus certus*.

Myzus (Sciamyzus) cymbalariae Stroyan, 1954 Figs 403, 404, 410

Apterae are dull yellowish green or yellowish brown, to dark brown or crimson red (more pigmented in cold conditions); BL 1.2-2.0 mm. Alatae, unlike most other *Myzus*, have more or less separate transverse dark bands on the dorsal abdomen. *M. cymbalariae* is polyphagous, colonising a similar range of hosts to *M. ascalonicus* (especially species in Alliaceae, Caryophyllaceae, Compositae, Iridaceae, Liliaceae, Scrophulariaceae, and Violaceae). It seems to be entirely parthenogenetic, although males have been obtained in trap catches and reared in laboratory cultures (Brown, 1983). Like the similar *M. ascalonicus*, its origin is unknown; it was first described in England in 1954 but is now found commonly in many other parts of the world.

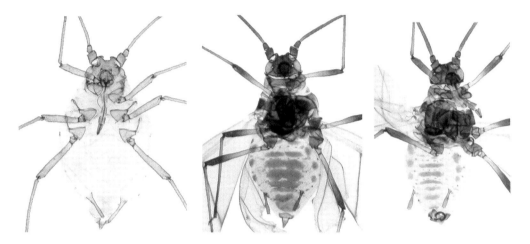

Figure 410. Aptera, alata and male of *Myzus cymbalariae*.

Myzus (Nectarosiphon) dianthicola Hille Ris Lambers, 1966

Apterae are deep yellow-green; BL 1.3-2.0 mm. They seem to be specific to *Dianthus caryophyllus*, usually in glasshouses, causing white or yellow spots or blotches on the leaves. *M. dianthicola* closely resembles *M. persicae,* but is distinguishable from that species by the reaction of the host plant, and from *M. certus* by its colour in life. No sexual morphs are known. It has been found in England, Denmark, North America, and New Zealand.

Myzus (Galiobium) langei (Börner, 1933) Figs 393, 394, 405, 411

Apterae are somewhat flattened, dull yellowish to pale green, the abdomen tinged anteriorly with rosy red; BL 1.3-1.9 mm. Immatures are bright rosy red. *M.langei* feeds only on *Galium* spp. (especially hedge bedstraw, *G. mollugo*, but not *G. aparine*), stunting and deforming new growth so that the foliage becomes bunched like a "witches' broom" (Stroyan, 1950). Colonies are visited by ants. Although said to overwinter in the sexual phase in central Europe (Börner, 1952), the sexual morphs do not seem to have been described. In England (all records south of the Wash), South Wales (Baker, 2009), continental Europe, and east to Kazakhstan.

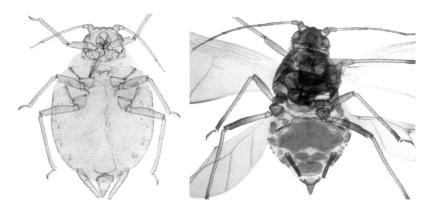

Figure 411. Aptera and alata of *Myzus langei*.

Myzus ligustri (Mosley, 1841) Figs 396, 412

Apterae are shiny yellow, with distal parts of siphunculi contrastingly brownish black; BL 1.0-1.5 mm. Alatae have secondary rhinaria distributed ANT III 10-19, IV 0-6. *M. ligustri* is sporadically common on privet, (*Ligustrum ovalifolium, vulgare*), feeding in leaves that are rolled longitudinally into narrow tubes and spotted with yellow. It lives all-year-round on privet, producing oviparae and alate males in November. Oviparae have only slightly swollen hind tibiae with 0-30 scent glands distributed over the middle parts. In England, Scotland, Wales, Europe, and introduced into North America.

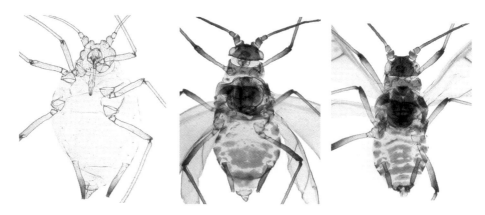

Figure 412. Aptera, alata and male of *Myzus ligustri*.

Myzus lythri (Schrank, 1801) Fig. 53b, 413

Apterae are pale green or yellowish green with pale appendages, often with brownish head and prothorax and reddish posterior abdomen; BL 1.5-2.1 mm. Alatae have 13-18 rhinaria on ANT III, 0 on IV. *M. lythri* is found on leaves and stems of Lythraceae (purple-loosestrifes, *Lythrum* spp.) and Onagraceae (*Epilobium, Fuschia*) and also sometimes on certain other plants in aquatic situations. In central Europe it has host alternation, with a sexual phase on *Prunus mahaleb*. It is not known how it overwinters in Britain, sexual morphs not having been collected. Shaposhnikov (1964) recorded a population in Russia living on *Lythrum salicaria* without host alternation. In England, Scotland, Isle of Man, Europe, Asia, and introduced to southern Africa (Burundi) and North America.

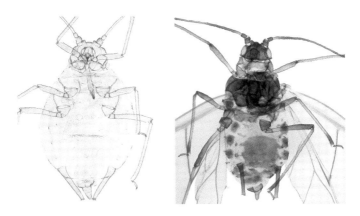

Figure 413. Aptera and alata of *Myzus lythri.*

Myzus (*Nectarosiphon*) *myosotidis* Börner, 1950 Figs 397, 414

Apterae are yellowish green; BL 1.5-1.9 mm. Alatae have secondary rhinaria distributed ANT III 8-14, IV (0-)2-5, V 0-2. *M. myosotidis* feeds specifically without host alternation on marsh forget-me-not, *Myosotis scorpioides* (= *palustris*), the leaves of which are rolled upwards. Oviparae and apterous males are produced in September-October. For a detailed account see Meier (1954). In England and parts of continental Europe (Netherlands, Germany, Poland, Russia, Switzerland).

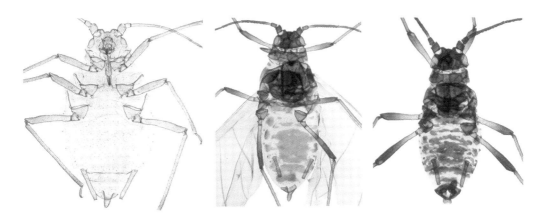

Figure 414. Aptera, alata and male of *Myzus myosotidis.*

Myzus ornatus Laing, 1932 **Violet Aphid** Fig. 415

Apterae are small, pale yellow or green, marked dorsally with a characteristic pattern of dark green or brownish dots and transverse streaks; BL 1.0-1.7 mm. Alatae have 4-14 secondary rhinaria on ANT III, 0 on IV. *M. ornatus* feeds dispersed on the leaves of plants in many different plant families including especially Bignonaceae, Compositae, Labiatae, Polygonaceae, Primulaceae, Rosaceae, and Violaceae, and tends to occur particularly on ornamental and potted plants in protected environments. Almost world-wide, and permanently parthenogenetic everywhere, except possibly in the Himalayas. See also Blackman & Eastop (2000).

Figure 415. Aptera and alatae (more and less pigmented forms) of *Myzus ornatus*.

Myzus (Prunomyzus) padellus Hille Ris Lambers & Rogerson, 1946 Fig. 416

Apterae forming red and yellow blistered leaf-galls on bird cherry *Prunus padus* in spring are bright saffron yellow with blackish brown head, legs bicoloured yellow and blackish brown, and black siphunculi; BL 2.0-2.3 mm. Emigrant alatae (with a rather small and relatively weakly pigmented dorsal abdominal patch) are produced in June, and are thought to migrate to *Galeopsis* (Labiatae), *Pedicularis* and *Rhinanthus* (Scrophulariaceae), as aphids identified as *M. padellus* have been collected from these plants in other parts of Europe. The apterae on secondary hosts are smaller (BL 1.3-1.9 mm), yellow or yellowish green and look very different from the bird cherry aphids. Secondary host populations have however not yet been found in Britain, and the host alternation has yet to be fully confirmed by host transfer experiments. The sexual morphs do not seem to have been described. In England, continental Europe, and Asia.

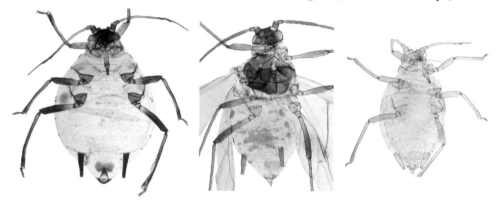

Figure 416. *Myzus padellus*; aptera and alata from *Prunus padus* in UK, and an aptera from a secondary host (*Pedicularis*) in Austria.

Myzus (Nectarosiphon) persicae (Sulzer, 1776) **Peach Potato Aphid, Green Peach Aphid** Figs 19c, 398, 400, 417

Apterae are whitish green, pale yellow-green, grey green, mid-green, pink or red, rather uniformly coloured, not shiny; BL 1.2-2.1 mm. Alatae have secondary rhinaria distributed ANT III 7-14, IV 0. Immature alatae are often pink or red, especially in autumn populations, and immature males are yellow. *M. persicae* is a well-known cosmopolitan and extremely polyphagous pest aphid colonising plants in over 40 different plant families. On most plants including field crops (e.g. potatoes, sugar-beet, brassicas) it feeds dispersed on the lower, older leaves, and its main economic importance is as an efficient vector of plant viruses. In countries with mild climates including Britain it mainly overwinters parthenogenetically, but in most of continental Europe there is a regular sexual phase, mainly on peach, *Prunus persica*. Spring colonies on peach twist and roll the leaves at right angles to the mid-rib (cf. *Myzus varians*). The fundatrix and her progeny on peach have tapering, unswollen siphunculi. Oviparae on peach leaves in autumn are reddish to plum-coloured with hind tibiae dark, swollen on basal two-thirds and bearing numerous scent glands. Populations colonising tobacco, and sometimes forming dense populations on young growth of other plants, are distinguished as a subspecies, **M. persicae ssp. nicotianae** Blackman, 1976. The most common form of this subspecies has pink apterae and seems to occur sporadically in Britain. See also Blackman & Eastop (2007).

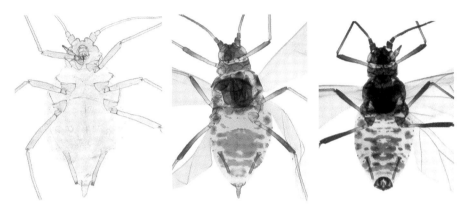

Figure 417. Aptera, alata and male of *Myzus persicae*.

Myzus varians Davidson, 1912 Figs 395, 418

Figure 418. Aptera (from *Clematis*), alata and male of *Myzus varians.*

Apterae are pale green to green, with distal parts of siphunculi conspicuously black; BL 1.7-2.3 mm. Spring populations cause characteristic longitudinal rolling and reddening of the leaves of peach trees (*Prunus persica*). Migration occurs to honeysuckles, *Clematis* spp., where they can sometimes build up damaging populations. Alatae have 7-15 secondary rhinaria on ANT III, 0 on IV. First records on *Clematis* in England were in the early 1970s, and included males and autumn migrant females collected in November (Stroyan, 1979). Males have subsequently been caught in traps and reared in laboratory cultures (R.L Blackman, unpublished data), and colonies have been found rolling peach leaves at Kew in June 1975 (coll. V.F. Eastop) and at Merton in south London in August 2005 (coll. J.H. Martin), indicating that sexual reproduction probably occurs regularly in England, although part of the population also overwinters parthenogenetically on *Clematis*. Apterae on peach have the distal half or more of the siphunculi black, whereas those on *Clematis* have only the tips of the siphunculi black. In south-east England, South Wales (Baker, 2009), Scotland (one trap record), continental Europe, East Asia, and also introduced to North America.

Nasonovia Mordvilko 1914

Medium-sized, often shiny aphids. The head is smooth with rather low antennal tubercles that have divergent inner faces, and the median tubercle is also somewhat developed. The antennae are frequently longer than the body, with a long PT, and with ANT III usually tapering to a narrow base. Apterae have secondary rhinaria on ANT III, often numerous, and sometimes also on IV; alatae have them on III-IV or III-V. Antennal and dorsal body hairs are often rather long. R IV+V is long and slender, longer than the HT II. First tarsal segments have 3-3-3 or 3-3-2 hairs. The dorsal cuticle is smooth, often with dark sclerotic segmental and/or intersegmental markings, in apterae as well as alatae. Spiracular apertures on the thorax are much larger than those on the abdomen, which may be broadly reniform to oval (subgenus *Nasonovia*) or narrowly reniform and almost covered by opercula (subgenus *Kakimia*). The siphunculi are usually fairly long and straight, cylindrical or tapering, with a slight constriction and some transverse striae below the rather well-developed flange. The cauda is finger-shaped, and normally bears either 5 (in *Kakimia*) or 7 hairs.

There are 42 species in the world; *Nasonovia* s. str. is palaearctic and oriental, but about two-thirds of the species are in subgenus *Kakimia*, which is predominantly nearctic. Nearly half the species are associated with Saxifragaceae and/or Grossulariaceae, the host-alternating species having *Ribes* as primary hosts. They are not visited by ants. For a full review of the genus see Heie (1979).

There are 5 species in Britain.

Key to apterous viviparae of British *Nasonovia*

1. Cauda almost always with 7 hairs (3 lateral pairs and one dorsoapical; e.g. Fig. 419). Abdominal spiracular apertures broadly reniform or oval, not covered by opercula (Fig. 420). R IV+V with 6-12 accessory hairs 2

- Cauda almost always with 5 hairs (2 lateral pairs and one dorsoapical; e.g. Fig. 421). Abdominal spiracular apertures crescent-shaped or narrowly reniform, partially covered by cowl-like opercula (Fig. 422). R IV+V with 11-24 accessory hairs (subgen. *Kakimia*) 5

419

420

421

422

2. Secondary rhinaria on ANT III tend to be concentrated on basal part of segment, which is often darker and somewhat swollen (Fig. 423). ANT PT 7.0-11.4 times longer than base of ANT VI. Longest hairs on ABD TERG 1-3 are 0.8-1.1 times longer than basal diameter of ANT III. Dorsum often with distinctive dark intersegmental markings (Fig. 428), but rarely with more extensive darker pigmentation. HT I almost always with 3 hairs .... *ribisnigri* (Mosley, 1841)

- Secondary rhinaria on ANT III spread out along one side of segment (Fig. 424). ANT PT 3.4-8.3 times longer than base of ANT VI. Longest hairs on ABD TERG 1-3 are 1.3-2.0 times longer than basal diameter of ANT III. Dorsum often with extensive dark pigmentation (Figs 425, 427). HT I almost always with 2 hairs 3

3. Dorsal pigmentation of abdomen often extensive, but variable and usually ill-defined, except for the dark intersegmental sclerites (Fig. 427). R IV+V 1.4-1.7 times longer than HT II .... *pilosellae* (Börner, 1933)

- Dorsal abdomen with extensive well-defined dark sclerotisation extending across to marginal areas of ABD TERG 1-5 (Fig. 425). R IV+V 1.1-1.5 times longer than HT II 4

4. ANT PT 3.3-6.7 (usually less than 5.7) times longer than base of ANT VI, 0.77-1.31 times longer than ANT III, and 1.5-1.9 times longer than siphunculi. Siphunculi 1.18-1.67 times longer than cauda .... *compositellae* s.str. (Theobald, 1924)

- ANT PT 5.3-7.8 (usually more than 5.7) times longer than base of ANT VI, 1.21-1.60 times longer than ANT III and 1.9-2.4 times longer than siphunculi. Siphunculi 1.46-1.85 times longer than cauda .... *compositellae* ssp. *nigra* (Hille Ris Lambers, 1931)

5. ANT PT (3.6-)5.1-8.4 times longer than base of ANT VI. R IV+V 1.6-2.3 times longer than HT II. Siphunculi (1.4-)1.8-2.5 times longer than cauda ... *dasyphylli* Stroyan 1957

- ANT PT 2.5-5.0 times longer than base of ANT VI. R IV+V 1.2-1.8 times longer than HT II. Siphunculi 1.2-1.6 times longer than cauda ....
.... *saxifragae* Doncaster and Stroyan, 1952

Key to alate viviparae of British *Nasonovia*

1. Cauda almost always with 7 hairs (3 lateral pairs and one dorsoapical). Dorsal abdomen with dark segmental markings not usually fused into a solid central patch (Figs 425, 427, 428). R IV+V with 6-12 accessory hairs 2

- Cauda almost always with 5 hairs (2 lateral pairs and one dorsoapical). Dorsal abdomen usually with a central solid dark patch extending at least across ABD TERG 3-5. R IV+V with more than 12 accessory hairs (subgenus *Kakimia*; Figs 426, 429) 5

2. HT I almost always with 3 hairs (median sense peg present). ANT PT 7.5-13.0 times longer than base of ANT VI. Siphunculi 1.6-2.4 times longer than cauda .... ***ribisnigri***

- HT I almost always with 2 hairs (no median sense peg). ANT PT 4.5-8.3(-8.8) times longer than base of ANT VI. Siphunculi 1.4-1.8 times longer than cauda 3

3. ANT PT 4.2-6.5 (usually less than 6.0) times longer than base of ANT VI, and 0.83-1.17 times longer than ANT III .... ***compositellae* s.str.**

- ANT PT 6.2-8.8 times longer than base of ANT VI, and 1.13-1.58 times longer than ANT III 4

4. Siphunculi 1.6-1.9 times longer than R IV+V. Secondary rhinaria distributed ANT III 18-41, IV 5-10, V 0-3 .... ***pilosellae***

- Siphunculi 2.0-2.4 times longer than R IV+V. Secondary rhinaria distributed ANT III 29-45, IV 4-17, V 0-1 .... ***compositellae* ssp. *nigra***

5. ABD TERG 2 usually with a pair of small spinal sclerites (Fig. 426). ANT V with (0-)5-11 secondary rhinaria. ANT PT 6.5-8.9 times longer than base of ANT VI. Siphunculi 1.5-2.1 times longer than cauda .... ***dasyphylli***

- ABD TERG 2 usually (and sometimes ABD TERG 1 also) with a transverse band (Fig. 429). ANT V with 0-5 secondary rhinaria. ANT PT 4.0-5.3 times longer than base of ANT VI. Siphunculi 1.2-1.5 times longer than cauda .... ***saxifragae***

Nasonovia compositellae (Theobald, 1924) Fig. 419, 424, 425

Apterae are shining dark green, often strongly tinged with orange-red, with an extensive black dorsal abdominal shield; BL 1.6-2.5 mm. Alatae have a pattern of dark dorsal abdominal segmental and intersegmental sclerites, and secondary rhinaria distributed ANT III 26-32, IV 8-12, V 0-3. *N. compositellae* lives all-year-round on hawkweeds, *Hieracium* spp., especially *H. exotericum* Jordan ex Boreau, in spring feeding on the upper sides of the leaves which fold upwards to enclose the colonies, and later colonising stems and inflorescences. Populations in Britain are currently regarded as comprising two subspecies, distinguishable mainly by different lengths of ANT PT. A detailed account is given by Stroyan (1953). **N. compositellae s.str.** (Theobald), is recorded from the north and west of England, Scotland, Wales and

Ireland, but outside Britain it is known only from Norway and Iceland. It produces oviparae and apterous males (on *H. exotericum* in Cumbria) in September-October (Prior & Stroyan, 1960, and BMNH collection). *N. compositellae* **ssp.** *nigra* (Hille Ris Lambers, 1931) has a more southerly distribution in England and Wales, and is widely distributed in Europe. Sexual morphs have been produced from populations of ssp. *nigra* collected in the Slovenia Alps (BMNH collection, leg R.N.B. Prior), but in Britain this subspecies seems to pass the winter exclusively in the parthenogenetic phase on the basal rosettes of *Hieracium*.

Figure 425. *Nasonovia compositellae* (s.str.) (left to right); aptera, alata, male and ovipara.

Nasonovia (*Kakimia*) *dasyphylli* Stroyan, 1957 Fig. 426

Apterae are pale green to yellowish green, sometimes tinged with red, and with a variably developed black dorsal abdominal patch, and siphunculi also variably pigmented, often paler in middle; BL 1.3-3.0 mm. Alatae have a central black abdominal patch and secondary rhinaria distributed ANT III 34-58, IV 13-31, V 0-11. *N. dasyphylli* was first described from Kidlington, Oxfordshire, living on stonecrop, *Sedum dasyphyllum* (Crassulaceae), in a shaded situation, and apparently persisting by exclusively parthenogenetic reproduction through numerous winters (Stroyan, 1957b). It has since been found in other parts of Europe on *Saxifraga* spp. (more typical hosts for a *Kakimia*), but it also feeds on other Crassulaceae besides *Sedum* (*Aichryson*, *Sempervivum*). Sexuales are still unknown in Britain, but oviparae and apterous males have been collected in Czech Republic, and there are alate males in the BMNH collection from Switzerland. In southern England (Oxon, Herts, London), parts of Europe, eastward to Caucasus and south to Spain and Italy; Madeira (BMNH collection, leg. J.H.Martin) and Canary Isles. Heie (1979) compared populations from different parts of Europe.

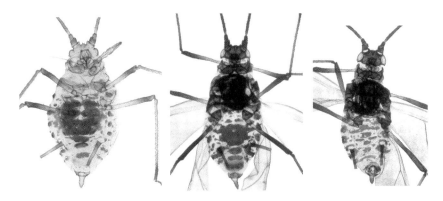

Figure 426. Aptera, alata and alate male (from Switzerland) of *Nasonovia dasyphylli*.

Nasonovia pilosellae (Börner, 1933) Fig. 427

Apterae are shining green to blackish; BL 1.2-2.5 mm. Alatae have a green abdomen with black marginal sclerites and variably developed dark green spino-pleural markings, and secondary rhinaria distributed III 18-41, IV 5-11, V 0-4. *N. pilosellae* lives all-year-round on mouse-ear hawkweed, *Hieracium pilosella* (= *Pilosella officinarum*) and the closely-related fox-and-cubs, *H. aurantiacum*, living in spring inside upwardly rolled leaves, later moving onto stems and flowers (Hille Ris Lambers, 1949). Oviparae and apterous males are produced in October. In England, Scotland, Wales, and most of Europe. Pale specimens of this species are easily confused with *N. ribisnigri* which is also frequently found on these plants.

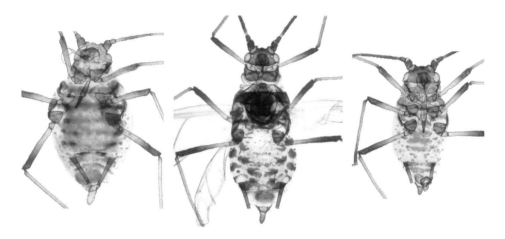

Figure 427. Aptera, alata and male of *Nasonovia pilosellae*.

Nasonovia ribisnigri (Mosley, 1841) **Currant-Lettuce Aphid** Figs 25, 420, 423, 428

Figure 428. Aptera, alata and male of *Nasonovia ribisnigri*.

Apterae are shiny straw-coloured, pale green or apple-green, sometimes reddish, with a dorsal pattern of dark brown markings when on secondary hosts; BL 1.3-2.7 mm. Alatae have a conspicuous pattern of black abdominal markings, and secondary rhinaria distributed III 23-66, IV 2-14, V 0. In spring the fundatrices form small colonies at the shoot tips and in curled young leaves of currant bushes (*Ribes* spp.), especially gooseberry and blackcurrant. Their progeny are almost all alatae which migrate to various plants in Compositae (*Cichorium, Crepis, Hieracium, Lactuca, Lampsana*), Cruciferae (*Alliaria, Sinapis, Sisymbrium*), Scrophulariaceae (*Euphrasia, Veronica*) and Solanaceae (*Nicotiana, Petunia*). Several generations occur on the secondary hosts, producing alatae to found more colonies. They seem more able to colonise plants with sticky hairs than most other aphids. The return migration to *Ribes* occurs in September and October. The alate males develop from reddish nymphs and fly to mate with yellowish to dark green oviparae maturing on undersides of leaves of *Ribes*. In England, Scotland, Wales, Ireland, and widely distributed through Europe, the Middle East, Central Asia, North and South America. See also Blackman and Eastop (2000).

Nasonovia (Kakimia) saxifragae (Doncaster & Stroyan, 1952) Figs 421, 422, 429

Apterae of early generations green, adults of later generations with dorsum shiny black due to extensive sclerotic shield; BL 1.4-2.1 mm. Alatae have dorsal cross bands usually fused on ABD TERG 3-5 into a solid patch, and secondary rhinaria distributed III 30-47, IV 9-13, V 0-5. This species lives all-year-round on *Saxifraga* spp. (*caespitosa, hypnoides, oppositifolia*). Oviparae and apterous males occur in August in Iceland (Prior and Stroyan, 1960), but have not yet been recorded in Britain. In northern England, Scotland, Wales, Jan Mayen Island (original description), Greenland, Iceland and Norway.

Figure 429. Apterae (from early and late generations) and alata of *Nasonovia saxifragae*.

Nearctaphis Shaposhnikov, 1950

Small to medium-sized oval aphids with rather short appendages, nearctic relatives of palaearctic *Anuraphis* and *Dysaphis*. The head has low antennal tubercles in apterae, so that the outline of the front of the head is almost straight. The antennae are much shorter than the body; apterae have no secondary rhinaria on ANT III, alatae have them on III-IV or III-V. Hairs on the dorsal body and appendages are quite long and numerous, with pointed or blunt apices. First tarsal segments have 3-3-3 hairs. The dorsal cuticle has a reticulate pattern of spicules, and apterae often have small dark scleroites at bases of dorsal hairs, sometimes fused on posterior tergites into larger spots or cross-bars. Alatae have dark marginal sclerites and dorsal cross-bands that are at least partially conjoined on tergites IV-

VI to form a large patch. Marginal tubercles may be present, but not spinal tubercles. Spiracular apertures are reniform, placed on posterior margins of spiracular sclerites. Siphunculi are rather short, tapering, and have close-set rows of small spinules (similar to those of *Anuraphis* but less regular and not quite so close-set), and end with a well-developed flange. The cauda is rather short, triangular or helmet-shaped.

There are 13 species in the world, of nearctic origin, typically host-alternating between Pyroidea and secondary hosts in the families Leguminosae and Scrophulariaceae, where they are attended by ants.

Nearctaphis bakeri (Cowen, 1895) **Short-Beaked Clover Aphid** Figs 81b, 83, 430

The only species introduced to Britain is the type species, the Short-Beaked Clover Aphid *Nearctaphis bakeri*, alatae of which were first trapped in 1969 (Stroyan, 1972), and colonies have subsequently been found, mostly on white clover, *Trifolium repens*, in southern England (Herts, Essex), Northern Ireland (BMNH collection, leg. A.R.Edwards), Scotland (trap records) and continental Europe (Heie, 1992). Apterae of *N. bakeri* are dark green to salmon pink with variably developed dorsal dark spots or patches; BL 1.1-2.4 mm. Alatae have broad dark dorsal abdominal cross-bands forming a large central patch, and secondary rhinaria distributed III 25-38, IV 3-11, V 0-4. In its native North America this species has a sexual phase on Pyroidea (*Crataegus, Cydonia, Malus*), and is a pest on red clover, *Trifolium pratense*. Secondary hosts also include *Lotus, Medicago* and *Meliliotus* and some non-leguminous plants such as shepherd's purse (*Capsella bursa-pastoris*) and speedwell (*Veronica persica*). European populations seem to be continuously parthenogenetic, although alate males have been trapped in Devon, Hertfordshire and Essex and reared in culture (BMNH collection). This species has also been introduced to the Middle East, Central Asia, India, Japan and South America.

Figure 430. Aptera, alata and male of *Nearctaphis bakeri*.

Neomyzus van der Goot, 1915

Small to medium-sized oval aphids with apterae having distinctive black dorsal markings, strongly resembling *Myzus* in the shape and spiculosity of the head and in having immatures with spinulose hind tibiae, but often placed as a subgenus of *Aulacorthum*, which it resembles in having long antennae and siphunculi with a large flange. It is an East Asian genus with one species that has become cosmopolitan, the Mottled Arum Aphid, *Neomyzus circumflexus*.

Neomyzus circumflexus (Buckton, 1876) **Mottled Arum Aphid** Fig. 431

Apterae are nearly white or pale yellow to bright green, with distinctive sclerotic dorsal markings, consisting of transverse bands or paired patches on the thorax and a large roughly U-shaped, patch on the abdomen; BL 1.2-2.6 mm. Alatae have dark dorsal cross-bands partially fused across ABD TERG 3-5 to form a transversely oval patch, and secondary rhinaria distributed III 14-28, IV 2-8. This species is extremely polyphagous, feeding on numerous species of both monocots and dicots, and even ferns and conifers, but in temperate climates found especially in glasshouses and on house plants (e.g. *Cineraria*, *Cyclamen*, *Fuschia*, *Zantedeschia*). Reproduction is apparently entirely parthenogenetic, no sexual morphs ever having been recorded. For further information see Heie (1994) and Blackman & Eastop (2000).

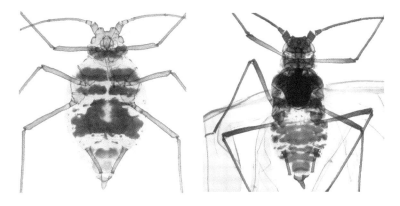

Figure 431. Aptera and alata of *Neomyzus circumflexus.*

Neotoxoptera Theobald, 1915

Small to medium-sized shining dark reddish oval aphids, with clavate siphunculi and morphology of apterae similar to *Myzus* subgenera *Nectarosiphon* and *Sciamyzus*, but the alatae have wing veins heavily bordered with fuscous, the radial sector very strongly curved, and numerous secondary rhinaria distributed over ANT III-V. The head is dark and spiculose with well-developed steep-sided antennal tubercles. Antennae are 6-segmented, similar in length to body. Dorsal body hairs are short and blunt. First tarsal segments have 3-3-2 hairs. The dorsal cuticle of apterae is mainly membranous, alatae have the abdomen with dark marginal sclerites and dorsal cross-bands partially fused across ABD TERG 4-5. Siphunculi are fairly short, moderately and rather symmetrically clavate. The cauda is elongate triangular or tongue-shaped, with 4-6 hairs.

Neotoxoptera formosana (Takahashi, 1921) **Onion Aphid** Figs 102b, 432

There are 5 species in the world, probably all of East Asian origin. One species, the Onion Aphid *Neotoxoptera formosana*, which is a cosmopolitan pest of *Allium* spp., was found on Welsh onion, *A. fistulosum*, and also on garlic chives ((*A. tuberosum*) and leeks (*A. porrum*), at the Royal Horticultural Society's garden at Wisley, Surrey in 1999 (Halstead, 2000), and has also been collected subsequently on other *Allium* spp. (*schoenoprasum*, *sphaerocephalum*) at the same location and in private gardens in Surrey and London (S. Reid, personal communication). An alata trapped at Kirton, Lincolnshire in 2002 (BMNH collection), and a destructive outbreak on *A. porrum* in a garden in Fife in 2008 (K. Davie, personal communication) indicates that it is widespread and well established in Britain. Apterae are shining magenta-red to almost black; BL 1.6-2.3 mm. Alatae have short broad dorsal abdominal cross-bands partly fused into a central patch, and secondary rhinaria distributed III 28-56, IV 8-35, V 0-9. This species is apparently entirely parthenogenetic, no sexual morphs having been found anywhere in the world. [Two other smaller but otherwise very similar *Neotoxoptera* species, *N. oliveri* (Essig, 1935) and *N. violae* (Pergande, 1900), have also spread around the world but are not yet recorded from Britain, although both have now been found in southern Europe. See Blackman and Eastop (2006) for further information.]

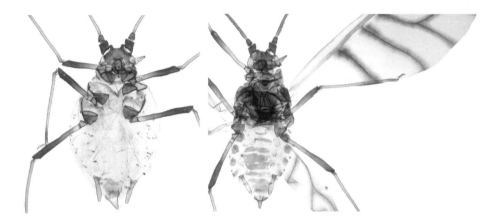

Figure 432. Aptera and alata of *Neotoxoptera formosana*.

Ovatomyzus Hile Ris Lambers, 1947

Small pale oval aphids with, as the name suggests, features of both *Ovatus* and *Myzus*. The cuticle of the head is much smoother than in *Myzus*, and the well-developed antennal tubercles have steep-sided inner faces which do not converge apically. Antennae are usually 6-segmented, as long as body or longer, with a very long PT. Antennae of apterae lack secondary rhinaria, those of alatae have numerous secondary rhinaria distributed over ANT III-V, as in *Ovatus*. Hairs of the dorsal body and antennae are short and blunt or slightly expanded apically. First tarsal segments have 3-3-2 hairs. The dorsal cuticle of apterae is only slightly sclerotic, but somewhat wrinkled or warty. Alatae have dark marginal sclerites and a dark dorsal abdominal patch on tergites 3-5 or 3-6 as in *Myzus*. Siphunculi are fairly long, cylindrical or with slight swelling near apex, imbricated, with a small flange or almost flangeless. The cauda is short, tongue-shaped with a slight constriction near base, and bears 4-8 hairs.

There are 3 species in the world, all European, living without host alternation, and apparently all entirely without sexual reproduction, on Labiatae and/or Boraginaceae. At least one of the species has a specialised overwintering morph adapted for surviving cold winters (Müller, 1969). They are not visited by ants. All three species are found in Britain.

Key to apterous viviparae of *Ovatomyzus*
(based on Eastop, 1987)

1. Siphunculi slender, tapering or cylindrical, almost flangeless (Fig. 433). ANT PT 1.4-1.8 times longer than siphunculi, 1.3-1.7 times longer than ANT III and 5.3-6.5 times longer than HT II. Triommatidium merged with underside of compound eye so that it is not visible from above (Fig. 434) .... **stachyos** Hille Ris Lambers, 1947

- Siphunculi slightly swollen on distal half, and with a distinct flange (Fig. 435). ANT PT 1.8-2.6 times longer than siphunculi, 1.4-2.4 times longer than ANT III and (5.7-) 6.5-9.7 times longer than HT II. Triommatidium not fully merged with compound eye and visible from above 2

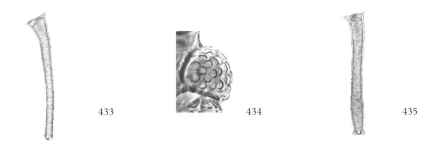

433   434   435

2. R IV+V usually bearing only 2 accessory hairs, and 0.8-1.1 times as long as base of ANT VI. Base of ANT VI 1.3-1.8 times longer than HT II. ANT PT 4.5-6.0 times longer than base of ANT VI, and 1.8-2.1 (-2.2) times longer than siphunculi. Cauda 0.9-1.2 times as long as base of ANT VI .... **boraginacearum** Eastop, 1952

- R IV+V bearing 2-5 accessory hairs, and 1.1-1.6 times as long as base of ANT VI. Base of ANT VI 1.1-1.4 times longer than HT II. ANT PT 5.6-7.7 times longer than base of ANT VI, and (1.9-) 2.0-2.6 times longer than siphunculi. Cauda (1.05-) 1.2-1.5 times longer than base of ANT VI .... **chamaedrys** (Passerini, 1879)

Key to alate viviparae of *Ovatomyzus*
(based mainly on Eastop, 1987)

1. ANT PT 1.6-2.0 times longer than ANT III, which bears 19-30 secondary rhinaria (ANT IV with 7-17 and V 1-7). ANT III 1.4-1.8 times longer than the siphunculi. Siphunculi 0.3-0.4 of length of ANT PT .... **boraginacearum**

- ANT PT 1.0-1.6 times longer than ANT III, which bears of 26-44 secondary rhinaria. ANT III 1.7-2.1 times longer than the siphunculi. Siphunculi 0.3-0.5 length of ANT PT ... 2

2. ANT PT 2.6-3.1 times longer than the siphunculi, and 1.4-1.6 times longer than ANT III. Secondary rhinaria distributed III 31-36 (at a density of 80-90 per mm), IV 11-15, V 0-4 Siphunculi slightly swollen on distal half, and about 8-14 times longer than their width at midlength .... *chamaedrys*

- ANT PT 2.0-2.5 times longer than the siphunculi, and 1.0-1.4 times longer than ANT III. Secondary rhinaria distributed III 26-44 (at a density of 50-80 per mm), IV (10-) 14-23, V 0-8. Siphunculi thin and cylindrical, about 17-20 times longer than their width at midlength .... *stachyos*

Ovatomyzus boraginacearum Eastop, 1952 Figs 26-28, 435, 436

Apterae are whitish to pale greenish yellow (brownish yellow to orange in overwintering populations); BL 0.9-1.6 mm. *M. boraginacearum* lives scattered on the undersides of leaves of its host plants, which are mainly Boraginaceae (*Anchusa, Pentaglottis, Pulmonaria, Symphytum*), and less commonly *Salvia* spp. (Labiatae). In addition there are records from *Geum urbanum* (Rosaceae), *Knautia arvensis* (Dipsacaceae), and also from *Eupatorium cannabinum* (Compositae) as *Myzus eupatorii* (Passerini) of Theobald (1926: 351) seems to be this species. In England, Scotland (one trap record), continental Europe (Germany, Netherlands, Sweden, Czech Republic) and Iran. Reproduction seems to be exclusively parthenogenetic, with a specialised hibernating apterous morph (Müller, 1969, as *O. calaminthae*).

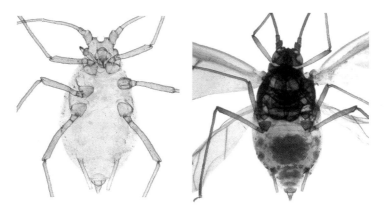

Figure 436. Aptera and alata of *Ovatomyzus boraginacearum*.

Ovatomyzus chamaedrys (Passerini, 1879)

Apterae are yellowish white to whitish green (darker at colder temperatures); BL 0.8-1.5 mm. They live on the undersides of leaves of certain labiates, especially *Teucrium* spp. and *Clinopodium vulgare*, and are also recorded from *Scabiosa columbaria* (Dipsacaceae) and *Lithodora diffusa* (Boraginaceae); the same plant families as *O. boraginacearum*, but with different preferred hosts (Eastop, 1987). The close similarity between *O.chamaedrys* and *O. boraginacearum* and their overlapping host ranges have led to confusion in the literature, with the name *O. calaminthae* Macchiati, 1885 applied to some populations of both species (Eastop, 1987). In England, Wales, and widely distributed in continental Europe. Apparently there is no sexual phase.

Ovatomyzus stachyos Hille Ris Lambers, 1947 Figs 433,434, 437

Apterae are pale greenish white; BL 1.0-1.5 mm. They seem to restrict their feeding exclusively to woundworts, *Stachys* spp., living dispersed on the undersides of older leaves, and often hidden under hairs. In England, Scotland, and widely distributed in continental Europe. Apparently there is no sexual phase.

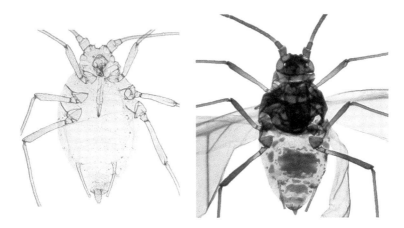

Figure 437. Aptera and alata of *Ovatomyzus stachyos*.

Ovatus van der Goot, 1913

Rather small to medium-sized oval aphids. The cuticle of the head is spiculose with well-developed antennal tubercles that are themselves divergent but have rounded spiculose to scabrous processes on their inner faces, which converge apically so they resemble those of *Myzus*. Antennae are 6-segmented, longer than the body, with a long PT. Antennae of apterae lack secondary rhinaria, those of alatae have often numerous secondary rhinaria distributed over segments III-V. R IV+V is usually longer than HT II. Hairs on the dorsal body and antennae are very short, and blunt or slightly expanded apically. First tarsal segments have 3-3-3 or 3-3-2 hairs. The dorsal cuticle of apterae is rather sclerotic, and variously sculptured with wrinkles, reticulation or small depressions. Alatae have dusky or dark marginal abdominal sclerites, and sometimes thin cross bands or intersegmental markings, but no central dark patch (c.f. *Myzus*). Spiracular apertures are narrowly reniform. Siphunculi are tapering or cylindrical, never clavate; imbricated, with a well-developed flange. The cauda is short, tongue-shaped, with 4-7 hairs.

There are 15 species in the world. Some have host alternation from Pyroidea (especially *Crataegus*) to members of the family Labiatae, while others live all-year-round on Labiatae. There are 6 British species, one of which is only known from a single collection of apterae and is yet to be described.

Key to apterous viviparae of British *Ovatus*

1. R IV+V 2.2-2.4 times longer than HT II, and bearing numerous (15-25) small accessory hairs (Fig. 438) .... *inulae* (Walker, 1849)

- R IV+V 0.9-2.0 times longer than HT II, and bearing 2-6 accessory hairs 2

438

2. Tergum of prepared specimens brownish, and siphunculi uniformly dusky to dark. ANT PT 3.5-4.3 times longer than base of ANT VI. R IV+V with 4-6 accessory hairs .... *glechomae* Hille Ris Lambers, 1949

- Tergum of prepared specimens pale, and siphunculi usually pale or only dusky towards apices, or if tergum brown and siphunculi dark then ANT PT more than 4.4 times longer than base of ANT VI. R IV+V with 2-6 accessory hairs (usually 2-4) 3

3. Inner angle of ANT I projecting forward as a rounded rugose protruberance (Fig. 439) .... *mentharius* (van der Goot, 1913)

- Inner side of ANT I without a forwardly-directed protruberance (e.g. Fig. 440) 4

439

440

4. R IV+V about 0.6-0.7 of length of base of ANT VI, and about equal in length to HT II. ANT PT about 2.2-2.3 times longer than base of ANT VI .... *Ovatus* sp. on *Mentha* (BMNH colln, leg. H.L.G. Stroyan)

- R IV+V 1.1-1.4 times longer than base of ANT VI, and 1.3-1.9 times longer than HT II. ANT PT 4.0-7.6 times longer than base of ANT VI 5

5. [This couplet gives limited discrimination and cannot be applied to early spring (April to mid-May) populations on *Crataegus*; see text under *O. insitus* concerning the difficulties of discriminating between apterae of these two species.]

ANT PT 1.1-2.1 times longer than ANT III (mostly more than 1.3 times), and 1.2-1.9 times longer than siphunculi (mostly more than 1.4 times). R IV+V usually with 2-3 accessory hairs (range 2-5). Tergum unpigmented and siphunculi pale or only darker towards apices .... ***crataegarius*** (Walker,1850)

- ANT PT 1.0-1.5 times longer than ANT III (mostly less than 1.3 times), and 1.1-1.6 times longer than siphunculi (mostly less than 1.4 times). R IV+V usually with 3-5 accessory hairs (range 2-6). (Tergum of apterae on secondary host may be brown and siphunculi dark) .... ***insitus*** (Walker, 1849)

Key to alate viviparae of British *Ovatus*

1. R IV+V more than 2.2 times longer than HT II, and bearing more than 15 small accessory hairs (as in Fig. 438) .... ***inulae***

- R IV+V 1.2-1.9 times longer than HT II, and bearing 2-6 accessory hairs 2

2. ANT III with 10-21 secondary rhinaria, IV with 5-11 and V with 0-5 3

- ANT III with 11-79 secondary rhinaria (but rarely less than 22); IV with 2-57 and V with 0-24 4

3. Primary rhinarium on ANT V enlarged, much larger than secondary rhinaria on same segment (Fig. 441). ANT III with 10-14 rhinaria. ABD TERG 1-4 usually with thin dark, somewhat fragmented cross-bands, and siphunculi rather uniformly dark. Inner side of ANT I without a forwardly-directed protruberance .... ***glechomae***

- Primary rhinarium on ANT V small, similar in size to secondary rhinaria on same segment (Fig. 442). ANT III with 12-21 rhinaria. No dorsal abdominal cross-bands, and siphunculi pale or dusky with paler bases. Inner angle of ANT I projecting forward as a rounded rugose protruberance .... ***mentharius***

441   442

4. ANT III with 11-52 secondary rhinaria (but rarely more than 43); ANT IV with 2-24 (rarely more than 20), and ANT V with 0-9 (rarely more than 5) .... ***crataegarius***

- ANT III with 25-83 secondary rhinaria (but rarely less than 43); ANT IV with 9-57 (rarely less than 18), and ANT V with 1-24 (rarely less than 6) .... ***insitus***

Key to alate males of British *Ovatus*

1. ANT III with 16-32 secondary rhinaria, IV with 7-13 and V with 2-7 2

- ANT III with 34-89 secondary rhinaria, IV with 14-47 and V with 7-22 3

2. R IV+V about 2.3 times longer than HT II, and bearing numerous small accessory hairs. Inner side of ANT I without a forwardly projecting protruberance .... *inulae*

- R IV+V about 1.5 times longer than HT II, with about 4 accessory hairs. Inner angle of ANT I projecting forward as a rounded rugose protruberance .... *mentharius*

3. R IV+V 0.12-0.15 mm long, 1.3-1.45 times longer than HT II. ANT III with 34-73 secondary rhinaria, IV with 14-41 and V with 7-22 .... *crataegarius*

- R IV+V 0.16-0.18 mm long, 1.55-1.7 times longer than HT II. ANT III with 54-89 secondary rhinaria, IV with 20-47 and V with 9-22 .... *insitus*

Ovatus crataegarius (Walker, 1850) **Mint Aphid** Figs 51, 440, 443

Apterae in spring are shining yellowish green to mid- or darkish green, BL 1.4-2.4 mm, feeding on young shoots and undersides of leaves of *Crataegus* spp. and certain other Pyroidea such as *Cydonia*, without causing leaf deformation. Alatae migrate in June to found colonies of yellowish green, mid- to pale green or greenish white apterae, BL 1.0-1.9 mm, on undersides of leaves of mints (*Mentha* ssp.) and some other Labiatae (*Melissa*, *Nepeta*); but colonies may also persist on pruned hawthorn hedges into the summer months. The return migration occurs in September; oviparae are red with dark, swollen hind tibiae bearing numerous scent glands. Parthenogenetic overwintering on *Mentha* also occurs where climatic conditions permit. Throughout Britain and Ireland; presumably European in origin, now of almost world-wide distribution.

Figure 443. Aptera (from mint), return migrant alata (gynopara) and male of *Ovatus crataegarius*.

Ovatus glechomae Hille Ris Lambers, 1947 Figs 441, 444

Apterae are rather dark, dirty brown or brownish green, usually darker laterally; BL 1.4-2.0 mm. They live in small colonies at soil level on etiolated stems and runners of ground-ivy, *Glechoma hederacea*, usually under stones, and drop readily when disturbed so that they are difficult to collect (Stroyan, 1950). There is no host alternation; very dark greenish brown oviparae and small apterous males are produced in late September and October (Hille Ris Lambers, 1947b), but have not yet been recorded in Britain. In southern England (only known from first collection at Great Wilbraham, Cambridgeshire, 1949, and subsequent trap catches), and other countries of north-west Europe.

Figure 444. Aptera and alata of *Ovatus glechomae*.

Ovatus insitus (Walker, 1849)

Apterae collected in spring on *Crataegus* are somewhat paler in life than *O. crataegarius* and may occur in mixed colonies with that species (see below); BL 1.6-2.6 mm. Some other Pyroidea are also utilised, especially medlar (*Mespilus germanica*) and occasionally *Cydonia*, *Malus*, *Pyrus* or *Sorbus*. Alatae migrate in June to give rise to colonies of shining green or greenish white apterae (BL 1.2-1.8 mm) at stem bases and on rhizomes of gypsywort, *Lycopus europaeus*. Later generations of apterae on rhizomes of *Lycopus* in August are mottled brown with dark siphunculi. In England, Scotland, and throughout most of Europe, south-west and central Asia, and Siberia. [*O. insitus* and *O. crataegarius* are very closely related, but there appears to be little or no gene flow between them even when sharing the same primary host plant. They are only really recognisable as distinct species by differences in the antennal sensoriation of the alatae, and by their different choice of, and appearance on, secondary host plants. Apterae of the two species from *Crataegus* in spring are virtually indistinguishable, although in autumn the oviparae of *O. insitus* have more scent glands on their hind tibiae than those of *O. crataegarius*. See Müller & Hubert-Dahl (1979) and Müller (1980) for further information.]

Ovatus (Ovatoides) inulae (Walker, 1849) Figs 438, 445

Apterae are yellow to lemon yellow or pale green; BL 1.0-1.6 mm. They live all-year-round on fleabane, *Pulicaria dysenterica*, feeding on the undersides of leaves, shoot apices and flowers, and on certain *Inula* spp., as well as being recorded from several other composite genera (*Adenostyles*, *Galactites*, *Helichrysum*). Alate males and small pale yellow oviparae (BL c.0.9 mm) having hind tibiae swollen basally with numerous scent glands, occur in October. In England, Wales, widely distributed in continental Europe, and also in central Asia.

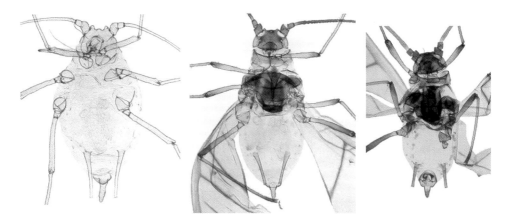

Figure 445. Aptera, alata and male of *Ovatus inulae*.

Ovatus mentharius (van der Goot, 1913) Figs 439, 442, 446

Apterae are greenish white; BL 1.2-1.8 mm. They live all-year-round on *Mentha* spp., feeding on the undersides of the leaves. Alatae are predominantly green, with blackish antennae. Pale greenish yellow oviparae, with hind tibiae swollen throughout length and bearing numerous scent glands, are produced along with alate males in October. Hille Ris Lambers (1947b) gave a full description of all morphs under the name *menthastri*. In England, Scotland, north-west, north, central and eastern Europe, south-west and central Asia, and recently (2006) introduced into USA (Florida).

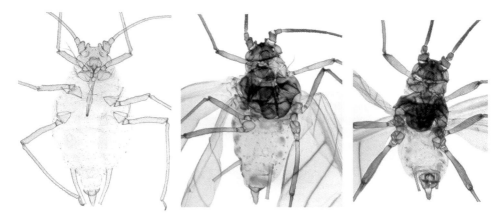

Figure 446. Aptera, alata and male of *Ovatus mentharius*.

Paramyzus Börner, 1933

Rather small pale shiny oval aphids resembling *Myzus* but probably closer to *Nasonovia*. The head is minutely spiculose with well-developed steep-sided antennal tubercles that are rounded apically. Antennae are longer than body, with a long PT. Apterae have rather large, somewhat protuberant secondary rhinaria on ANT III, and alatae have them on III-IV or III-V. Antennal and dorsal body hairs are very short and blunt. R IV+V is much longer than HT II. The thoracic sternites each have a pair of low, spiculose processes. First tarsal segments have 3-3-2 hairs. The siphunculi are rather long and straight, slightly clavate, strongly imbricated to almost scabrous, with a distinct flange. The cauda is rather short, tongue-shaped, and bears 4-6 hairs.

Paramyzus heraclei Börner, 1933 Figs 42, 447

There are 2 species in the world, one of which, *Paramyzus heraclei*, occurs in Britain, and is recorded from England, Scotland and Wales. Apterae of *P. heraclei* are shiny, either white or yellow, with black eyes and pale appendages, only the tarsi being darker; BL 1.3-1.9 mm. Alatae have dark head, thorax and antennae, and white to greenish yellow abdomen with dark marginal sclerites, an irregularly quadrate dark dorsal patch on ABD TERG 3-5, and other dark markings. This species lives without host alternation on hogweed, *Heracleum sphondylium*, causing yellow spotting of the leaves. Yellowish oviparae, with basal halves of hind tibiae only slightly swollen but bearing 34-104 scent glands, are produced along with alate males (with secondary rhinaria distributed III 20-43, IV 8-22, V 2-9) in September to November. Müller (1977) gave a full account of this species in Germany.

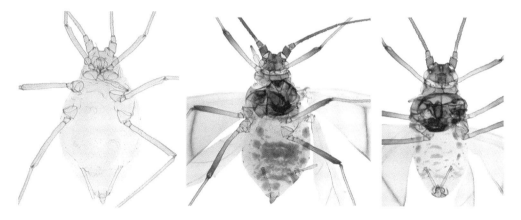

Figure 447. Aptera, alata and male of *Paramyzus heraclei*.

Pentalonia Coquerel, 1859

Rather small, oval, reddish brown to blackish aphids with distinctive features of the wings, dorsal body hairs and cuticle, and siphunculi. The head is spiculose, with rather small conical scabrous antennal tubercles. The median tubercle is undeveloped. The antennae are 6-segmented, about as long as body, with a very long PT. Antennae of apterae lack secondary rhinaria, those of alatae have a few scattered rhinaria on III-IV or III-V. Hairs on antennae are short and blunt, those on dorsal body are short and broadly fan-shaped. First tarsal segments have 3-3-2 hairs. The dorsal cuticle is wrinkled, with minute spinules forming a reticulation. Alatae have distinctive forewings with all veins thickly brown-bordered, and with the radial sector strongly curved and fused with the media for part of its length, forming a closed or partly closed cell. The hind wing is somewhat reduced and has only one oblique vein. The siphunculi are distinctively shaped, rather thick, symmetrically clavate, scabrous, black on distal part, with a large flange. The cauda is tongue-shaped, with 4 hairs.

There are 4 species in the world, living without host alternation on tropical monocotyledenous plants of the families Araceae, Musaceae, Zingiberaceae and Gramineae. Two species are widely distributed in temperate regions in hothouses. One of these is the cosmopolitan Banana Aphid, *Pentalonia nigronervosa* Coquerel, 1859, which normally restricts its feeding to bananas and other Musaceae. Until recently the other widely-distributed species, *Pentalonia caladii*, which feeds on plants in the families Araceae and Zingiberaceae, was generally regarded as a 'form' of the banana aphid, but molecular work (Foottit *et al.*, 2010) has now shown that it should be treated as a separate species. *P. caladii* has a shorter rostrum (R IV+V is 0.106-0.130 mm in *caladii* compared with 0.137-0.170 mm in *nigronervosa*), and slightly longer and thinner siphunculi than the banana aphid.

Pentalonia caladii van der Goot, 1919 Figs 40, 448

As yet, no *Pentalonia* have been recorded from bananas growing in UK hothouses, but aphids conforming to the morphology of *P. caladii* have been collected since 1922 at Kew Gardens on Araceae (*Caladium*, *Xanthosoma*) and Zingiberaceae (*Alpinia*, *Hedychium*, *Zingiber*). Apterae in life are brown, with dark siphunculi, mainly pale antennae, pale tibiae and a whitish cauda. Immatures are reddish brown. They live at the base of the top leaf and on the young stem, on inwardly rolled top leaves, or at the bases of older leaves surrounded by bracts. Colonies are visited by ants, and reproduce parthenogenetically throughout the year.

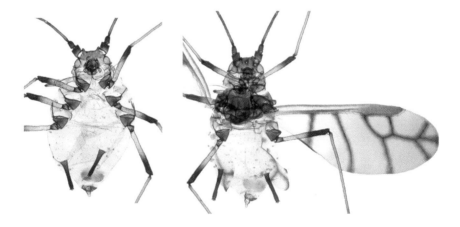

Figure 448. Aptera and alata of *Pentalonia caladii*.

Phorodon Passerini, 1860

Small to medium-sized broadly spindle-shaped aphids. The cuticle of the head is spiculose with well-developed antennal tubercles that are themselves divergent but have finger-like forwardly-directed processes on their inner faces, and the inner angles of ANT I also project forward. The antennae of apterae are shorter than the body, usually 6-segmented or occasionally 5-segmented, with a rather long PT. Secondary rhinaria are absent from the antennae of apterae, present on segments III-IV or III-V of alatae. R IV+V is longer than HT II. Hairs on the dorsal body and antennae are short and blunt or somewhat expanded apically. First tarsal segments have 3-3-3 or 3-3-2 hairs. The dorsal cuticle of apterae is variously sculptured with wrinkles, reticulation or small depressions. Alatae have secondary rhinaria on ANT III-IV and sometimes also on ANT V, dark marginal abdominal sclerites and a *Myzus*-like dark central dorsal patch. The siphunculi are long and gradually tapering, often slightly curved outward distally, strongly imbricated, and with a distinct flange. The cauda is elongate triangular, rather pointed, with 6-10 hairs.

There are 5 species in the world, which either have host alternation from *Prunus* to members of the family Cannabidaceae, or live all year on Cannabidaceae. They are not visited by ants.

Phorodon humuli (Schrank, 1801), the **Damson-Hop Aphid** Figs 50, 449

There is only one species in Britain, *Phorodon humuli*, which is an important pest of hops. Apterae are rather shiny pale green to yellowish green, with three darker green longitudinal dorsal stripes; BL 2.0-3.0 mm on *Prunus*, 1.0-2.1 mm on hops. Alatae have secondary rhinaria distributed ANT III 23-35, IV 1-11. Colonies occur in spring on new growth of certain *Prunus* spp. (*spinosa, insititia, domestica*), the leaves being only slightly curled by this species. This was the aphid in which host alternation was first recognised, when Walker (1849) advised hop growers to prune blackthorn hedges in order to destroy the aphid's overwintering eggs. Migration occurs in June to hops (*Humulus lupulus*), where colonies form on the undersides of leaves and on flowers and fruits. The return migration to *Prunus* occurs in late August-September. Oviparae are small (BL 1.0-1.3 mm), red or yellowish green with thickened dark hind tibiae bearing about 50 rather large scent glands. The alate males are larger (BL 1.3-2.1 mm) with an extensive pattern of dark dorsal abdominal sclerotisation. *P. humuli* is widely distributed through Europe and Asia, and introduced to North America and New Zealand. See also Blackman and Eastop (2000).

Figure 449. *Phorodon humuli* (left to right); aptera (from hops), spring migrant alata, autumn migrant alata (gynopara), male.

Pleotrichophorus Börner, 1930

Medium-sized, usually pale spindle-shaped aphids with long appendages. The head has fairly low antennal tubercles with divergent inner faces, and the median tubercle is better developed than in the related genus *Capitophorus*. Antennae are normally 6-segmented, with a very long PT; apterae have small secondary rhinaria on ANT III, and alatae have them on III, III-IV, or III-V. Alatae have dark-bordered wing veins. Males are apterous, small and slender, and have numerous rhinaria on ANT III-V. Dorsal hairs of apterae are numerous, thick and rather short, capitate or fan-shaped, in 2-3 rather irregular tranverse rows on each segment. Antennal hairs are short and blunt. Alatae have thinner hairs than apterae. R IV+V is typical of aphids feeding on Anthemideae; pointed or stiletto-shaped, with straight or concave sides, and usually with a pair of very long accessory hairs on the basal part. First tarsal segments have 3-3-3 hairs. Forewing veins are conspicuously dark-bordered. The dorsal abdomen is membranous in apterae, and alatae only have dark intersegmental sclerites and dusky marginal sclerites. The siphunculi are long and slender, cylindrical for most of length but often slightly expanded at apex, with a small flange. The cauda is finger-shaped, tongue-shaped or triangular, with 5-8 hairs.

There are about 60 species in the world, 49 of which are nearctic and 7 European. They all live without host alternation on Compositae, mostly on Anthemideae and Astereae, with a few on Inuleae. They are not visited by ants. Nominally there are 3 British species, although one of them may not deserve separate species status (see below under *P. chrysanthemi*). The keys include *P. filaginis* (Schouteden, 1906) not yet recorded from Britain, but with a strong likelihood of occurring here, and *P. persimilis*, added on the basis of a single trapped alata (but see text).

Key to apterous viviparae of British *Pleotrichophorus*
(Most single specimens of *P. chrysanthemi* cannot be distinguished from *P. glandulosus*.)

1. Siphunculi longer than ANT III. R IV+V with all accessory hairs of similar length .... ***persimilis*** Börner, 1950

- Siphunculi no longer than and usually shorter than ANT III. R IV+V with the basal pair of accessory hairs much longer than those more distal 2

2. PT 3.1-3.8 times longer than base of ANT VI. Siphunculi 1.5-1.9 times longer than cauda .... ***duponti*** Hille Ris Lambers, 1935

- PT 4.8-6.9 times longer than base of ANT VI. Siphunculi 1.9-2.5 times longer than cauda 3

3. Tergum dusky. Antennae and legs rather dark, darker than tergum, with tibial apices often very dark .... ***filaginis*** (Schouteden, 1906)

- Tergum pale. Antennae and legs mainly pale with only apex of ANT V, base VI around primary rhinartium and tarsi ever really dark 4

4. ABD TERG 8 with 5-11 hairs (mostly with 7-8) .... ***chrysanthemi*** (Theobald, 1920)

- ABD TERG 8 with 8-13 hairs (mostly with 9-10) .... ***glandulosus*** (Kaltenbach, 1846)

Key to alate viviparae of British *Pleotrichophorus*

1. Siphunculi longer than ANT III. R IV+V with all accessory hairs of similar length .... ***persimilis***

- Siphunculi no longer than and usually shorter than ANT III. R IV+V with the basal pair of accessory hairs much longer than those more distal 2

2. ANT PT less than 4.5 times longer than base of ANT VI .... *duponti*

- ANT PT more than 4.8 times longer than base of ANT VI 2

3. Femora dark on distal half or more ....*filaginis*

- Femora mainly pale, at most with a dusky spot near apices 3

4. ANT III with 9-20 rhinaria (mostly 12-16), and IV without any. ABD TERG 8 with 5-11 hairs (mostly with 7-8) .... *chrysanthemi*

- ANT III with 9-23 rhinaria (but mostly 16-19), and IV with 0-8 (usually with at least 1 on IV on one antenna). ABD TERG 8 with 8-14 hairs (mostly with 9-10) ....
.... *glandulosus*

Pleotrichophorus chrysanthemi (Theobald, 1920)

Apterae are pale green to yellowish; BL 1.8-2.4 mm. They feed on the undersides of the leaves of florists' chrysanthemums, (*Dendranthema* spp.), often forming large colonies on yellowing leaves. Alatae have paired dusky dorsal intersegmental markings. *P. chrysanthemi* apparently reproduces entirely by parthenogenesis, no sexual morphs being known; possibly it arose quite recently in east Asia as a clone of *P. glandulosus* able to feed on *Dendrathema*, and subsequently dispersed widely on chrysanthemum cuttings. In most respects it is morphologically indistinguishable from *P. glandulosus*. In England, Ireland, and most parts of the world where chrysanthemums are cultivated.

Pleotrichophorus duponti Hille Ris Lambers, 1935 Fig. 450

Apterae are dull greyish green with green transverse intersegmental stripes; BL 1.6-2.1 mm. They feed on the lower leaves of yarrow, *Achillea millefolium*, from which they fall readily when disturbed. Oviparae and apterous males are produced in September to October in the Netherlands (Hille Ris Lambers, 1953). In England, Scotland, and northern, central and eastern Europe.

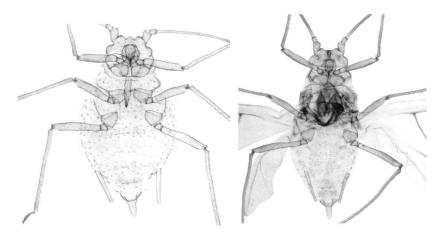

Figure 450. Aptera and alata of *Pleotrichophorus duponti*.

Pleotrichophorus filaginis (Schouteden, 1906)

Apterae are purplish grey, BL 1.5-2.2 mm. They feed on cudweed, *Gnaphalium sylvaticum*, solitarily or in small single-parent families on upper- and undersides of leaves. Oviparae and apterous males are produced in October (Hille Ris Lambers, 1953). Not yet recorded in Britain, possibly because of host scarcity; present in France, Belgium, Netherlands and Germany.

Pleotrichophorus glandulosus (Kaltenbach, 1846) Figs 22, 451

Apterae are yellowish white, sometimes greenish, occasionally with a pale green median stripe; BL 1.4-2.6 mm. They live on the undersides of lower leaves of mugwort, *Artemisia vulgaris*, and sometimes on other *Artemisia* spp., and *Anthemis arvensis*. Alatae have a yellowish abdomen with pale brown marginal sclerites and darker pleural intersegmental sclerites. Oviparae with the basal part of the hind tibia swollen and small, slender apterous males are produced in late September and October. Eggs are laid on the undersides of the leaves. In England, Scotland, Wales, Ireland, throughout most of Europe and Asia, and introduced to eastern North America.

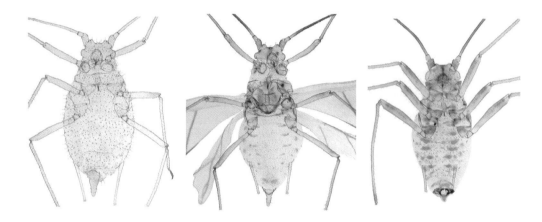

Figure 451. Aptera, alata and male of *Pleotrichophorus glandulosus*.

Pleotrichophorus persimilis Börner, 1950

Apterae are pale yellowish red to brownish, appearing wax-powdered; BL 1.9-2.6 mm. On *Artemisia campestris* and *A. scoparia* in continental Europe, and east to Iran and Kazakhstan. Not yet found on *Artemisia* in Britain, but an alata that appears to be this species was recently (May, 2007) trapped at Silwood Park in Buckinghamshire (V.F. Eastop, pers. comm.). However, this alata had many more secondary rhinaria (III 26-29, IV 7-8, V 4-6) than those recorded from continental Europe (III 2-8, IV and V 0). Oviparae and apterous males occur on *A. campestris* in September in Germany (Hille Ris Lambers, 1953).

Pseudacaudella Börner, 1950

Very small shiny olive green or brown moss-feeding aphids. The head is broad with very low antennal and median tubercles, so that the outline of the front of the head is almost straight. The antennae are short, 6-segmented, with PT longer than base of segment VI and tapering to a pointed apex. Antennae of apterae lack secondary rhinaria, those of alatae have rhinaria on III-IV or III-V. Hairs on dorsal body and appendages are sparse, short and blunt. First tarsal segments all have 2 indistinct hairs. The forewings of the alatae usually have the media only once-branched, and the veins are dark-bordered. The dorsum of the aptera is sclerotic, dark-pigmented and mainly smooth except for marginal areas. The siphunculi are cylindrical, strongly imbricated, with a subapical constriction and a large flange. The cauda is short, with swollen basal part and narrow apical part typical of moss-feeding aphids, and bearing 4 hairs.

Pseudacaudella rubida Börner Figs 74b, 75, 452

There is only one species in the genus, *Pseudacaudella rubida*. It lives without host alternation on mosses in various genera (*Climacium, Dicranum, Hylocomium, Mnium, Pleurozium, Polytrichum, Pseudoscleropodium, Thuidium*), and is able to live in dry as well as humid habitats. Apterae are shining olive green to brown, with rusty spots at the bases of the siphunculi. Alatae have secondary rhinaria distributed III 7-15, IV 3-7, V 0-2. It is adapted for continuous all-year round parthenogenesis, with a specialised overwintering second instar having a dark sclerotic cuticle and a wax coat (Müller, 1973; Tinguely, 1993). In England, Scotland, Wales, Ireland, and also recorded from continental Europe, North Africa, North and South America, and New Zealand.

Figure 452. Aptera and alata of *Pseudacaudella rubida*.

Pseudobrevicoryne Heinze, 1960

Medium-sized wax-powdered, oval aphids. The head is without antennal or median tubercles, so that the outline of the front of the head is straight to slightly convex. Antennae of apterae are 5- or 6-segmented (4-segmented in fundatrices), shorter than body, although the PT is relatively long. Antennae of apterae lack secondary rhinaria, those of alatae have numerous rhinaria on III-V. Dorsal body hairs have blunt apices. First tarsal segments have 3-3-2 hairs. Alatae have dark segmental cross-bands on the dorsal abdomen, sometimes fragmented. The siphunculi are short, truncate flangeless cones, about as long as their basal width (in fundatrices they are merely thick-rimmed pores). The cauda is short, tongue-shaped to triangular, with 5-6 hairs.

Pseudobrevicoryne buhri (Börner, 1952) Figs 57, 453

There are 3 species in the world, one of which, *Pseudobrevicoryne buhri*, has been recorded in Britain. Apterae are yellowish, wax-powdered; BL 1.5-2.3 mm. Alatae have secondary rhinaria distributed III 35-56, IV 5-11, V 3-6. This little-known species lives without host alternation on *Barbarea* sp. (*stricta*, *vulgaris*), feeding in leaves that are rolled upwards. Fundatrices have been found in mid-May in southern England, but sexual morphs have not been described. In England (only collected at one location in Berkshire in 1948/49; see Stroyan, 1955), and in countries of north-west, northern and eastern Europe

Figure 453. Aptera and alata of *Pseudobrevicoryne buhri*.

Rhodobium Hille Ris Lambers, 1947

Medium-sized spindle-shaped shiny aphids combining some features of *Aulacorthum* and *Macrosiphum*. The head has well-developed antennal tubercles, with their inner faces spiculose and steep-sided, almost parallel or slightly convergent apically. The median tubercle is also evident. Antennae of apterae have 2-18 rather large secondary rhinaria on III, arranged in a row; alatae have them on III-IV or III-V. Hairs on the dorsal body and antennae are very short and blunt. First tarsal segments have 3-3-3 hairs. Alatae have very dark wing veins. The dorsal cuticle of the aptera is slightly sclerotic, unpigmented and mostly smooth. Alatae have dusky marginal abdominal sclerites and sometimes faint spinopleural markings. The siphunculi are rather thick, tapering or cylindrical, pale with darker apices, without polygonal reticulation, and with a distinct flange. The cauda is pale and finger-shaped, and has 2 pairs of lateral hairs and usually 1-3 much shorter, blunt hairs near the apex.

Rhodobium porosum (Sanderson, 1900) Figs 45, 46, 454

There is only one nominal species in the genus, *Rhodobium porosum*, probably of North American origin but now widely distributed. It lives without host alternation on *Rosa* spp., especially cultivated varieties. In North America it also occurs in a yellow form regularly on strawberry, *Fragaria vesca*, and British populations will feed on *Fragaria* when transferred artificially (BMNH collection, leg. H.L.G.Stroyan). Apterae on roses are rather shiny, bright green or yellowish green with a brownish yellow head, BL 1.2-2.5 mm, and are found usually on young, partly unfolded leaves. Alatae have a bright green abdomen without any distinct dark markings. In Britain all the records so far are from England, apart from one alata trapped in Scotland, and it tends to occur mainly in sheltered situations and glasshouses, where it overwinters parthenogenetically, but oviparae and alate males have been obtained in the laboratory (BMNH collection, leg. H.L.G.Stroyan). In North America there is a sexual phase on both *Rosa* and *Fragaria*, and fundatrices and sexual morphs are recorded from some parts of continental Europe (Müller & Steiner, 1988).

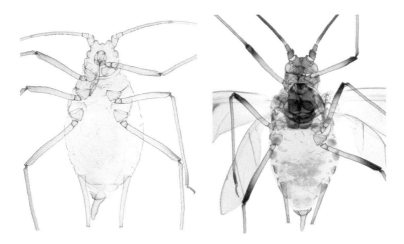

Figure 454. Aptera and alata of *Rhodobium porosum*.

Rhopalomyzus Mordvilko, 1921

Small to medium-sized oval aphids, yellowish or dark reddish brown to black. The cuticle of the head is spiculose in *Rhopalomyzus* sensu stricto, or smooth (in subgenus *Judenkoa*), with small but evident antennal tubercles, their inner faces scabrous and converging apically, or smooth and divergent (in *Judenkoa*). The median tubercle is usually also evident. Antennae are 6-segmented, slightly shorter than or about as long as body in apterae, with PT 3-5 times longer than base of last segment. Antennae of apterae lack secondary rhinaria, those of alatae have numerous protruberant secondary rhinaria on segments III-IV, or III-V. The hairs on the dorsal body and antennae are short and blunt or somewhat expanded apically. First tarsal segments have 3-3-2 hairs (sometimes 2-2-2 in fundatrices). The dorsal cuticle of apterae is smooth or somewhat wrinkled, and there may be dark cross bands on posterior abdominal tergites. Alatae have dark marginal abdominal sclerites and dorsal cross-bands, often fused across tergites III-V or III-VI into a large dark dorsal abdominal patch. There are often marginal tubercles on the prothorax and abdominal segments II-VI. Spiracular apertures are partially covered by opercula. Siphunculi are rather strongly clavate, with fairly symmetrical swelling, and a slight constriction below the small but distinct flange. The cauda is rather short, tongue-shaped or triangular, with 5-11 hairs.

There are 7 species in the world, typically host alternating between *Lonicera* as primary host and secondary hosts in Gramineae. The colonies deforming the leaves of *Lonicera* in spring consist only of fundatrices and developing spring migrant alatae. In Britain there are two very different species, belonging to different subgenera.

Key to fundatrices of British *Rhopalomyzus*

- R IV+V longer than HT II. Siphunculi 1.9-2.1 times longer than cauda ....
  .... ***poae*** (Gillette, 1908)

- R IV+V shorter than HT II. Siphunculi 1.5-1.8 times longer than cauda ....
  .... ***lonicerae*** (Siebold, 1839)

Key to apterous viviparae of British *Rhopalomyzus* species on grasses

- Frontal tubercles scabrous, bearing hairs with swollen apices. Siphunculi 1.9-2.5 times longer than cauda, which is triangular and bears 5-7 hairs. R IV+V longer than HT II .....
  .... ***poae***

- Frontal tubercles almost smooth, with hairs blunt or pointed. Siphunculi 1.3-1.6 times longer than cauda, which is tongue-shaped and bears 6-11 hairs. R IV+V shorter than HT II .... ***lonicerae***

Key to alate viviparae of British *Rhopalomyzus*

- Siphunculi 2.4-3.3 times longer than cauda. R IV+V longer than HT II. Dorsum usully with well-developed but more-or less separate cross-bands on all of ABD TERG 3-7 ...... ***poae***

- Siphunculi 1.5-2.1 times longer than cauda. R IV+V shorter than HT II. Dorsum with a variably developed patch on ABD TERG 3-5, and ABD TERG 6 and 7 usually with poorly developed or fragmented cross-bands .... ***lonicerae***

Key to alate males of British *Rhopalomyzus*

- R IV+V longer than HT II. Cauda with 5 hairs .... ***poae***

- R IV+V shorter than HT II. Cauda with 8-10 hairs .... ***lonicerae***

Rhopalomyzus (Judenkoa) lonicerae (Siebold, 1839) Fig. 455

Spring colonies on *Lonicera* spp. cause the leaves to roll or fold towards their undersides and become mottled with pale yellow, sometimes with red spots. The plump adult apterae found inside these pseudogalls are all fundatrices, bluish green with dark head and appendages, powdered with greyish wax; BL 1.7-2.6 mm. Their whitish progeny all become alatae (BL 1.9-2.4 mm, with secondary rhinaria distributed III 31-51, IV 16-27, V 0-4), migrating in May-June to grasses in damp situations, mainly *Phalaris arundinacea*. Apterae on *Phalaris* are pale yellowish, not wax-powdered, with antennae conspicuously dark beyond ANT III. As summer progresses they may develop dense colonies on the leaf-blades. The return migrants (BL 2.4-3.0 mm, secondary rhinaria distributed III 40-62, IV 23-31, V 0-3) fly back to *Lonicera* in late September-October and aggregate on the undersides of the leaves, which turn bright yellow where they and their progeny are feeding. The mature oviparae (not yet recorded from Britain) are rather small (BL 1.5-2.0 mm) and pale yellow with conspicuously dark and swollen hind tibiae. Males have dorsal abdominal cross-bands, and secondary rhinaria distributed III 54-75, IV 27-40, V 8-17. Some colonisation of the common garden shrub *Symphoricarpos racemosus* also occurs in autumn, but the oviparae deposited on this plant apparently fail to mature (Hille Ris Lambers, 1953). In England, Scotland, most parts of continental Europe, Central Asia, Siberia, and North America.

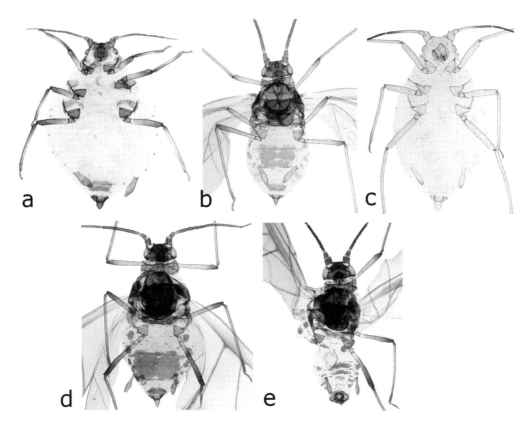

Figure 455. Various morphs of *Rhopalomyzus lonicerae*; (a) fundatrix on *Lonicera*, (b) spring migrant alata, (c) aptera on *Phalaris*, (d) autumn migrant alata, (e) male.

Rhopalomyzus poae (Gillette, 1908) Figs 41, 456

Spring colonies of this species form large red and yellow speckled pseudogalls specifically on alpine honeysuckle, *Lonicera alpigena*, which is cultivated in many parks and gardens in the UK. The fundatrices (BL 2.3-3.5 mm) are on average larger than those of *R. lonicerae*, and feed inside the folded-down margins of the leaves. Their progeny are all alatae (BL 2.3-2.5 mm, secondary rhinaria distributed III 19-46, IV 4-16, V 0-3) which migrate in late May-June to grasses (*Agrostis, Dactylis, Festuca, Glyceria, Phalaris, Poa*), giving rise to colonies on the basal parts of stems, often where these are etiolated under stones. Apterae on grasses are reddish brown, dark brown or blackish, wax-powdered on the underside, with dusky/dark appendages; BL 1.3-1.8 mm. Alatae produced in August-September (BL 1.8-2.1 mm, secondary rhinaria distributed III 45-65, IV 18-32, V 0-4) migrate back to *Lonicera* to produce very small (BL 1.1-1.3 mm) oviparae on the leaves. Observations by Wood-Baker (1970) indicate that parthenogenetic overwintering on grasses occurs commonly in UK and Ireland. In England, Scotland, Wales, Isle of Man, Ireland, continental Europe, USA, and there are also records from Pakistan, Bolivia and Peru.

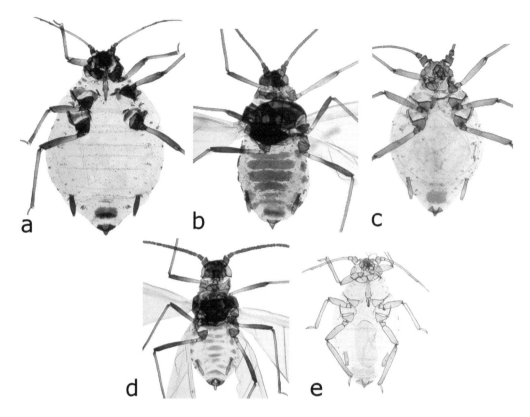

Figure 456. Various morphs of *Rhopalosiphun poae*; (a) fundatrix, (b) spring migrant alata, (c) aptera on grass, (d) male, (e) ovipara.

Rhopalosiphoninus Baker, 1920

Medium-sized oval aphids, usually dark and shiny. The cuticle of the head is spiculose, with well developed antennal tubercles, their inner faces scabrous and steep-sided, parallel or converging apically. The median tubercle is not developed. Antennae are 6-segmented, longer than or about as long as body in apterae, with a long PT. Antennae of apterae are with or without secondary rhinaria, those of alatae have secondary rhinaria on segment III only, III-IV, or (rarely) III-V. Hairs on the dorsal body and antennae are usually short, and blunt or somewhat expanded apically. First tarsal segments have 3-3-3 or 3-3-2 hairs. The dorsal cuticle of apterae may be mainly membranous but is often sclerotic with very extensive dark pigmentation (but this varies seasonally within some species); the surface may be smooth or have reticulate pattern of small spicules. Alatae have dark marginal abdominal sclerites and a varying amount of mid-dorsal sclerotisation, from intersegmental markings to a complete black shield. Siphunculi are large and very strongly clavate, with fairly symmetrical swelling, relatively smooth-surfaced and often dark, and strongly constricted below the well-developed flange. The cauda is rather short, tongue-shaped or triangular, with 4-7 hairs.

There are 19 species in the world, living on a variety of plants, mostly without host alternation, and mostly feeding at or even below ground level, but unattended by ants, so they are easily overlooked. They are divided into four subgenera. In Britain there are 6 species/subspecies, including representatives of all four subgenera.

Key to apterous viviparae of British *Rhopalosiphoninus*
(I thank Dr V.F. Eastop for his help in suggesting morphometric discriminants for separating *staphyleae* and *tulipaellus*.)

1. ANT III without secondary rhinaria. Siphunculi with swollen part 3.7-4.8 times thicker than narrowest part of stem, and with a cylindrical, reticulated distal part (Fig. 457). HT I with 2 hairs .... *latysiphon* (Davidson, 1912)

- ANT III with 1-30 rhinaria. Siphunculi with swollen part no more than 3.2 times thicker than narrowest part of stem, and with distal part tapering to flange (Figs 458, 459). HT I with 3 hairs 2

457   458   459

2. Dorsal abdomen with an extensive dark sclerotic shield encompassing marginal sclerites. ANT III with 5-30 rhinaria 3

- Dorsal abdomen membranous or with spino-pleural sclerotisation not extending laterally to marginal sclerites. ANT III with 1-9 rhinaria 4

3. Siphunculi with narrow, almost cylindrical stem, widening abruptly to swollen half which is about 3 times thicker than narrowest part of stem (Fig. 458). Tergum smooth without any trace of reticulation .... *calthae* (Koch, 1854)

- Siphunculi with thick stem widening gradually to swollen part that is about twice as thick as narrowest part of stem (Fig. 459). Tergum coarsely reticulated .... *ribesinus* (van der Goot, 1912)

4. Apices of femora contrastingly black. Dorsal abdomen membranous, pale, without any spino-pleural sclerotisation anterior to siphunculi; only with small marginal sclerites, antesiphuncular and post-siphuncular sclerites, and cross-bands on ABD TERG 7 and 8 .... *heikinheimoi* (Börner, 1952)

- Femora pale or dusky, without contrastingly black apices. Dorsal abdomen usually with at least some spino-pleural dusky/dark sclerotisation anterior to siphunculi 5

5. Dorsal abdomen with variably developed dusky to dark, often fragmented cross-bands, usually divided in midline and only partially fused across segments (see Fig. 464). ANT III with 1-2 rhinaria in 90% of specimens. ANT V 2.1-3.1 (but mostly 2.3-2.8) times longer than base of ANT VI. Distance from base of ANT III to first rhinarium 0.07-0.22 (mostly 0.13-0.16) of length of ANT III .... ***staphyleae* s. str.**(Koch, 1854)

- Dorsal abdomen with a distinct dark sclerotic pattern including complete cross-bands on ABD TERG 1-3, with bands usually coalesced across tergites to form a trapezoid central patch on ABD TERG 3-5 or 4-5 (Fig. 464). ANT III with 1-7 rhinaria, usually 2-4. ANT V 1.8-2.6 (but mostly 1.9-2.4) times longer than base of ANT VI. Distance from base of ANT III to first rhinarium 0.14-0.30 (but mostly 0.16-0.21) of length of ANT III .... ***staphyleae* ssp. *tulipaellus*** (Theobald, 1916)

Key to alate viviparae of British *Rhopalosiphoninus*

Note that single alatae of *staphyleae* s.str. and *staphyleae tulipaellus* cannot be reliably distinguished.

1. Media of forewing once-branched. Dorsal abdomen membranous except for marginal and pre- and post-siphuncular sclerites .... ***heikinheimoi***

- Media of forewing almost always twice-branched. Abdomen with at least some spino-pleural sclerotisation; often with a central black patch, or at the very least with blackish pleural intersegmental sclerites 2

2. ABD TERG 3-6 membranous except for blackish pleural intersegmental sclerites and marginal sclerites (see Fig. 463) .... ***ribesinus***

- ABD TERG 3-6 mostly covered by a large dark central patch 3

3. Siphunculi with swollen part 3 or more times thicker than narrowest part of stem 4

- Siphunculi with swollen part much less than 3 times thicker than narrowest part of stem 5

4. ANT III with 35-55 rhinaria, and ANT IV with 2-8. Hairs on ANT III all shorter than basal diameter of segment. Siphunculi without cylindrical part distal to swelling. All first tarsal segments with 3 hairs .... ***caltheae***

- ANT III with 16-25 rhinaria, ANT IV without any. Longest hairs on ANT III as long as or longer than basal diameter of segment. Siphunculi with a cylindrical part distal to swelling. First tarsal segments with 3-3-2 hairs (HT I without medial sense peg) .... ***latysiphon***

5.   ANT III with (13-)16-32 rhinaria (note:spring migrants from *Staphylea* may have fewer rhinaria, but are not known from Britain). Distance from base of ANT III to first rhinarium 0.08-0.17 of length of ANT III. ANT V (2.4-) 2.6-3.2 times longer than base of ANT VI .... ***staphyleae***

-     ANT III with 6-14(-15) rhinaria. Distance from base of ANT III to first rhinarium 0.15-0.28 of length of ANT III. ANT V 1.8-2.8 times longer than base of ANT VI ......
....*staphyleae* ssp. *tulipaellus*

Rhopalosiphoninus (Pseudorhopalosiphoninus) calthae (Koch, 1854)
Figs 458, 460

Apterae are shining brownish black with yellow legs, the antennae being dark except for basal part of ANT III; BL 2.1-3.0 mm. They form dense colonies on the undersides of the leaves of *Caltha palustris*, especially on plants growing in shady conditions. Alatae have a large black dorsal abdominal patch and secondary rhinaria distributed III 35-55, IV 2-8, V 0-2. There is no host alternation; small (BL c.1.7 mm) black apterous males, and oviparae lacking the sclerotic tergum of the viviparae and with only slightly swollen hind tibiae, are produced in October. In England, Scotland, and most parts of continental Europe.

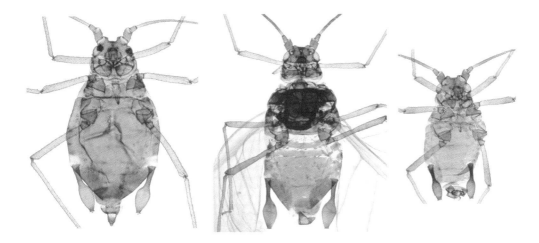

Figure 460. Aptera, alata and male of *Rhopalosiphoninus calthae*.

Rhopalosiphoninus (Submegoura) heikinheimoi (Börner, 1952) Fig. 461

Apterae are very dark brown to almost black, slightly shiny, with antennae mainly dark, and legs mainly brownish yellow but with distal parts of femora, tibial apices and tarsi contrastingly black; BL 2.0-2.8 mm. They feed on *Vicia cracca*, and possibly also sometimes on *Lotus corniculatus*, at stem bases close to ground usually hidden by tall grass or fallen leaves, and can form large colonies, but are easily overlooked. Alatae are without a dorsal abdominal patch and have secondary rhinaria distributed III 12-20, IV 7-17, V 0-3. There is no host alternation, oviparae and apterous males being produced in October in the Netherlands (Hille Ris Lambers, 1953), but not yet recorded in Britain. In England – where it has apparently not been collected since 1949, the only records being from two localities, in Surrey and Lincolnshire, given by Stroyan (1950, under the name *obscurata*) - and countries of northern and central Europe.

Figure 461. Aptera and alata of *Rhopalosiphoninus heikinheimoi*.

Rhopalosiphoninus latysiphon (Davidson, 1912) **Bulb-and-Potato Aphid**
Figs 457, 462

Apterae are shiny dark olive green with very striking swollen shiny black siphuculi; BL 1.4-2.5 mm. Alatae have a shiny olive-green to black dorsal abdominal patch and other markings. It lives on bulbs (*Tulipa*, *Gladiolus*) and potato tubers in store, and on roots of a variety of plants, especially in clay soils (e.g. potato crops), or on etiolated stems or runners growing in darkness under stones (e.g. *Bromus sterilis*, *Convolvulus arvensis*, *Potentilla anserina*, *Vinca major*, *Urtica* spp.). This species reproduces all the year round by parthenogenesis, surviving cold winters on stored bulbs and potatoes. Sexual morphs have not been recorded, apart from one alate male trapped in Scotland (BMNH collection, 11.xi.1975). In England, Scotland, Wales, and almost cosmopolitan (but strangely there are no published records from Ireland).

Figure 462. Aptera and alata of *Rhopalosiphoninus latysiphon*.

Rhopalosiphoninus ribesinus (van der Goot, 1912) **Currant Stem Aphid**
Figs 459, 463

Apterae are shining reddish brown to brownish black, with black siphunculi; BL 2.2-3.0 mm. They feed on old canes or on young shoots and leaves of redcurrant, *Ribes rubrum*, and sometimes on blackcurrant, *R. nigrum*, the colonies always being close to the ground in rather damp and shady places. Alatae have no black dorsal abdominal patch and their secondary rhinaria are distributed III 40-60, IV 6-16, V 0-1. There is no host alternation; the small apterous males (BL 1.6-1.8 mm), and oviparae (BL 2.4-2.7 mm) with hardly swollen hind tibiae bearing only a few scent glands on the basal halves, are produced in October, and large numbers of eggs are laid on old canes. It seems to be a rare species; the few samples in the BMNH collection include sexual morphs collected in the north of England on *R. nigrum* (18.x.1935, leg. J.P. Rogerson). In England, Scotland, northern Europe and west Siberia.

Figure 463. Aptera, alata and male of *Rhopalosiphoninus ribesinus.*

Rhopalosiphoninus (Myzosiphon) staphyleae (Koch, 1854) Figs 39b, 464

Apterae are dark olive green or brownish with very dark green or black dorsal markings, the siphunculi having their swollen part paler than the base or apex; BL 1.5-2.4 mm. Alatae have an extensive dark green to black sclerotic dorsal patch. **R. staphyleae s. str.** lives on the subterranean parts of Liliaceae and Iridaceae (*Tulipa, Hemerocallis, Crocus, Anthericum*), and occasionally on roots or etiolated parts of plants in at least 11 other plant families (e.g. *Anemone, Capsella, Cardamine, Dentaria, Lamium, Oxalis, Vinca*). It occurs throughout the British Isles. In continental Europe it has host alternation, with a sexual phase on *Staphylea* (Hille Ris Lambers, 1953), but this has not been recorded fom Britain or in other parts of the world to which it has been introduced (Africa, Australia, New Zealand, North and South America). Presumably overwintering in Britain is mainly in the parthenogenetic phase, but alate males appear in October, and have been reared in culture from specimens collected in London on *Oxalis* (BMNH, 29.x.1968, leg. H.L.G.Stroyan). These males are much smaller than those described by Hille Ris Lambers (1953) from the Netherlands (BL 1.3-1.6 mm compared with 2.1 mm) and have fewer rhinaria (III 14-23, IV 7-15, V 5-10 as opposed to III 28-40, IV 16-23, V 6-12), so there is some doubt about their identity. **R. staphyleae ssp. tulipaellus** (Theobald, 1916), the **Mangold Aphid**, is particularly a pest of stored mangold beets (*Beta vulgaris*), but is also recorded from roots of a wide range of other plant genera including *Galium, Lycopersicon, Rumex, Tulipa*, and *Viola*. This form was described from England, and is apparently widely distributed in continental Europe. However, although treated as a separate species by some authors including Heie (1994), the morphological discrimination from *staphyleae*, particularly in the case of alatae, is not at all clear, and there are details of the life cycles of the two forms that need to be clarified. Like *staphyleae*, *tulipaellus* probably overwinters in Britain mostly in the parthenogenetic phase, on stored beets for example, but Müller (1959) reared apterous males from a sample collected on *Lamium* in northern Germany and identified as *tulipaellus*, along with oviparae with unthickened hind tibiae that laid infertile eggs. In the BMNH collection there is other evidence of a sexual phase occurring without migration to *Staphylea*; four oviparae collected on *Oxalis acetosella* in Czech Republic, 8.ix.1960 (leg. D. Hille Ris Lambers), and one beaten from grass and *Achillea* in England, 16.xi.78 (leg. H.L.G.Stroyan). These oviparae are very different from those obtained by Müller (1959), being much smaller than viviparae and having swollen hind tibiae with numerous scent glands. They are also very different from the oviparae produced by *staphyleae* on *Staphylea*, which have much less swollen siphunculi. Some apterae collected along with the Czech oviparae were however morphologically closer to *staphyleae* than to *tulipaellus*. Further investigation is need to clarify life cycles and relationships within this group.

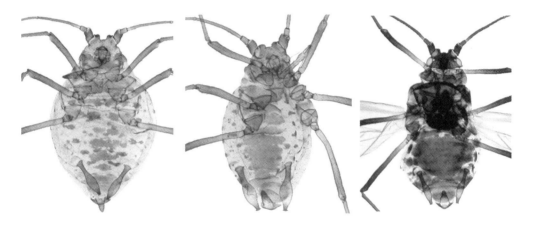

Fgure 464. Aptera of *Rhopalosiphoninus staphyleae* s. str. (left), and aptera and alata of *R. staphyleae* ssp. *tulipaellus*.

Semiaphis van der Goot, 1913

Lightly wax-powdered, greenish, oval aphids, usually with dark brown head, legs, siphunculi and cauda. The cuticle of the head is smooth, with antennal tubercles undeveloped, so that the outline of the front of the head is almost straight. The antennae are usually 6-segmented, sometimes 5-segmented, much shorter than body, with PT more than twice as long as base of last segment. Antennae of apterae lack secondary rhinaria, those of alatae have them on III-IV or III-V. The dorsal body hairs are short and blunt. First tarsal segments have 3-3-3 or 3-3-2 hairs. The dorsal cuticle of apterae is rather smooth, with abdomen membranous except for dusky/dark tranverse sclerites on ABD TERG 7 and 8. Alatae also have the dorsal abdomen mainly membranous with small marginal sclerites, and dorsal cross-bands only on posterior tergites. The siphunculi are very small cylinders, sometimes curved outwards, flangeless, and much shorter than the cauda. The cauda is tongue-shaped or elongate triangular, as long as the siphunculi or longer, with 5-7 hairs.

There are 14 species in the world, all palaearctic. Some have host alternation between *Lonicera* and Umbelliferae (showing their affinity to *Hyadaphis*), others live without host alternation on one of these host groups. Two species have moved onto *Impatiens*. They are not visited by ants. There are 2 species recorded in Britain, but both of them have only been found once. Both species live without host alternation on Umbelliferae.

Key to apterous and alate viviparae of British *Semiaphis*

- HT I with 3 hairs like the fore and mid tarsi (but this may be a peculiarity of the only recorded British (clonal?) population, as individuals from continental European populations can have HT I with either 2 or 3 hairs). Longest hair on ABD TERG 8 is 8-25 μm (mostly 12-20 μm). Genital plate with 13-20 (mostly 14-17) hairs on posterior margin. ANT PT 1.7-2.5 times longer than base of ANT VI in apterae, and 2.4-3.4 times longer than base of ANT VI in alatae .... ***dauci*** (Fabricius, 1775)

- HT almost always with 2 hairs, rarely 3. Longest hair on ABD TERG 8 is 15-47 μm (mostly 18-30 μm). Genital plate with 7-20 (but mostly 11-13) hairs on posterior margin. ANT PT (1.8-) 2.2-3.2 times longer than base of ANT VI in apterae, and 3.1-4.4 times longer than base of ANT VI in alatae .... ***pimpinellae*** (Kaltenbach, 1843)

Semiaphis dauci (Fabricius, 1775) Figs 60a, 465

Apterae are pale blue-green with dark brown head and waxy bloom; BL 1.3-2.1 mm. They live all-year-round on wild and cultivated carrot, *Daucus carota*, in spring feeding on upper sides of young leaves and leaflets which become rolled and curled. In summer they may be found in the umbels. It is also recorded from *Aegopodium podagraria* and *Scandix pecten-veneris*. Alatae have a green abdomen with dark cross-bands only on the posterior tergites, and secondary rhinaria distributed III 16-24, IV 1-7, V 0-3. Overwintering in Britain seems to be in the parthenogenetic phase although small alate males (BL 0.9-1.3 mm) have been reared in culture (Prior, 1971). In southern England (one record from Soar Mill Cove near Salcombe, Devon), continental Europe, Middle East and Central Asia.

Figure 465. Aptera, alata and male of *Semiaphis dauci*.

Semiaphis pimpinellae (Kaltenbach, 1843) Figs 60b, 466

Apterae are dull green mottled with darker green, coated with greyish wax powder; BL 1.4-1.8 mm. They live on burnet-saxifrage, *Pimpinella saxifraga*, causing leaves to curl upwards, and later in season they feed in umbels. There is also a Swedish record from *Aegopodium podagraria*. Alatae have a green abdomen with long dark bands across ABD TERG 7 and 8, and secondary rhinaria distributed III 16-59, IV 2-12, V 0-4. In England it has only been recorded once, from Fulford Ings, Yorkshire in 1948 (Stroyan, 1955). In north, central and eastern Europe.

Figure 466. Aptera and alata of *Semiaphis pimpinellae*.

Sitobion Mordvilko, 1914

Medium-sized to rather large broadly spindle-shaped or oval aphids. The head has rather low, smooth, divergent antennal tubercles like *Metopolophium*, but the median tubercle is less well developed, so that the outline of the front of the head is concave in dorsal view. The antennae of apterae are slightly shorter or longer than body, usually with 1-4 small rhinaria on segment III near base (more in subgenus *Metobion*). Alatae usually have secondary rhinaria only on segment III, in some species on IV or IV-V also, but they are never very numerous. Males have them on III-V. Antennal and dorsal body hairs are short and blunt; those on the antennae are almost always less than half the width of the base of ANT III, and often much shorter. This is a useful distinguishing feature from most *Macrosiphum*, which slide-mounted *Sitobion* often superficially resemble. The rostrum is short, with R IV+V often short, blunt and rounded at base. First tarsal segments all have 3 hairs. The dorsal cuticle of apterae is smooth, sclerotic, and often with ill-defined dark pigmentation and dark intersegmental markings, but in some species there is a very well-defined black sclerotic pattern. Alatae have dorsal abdominal markings varying between species, sometimes including dark transverse markings but usually not much more developed than in apterae. The siphunculi are broad-based, tapering, usually dark, with a subapical zone of polygonal reticulation which is often rather extensive, and a small but distinct flange. The cauda is pale or dusky, finger-shaped, often with a midway constriction.

There are about 65 species in the world, many of them in Asia and Africa. They are about equally distributed between dicots and monocots (especially grasses and orchids). Some host-alternate between a dicotyledonous primary host (such as *Rosa*, *Rubus* and *Akebia*) and grasses. Subgenus *Metobion* is a boreal group of five species mainly living on grasses. *Sitobion* are not visited by ants.

There are only five species in Britain, including one member of subgenus *Metobion*.

Key to apterous viviparae of British *Sitobion*

1. ANT III with 8-17 rhinaria. R IV+V very short and stubby, with only 2 accessory hairs. Siphunculi pale, only dark at apices where there are only 3-4 rows of imperfectly formed polygonal reticulation (see Fig. 34) .... ***scoticum*** (Stroyan, 1969)

- ANT III with 0-6 rhinaria, mostly 1-4. R IV+V with 4-6 accessory hairs. Siphunculi pale or dark, distinctly reticulated over distal 0.1-0.3 of length 2

2. Dorsal abdomen with a rather distinctly defined central dark, more-or-less ovoid patch (see Fig. 470). ANT III 1.0-1.1 times longer than ANT IV. R IV+V a little longer than HT II .... ***luteum*** (Buckton, 1876)

- Dorsal abdomen pale or with variable rather vaguely-defined dark sclerotisation. ANT III at least 1.2 times longer than IV. R IV+V shorter than HT II 3

3. Siphunculi 1.7-2.7 times longer than cauda which is rounded at apex (see Fig. 469c) .... ***fragariae*** (Walker, 1848)

- Siphunculi 1.1-1.4 times longer than cauda which tapers distally to a more pointed apex 4

4. Siphunculi dark, almost black .... ***avenae*** (Fabricius, 1775)

- Siphunculi pale or dusky .... ***alopecuri*** (Takahashi, 1921)

Key to alate viviparae of British *Sitobion*

1. Hind femora dark only at apices. Dorsal abdomen with only pale to dusky markings. R IV+V very short and stubby, with only 2 accessory hairs. ANT III with 19-36 rather protruberant rhinaria .... ***scoticum***

- Hind femora dark over about distal half of length. Dorsal abdomen with at least the pleural intersegmental sclerites quite dark. R IV+V with 4-6 accessory hairs. ANT III with 4-23 rhinaria 2

2. ANT III 0.9-1.1 times longer than ANT IV. R IV+V a little longer than HT II .... ***luteum***

- ANT III at least 1.2 times longer than ANT IV. R IV+V shorter than HT II 3

3. Siphunculi 1.8-2.8 times longer than cauda, with reticulation on distal 0.15-0.26 of length .... ***fragariae***

- Siphunculi 1.1-1.8 times longer than cauda, with reticulation on distal 0.27-0.45 of length 4

4. Siphunculi entirely black .... ***avenae***

- Siphunculi pale or dusky, or pale basally becoming dark towards apices .... ***alopecuri***

Key to alate males of British *Sitobion*

1. Hind femora dark only at apices. Dorsal abdomen with only marginal and intersegmental sclerites. R IV+V very short and stubby, with only 2 accessory hairs .... ***scoticum***

- Hind femora dark over about distal half of length. Dorsal abdomen usually with short spinopleural cross-bands as well as the marginal and intersegmental sclerites. R IV+V with 4-6 accessory hairs 2

2. Siphunculi 2.7-3.4 times longer than cauda .... ***fragariae***

- Siphunculi 1.4-2.0 times longer than cauda 3

3. Siphunculi black, 1.4-1.7 times longer than cauda. ANT III with 43-74 rhinaria .... ***avenae***

- Siphunculi dusky, 1.7-2.0 times longer than cauda. ANT III with 32-47 rhinaria .... ***alopecuri***

Sitobion alopecuri (Takahashi, 1921) Fig. 467

Apterae are mid apple-green with pale to dusky siphunculi; BL 1.8-2.7 mm. Alatae have 4-16 secondary rhinaria on ANT III. *S. alopecuri* lives all-year-round on water foxtail, *Alopecurus geniculatus*; this is the only known British host, but elsewhere it has been recorded from other grass species growing in sandy habitats. Oviparae and alate males (with secondary rhinaria distributed III 32-47, IV 10-22, V 6-13, VI base 0-1) are produced in October. In England (Stroyan, 1991), Scotland (trap records), the Netherlands, North America, northern India, and originally described from Taiwan.

Figure 467. Aptera, alata and male of *Sitobion alopecuri*.

Sitobion avenae (Fabricius, 1775) **Grain Aphid** Fig. 468

Apterae are yellowish green or dirty reddish brown, sometimes rather shiny, with black antennae and siphunculi; BL 1.3-3.3 mm. They are found on numerous species of grasses, including all the cereals and pasture grasses of temperate climates, and many other monocots. Certain dicots may also occasionally be colonised, e.g. shepherd's purse, *Capsella bursa-pastoris* (Wood-Baker, 1972), and corn spurrey, *Spergula arvensis* (Hille Ris Lambers, 1939a). On cereals the aphids prefer to feed on the upper leaves, and on the ears once these have emerged. Alatae have a pattern of dark intersegmental and marginal sclerites, and 4-20 rhinaria on ANT III. Populations in southern England mostly overwinter parthenogenetically, but Newton & Dixon (1988) found that more than 90% of the clones that they studied from Scotland produced sexual morphs in autumn, as do populations in continental Europe. Oviparae, with hind tibiae markedly swollen and with numerous scent glands on basal half , and alate males (with secondary rhinaria distributed III 43-74, IV 0-29, V 6-14) are produced in October, and eggs are laid on numerous grass species (Müller, 1977). DNA studies in southern England and France have revealed host specialisation, including races preferentially colonising wheat and *Dactylis glomerata*, the latter form apparently hybridising naturally with *S. fragariae* (reviewed in van Emden & Harrington, 2007). In England, Scotland, Shetland, Wales, Isle of Man, Ireland, throughout Europe and most of Asia except the Far East, and in Africa and the Americas.

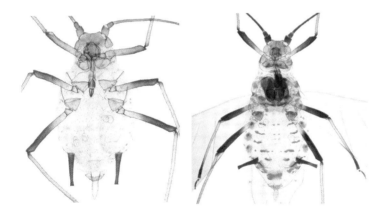

Figure 468. Aptera and alata of *Sitobion avenae*.

Sitobion fragariae (Walker, 1848) **Blackberry-Cereal Aphid** Fig. 469

Apterae on *Rubus* in spring are yellowish green with small brown intersegmental markings, with siphunculi either entirely dark or pale with darker apices; BL 2.0-3.3 mm. After two generations alatae are produced which migrate to grasses, where the apterae produced are dirty greenish yellow - sometimes becoming quite dark and shiny in the central of the dorsum - with black antennae and siphunculi; BL 1.6-3.1 mm. Alatae have a pattern of dorsal dark intersegmental markings that is usually more extensive than in *S. avenae* (especially those produced on grasses in early summer), and 6-23 rhinaria on ANT III. The return migration to *Rubus* occurs in late September to November. Oviparae are rather small (BL c.1.9 mm) and plump, usually pale yellow, with hind tibiae markedly swollen and bearing numerous scent glands. Males are larger (BL c. 2.4 mm), dirty green with dark dorsal markings, and secondary rhinaria distributed III 32-62, IV 5-19, V 8-18. Although the principal primary hosts are *Rubus*, especially *R. fruticosus*, the sexual phase may also sometimes occur on *Fragaria*, *Rosa* or *Geum*. In England, Scotland, Wales, Ireland, throughout Europe and Asia except the Far East, and introduced to South Africa, and the Americas.

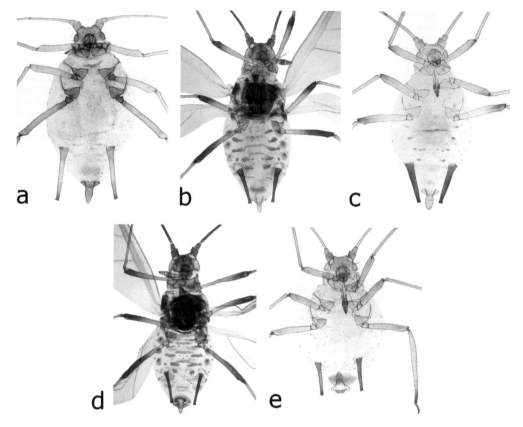

Figure 469. Various morphs of *Sitobion fragariae;* (a) aptera on *Rubus*, (b) spring migrant alata, (c) aptera on grass, (d) male, (e) ovipara on *Rubu*s.

Sitobion luteum (Buckton, 1876) **Yellow Orchid Aphid** Fig. 470

Apterae are bright greenish yellow to pale yellowish green, with an oval black dorsal abdominal patch, antennae black except for base of III, black siphunculi and a pale cauda; BL 1.3-2.1 mm. Alatae lack the central black patch having only dark intersegmental and marginal sclerites, and have 10-19 rhinaria on ANT III. *S. luteum* feeds on many species of orchids (*Dendrobium*, *Epidendrum*, etc.), and in temperate climates it is usually found only in glasshouses. It reproduces entirely by parthenogenesis, no sexual morphs having been recorded anywhere in the world. Distributed throughout the world, but all British records are from England.

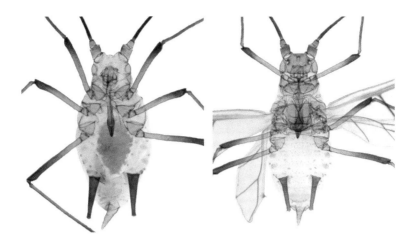

Figure 470. Aptera and alata of *Sitobion luteum.*

Sitobion (*Metobion*) *scoticum* (Stroyan, 1969) Figs 34, 471

Apterae are dull apple-green with dark antennae and pale brownish siphunculi; BL 2.3-3.0 mm. Alatae are green with a dark brown head, thoracic lobes, antennae and siphunculi. *S. scoticum* lives all-year-round on *Poa trivialis*, feeding on uppersides of leaves and hidden in inflorescences, in a marshy habitat. Oviparae with only slightly swollen hind tibiae having scent glands distributed over their entire length, and smaller alate males (BL 1.7-2.0 mm) with secondary rhinaria distributed III 36-44, IV 0-2, V 7-11, were produced in laboratory cultures in September (Stroyan, 1969b). This species is still only known from the original collection, at Loch an Eilein, Inverness-shire, Scotland.

Figure 471. Aptera, alata and male of *Sitobion scoticum.*

Staegeriella Hille Ris Lambers, 1947

Greyish-green oval aphids with rather short appendages, superficially resembling *Hydaphias* and sharing the same host plants, but differing markedly in biology and easily distinguished by the shape of the siphunculi and absence of rhinaria from ANT III of apterae. The cuticle of the head is smooth, with very low divergent antennal tubercles, so that the outline of the front of the head is convex or slightly sinuate in dorsal view. The antennae are 5- or 6-segmented, much shorter than the body, with PT about twice as long as base of last segment. Apterae lack secondary rhinaria, alatae have them on ANT III or III-IV. The dorsal body hairs are extremely short. First tarsal segments usually all have only 2 hairs. The dorsal cuticle of apterae is membranous except for dusky tranverse sclerites on ABD TERG 7 and 8. Alatae also have dorsal abdomen mainly membranous with pale marginal sclerites, and dorsal cross-bands only on posterior tergites. Marginal tubercles are absent. Spiracular apertures are broadly reniform. The siphunculi are short, broad-based, tapering or slightly swollen, with a distinct flange. The cauda is tongue- or finger-shaped, with 5-7 hairs.

Staegeriella necopinata (Börner, 1939) Figs 95, 472

There are 2 species in the world, one of which, *Staegeriella necopinata*, occurs in Britain. It lives without host alternation on bedstraws, *Galium* spp., (all the British records being from *G. verum*), colonising the stems and flowerheads and causing stunting and twisting of new growth. It may possibly also occur on *Asperula*, although there are no British records of this as a host. Colonies are not visited by ants. Apterae are greyish green to lead-coloured, with head darker, and dusky-dark siphunculi and cauda; BL 1.3-2.2 mm. Alatae have secondary rhinaria distributed III 10-19, IV 0-5. Oviparae and alate males occur in October in Switzerland (Hille Ris Lambers, 1947b), but the single British ovipara in the BMNH collection was found in mid-July. *S. necopinata* is recorded from England, Scotland and Wales, and throughout Europe.

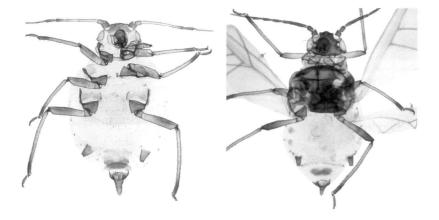

Figure 472. Aptera and alata of *Staegeriella necopinata*.

Staticobium Mordvilko, 1914

Medium-sized broadly spindle-shaped aphids, similar to *Macrosiphoniella*, but with adaptations, such as the protected spiracles, for living in saltmarsh habitats. The head is smooth with broadly divergent antennal tubercles, and a low median tubercle. Antennae are 6-segmented, with a long PT. Apterae and alatae both have only a few secondary rhinaria on basal part of ANT III. Males have secondary rhinaria on segments III-V. Dorsal body and antennal hairs are rather short and blunt or slightly expanded apically. First tarsal segments have 3-3-3 hairs. The dorsum is smooth and membranous except for small dark scleroites at the hair bases. Spiracular apertures are covered by cowl-like opercula. The siphunculi are tapering, with coarse spiculose imbrication on the basal part and an extensive zone of distal reticulation below a small flange. The cauda is long and finger-shaped, with relatively few hairs.

There are about 12 species in the world, of holarctic distribution, all living without host alternation on Plumbaginaceae. Most seem to be highly host-specific, although the taxonomy is difficult and some of the names may be synonyms. They are not visited by ants.

Staticobium staticis (Theobald, 1923) Figs 13, 473

Nominally there is one species in Britain, *Staticobium staticis*, which colonises the upper parts of the stem and inflorescences of the sea-lavenders, *Limonium humile* and *L. vulgare*. Foster (1984) in a four-year study found heavy infestations on these two plant species at a site in Norfolk, but only rare, small colonies on *L. binervosum*, and only a single aphid on *L. bellidifolum*. Apterae are shiny, deep green or brown or dirty greenish or reddish; BL 2.3-2.7 mm. They can survive on plants that are often temporarily submerged by high tides, becoming encrusted with mud. Alatae have 1-6 rhinaria on basal half of ANT III. Sexual morphs were found in North Wales (Anglesey) in early September (Jacob 1948, as *S. limonii*). The Welsh oviparae were pale reddish and had hind tibiae moderately swollen on basal half with 17-55 scent glands, and the apterous males were small (BL 1.6-2.0 mm), and dark green, with secondary rhinaria distributed III 17-35, IV 7-17, V 3-9. Two oviparae collected by Walker at Fleetwood in October have longer hind tibiae more strongly swollen on basal half with 64-69 scent glands (Doncaster, 1961, as *S. limonii*), and sexuales described by Müller (1975a, as *S. limonii*) from northern Germany also differed from the Welsh aphids in several respects. There seems to be significant geographical variation within this species in several characters, e.g. lengths of PT and siphunculi, perhaps because populations are distributed linearly along coasts or isolated in salt marshes. In coastal areas of England, Scotland, Wales, Ireland, and northern Europe.

Figure 473. Aptera, alata and male of *Staticobium staticis*.

Subacyrthosiphon Hille Ris Lambers, 1947

Medium-sized, pale, broadly oval aphids with characters intermediate between *Acyrthosiphon* and *Aulacorthum*, the long appendages seeming strangely ill-adapted to its cryptic habitat. The head has well-developed antennal tubercles, with inner faces steep-sided and distinctly scabrous, and the median tubercle is undeveloped. Antennae of apterae have 2-9 secondary rhinaria on segment III near base, and alatae also have only a few secondary rhinaria (2-14), usually restricted to basal half of segment III; males have them on III-V. Hairs on the dorsal body and antennae are short and blunt. First tarsal segments have 3-3-3 hairs. Apterae have a wrinkled or somewhat reticulate dorsal cuticle, and dark antesiphuncular and postsiphuncular sclerites; alatae have abdomen pale except for dusky/dark marginal sclerites, and larger ante- and postsiphuncular sclerites. Spiracular apertures are small and partially covered by dark opercula. Siphunculi are long, broad-based, cylindrical, dark distally with a few transverse striae below a distinct flange. The cauda is tongue-shaped to triangular, with 6-8 hairs, the apical ones being shorter and having spear-shaped apices.

Subacyrthosiphon cryptobium Hille Ris Lambers 1947 Fig. 474

There is only one species, *Subacyrthosiphon cryptobium*, which lives cryptically without host alternation on older parts of prostrate stems of white clover, *Trifolium repens*. Apterae are pale olive-green with the head sometimes slightly reddish, and the bases and apices of the antennae as well as the tips of the siphunculi are black; BL 1.6-2.3 mm. The aphids drop when disturbed, so they are rarely observed or collected. They are not visited by ants. Oviparae, with basal part only slightly swollen with a few rather large scent glands, and small apterous males (BL 1.2-1.6 mm) are produced in September-October. There are records from England, Scotland, northern Europe, and USA.

Figure 474. Aptera and alata of *Subacyrthosiphon cryptobium.*

Trichosiphonaphis Takahashi, 1922

Trichosiphonaphis is a mainly East Asian genus of *Myzus*-like species with hairs on the siphunculi, typically host alternating between *Lonicera* and *Polygonum*. The head is spiculose both dorsally and ventrally, with variably developed antennal tubercles. The antennae of apterae lack secondary rhinaria, those of alatae generally have them on III-V. Alatae lack a dorsal abdominal dark patch. The siphunculi are peculiar not only for bearing hairs (in the single species introduced to Britain these are very small and easily overlooked) but in the structure of the apex; there is no reflexed flange and the apical pore is much reduced in size, although it may be surrounded by a swollen rim. The cauda is short and usually bears more than 7 hairs. Remaudière *et al.* (1992) provided a review of the genus and key to species.

Trichosiphonaphis polygonifoliae (Shinji, 1944) Figs 43, 475

The single species in Britain, *Trichosiphonaphis polygonifoliae*, which was introduced to Europe in about 1990, has host alternation between *Lonicera* and Polygonaceae (*Polygonum*, *Persicaria*) although only the spring populations on *Lonicera tatarica* have so far been located in Britain (Martin, 2000). Fundatrices were found on woody stems in early April in south London, developing colonies of plump-bodied greenish brown to brownish black apterae (BL 1.8-3.0 mm), vigorously attended by the ant *Lasius niger*. Small emigrant alatae (BL 1.6-1.9 mm, with secondary rhinaria distributed III 12-32, IV 0-14, V 0-2) were produced in June. Return migrant alatae trapped in France in September to November are larger (BL 2.1-2.5 mm) and have much more numerous strongly protruberant secondary rhinaria crowded on ANT III-IV (III c.80-100, IV 40-63, V 0-9), and males have III c.100-120, IV c.40-60, V 3-9 (Remaudière *et al.*, 1992). Oviparae with strongly swollen hind tibia bearing numerous scent glands have subsequently been found, again on *L. tatarica*, in Hungary in late October (BMNH collection, leg. G . Remaudière).

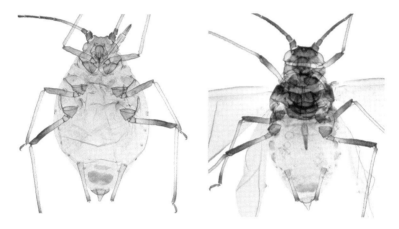

Figure 475. Aptera and alata of *Trichosiphonaphis polygonifoliae*.

Tubaphis Hille Ris Lambers, 1947

Small pale broadly spindle-shaped aphids. The cuticle of the head is spinulose, and has fairly well-developed antennal tubercles that are rather widely separated and have scabrous, steep-sided inner faces which may converge slightly at their apices. Antennae are 6-segmented, as long as body or longer, with an unusually thin basal part to the last segment. Antennae of apterae lack secondary rhinaria, those of alatae have numerous secondary rhinaria distributed over the whole surface of segment III, but only a few (or none) on IV and V. Hairs on the dorsal body and antennae are very short and blunt. First tarsal segments have 3-3-3 hairs. The dorsal cuticle of apterae is markedly wrinkled. Spiracular apertures are broadly reniform. Siphunculi are cylindrical, thin but broad-based, coarsely imbricated, with a constriction below a distinct apical flange. The cauda is short, tongue-shaped, constricted at base, with a slightly swollen basal part and thinner distal part, and 4 hairs.

Tubaphis ranunculina (Walker, 1852) Figs 52, 476

There are 2 species in the world, both living without host alternation on Ranunculaceae. They are not visited by ants. One widely distributed species, *Tubaphis ranunculina*, is found in Britain. Apterae are yellowish, with pale appendages; BL 1.2-1.9 mm. They are found on the undersides of leaves of buttercups (*Ranunculus acris, R. repens*). Alatae have a yellowish green abdomen with dusky, rather ill-defined marginal sclerites and thin transverse cross-bands, and secondary rhinaria distributed III 23-48, IV 0-10, V 0-6. Oviparae (BL 1.2-1.7 mm), with hind tibiae moderately swollen and bearing c.30-50 scent glands, and alate males (BL c.1.5 mm), with secondary rhinaria distributed III 42-48, IV 12-14, V 2-8, VI base 0-1, are produced in October. In England, Scotland, Wales, Ireland, continental Europe, and across Asia to Japan.

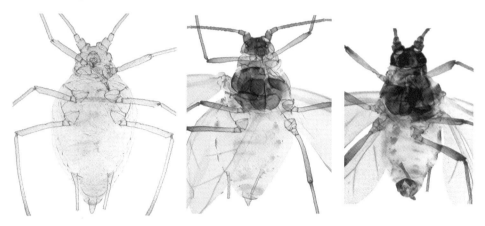

Figure 476. Aptera and alata of *Tubaphis ranunculina*.

Uroleucon Mordvilko, 1914

Most European species of *Uroleucon* are rather large shiny red, brown or bronze-coloured, black-eyed, broadly oval to spindle-shaped aphids with black siphunculi. The head is smooth with well-developed, divergent antennal tubercles, and the median tubercle is undeveloped. Antennae are 6-segmented, similar in length to body, with secondary rhinaria, often numerous, on segment III in both apterae and alatae. Males have secondary rhinaria on segments III-V. The PT is often very long, rarely less than 4 times longer than base of segment VI. Antennal hairs are rather long and often have slightly expanded apices. R IV+V is variable in length and number of accessory hairs, but always with blunt apex. First tarsal segments usually have 5-5-5 hairs, but a few species have 3-3-3. Dorsal body hairs are often quite long, and usually placed on dark scleroites. In addition to these scleroites both apterae and alatae usually have large dark postsiphuncular sclerites, but antesiphuncular sclerites are often absent and only ever developed in association with the postsiphuncular ones. The siphunculi are dark or mainly dark, cylindrical or tapering, varying in length, but in most species they are rather long, much longer than the cauda, with polygonal reticulation on distal 0.1-0.4 of length, comprising numerous small closed polygonal cells. There is usually a small apical lip or flange. The cauda is long, sometimes very long, finger-shaped, usually with a pointed apex, and may be pale or dark.

There are about 180 species in the world, almost all living without host alternation on Compositae (particularly Cichoreae and Cynareae) or Campanulaceae, and usually found colonising the upper parts of the flower stalks. They are not visited by ants. Most show host specificity at least at the level of plant genus, and there are some taxonomically difficult species complexes, especially among European species around *cichorii* and *jaceae*, where the evidence of species distinction is more biological than morphological, depending largely on field and experimental observations of differential colonisation of particular plants, and requiring additional confirmation. Native European species can be placed in the two subgenera, *Uroleucon* and *Uromelan*, but the subgeneric classification on a world scale is less certain.

There are 24 species in Britain, including 10 species of subgenus *Uromelan* and one introduced species of the nearctic subgenus *Lambersius*. (One species on the British list, *U. pilosellae*, should be removed as the record is based on two trapped alatae of uncertain identity; see under *pilosellae* below).

Key to apterous viviparae of British *Uroleucon*

The key includes one additional species, *U. rapunculoides*, likely to occur in Britain but not yet recorded. *U. pilosellae* is also included as likely to occur, although its presence needs confirmation.

1. Siphunculi pale basally (Fig. 477). ANT I and II pale ....
.... ***erigeronense*** (Thomas, 1878)

- Siphunculi entirely black, or at least black basally and distally, although sometimes with middle section paler. ANT I and II dark
.... 2

477

2. Cauda pale or dusky, much paler than siphunculi (subgen. *Uroleucon*) 3

- Cauda as dark as, or almost as dark as, siphunculi (subgen. *Uromelan*) 15

3. Scleroites at bases of dorsal hairs absent or indistinct, where present pale and not much larger than hair-bases 4

- Dorsal hairs all or almost all arising from dark scleroites, much larger than and sometimes fused between hair-bases, forming rows of dark spots (see Fig. 6a) 5

4. Coxae and apices of femora pale or dusky (see Fig. 504). Siphunculi 2.1-2.6 times longer than cauda, with reticulation on distal 0.11-0.15 of length. ANT PT 5.7-9.3 times longer than base of ANT VI. Cauda with 12-25 hairs .... ***tussilaginis*** (Walker, 1850)

- Coxae and apices of femora dark (see Fig. 501). Siphunculi 1.4-1.9 times longer than cauda, with reticulation on distal 0.16-0.27 of length. ANT PT 4.1-5.6 times longer than base of ANT VI. Cauda with 18-35 hairs .... ***sonchi*** (Linnaeus, 1767)

5. Crescent-shaped antesiphuncular sclerites present (see Fig. 6a) 6

- Antesiphuncular sclerites absent or vestigeal 12

6. Spinal hairs on ABD TERG 2-4 in groups of 2-4, but usually 3, arising from separate or fused scleroites, on each side of midline (Fig. 478, below). ABD TERG 8 with 6-10 hairs .... ***cirsii*** (Linnaeus, 1758)

- ABD TERG 2-4 usually with only 1-2 spinal hairs on each side of midline. ABD TERG 8 with 4-5, rarely 6, hairs 7

7. R IV+V long and slender, 1.32-1.85 times longer than HT II (measure several specimens) 8

- R IV+V 0.84-1.35 times longer than HT II 9

8. Hind coxae dusky to dark, like distal parts of femora. R IV+V 1.32-1.57 times longer than HT II, with 8-15 accessory hairs. Small marginal tubercles, mostly smaller than hair-bases, irregularly present on marginal sclerites of ABD TERG 2-4, rarely on 5. ANT PT 5.1-6.7 times longer than base of ANT VI ... ***leontodontis*** (Hille Ris Lambers, 1939)

- Hind coxae much paler than distal parts of femora. R IV+V 1.45-1.85 times longer than HT II, with 8-9 hairs. Well-developed marginal tubercles, often larger than hair-bases, usually present on marginal sclerites of ABD TERG 2-4, and on antesiphuncular sclerites (Fig. 479). ANT PT 4.4-5.8 (-6.3) times longer than base of ANT VI (often less than 5.0 in British populations) .... ***picridis*** (Fabricius, 1775)

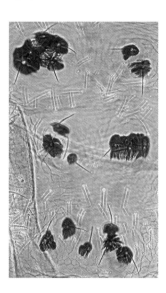 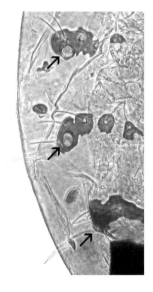

478

479

9. R IV+V 0.84-1.08 of length of (rarely longer than) HT II ....
.... ***hypochoeridis*** (Hille Ris Lambers, 1939)

- R IV +V 1.04-1.35 times longer than HT I 10

10. Siphunculi 1.6-1.9 times longer than cauda, with reticulation over distal 0.33-0.40 of length. Cauda with 12-18 hairs. First tarsal segments almost always with 3 hairs .... *pilosellae* (Börner, 1933)

- Siphunculi 1.0-1.7 times longer than cauda, with reticulation over distal 0.16-0.33 of length. Cauda with 16-33 hairs. First tarsal segments with 5 hairs 11

11. ANT PT 3.8-5.3 (-6.2) times longer than base of ANT VI. ANT III with 13-54 rhinaria. Siphunculi 1.0-1.4 times cauda. Hind coxae pale or dark. BL usually less than 3 mm .... *obscurum* (Koch, 1855)

- ANT PT 5.4-8.4 times longer than base of ANT VI. ANT III with 26-97 rhinaria. Siphunculi 1.1-1.7 times cauda. Hind coxae dark. BL usually more than 3 mm .... *cichorii* (Koch, 1855) or *grossum* (Hille Ris Lambers, 1939) (see text)

12. R IV+V 0.75-0.95 of length of HT II. Siphunculi 1.4-2.0 times longer than cauda. Dorsal hairs shorter than diameters of scleroites on which they are based .... *murale* (Buckton, 1876)

- R IV+V 1.0-1.6 times longer than HT II. Siphunculi 1.9-2.8 times longer than cauda. Dorsal hairs longer than diameters of scleroites on which they are based (e.g. Fig. 480) 13

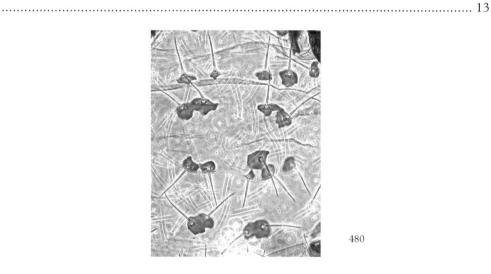

480

13. ANT III with 35-66 rhinaria. Cauda with (8-)11-18 hairs. Siphunculi with reticulation restricted to distal 0.12-0.17 of length .... *jaceicola* (Hille Ris Lambers, 1939)

- ANT III with 7-26 rhinaria. Cauda with 5-9 hairs. Siphunculi with reticulation over distal 0.17-0.30 of length 14

14. Distal parts of femora and bases of tibiae black (Fig. 485). R IV+V 1.27-1.50 times longer than HT II. Siphunculi uniformly dark .... *achilleae* (Koch, 1855)

- Femora entirely pale or only slightly dusky towards apices, and tibiae black only at apices (Fig. 502). R IV+V 1.02-1.15 times longer than HT II. Siphunculi usually with middle section paler .... *tanaceti* (Linnaeus, 1758)

15. Siphunculi 0.7-1.2 times longer than cauda. R IV+V 0.8-1.1 times longer than HT II and bearing 4-5 accessory hairs. First tarsal segments all with 3 hairs .... *campanulae* (Kaltenbach, 1843)

- Siphunculi 1.3-2.6 times longer than cauda. R IV+V 1.0-1.8 times longer than HT II and bearing 4-12 accessory hairs. First tarsal segments with 3 or 5 hairs 16

16. Siphunculi 2.2-2.6 times longer than cauda which bears 8-12 hairs. R IV+V 1.0-1.2 times longer than HT II. First tarsal segments usually all with 3 hairs .... *taraxaci* (Kaltenbach, 1843)

- Siphunculi 1.2-2.2 times longer than cauda which bears 7-33 hairs. R IV+V 1.1-1.8 times longer than HT II. First tarsal segments with 5 hairs 17

17. ANT III 1.6-2.4 times longer than ANT IV, with secondary rhinaria extending over 0.64-0.95 of its length. R IV+V 1.4-1.8 times longer than HT II 18

- ANT III 1.1-1.6 times longer than ANT IV, with secondary rhinaria extending over 0.36-0.80 of its length. R IV+V 1.1-1.6 times longer than HT II 20

18. ANT III with 55-122 rhinaria .... *nigrocampanulae* (Theobald, 1928)

- ANT III with 25-52 rhinaria 19

19. Cauda with 7-12 hairs. Siphunculi 2.0-2.2 times longer than cauda and reticulated on at least distal 0.28-0.33 of length ....*helenae* (Hille Ris Lambers, 1950)

- Cauda with 14-24 hairs. Siphunculi 1.5-1.8 times longer than cauda and reticulated on distal 0.19-0.29 of length .... *rapunculoides* (Börner, 1939)

20. Tibiae wholly black, or with middle part only slightly paler. Cauda with 22-33 hairs 21

- Tibiae pale on middle part with black bases and apices. Cauda with 11-24 hairs 22

21. R IV+V 0.23-0.26 mm long. ABD TERG 2-4 with tubercles on marginal sclerites often larger than adjacent hair bases (Fig. 481). Tibiae usually slightly paler on middle part. Hind tibia without a row of distinctly peg-like hairs on inner side .... *aeneum* (Hille Ris Lambers, 1939) (part)

- R IV+V 0.17-0.225 mm long. ABD TERG 2-4 with marginal tubercles if present not larger than adjacent hair bases (Fig. 482). Tibiae usually entirely black. Hind tibia with a row of very short and thick peg-like hairs on inner side (Fig. 483) .... *jaceae* (Linnaeus, 1758)

481   482   483

22. Primary rhinarium on ANT V enlarged and protuberant, 25-40 μm long (Fig. 484, two views). ANT III-V pale/dusky except for dark apices of segments and rhinariated section of III .... *solidaginis* (Fabricius, 1779)

- Primary rhinarium on ANT V not distinctly enlarged or protrusive, 16-27 μm long. ANT III-VI entirely dark, except for base of III 23

484

23. ANT III with 38-62 rhinaria extending over 0.66-0.80 of length. R IV+V with 10-12 accessory hairs .... *simile* (Hille Ris Lambers, 1935)

- ANT III with 13-35 rhinaria extending over 0.36-0.61 of length. R IV+V with 7-9 accessory hairs 24

24. R IV+V 0.23-0.26 mm long. ABD TERG 2-4 with tubercles on marginal sclerites often larger than adjacent hair bases (Fig. 481) ..... *aeneum* (Hille Ris Lambers, 1939) (part)

- R IV+V 0.15-0.20 mm long, ABD TERG 2-4 with or without marginal tubercles but these are rarely larger than hair bases 25

25. HT II 0.14-0.18 mm long, 0.86-1.05 of length of base of ANT VI .... *riparium* (Stroyan, 1955)

- HT II 0.11-0.14 mm long, 0.72-0.84 of length of base of ANT VI ... *minor* (Börner, 1940)

Key to alate viviparae of British *Uroleucon*

One additional species, *U. rapunculoides*, not yet recorded from Britain, is included. *U. pilosellae* is also included, although the British specimens under that name lack the antesiphuncular sclerites that are a distinctive feature of this species in continental Europe).

1. Siphunculi pale basally. ANT I and II pale or dusky .... ***erigeronense***

   - Siphunculi entirely dark, or sometimes dark basally and distally with middle section paler. ANT I and II dark 2

2. Cauda pale or dusky, much paler than siphunculi (subgen. *Uroleucon*) 3

   - Cauda dark like siphunculi (subgen. *Uromelan*) 15

3. Spinal hairs on ABD TERG 2-4 in groups of 2-4, usually 3, arising from separate or fused scleroites, on each side of midline. ABD TERG 8 with 6-10 hairs. Cauda dusky with 20-30 hairs (Fig. 487) .... ***cirsii***

   - ABD TERG 2-4 with only 1-2 spinal hairs on each side of midline. ABD TERG 8 with 4-5, rarely 6, hairs. Cauda pale with 7-32 hairs 4

4. Siphunculi 2.3-3.3 times longer than cauda 5

   - Siphunculi 1.3-2.2 times longer than cauda 8

5. Scleroites at bases of dorsal hairs absent or very indistinct. ANT III with 11-23 rhinaria. .... ***tussilaginis***

   - Scleroites at bases of dorsal hairs distinct. ANT III with 26-69 rhinaria 6

6. Tibiae entirely pale or dusky except at apices (Fig. 502). Siphunculi often with middle section paler. R IV+V 1.0-1.2 times longer than HT II .... ***tanaceti***

   - Tibiae black at bases ('knees') as well as at apices (e.g. Fig. 485). Siphunculi uniformly dark. R IV+V 1.25-1.5 times longer than HT II 7

7. Crescent-shaped antesiphuncular sclerites present (Fig. 485). Siphunculi rather thick, less than 0.3 of BL, with reticulation over distal 0.24-0.32 of length .... ***achilleae***

   - Antesiphuncular sclerites absent or incomplete. Siphunculi long and thin, more than 0.3 of BL, with reticulation over distal 0.14-0.19 of length .... ***jaceicola***

8. R IV+V shorter than or similar in length to HT II 9

- R IV+V distinctly (1.05-1.65 times) longer than HT II 11

9. Siphunculi rather thick, 1.4-1.8 times longer than cauda. Crescent-shaped antesiphuncular sclerites present .... *hypochoeridis*

- Siphunculi long and thin, 1.9-2.2 times longer than cauda. Antesiphuncular sclerites absent or incomplete 10

10. ANT IV usually with 1-8 rhinaria, and ANT III with 29-47 .... *murale*

- ANT IV always without rhinaria, ANT III with (42-)48-65 .... *sonchi*

11. Siphunculi reticulated over distal 0.33-0.49 of length. First tarsal segments with 3 hairs .... *pilosellae*

- Siphunculi reticulated over distal 0.20-0.30 of length. First tarsal segments with 5 hairs 12

12. Siphunculi 1.0-1.4 times longer than cauda. ANT PT 4.3-5.3 times longer than base of ANT VI .... *obscurum*

- Siphunculi 1.2-1.9 times longer than cauda, but if less than 1.5 times longer than cauda then ANT PT is more than 5.7 times longer than base of ANT VI 13

13. ANT PT 4.7-5.8 times longer than base of ANT VI. Well-developed marginal tubercles, often larger than hair-bases, usually present on marginal sclerites of ABD TERG 2-4, and on 5, on the antesiphuncular sclerites. R IV+V very long and slender, 1.45-1.65 times longer than HT II, at least 4 times its basal width .... *picridis*

- ANT PT 5.8-8.4 times longer than base of ANT VI. Small marginal tubercles, mostly smaller than hair-bases, irregularly present on marginal sclerites of ABD TERG 2-4, more rarely on V. R IV+V 1.05-1.57 times longer than HT II, usually less than 4 times longer than its basal width 14

14. R IV+V 1.3-1.6 times longer than HT II .... *leontodontis*

- R IV+V 1.05-1.4 times longer than HT II .... *cichorii* or *grossum* (see text)

15. Siphunculi 1.0-1.3 times longer than cauda. R IV+V 0.8-1.2 times longer than HT II and bearing 4(-5) accessory hairs. First tarsal segments all with 3 hairs ..... *campanulae*

- Siphunculi 1.5-3.1 times longer than cauda. R IV+V 1.0-1.6 times longer than HT II and bearing 4-9 accessory hairs. First tarsal segments with 3 or 5 hairs 16

16. Siphunculi 2.4-3.1 times longer than cauda which bears 7-10 hairs. R IV+V 1.0-1.2 times longer than HT II. First tarsal segments usually all with 3 hairs .... **taraxaci**

- Siphunculi 1.5-2.35 times longer than cauda which bears 7-28 hairs. R IV+V 1.1-1.6 times longer than HT II. First tarsal segments with 5 hairs 17

17. ANT III 1.57-2.15 times longer than ANT IV 18

- ANT III 1.10-1.55 times longer than ANT IV 20

18. Cauda with 6-9 hairs . ANT III with 68-83 rhinaria. Siphunculi reticulated over 0.33-0.42 of length .... **helenae**

- Cauda with 15-26 hairs. ANT III with 43-137 rhinaria. Siphunculi reticulated over 0.20-0.25 of length 19

19. ANT III with 75-137 rhinaria, and IV occasionally with 1-10 .... **nigrocampanulae**

- ANT III with 43-69 rhinaria, IV with 0 .... **rapunculoides**

20. Siphunculi 1.5-1.7 times longer than cauda. R IV+V with 9-12 accessory hairs ....
.... **simile**

- Siphunculi 1.8-2.35 times longer than cauda. R IV+V with 7-9 accessory hairs 21

21. Primary rhinarium on ANT V elongate, 25-40 μm long (as in Fig. 484). Cauda with 12-14 hairs .... **solidaginis**

- Primary rhinarium on ANT V not elongate, 16-27 μm long. Cauda with 14-28 hairs ...
.... 22

22. ANT III with 33-40 rhinaria (based on 1 specimen) .... **riparium**

- ANT III with 41-90 rhinaria 23

23. R IV+V 0.22-0.26 mm long. ABD TERG 2-4 with tubercles on marginal sclerites often larger than adjacent hair bases. Hind tibia without a row of distinctly shorter and thicker peg-like hairs on inner side .... **aeneum**

- R IV+V 0.15-0.21 mm long. ABD TERG 2-4 with marginal tubercles if present rarely larger than adjacent hair bases. Hind tibia with a row of short thick peg-like hairs on inner side (as in Fig. 483) 24

24. Hind tibia with paler middle section. R IV+V 0.15-0.17 mm .... *minor*

-   Hind tibia entirely dark. R IV+V 0.17-0.21 mm .... *jaceae*

Key to alate males of British *Uroleucon*

(This is a tentative key based in some cases on very few specimens. Males of *helenae* and *minor* are apparently unknown.)

1. Siphunculi paler at base .... *erigeronense*

-   Siphunculi dark at base, and usually entirely black, sometimes black basally and distally with middle section paler 2

2. Cauda pale or dusky, paler than siphunculi (subgen. *Uroleucon*) 3

-   Cauda dark like siphunculi (subgen. *Uromelan*) 11

3. Tibiae entirely pale or dusky except at apices .... *tanaceti*

-   Tibiae black at bases ('knees') as well as at apices 4

4. R IV+V not longer than HT II .... *hypochoeridis*

-   R IV+V distinctly (1.05-1.65 times) longer than HT II 5

5. Spinal hairs on ABD TERG 2-4 in groups of 2-4, often 3, arising usually from fused scleroites, on each side of midline. ABD TERG 8 with 6-8 hairs. Cauda dusky ...... *cirsii*

-   ABD TERG 2-4 with only 1-2 spinal hairs on each side of midline, usually on separate scleroites. ABD TERG 8 with 4-5 hairs. Cauda pale 6

6. Cauda elongate triangular, tapering almost to a point (Fig. 485) .... *achilleae*

-   Cauda tongue-shaped with rounded apex 7

7. ANT III less than 1.4 times longer than ANT IV, and bearing 36-60 rhinaria 8

-   ANT III more than 1.4 times longer than ANT IV, and bearing 46-73 rhinaria 9

8. Coxae dark. R IV+V 1.3-1.5 times longer than HT II, 4 or more times longer than its basal width .... *leontodontis*

- Coxae pale or dusky, like trochanters. R IV+V 1.05-1.3 times longer than HT II, less than 4 times longer than its basal width .... *obscurum*

9. Coxae pale or dusky. Well-developed marginal tubercles, often larger than hair-bases, usually present on marginal sclerites of ABD TERG 2-4, and on 5, on antesiphuncular sclerites . ANT PT 4.6-5.8 times longer than base of ANT VI. R IV+V 1.45-1.65 times longer than HT II .... *picridis*

- Coxae black. Small marginal tubercles, mostly smaller than hair-bases, irregularly present on marginal sclerites of ABD TERG 2-4, more rarely on 5. ANT PT 5.8-8.4 times longer than base of ANT VI. R IV+V 1.05-1.4 times longer than HT II 10

10. Secondary rhinaria distributed ANT III 56-73, IV 4-19, V 2-16 .... *grossum*

- Secondary rhinaria distributed ANT III 47-55, IV 4-10, V 5-11 .... *cichorii*

11. Siphunculi 0.95-1.30 times longer than cauda. First tarsal segments with 3 hairs .... *campanulae*

- Siphunculi 1.7-2.7 times longer than cauda. First tarsal segments with 5 hairs 12

12. ANT III with 61-95 rhinaria. ABD TERG 2-4 with tubercles on marginal sclerites regularly present and often much larger than adjacent hair bases 13

- ANT III with 31-57 rhinaria. ABD TERG 2-4 with marginal tubercles absent or sporadically present but mostly not larger than adjacent hair bases 14

13. ANT IV with 2-12 rhinaria, and ANT V with 2-8. R IV+V 1.5-1.6 times longer than HT II .... *nigrocampanulae*

- ANT IV with 12-16 rhinaria, and ANT V with 10-13. R IV+V 1.2-1.5 times longer than HT II .... *aeneum*

14. Primary rhinarium on ANT V enlarged, elongate, 25-36 μm long .... *solidaginis*

- Primary rhinarium on ANT V normal, rounded, 16-22 μm long 15

15. Secondary rhinaria distributed ANT III 31-53, IV 10-19, V 10-20 .... *riparium*

- Secondary rhinaria distributed ANT III 48-56, IV 4-14, V 6-14 .... *jaceae*

Uroleucon achilleae (Koch, 1855) Figs 480, 485

Apterae are vivid red or brownish red with rows of black dorsal spots, yellow and black-banded legs, black siphunculi and a yellow cauda; BL 2.2-2.6 mm. They feed on the undersides of the lower leaves of yarrow, *Achillea millefolium*. Large colonies may be formed that cause the leaves to wither and turn brown, at which stage the whole colony develops into alatae. Sometimes they form mixed colonies with *Macrosiphoniella sejuncta* and/or *M. usquertensis*. Oviparae, with hind tibiae swollen with numerous scent glands on basal two-thirds, and alate males with secondary rhinaria distributed ANT III c.35-36, IV 8-14, V 5-9, are found in October (but some males may be produced as early as August). An account of the biology, life cycle and morphology of *U. achilleae* in Germany is given by Sobhani (1970). In England, Scotland, Wales, Ireland, continental Europe, and introduced to USA (California, Oregon).

Figure 485. Aptera, alata and male of *Uroleucon achilleae*.

Uroleucon (*Uromelan*) *aeneum* (Hille Ris Lambers, 1939) Fig. 481

Apterae are large shiny metallic bronze-black aphids with dorsal rows of black spots, antennae, siphunculi and cauda black, legs mainly black except that tibiae are brownish in middle and femora yellowish basally; BL 3.0-4.3 mm. They feed on the upper parts of the stems of thistles, mainly on *Carduus* spp. (*acanthoides, crispus, nutans*) where very larger colonies may be formed, but they can sometimes occur on *Cirsium* spp. (*arvense, palustre*), *Onopordon acanthium* or *Silybum marianum*. Alatae are produced mainly in the third generation (Hille Ris Lambers, 1939a). Oviparae and alate males (with secondary rhinaria distributed 61-95, IV 12-16, V 10-13) appear from mid-September in the Netherlands (Hille Ris Lambers, 1939a), but are not yet reported in Britain. In England, Wales, throughout Europe, and across Asia. *U. aeneum* is very similar in appearance to *U. jaceae*, and was originally described as a subspecies.

Uroleucon (*Uromelan*) *campanulae* (Kaltenbach, 1843) Figs 1u, 486

Apterae are shiny reddish brown to black, with black antennae, siphunculi and cauda, and legs bicoloured yellow and black; BL 2.1-3.7 mm. They colonise the upper parts of the stems and the flowers of Campanulaceae (bellflowers, *Campanula* spp., most commonly *C. rotundifolia*, and sheep's bit. *Jasione montana*). Specimens from *Jasione* have longer siphunculi than those from *Campanula*; siphunculi are 1.01-1.14 times cauda in apterae from *Jasione*, but 0.72-0.98 times cauda in apterae from *Campanula*, and R IV+V is also longer relative to HT II in *Jasione*-feeding aphids (Heie, 1995, and V.F.Eastop, unpublished data). This suggests that there may be two distinct species. Hille Ris Lambers (1939a) also observed that the form on *Jasione* usually had little success in colonising *Campanula* spp. Oviparae with markedly swollen dark hind tibiae bearing numerous scent glands are produced in September, while the rather small alate males (BL 1.8-2.2 mm, with secondary rhinaria distributed III 45-60, IV 8-18, V 8-15) are recorded from July to September. In England, Scotland, Wales, continental Europe, Transcaucasus and Central Asia.

Figure 486. Aptera, alata and male of *Uroleucon campanulae*.

Uroleucon cichorii (Koch, 1855)

Apterae are shining metallic brown with black antennae and siphunculi, legs with femora yellow on basal halves and black distally, tibiae entirely dark (cf. *grossum*), and a pale yellow cauda; BL 2.7-4.7 mm. They live on the upper parts of the stems of chicory, *Cichorium intybus*. *U. cichorii* is also recorded from several related composite genera (e.g. *Crepis*, *Hieracium*, *Hypochaeris*, *Lactuca*, *Lapsana*, *Leontodon*). Oviparae and alate males (with secondary rhinaria distributed III 45-65, IV 4-10, V 5-11) occur in September. The exact host range of *U. cichorii* is uncertain because it is a member of a group of closely related species in Europe with different host associations. Some of these are host specialists clearly functioning as distinct species, although difficult to distinguish morphologically (*U. grossum* feeding specifically on *Crepis*, *U. hypochoeridis* on *Hypochaeris*, and *U. leontodontis* specialising on *Leontodon*). Much further work is needed on the stability of host associations and taxonomic relationships within this group, and the host specificity of *Cichorium*-feeding populations in particular is not clearly established, nor is it supported by consistent morphological differences. *U. cichorii* is therefore perhaps best regarded as a less host-specific taxon potentially capable of living on plants in several genera, including the hosts of more specialised members of the group. It is also likely that some records of *U. cichorii* are misidentified *U. picridis* (and vice versa). In England, Ireland, continental Europe and Asia.

Uroleucon cirsii (Linnaeus, 1758) Figs 6a, 478, 487

Apterae are bronze brown, with dark head and prothorax, rows of black dorsal abdominal spots, antennae black beyond the base of III, yellow- and black-banded legs, black siphunculi and a yellow cauda; BL 3.2-5.2 mm. They feed on *Cirsium* spp., forming colonies on upper parts of stems and upper leaves. Alatae are produced mainly in the third generation. Oviparae and alate males (dark green as both immatures and adults, with secondary rhinaria distributed III 45-65, IV 9-14, V 11-18) appear in late September-October, and eggs are laid on the undersides of the radical leaves (Hille Ris Lambers, 1939a). In England, Scotland, Wales, Ireland, very common throughout Europe, and introduced to North America.

Figure 487. Aptera, alata and male of *Uroleucon cirsii*.

Uroleucon (*Lambersius*) *erigeronense* (Thomas, 1878) Figs 477, 488

Apterae are yellowish green with a darker spinal stripe, or uniformly pale green, the siphunculi dark distally with pale bases, the antennae and legs also dark distally and pale basally; BL 2.3-2.8 mm. They live on the upper parts of the stems of Canadian fleabane, *Conyza canadensis*; this seems to be its only host in Europe, although in South America populations have been found on plants in several other composite genera including *Aster*, *Baccharis*, *Haplopappus*, *Heterotheca*, *Grindelia* and *Lactuca*. Alatae are produced in large numbers from early summer to autumn. Oviparae, with hind tibiae darkened and swollen on basal half, and small alate males (BL 1.5-2.0 mm, with secondary rhinaria distributed III 33-53, IV 5-21, V 7-11) occur from mid-September to October. *U. erigeronense* like its host is of North American origin, introduced to Central and South America, and (in the 1970's) to Europe, and now also in Asia (Kazakhstan, Korea). In Britain a single alata was trapped in 1973 in Berkshire, but the first colonies were not found until 1982, in London (Martin, 2000), and it has still not been collected outside of south-east England.

Figure 488. Aptera, alata and male of *Uroleucon erigeronensis*.

Uroleucon grossum (Hille Ris Lambers, 1939) Fig. 489

Apterae are shining metallic brown with black antennae and siphunculi, legs with femora yellow on basal halves and black distally, tibiae dark but with much of the basal half generally yellow-brown rather than black (cf . *cichorii*), and a yellow cauda; BL 2.8-4.9 mm. They are found on the upper parts of stems of hawk's-beards, *Crepis* spp., most commonly *C. biennis*. Oviparae and alate males (with secondary rhinaria distributed III 56-73, IV 4-19, V 2-16) occur from the end of August (Heie, 1995). Further work is needed to confirm its distinction from *U. cichorii*, which is still based mainly on the field observations of the host association with *Crepis* by Hille Ris Lambers (1939a). In England, Scotland, Wales, continental Europe, and Asia.

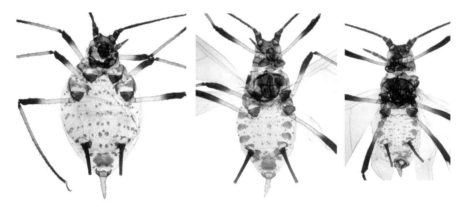

Figure 489. Aptera and alata of *Uroleucon grossum*, and male of *U. leontodontis.*

Uroleucon (Uromelan) helenae (Hille Ris Lambers, 1950) Fig. 490

Apterae are shining black with a bronze tinge, with black antennae and siphunculi, legs mainly brownish yellow with distal thirds of femora, apices of tibiae and tarsi black, and a dark brown cauda; BL 1.6-2.6 mm. They live in large, rather diffuse colonies on the stems of carline thistle, *Carlina vulgaris* (Stroyan, 1957b). Oviparae (small, with only slightly swollen hind tibiae bearing few scent glands) have been reared in culture in late September (BMNH collection, leg. H.L.G.Stroyan), but males are unknown. In England and Wales (coastal sites in Devon, Glamorgan, Gwynedd and Denbighshire), and several countries of continental Europe (Croatia, Czech Republic, France, Italy, Switzerland).

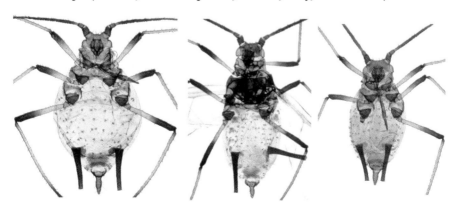

Figure 490. Aptera, alata and ovipara of *Uroleucon helenae.*

Uroleucon hypochoeridis (Hille Ris Lambers, 1939) Fig. 491

Apterae are brown or reddish brown with black antennae and siphunculi, longitudinal rows of black spots on dorsum, legs banded yellow and black, and a yellow cauda; BL 2.8-4.4 mm. They feed on the upper parts of the flowerstalks of cat's-ears, *Hypochaeris* spp., and also colonise autumn hawkbit, *Leontodon autumnalis*. There are also records from *Crepis* and *Taraxacum*, but these could be due to confusion with other members of the *U. cichorii* group. Oviparae with dark, swollen hind tibiae and alate males (secondary rhinaria distributed III 63-74, IV 6-10, V c.10) appear in late August to October. In England, Scotland, Wales and Ireland, and widely distributed in Europe, although records may be confused with other similar species, especially *U. cichorii*.

Figure 491. Aptera, alata and male of *Uroleucon hypochoeridis*.

Uroleucon (Uromelan) jaceae (Linnaeus, 1758) Figs 482, 483, 492

Figure 492. Aptera, alata and male of *Uroleucon jaceae*.

Apterae are reddish brown or blackish brown, often shiny, with rows of black spots on dorsal abdomen, and black antennae, legs (except for yellowish-brown basal halves of femora), siphunculi and cauda; BL 2.8-4.7 mm. They form colonies on the upper parts of the stems of knapweeds, *Centaurea* spp. There are records from other composite genera, especially *Cirsium*, and certain Boraginaceae, but at least some of these may be misidentifications. Oviparae with strongly swollen hind tibiae, and alate males with secondary rhinaria distributed III 48-56, IV 4-14, V 6-14, appear in late September. The name is perhaps being applied to a group of closely-related species with more specific host associations. Apterae on *Centaurea nigra* usually have rhinaria confined to the basal half of ANT III, whereas those on other *Centaurea* spp. (e.g. *jacea, cyanus*) have secondary rhinaria extending to 60-80% of the length of the segment. Börner (1950) described populations on *C. scabiosa* as a subspecies, *U. jaceae* ssp. *henrichi*, but his discriminants do not hold for all populations (Heie, 1995). In England, Scotland, Wales, Ireland, continental Europe, Middle East, Central Asia and Pakistan.

Uroleucon jaceicola (Hille Ris Lambers, 1939) Fig. 493

Apterae are dark bronze-brown, with black antennae and siphunculi, legs mainly yellow with "knees", tibial apices and tarsi black, and a yellow cauda; BL 2.9-3.3 mm. They colonise the stems of common knapweed, *Centaurea nigra*, occurring low on the stem in spring and later on the upper parts. Oviparae and small dark apterous males have been found on the petioles of radical leaves in October (Hille Ris Lambers, 1939a and J.H. Martin, pers. comm). In England, Scotland, Wales, Channel Isles, continental Europe, and Central Asia.

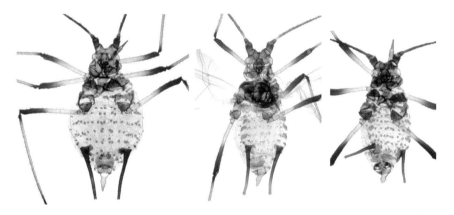

Figure 493. Aptera, alata and male of *Uroleucon jaceicola*

Uroleucon leontodontis (Hille Ris Lambers, 1939) Fig. 489

Apterae are shining brown with black antennae and siphunculi, legs mainly black except for basal parts of femora, and a yellow cauda; BL 3.2-4.3 mm. They feed on hawkbits, *Leontodon* spp. Oviparae and alate males (Fig. 489) occur in September and October. Described as a subspecies of *U. cichorii*, this aphid has a long narrow R IV+V similar to that of *U. picridis*, and is easily confused with that species, but has less well-developed marginal abdominal tubercles and a relatively longer PT. In England, Scotland, Wales, and continental Europe.

Uroleucon (*Uromelan*) *minor* (Börner, 1940)

Apterae are brown with longitudinal rows of black dorsal spots, legs yellow banded with black, antennae, siphunculi and cauda black; BL 2.6-4.5 mm. They live on saw-wort, *Serratula tinctoria*. Small numbers were found at the Usk Reservoir, Powys (South Wales) on various dates between 1976 and 1986 (Stroyan, 1991); these are the only British records and, as noted by Stroyan, some of the differences from *U. jaceae* could be host plant-related, although there do seem to be consistent host-related differences in the pigmentation of the tibiae of both apterous and alate morphs. Sexual morphs have not been recorded. In Wales and several countries of continental Europe.

Uroleucon murale (Buckton, 1876) Fig. 494

Apterae are reddish brown with black siphunculi, mainly yellow-brown legs and a yellow cauda; BL 2.1-3.2 mm. They are found on the upper parts of the stems and in the inflorescences of wall lettuce, *Mycelis muralis*. Elsewhere in Europe there are records from *Lactuca quercina* and *Crepis* spp. Oviparae and small apterous males (BL 1.7-2.0 mm) occur in October-November. One specimen in the BMNH collection contains an internal cecidomyid parasitoid (?*Endaphis* sp.). In England, Wales, and continental Europe, eastward to Poland and Ukraine.

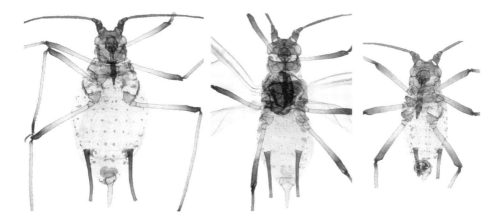

Figure 494. Aptera, alata and male of *Uroleucon murale*.

Uroleucon (Uromelan) nigrocampanulae (Theobald, 1928) Fig. 495

Apterae are dark brown with black antennae, siphunculi and cauda, and bicoloured yellowish brown/black legs; BL 2.7-4.0 mm. They live on bellflowers, *Campanula* spp., (*glomerata*, *latifolia*, *persicifolia*, *rapunculoides*, *trachelium* - but not harebells, *rotundifolia*), feeding on the leaves and causing them to become curled in spring, and later spotted with yellow. Oviparae and alate males (BL 2.3-2.8 mm, with secondary rhinaria distributed III 74-87, IV 2-5, V 2-8) occur in late September to October. It is very similar to the host-specific *U. rapunculoides*, but easily recognisable by the very large numbers of secondary rhinaria in both apterae and alatae. In England, Scotland, continental Europe, and Asia.

Figure 495. Aptera, alata and male of *Uroleucon nigrocampanulae*.

Uroleucon obscurum (Koch, 1855) Fig. 496

Apterae are reddish brown to bronze with black antennae and siphunculi, legs black except for yellow basal parts of femora and yellowish brown basal halves of tibiae, and a yellow cauda; BL 1.8-2.9 (-3.7) mm. They feed on the upper parts of the stems of hawkweeds, *Hieracium* spp., especially *H. laevigatum*. Oviparae with black hind tibiae swollen and bearing very numerous scent glands, and alate males (BL 1.6-2.4 mm, with secondary rhinaria distributed III 36-55, IV 7-14, V 7-14) occur in September. There was early confusion with *U. picridis*, and records of *picridis* from *Hieracium* are probably all or mostly referable to this, typically much smaller species. In England, Wales, continental Europe, and Central Asia.

Figure 496. Aptera, alata and male of *Uroleucon obscurum*.

Uroleucon picridis (Fabricius, 1775) Figs. 479, 497

Apterae are dark shiny reddish brown to almost black, with black antennae and siphunculi, legs brown-black except that basal halves of femora are yellow, cauda yellow; BL 2.6-3.7 mm. They feed on ox-tongues, *Picris* spp., usually *P. hieracioides*, forming colonies on the stems just below the flowers. There are records from other composite genera, but a lot of these are probably misidentifications of other *Uroleucon* species. Sexuales are produced in October; oviparae have hind tibiae entirely black and only slightly swollen, but with numerous scent glands, and alate males have secondary rhinaria distributed III 50-68, IV 6-12, V 6-13. Eggs are laid on the undersides of the radical leaves (Hille Ris Lambers, 1939a). In southern England (Beds, Bucks, Sussex), continental Europe, and across Asia.

Figure 497. Aptera, alata and male of *Uroleucon picridis*.

Uroleucon pilosellae (Börner, 1933)

Apterae are dark reddish brown with black siphunculi, brown-black antennae, yellow- and black-banded legs and a yellow cauda; BL 2.2-2.5 mm. They feed on the flower stems of mouse-ear hawkweed, *Hieracium pilosella*, and its close relative *H. aurantiacum*. The British record is based on five trapped alatae (Stroyan, 1950), of which two trapped in Lincolnshire in 1944 are in the BMNH collection; but on re-examination these are unlikely to be *pilosellae*, as they lack the well-developed antesiphuncular sclerites of this species, and are of indeterminate identity. The sexual morphs are undescribed; the male is reportedly alate (Hille Ris Lambers, 1939a, citing Börner). This species occurs throughout continental Europe.

Uroleucon (Uromelan) rapunculoides (Börner, 1939)

Apterae are shiny dark brown with black antennae, siphunculi, yellow- and black-banded legs and a black cauda; BL 3.0-3.9 mm. It feeds specifically on the stems and flowers of *Campanula rapunculoides* but has not yet been recorded from Britain. Oviparae were found in October in the Netherlands (Hille Ris Lambers, 1939a). Although very similar to *U. nigrocampanulae*, the differences are consistent enough to indicate its separate existence as a host-specific taxon. In continental Europe, Middle East and Central Asia.

Uroleucon (Uromelan) riparium (Stroyan, 1955) Fig. 498

Apterae are dark bronze-brown with black antennae, siphunculi, cauda, apices of femora and tibiae, and tarsi; BL 2.9-4.1 mm. They live in small colonies on the flower stems of marsh hawk's-beard, *Crepis paludosa*. In Finland this species has been recorded from *C. tectorum*, and also from *Taraxacum* (Heie, 1995, citing Heikinheimo). Oviparae with darkened and moderately swollen hind tibiae, and alate males with secondary rhinaria distributed III 31-53, IV 10-19, V 10-20, occur from late July to September. In Scotland, Sweden and Finland.

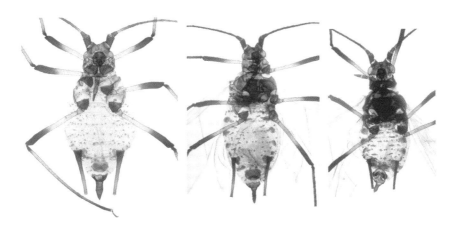

Figure 498. Aptera, alata and male of *Uroleucon riparium*.

Uroleucon (Uromelan) simile (Hille Ris Lambers, 1935) Fig. 499

Apterae are shining reddish brown, with black antennae, siphunculi and cauda, and legs yellowish brown with apices of segments black; BL 2.3-4.1 mm. Colonies form on the flowerstalks of blue fleabane, *Erigeron acer*, apparently the preferred host, although there are records from several other (non-British) *Erigeron* spp., and from *Conyza canadensis*, and it has been noted as a pest of hybrids of *E. speciosum* x *macranthus* grown as ornamentals (Hille Ris Lambers, 1967). Oviparae and small dark brown apterous males were found on *E. acer* in September in the Netherlands, on the undersides of radical leaves (Hille Ris Lambers, 1939a). In England, throughout Europe, and across Asia.

Figure 499. Aptera, alata and ovipara of *Uroleucon simile*.

Uroleucon (*Uromelan*) *solidaginis* (Fabricius, 1781) Figs 484, 500

Apterae are shining reddish brown with black dorsal spots, black antennae, siphunculi and cauda, and legs mainly yellowish brown with darker bands; BL 2.3-4.1 mm. They are found on the upper parts of the stems of goldenrod, *Solidago virgaurea*. Immatures are bright red in colour. Oviparae, with darkened rather strongly swollen hind tibiae bearing very numerous scent glands, may be found in September to October, and alate males with secondary rhinaria distributed III 40-50, IV 9-14, V 7-14, are recorded from mid-July to October. In England, Scotland, Wales, Ireland, continental Europe, Asia, North Africa and North America.

Figure 500. Aptera, alata and male of *Uroleucon solidaginis*.

Uroleucon sonchi (Linnaeus, 1767) Fig. 501

Apterae are shiny dark brown, with antennae mainly dark, legs mainly pale with black apices to femora and tibiae, siphunculi black and cauda yellow; BL 2.9-4.5 mm. They live mainly on stems and among flowerheads of sow-thistles, *Sonchus* spp. and other genera in the tribe Lactuceae (*Lactuca*, *Cichorium*, *Hieracium*, *Picris*), with occasional records from other composite genera including *Chrysanthemum*. Oviparae, with hind tibia swollen and bearing numerous small scent glands on basal halves, together with slender dark brown apterous males (BL 2.0-2.5 mm), may be found on the radical leaves of *Sonchus* in September and October. In England, Wales, Ireland, and almost world-wide.

Figure 501. Aptera, alata and male of *Uroleucon sonchi*.

Uroleucon tanaceti (Linnaeus, 1758) Fig. 502

Apterae are bright red or reddish brown, with yellowish, black-banded antennae and legs, longitudinal rows of black spots on the dorsum, brown-black siphunculi usually paler in middle, and a yellow cauda; BL 2.2-3.4 mm. They feed on tansies, *Tanacetum* spp., primarily on the lower, often yellowing, leaves. Oviparae, with basal halves of hind tibiae pale and only slightly swollen, and alate males (BL about 2.2 mm, with secondary rhinaria distributed III 35-50, IV 4-12, V 5-15, occur in October-November in southern England (BMNH collection, leg. V.F. Eastop). In Finland oviparae have been found on cultivated *Chrysanthemum* (Heie, 1995). In England, Scotland, continental Europe, Central Asia and North America.

Figure 502. Aptera, alata and male of *Uroleucon tanaceti*.

Uroleucon (*Uromelan*) *taraxaci* (Kaltenbach, 1843) Fig. 503

Apterae are shining dark bronze-brown, with black dorsal spots, and black antennae, legs (except femoral bases), siphunculi and cauda; BL 2.5-3.8 mm. They live on dandelions, *Taraxacum* spp., feeding on the undersides and basal parts of the leaves near ground level. Dark reddish brown oviparae with slightly swollen hind tibiae bearing numerous scent glands, and small, slender apterous males (BL about 2 mm), appear in late September. In England, Scotland, Wales, Ireland, continental Europe, Central Asia, and introduced to North America.

Figure 503. Aptera, alata and male of *Uroleucon taraxaci*.

Uroleucon tussilaginis (Walker, 1850) Fig. 504

Apterae are shining brown, their antennae pale basally and dark distally, their siphunculi black at base and apex but with yellowish brown middle section, and cauda yellow; BL 2.4-4.3 mm. They feed on the undersides of the leaves of colt's-foot, *Tussilago farfara*, and butterbur, *Petasites hybridus*. Oviparae with pale swollen hind tibiae bearing numerous scent glands, and slender apterous males (BL 2.7-3.0 mm) occur in September to November. In England, Scotland, Wales, continental Europe and Central Asia.

Figure 504. Aptera, alata and male of *Uroleucon tussilaginis*.

Utamphorophora Knowlton, 1947

Medium-sized, pale, oval grass-feeding aphids. The head has well-developed antennal tubercles, their inner faces steep-sided and scabrous. The median tubercle is not developed. The antennae of apterae are 6-segmented, similar in length to body, with or without a few secondary rhinaria on III, and with a long PT. Alatae have protruberant secondary rhinaria on III or III-IV, and males have them on III-V. Antennal and dorsal body hairs are very short and blunt. R IV+V is rather short and blunt, as in most grass-feeding aphids. First tarsal segments all have 3 hairs. The dorsal cuticle of apterae is somewhat wrinkled. Alatae look very different, with mainly dark legs and antennae and a pattern of dark dorsal markings. Spiracular apertures are broadly reniform. Siphunculi are moderately clavate. The cauda is finger-shaped.

There are 13 species in the world, mostly nearctic, and the primitive life cycle for the genus is probably host alternation between Rosaceae and grasses, as in the mainly palaearctic genus *Metopolophium*. They are not visited by ants.

Utamphorophora humboldti (Essig, 1941) Fig. 505

One species, *Utamphorophora humboldti*, was introduced into Britain in about 1974, and has since been found in all countries of the British Isles. Apterae are apple green with light brown head and siphunculi. They feed along the upper sides of leaf blades, or concealed in the inflorescences, of various grasses; *Dactylis*, *Festuca*, *Poa*, *Lolium*, etc., but the favoured host seems to be *Poa trivialis*. Alatae have much darker pigmentation, the green abdomen having dark marginal sclerites, variably developed intersegmental markings and usually two rows of rather large and dark paired pleural spots as well as a pattern of paler sclerotisation. In North America this species has host alternation to *Physocarpus*, and alate males and oviparae have been produced in culture in England, the latter by transferring alatae reared on *Poa* to *Physocarpus opulifolius* (Stroyan, 1979). However, the introduced population in Britain apparently mainly overwinters parthenogenetically on grasses.

Figure 505. Aptera, alata and male of *Utamphorophora humboldti*.

Vesiculaphis del Guercio, 1911

Rather small, oval or spindle-shaped aphids. The head is spiculose or nodulose, with frontal part developed either as a ledge or as three rounded lobes between the antennal bases (the latter in the case of the single species occurring in Britain). The antennae are short, 5- or 6-segmented in apterae, with PT not much longer than base of last segment; those of apterae lack secondary rhinaria, those of alatae have secondary rhinaria on III-V. Hairs on the dorsal body and appendages (except those on frontal lobes) are very short, and pointed. First tarsal segments have 3-3-2 hairs. The media of the forewing of the alata may be once- or twice-branched. The dorsum of the aptera is sclerotic and rugose or strongly wrinkled. Siphunculi are very thick and scabrous, curved inward at the base and outward at the apex, swollen on distal part and abruptly narrowed at apex, so that the aperture is small, although there is a well-developed flange. ABD TERG 8 often tends to project over the cauda in apterae. Cauda is tongue-shaped, with a constriction between the swollen basal part and narrower distal part, and bears 4-5 hairs.

There are 9 species in the world, predominantly in East Asia, where there is host alternation between Ericaceae (*Rhododendron*, *Pieris*) and Cyperaceae.

Vesiculaphis theobaldi Takahashi, 1930 Figs 1o, 20c, 79a, 80, 506

One species, *Vesiculaphis theobaldi*, is more widely distributed, and occurs in England, Scotland and Ireland. Apterae are yellowish green with red eyes. They live without host alternation on Cyperaceae, mainly in damp places, and are visited by ants. Probably it mainly overwinters parthenogenetically, although oviparae with slightly swollen hind tibiae bearing 25-30 scent glands were reared by Wood-Baker (1958), and oviparae and one alate male (with secondary rhinaria distributed III 25-26, IV 13-15, V 6-7) have subsequently been collected in Yorkshire in October (BMNH collection, leg. R.N.B. Prior).

Figure 506. Aptera, alata and male of *Vesiculaphis theobaldi*.

Wahlgreniella Hille Ris Lambers, 1949

Pale, medium-sized spindle-shaped aphids. The head has well-developed antennal tubercles, with inner faces divergent and smooth or with a few small spicules. The median tubercle is usually undeveloped. Antennae of apterae are as long as or longer than body, and usually have 0-1 secondary rhinaria on III (more in alatiform specimens). Alatae have secondary rhinaria on III, or sometimes III-IV. PT is usually very long. Hairs on dorsal body and antennae are short and blunt. First tarsal segments have 3-3-3 hairs. Dorsal abdomen is membranous in apterae, but alatae have variably developed dark sclerotisation, sometimes coalesced into an irregular, much perforated central patch. Siphunculi are long and distinctly swollen on distal part, like those of *Amphorophora*. The cauda is tongue- or finger-shaped, rather pointed at apex, and usually bears 5 hairs.

There are 6 species in the world, mostly associated with Ericaceae. One species occurs on *Rosa* and possibly has host alternation in North America between *Rosa* and various Ericaceae. They are not visited by ants. There are 3 species in Britain, one of which has two forms with different host associations, presently regarded as subspecies, and probably representing two separate introductions from North America.

Key to apterous viviparae of British *Wahlgreniella*

1. Femora dark at apices. ANT III with 1-4 (exceptionally 0) rhinaria on basal part, which is often somewhat swollen. Dorsal body cuticle dusky. Siphunculi swollen mainly on inner sides, often darker on distal half, and almost smooth, except for a subapical annular incision (Fig. 507). ABD TERG 8 with 5-7 (typically 6) hairs .... ***ossiannilssoni*** Hille Ris Lambers, 1949

507

- Femora not dark at apices, sometimes with a dusky spot. ANT III in true apterae without rhinaria (but alatiform apterae with rhinaria in a row along ANT III occur frequently). Dorsal cuticle pale. Siphunculi swollen more-or-less symmetrically, pale and with moderate imbrication throughout. ABD TERG 8 with 3-6 hairs, typically with 4 hairs ... 2

2. Antennal tubercles with very steep, almost parallel, inner faces, and distinctly scabrous, particularly ventrally (Fig. 508). Siphunculi with flanges well-developed (Fig. 509) .... ***vaccinii*** (Theobald, 1924)

- Antennal tubercles with inner faces divergent and smooth, or at most very finely spinulose ventrally. Siphunculi with small flanges (Fig. 510) 3

508

509

510

3. R IV+V 1.33-1.51 times longer than HT II. Hairs on antennal tubercles are maximally 12-28 μm long, and on ABD TERG 3 are maximally 13-24 μm long .... ***nervata* ssp. *arbuti*** (Davidson, 1910)

- R IV+V (0.91-)1.14-1.27 times longer than HT II. Hairs on antennal tubercles are maximally 8-16 μm long, and on ABD TERG 3 are maximally 8-11 μm long .... ***nervata*** (Gillette, 1908)

Key to alate viviparae of British *Wahlgreniella*

1. Dorsal abdomen with a dusky to dark central sclerite (with large "windows") on ABD TERG 4-5 or 4-6 (Fig. 511). Tibiae mostly very dark, slightly paler in middle .... ***nervata* ssp. *arbuti***

- Dorsal abdomen usually without any central sclerite. Tibiae mainly pale except apically and/or basally 2

2. Abdomen without any distinct dorsal sclerotisation; marginal sclerites if discernible are pale with a small brown central spot .... ***vaccinii***

- Abdomen with variable dorsal sclerotisation; at least with large rather uniformly pigmented marginal sclerites 3

3. Hairs on front of head and antennal tubercles conspicuous, maximally 18-58 μm long. ABD TERG 8 with 5-7 hairs, typically 6 .... ***ossiannilssoni***

- Hairs on front of head and antennal tubercles inconspicuous, maximally 8-15 μm long. ABD TERG 8 usually with 4 hairs .... ***nervata***

Wahlgreniella nervata (Gillette, 1908) Figs 510, 511

Apterae in spring and summer are pale green to dull mid-green, with pale, dark-ringed antennae and pale, dark-tipped siphunculi; BL 1.4-2.5 mm. Alatae are much more pigmented with variably-developed dark dorsal markings and 12-20 rhinaria in a row on ANT III. Alatiform apterae, with rhinaria on ANT III and rather longer siphunculi, occur commonly. Colonies occur on the shoots or mature leaves of wild and cultivated *Rosa*. British populations reproduce parthenogenetically throughout the year on roses, and males are unrecorded, but one ovipara has been obtained in culture (BMNH collection, leg. H.L.G. Stroyan). This rose-feeding form of *W. nervata* was apparently introduced in about 1973 from western North America, where there may be a migration from *Rosa* to Ericaceae (*Arbutus*, *Arctostaphylos*, *Pieris*. This needs further confirmation (see Stroyan, 1979), but is interesting in view of the fact that an Ericaceae-feeding population, regarded by Hille Ris Lambers (1949) as a subspecies and assigned the name ***W. nervata* ssp. *arbuti*** (Davidson, 1910), has been known in Britain and France since the the 1940's. Apterae of this form in spring and summer are shining yellowish green, BL 2.1-2.9 mm, and alatae usually have a much-perforated and irregularly-shaped dorsal abdominal patch. It lives on the undersides of the leaves of Ericaceae (*Arbutus*, *Arctostaphylos*) and occasionally crowberry (*Empetrum nigrum*, Empetraceae), and overwinters parthenogenetically, although again, oviparae have been obtained in culture (BMNH collection, leg. R.N.B. Prior). Overwintering individuals of both forms are more deeply pigmented. The two British populations maintain their specific host associations and morphological differences in the field, and in Europe they clearly function as distinct species, although they can be reared on each other's host plants in the laboratory (Stroyan, 1979). Originating in North America, the rose-feeding form of *W. nervata* now occurs in England, Scotland, Brazil, Africa and Pakistan, and the Ericaceae-feeding form (*arbuti*) is recorded from England, Scotland, Wales, Ireland, France, Madeira, Israel and India.

Figure 511. Aptera and alata of *Wahlgreniella nervata* and (right) alata of *W. nervata* ssp. *arbuti*.

Wahlgreniella ossiannilssoni Hille Ris Lambers, 1949 Figs 507, 512

Apterae in Britain (Scotland) are shining pale yellow, but apterae with much darker pigmentation are recorded from other European countries; BL 1.5-2.3 mm. They feed on the undersides of the leaves and shoots of bearberry, *Arctostaphylos uva-ursi*. Alatae are much more pigmented and have 10-16 rhinaria in a row on ANT III. It has a boreo-alpine distribution (northern Europe, Alps and Pyrenees), and in Britain is only known from Scotland. A single alate male (BL 1.9 mm, secondary rhinaria distributed III 24-27, IV 1-3, V 6-9) has been trapped in Scotland (BMNH collection, leg. J. Cole, 10.ix.1973) and oviparae and eggs were collected on *A. uva-ursi* in Sweden in early November (Hille Ris Lambers, 1949).

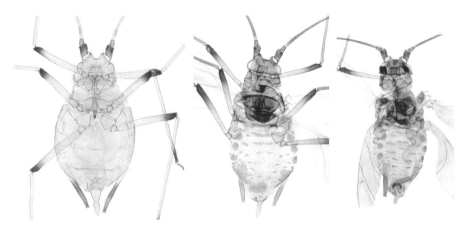

Figure 512. Aptera, alata and male of *Wahlgreniella ossiannilssoni*.

Wahlgreniella vaccinii (Theobald, 1924) Figs 508, 509, 513

Apterae are shining greenish yellow or yellowish green, with antennae ringed with black; BL 1.6-2.3 mm. They feed on the undersides of the leaves of *Vaccinium* spp., usually cowberry (*V. vitis-idaea*). Alatae have much darker appendages and 11-17 rhinaria on ANT III. Small yellow-orange oviparae (BL 1.4-1.7 mm) and apterous males (BL also 1.4-1.7 mm) were found on *V. vitis-idaea* in Yorkshire in October, 1972 (BMNH collection, R.N.B. Prior), and have previously been collected in England (Cheshire) on *V. vitis-idaea* (BMNH collection, leg. H. Britten, 5.x.1948) and on *V. myrtillus* in North Wales (BMNH collection, F.H. Jacob, 22.viii.55). These British records of sexual morphs of *W. vaccinii* seem to have been overlooked, and the apterous male has not previously been recorded in the literature. In northern England, North Wales, Scotland, northern continental Europe, and also in North America.

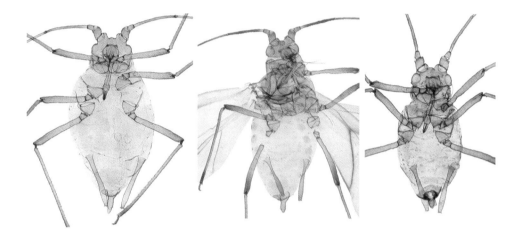

Figure 513. Aptera, ovipara and male of *Wahlgreniella vaccinii*.

Collecting, rearing and studying aphids

Techniques for studying aphids have been detailed in van Emden (1972) and Minks and Harrewijn (1988), so that I shall confine myself here to a few points that I think are the most important for anyone starting work on aphids.

Collecting is simply a matter of careful examination of all parts of plants, not neglecting to look on the undersides of leaves, and in the inflorescences. Aphids colonising the basal parts of plants are often detectable by the presence of attendant ants, or may be covered by earthen shelters built by the ants. Some aphids tend to live on etiolated stems or runners growing in darkness under stones. Some aphids are highly cryptic and may only be revealed by use of a beating tray. Beating may also be the best method of collecting certain aphids that escape by falling off the plant at the least disturbance. Sweeping is not recommended as it is rarely possible to ensure that only one species of plant is being swept at a time, and it is always important to know the identity of the host whenever possible. Field notes should include as much as possible about appearance in life, size of colony, feeding site and identity of the host plant, taking a sample of the plant for identification if necessary. A fine sable hair paint brush for handling aphids and a small pair of secateurs are essential field equipment.

It is a good idea to keep the aphids alive for at least 2-3 days after collection, in a tied polythene bag or a fairly large capped Perspex tube (making sure that no predators are present). Include a piece of the host plant, and a paper tissue to absorb excess moisture. Protect the aphids from overheating in a cool-box or cool-bag in the field or during transport (and remember not to leave this in the car on a hot sunny day while having a pub lunch!). Collecting in this way has several advantages: (1) detailed colour notes of living specimens can be made at leisure; (2) aphids that were 4th instar immatures at the time of collection will reach adulthood, increasing the number of adult specimens for identification, and perhaps rearing adult alatae where there were none before; (3) hymenopterous parasitoids that were present in the colony at the time of collection are given time to emerge, or to form aphid 'mummies' from which they can subsequently be reared.

It is also possible to gain much new information about British aphids by rearing them for a more extended period, either on whole potted plants or on excised leaves or shoots. Cages can be constructed simply from cellulose acetate sheets formed into cylinders to fit inside flowerpots, or by modifying polystyrene food boxes to include a compartment with wet sponge into which the plant stem or leaf petiole can be inserted. Large holes covered with fine mesh nylon or Terylene net are needed to provide adequate ventilation. The most important point about rearing aphids is to keep the numbers under control, by transferring just a few individuals to fresh plant material at frequent intervals. Once a culture is established, two potentially useful and productive lines of investigation are (1) investigating host specificity and host range by means of transfer experiments, and (2) monitoring the response to decreasing daylength and producing sexual morphs.

The host specificity and host range of an aphid species has often been investigated by simply transferring some apterae between plants with a paint brush and observing whether colonisation occurs. This can give misleading results. Probably the biggest problem is that the natural colonisation of new hosts is usually done by alatae after a period of flight, sometimes using sensory equipment and patterns of behaviour not available to apterae. Transfer experiments are therefore best done with alatae, which can often be produced in large numbers by crowding cultures. If this is done in large cages, alatae can have a period of flight activity and then be given a choice between potential host plants. Providing a fresh specimen of the original host together with closely related plants and a more distantly related one, and repeating the experiment several times with the plants in the cage in different positions, counting the progeny produced on each plant after 48 hours, is likely to give the most reliable results. Detailed observations of the behaviour of individual alighting alatae and the time that they spend probing each plant before either settling or take-off can also provide useful additional data.

Cultures of most British species kept under natural conditions of gradually reducing daylength in August and September will produce sexual morphs, as long as the temperature is at or below 15°C. Host-alternating species will first produce a generation of return migrant alate females (gynoparae), and these may be reluctant to produce oviparae unless provided with the primary, woody host. Males tend to be produced later in the reproductive life of their mothers, after several days' production of exclusively female progeny, so in order to ensure male production it will be necessary to make sure that at least some apterous viviparae remain alive and reproducing for about 1-2 weeks after they become adult. Immature males can usually be detected early because they generally differ in colour and/or size and shape from females (gynoparae or oviparae) of the same developmental stage and generation.

Mating usually occurs very readily once both oviparae and males are mature, and eggs may be laid on the sides of the container as well as on any available host plant material, so that it is difficult to determine the natural oviposition site. The eggs are yellow when first laid but soon become shiny black if fertile. Unfortunately this is often as far as you will get, as aphid winter egg mortality can be very high. Typically there is a rather long diapause requiring a period of low temperature before warmer weather leads to completion of embryonic development and hatching. In nature eggs must encounter very different conditions according to where they are laid – on twigs or leaves, or in soil or leaf litter – and to achieve any level of hatching success it is probably best to obtain large numbers and give them as close to natural conditions as possible. With luck, a few adult apterae of the first parthenogenetic generation – fundatrices – may be obtained, a worthwhile result because these differ to a greater or lesser extent in morphology from subsequent generations, yet have not been studied in the majority of British species.

Preservation and slide preparation

Aphids for microscopic examination should be preserved in tightly stoppered tubes filled with 80-95% ethanol. It is best not to leave any air space, so that specimens are less likely to be damaged if the tube is shaken. Avoid prolonged storage as in the course of time specimens may become brittle and lose appendages during the mounting procedure.

Various methods for preparing aphids and mounting them on slides for microscopic examination are given in detail in several publications (e.g. Minks & Harrewijn, 1988, Blackman & Eastop 2000). These may tend to discourage people who do not have ready access to laboratory facilities, as they involve some chemicals that are not readily available and/or procedures that are not really suitable for home use. However it is possible to make good preparations by the following relatively simple procedure:

1. Gently boil the specimens in 90% ethanol in a specimen tube in a water bath for 5-10 mins. (For a home-made water-bath, tightly wedge a circle of expanded polystyrene into the bottom of a small saucepan, having first cut holes in the polystyrene of the right diameter to grip the tubes).

2. Transfer specimens to 50% ethanol in a watch-glass, sort specimens for mounting and prick the abdomens with a sharp needle or fine entomological pin.

3. Transfer specimens (best done by lifting them carefully from underneath with curved, fine forceps) to a tube with 1 cm depth of 10% potassium hydroxide (KOH) solution and simmer in the water bath for about 5 min. Check that body contents have become transparent; if not, leave for an extra 2-3 min, or if necessary expel some of the body contents by gently squeezing the abdomen with forceps.

4. Wash the specimens free of all KOH using one change of distilled water with a drop of liquid detergent for 10 min, and then at least five changes of distilled water, each for an hour or more at room temperature, or 10-20 min if warmed to 80°C.

5. Transfer specimens from final wash to 20% PVA clear glue (e.g. 'Pritt in a tube', available from stationers and art shops) in distilled water (shake the liquid thoroughly and leave for an hour before use).

6. Transfer to a watch-glass, and transfer a specimen to a drop of PVA clear glue squeezed straight from the tube onto the centre of a clean microscope slide. Alternatively, for a better refractive index and longer-lasting result use PVA/borax/glycerol mountant ("PVA-G"; see Dioni, 2003). To make this add 6 ml of glycerol to 10 ml of PVA clear glue, then add 4 ml of distilled water saturated with borax, mix well and leave for at least 24 hours, with occasional gentle warming until the liquid is clear of air bubbles. (Note: a great mass of small air bubbles is initially produced; these same ingredients are used to produce artificial "slime"!) Decant the clear mountant into a fresh container before use.

7. Arrange the specimen quickly with body untwisted, dorsal side uppermost and appendages spread out. When mounting aphids with a heavily sclerotised dorsum, try to displace the rostrum to one side so that R IV+V can be clearly observed. Apply a 16mm round cover-slip, lowering it carefully and pressing gently with the forceps to spread the mountant evenly without trapping air bubbles. Leave to dry overnight. If PVA is used as a mountant on its own then the cover-slip will need to be ringed after 24 hours with nail varnish to prevent ingress of air. The PVA/borax/glycerol mountant does not require sealing, but ringing with nail varnish will help to keep the cover-slip in place.

8. Label and store the slides in a cool dry place. For labelling it is best to use 22 mm squares of thick card, stuck on each end of the slide (the same PVA glue can be used for this purpose). These will protect the cover-slip, and enable slides to be stacked on top of one another if required. A suggested format for labelling is shown in Fig. 514.

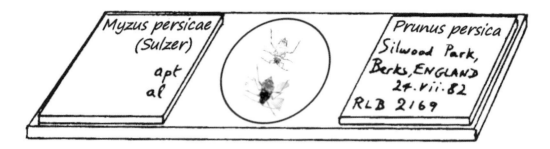

Fig 514. Labelled slide preparation. (Note that the orientation of the labels is reversed in comparison with that of the specimens, to allow for the inversion of the image in a compound microscope.)

The method described above can provide slide preparations of excellent clarity that will enable aphids to be worked through the keys in this handbook and identified to species. However for preparations of proven permanency it is necessary to use a mounting medium that has stood the test of time, such as Canada balsam (see Blackman & Eastop 2000, pp.363-5). It may therefore be wise to proceed by mounting only a part of each sample in PVA, keeping some representative specimens in alcohol in case the identity of the sample cannot be established, and it is necessary to consult a specialist.

Glossary

Aphid morphology is relatively simple and the characters used are illustrated in Figs 2-6, and described on pages 3-7. However the terminology used in connection with the description of the different morphs and life cycle stages can be daunting to the non-specialist. Such terms have been kept to a minimum in this handbook, but a fuller list including some of those likely to be encountered in the aphid literature may be useful.

alatae. Winged morphs, usually referring to winged parthenogenetic females

alienicolae. Host-alternating aphids living on their secondary host plants (= exules)

androcyclic. Reproducing by parthenogenesis throughout the year, but producing some males to contribute to the sexual phase

androparae. Parthenogenetic females that produce males

anholocyclic. Reproducing by parthenogenesis throughout the year, without a sexual phase

apomixis. Reproduction that does not involve genetic recombination

apterae. Wingless morphs, usually referring to wingless parthenogenetic females

autoecious. Living all-year-round on one type of host, i.e not host-alternating (= monoecious)

exules. Host-alternating aphids when on their secondary host-plant (= alienicolae)

fundatrigeniae. Progeny of the fundatrix, often with morphology intermediate between the fundatrix and subsequent generations (alate fundatrigeniae of host-alternating aphids = spring migrants)

fundatrix. The founding female of a clone, hatching from a sexually-produced egg and therefore with a unique combination of genes (pl. fundatrices) (= foundress)

gynoparae. Parthenogenetic females that produce sexual females; in host alternating Aphidinae these are the return migrant alatae

heteroecious. Host-alternating between a primary host (usually woody) and a secondary host (usually herbaceous)

holocyclic. Having a complete life cycle in which parthenogenetic reproduction is interrupted, usually each autumn, by production of sexual morphs and overwintering eggs

migrants. In aphids this term is normally applied to winged individuals that fly in spring and autumn between the primary and secondary hosts

monoecious. Living without host alternation all year on one type of host

oviparae. Sexual females that mate with males and lay fertilised eggs

parthenogenesis. Reproduction by development from unfertilised eggs

primary host. In host-alternating aphids, the plant on which the sexual phase of the life cycle occurs

return migrants. Winged aphids (in Aphidinae these are gynoparae and males) returning to the primary host in autumn

secondary host. In host-alternating aphids, the plant on which only parthenogenetic reproduction takes place

sexuales. Sexual morphs; males and oviparae

sexuparae. Parthenogenetic females producing both sexual females (oviparae) and males (in Aphidinae these only occur in species without host alternation)

stem mother. Another term for the fundatrix

thelytoky. Parthenogenetic reproduction in which a succession of all-female generations are produced from unfertilised (diploid) eggs

virginoparae. Parthenogenetic female aphids that give birth to more parthenogenetic female aphids ('virgin producers')

viviparae. Females that produce live young; in aphids this is always by parthenogenesis (cf. oviparae)

References

Andreev, A. (2004). The subgeneric classification of *Brachycaudus*. pp. 111-117 in Simon, J.-C., Dedryver, C.A., Rispe, C. & Hullé, M. (eds) *Aphids in the New Millenium*. INRA, Paris.

Badmin, J.S. (1991). Biology of *Helleborus foetidus* and the aphid *Macrosiphum hellebori*. *Transactions of the Kent Field Club* 11: 81-92.

Baker, E.A. (2009) Observations of aphids (Aphidoidea) new to Wales. *British Journal of Entomology and Natural History* 22: 235-246.

Barbagallo, S. & Patti, I. (1998). Acquisizioni bio-ecologiche sugli Afidi del territorio centro-orientale italiano. *Bollettino di Zoologia agraria e di Bachicoltura* 30: 223-310.

Bell, A.C. (1983). The life history of the leaf-curling plum aphid *Brachycaudus helichrysi* in Northern Ireland and its ability to transmit potato virus Y[C(AB)]. *Annals of Applied Biology* 102: 1-6.

Bennett, S.H. (1955). The biology, life history and methods of control of the leaf-curling plum aphid *Brachycaudus helichrysi*. *Journal of the Horticultural Society* 30: 252-259.

Blackman, R.L. (1967). The effects of different aphids foods on *Adalia bipunctata* and *Coccinella 7-punctata* L. *Annals of Applied Biology* 59: 207-219.

Blackman, R.L. (1984). Two species of Aphididae (Hemiptera) new to Britain. *Entomologist's Monthly Magazine* 120: 185-186.

Blackman, R.L. (2006). Mugwort aphid turns yellow. *Antenna* 30: 155.

Blackman, R.L. & Eastop, V.F. (2000). *Aphids on the World's Crops*. 2nd edition. John Wiley, Chichester UK, 466 pp.

Blackman, R.L. & Eastop, V.F. (2006). *Aphids on the World's Herbaceous Plants and Shrubs*. (2 vols) John Wiley, Chichester UK, 1440 pp.

Blackman, R.L. & Eastop, V.F. (2007) Taxonomic issues. pp. 1-29 in van Emden, H.F. & Harrington, R., *Aphids as Crop Pest*s. CAB International, Wallingford UK.

Blackman R.L. & Paterson, A.J.C. (1986). Separation of *Myzus (Nectarosiphon) antirrhinii* from *M. (N.) persicae* and related species in Europe. *Systematic Entomology* 11: 267-276.

Blackman, R.L., Eastop, V.F. & Hills, M. (1977). Morphological and cytological separation of *Amphorophora* Buckton (Homoptera: Aphididae) feeding on European raspberry and blackberry (*Rubus* spp.). *Bulletin of Entomological Research* 67: 285-296.

Börner, C. (1950). Neue europäische Blattlausarten. Selbstverlag, Naumberg. 19 pp.

Börner, C. (1952, 1953). Europae centralis Aphides. *Mitteilungen der Thüringischen Botanischen Gesellschaft* 4: 1-484 (1952); 485-488 (1953).

Brown, P.A. (1983). A note on *Myzus (Sciamyzus) cymbalariae*, with a description of the male. *Journal of Natural History* 17: 875-880.

Brown, P.A. & Blackman, R.L. (1985). A new species of *Amphorophora* (Homoptera: Aphididae) on *Geranium macrorrhizum* in Britain. *Journal of Natural History* 19: 225-232.

Burger, H.C. (1975). Key to the European species of *Brachycaudus,* subgenus *Acaudus* with redescriptions and a note on *B. persicae*. *Tijdschrift voor Entomologie* 118: 99-116.

Carter, C.I. & Nichols, J.F.A. (1989). Winter survival of the lupin aphid *Macrosiphum albifrons* Essig. *Journal of Applied Entomology* 108: 213-216.

Carter, C.I., Wood-Baker, C.S. & Polaszek, A. (1987). Species, host plants and distribution of aphids occurring in Ireland. *Irish Naturalist's Journal* 22: 266-284.

Coeur d'Acier, A., Cocuzza, G., Jousselin, E., Cavalieri, V. & Barbagallo, S. (2008). Molecular phylogeny and systematic in the genus *Brachycaudus* (Homoptera: Aphididae): insights from a combined analysis of nuclear and mitochondrial genes. *Zoologica Scripta* 37: 175-193.

Dahl, M.L. (1968). Biologische und morphologische Untersuchungen uber den Formenkreis der *Myzus cerasi*. *Deutsche Entomologische Zeitschrift* (N.F.) 15: 28-312.

Darwish, E.T.E. (1983). On the morphology of *Brachycaudus schwartzi* CB. and *B. amygdalinus* (Schout.) (Homoptera: Aphidinea). *Folia Entomologica Hungarica* **44**: 165-173.

Dioni, W. (2003). Safe microscopic techniques for amateurs. I. Mounting microscopic subjects. Pt 3b. PVA-lactic acid and PVA-glycerol mountants. In *Alternative mounting media revisited.* http://www.microscopy-uk.org.uk/mag/artjun04/wdmtmedia.html

Doncaster, J.P. (1946). The shallot aphis, *Myzus ascalonicus* sp.n. *Proceedings of the Royal Entomological Society of London* (B) **15**: 27.

Doncaster, J.P. (1961). *Francis Walker's Aphids.* British Museum (Natural History), London. 165 pp.

Dunn, J.A. (1965). Studies on the aphid *Cavariella aegopodii* Scop. I. On willow and carrot. *Annals of Applied Biology* **56**: 429-438.

Eastop, V.F. (1966). A taxonomic study of Australian Aphidoidea. *Australian Journal of Zoology* **14**: 399-592.

Eastop, V.F. (1971) Keys for the identification of *Acyrthosiphon. Bulletin of the British Museum (Natural History) (Entomology)* **26**: 1-115.

Eastop, V.F. (1987). Key to the European species of *Ovatomyzus* Hille Ris Lambers (Aphididae: Hemiptera). *Systematic Entomology* **12**: 433-436.

Foottit, R.G., Maw, H.E.L., Pike, K.S. & Miller, R.H. (2010). A molecular and morphometric analysis of the banana aphid, *Pentalonia nigronervosa* Coquerel (Hemiptera: Aphididae). *Zootaxa* **2358**:25-38.

Forrest, J.M.S. (1970). The effect of maternal and larval experience on morph determination in *Dysaphis devecta. Journal of Insect Physiology* **16**: 2281-2292.

Forrest, J.M.S. & Dixon, A.F.G. (1975). The induction of leaf-roll galls by the apple aphids *Dysaphis devecta* and *D. plantaginea. Annals of Applied Biology* **81**: 281-288.

Foster, W.A. (1984). The distribution of the sea-lavender aphid *Staticobium staticis* on a marine saltmarsh and its effect on host plant fitness. *Oikos* **42**; 97-104.

Gimingham, C.T. (1942). *Clypeoaphis suaedae* Soliman, a genus and species of Aphididae new to Britain. *Entomologist's Monthly Magazine* **78**: 32-34.

Gruppe, A. (1988). Elektrophoretische Untersuchungen zur Unterscheidung der Subspezies von *Myzus cerasi* F. (Homoptera: Aphididae). *Zeitschrift angewandte Entomologie* **105**: 460-465.

Guldemond, J.A. (1990). Evolutionary genetics of the aphid *Cryptomyzus,* with a preliminary analysis of the inheritance of host plant preference, reproductive performance and host-alteration. *Entomologia experimentalis et applicata* **57**: 65-76.

Guldemond, J.A. (1991a). Biosystematic and morphometric study of the *Cryptomyzus galeopsidis/alboapicalis* complex (Homoptera, Aphididae). *Netherlands Journal of Zoology* **41**: 1-31.

Guldemond, J.A. (1991b). Host plant relationships and life cycles of the aphid genus *Cryptomyzus.. Entomologia experimentalis et applicata* **58**: 21-30.

Halstead, A.J. (2000). An onion aphid, *Neotoxoptera formosana* (Takahashi) (Hemiptera:Aphididae), new to Britain. *British Journal of Entomology and Natural History* **13**: 94.

Heie, O.E. (1960). *Aulacorthum knautiae* n. sp. (Homoptera: Aphididae). *Entomologiske Meddelelser* **29**: 304-311.

Heie, O.E. (1979). Revision of the aphid genus *Nasonovia,* including *Kakimia,* with keys and descriptions of the species of the world. *Entomologica Scandinavica. Supplement* **9**: 105 pp.

Heie, O.E. (1980). The Aphidoidea of Fennoscandia and Denmark. I. Mindaridae, Hormaphidae, Thelaxidae, Anoeciidae and Pemphigidae. *Fauna Entomologica Scandinavica* **9**: 236 pp.

Heie, O.E. (1982). The Aphidoidea of Fennoscandia and Denmark. II. Drepanosiphidae. *Fauna Entomologica Scandinavica* **11**:176 pp.

Heie, O.E. (1986). The Aphidoidea of Fennoscandia and Denmark. III. Aphididae: Pterocommatinae and Aphidini. *Fauna Entomologica Scandinavica* **17**: 314 pp.

Heie, O.E. (1992). The Aphidoidea of Fennoscandia and Denmark. IV. Aphididae: Part 1 of Macrosiphini. *Fauna Entomologica Scandinavica* **25**: 190 pp.

Heie, O.E. (1994). The Aphidoidea of Fennoscandia and Denmark. V. Aphididae: Part 2 of Macrosiphini. *Fauna Entomologica Scandinavica* **28**: 242 pp.

Heie, O.E. (1995). The Aphidoidea of Fennoscandia and Denmark. VI. Aphididae: Part 3 of Macrosiphini, and Lachnidae. *Fauna Entomologica Scandinavica* **31**: 222 pp.

Hille Ris Lambers, D. (1938). Contributions to a monograph of the Aphididae of Europe. I. The genus *Macrosiphoniella* Del Guercio, 1911. *Temminckia* **3**: 1-44.

Hille Ris Lambers, D. (1939a). Contributions to a monograph of the Aphididae of Europe. II. *Dactynotus, Staticobium, Macrosiphum, Masonaphis... Temminckia* **4**: 1-134.

Hille Ris Lambers, D. (1939b). On some western European aphids. *Zoologische Mededelingen* **22**: 79-119.

Hille Ris Lambers, D. (1947a). Contributions to a monograph of the Aphididae of Europe. III. *Microsiphum, Anthracosiphon, Delphiniobium, Acyrthosiphon, Subacyrthosiphon, Silenobium, Titanosiphon, Metopolophium, Cryptaphis, Rhodobium, Impatientinum, Aulacorthum* (part). *Temminckia* **7**: 179-319.

Hille Ris Lambers, D. (1947b). On some mainly western European aphids. *Zoologische Mededelingen* **28**: 291-333.

Hille Ris Lambers, D. (1949) Contributions to a monograph of the Aphididae of Europe. IV. *Aulacorthum* (part), *Microlophium, Hyalopteroides, Idiopterus, Pentalonia, Amphorophora, Amphorosiphon, Wahlgreniella, Megoura, Megourella, Hyperomyzus, Nasonovia. Temminckia* **8**: 182-329.

Hille Ris Lambers, D. (1953). Contributions to a monograph of the Aphididae of Europe. V. *Capitophorus, Chaetosiphon, Cryptomyzus, Eucarazzia, Rhopalomyzus, Rhopalosiphoninus. Temminckia* **9**: 1-176.

Hille Ris Lambers, D. (1967). New and little-known members of the aphid fauna of Italy. *Bollettino di Zoologia agraria e Bachicoltura* [1966] **8**: 1-32.

Hille Ris Lambers, D. (1970). Four new species of *Cavariella* del Guercio, 1911. *Memorie della Societa Entomologica Italiana* [1969] **48**: 285-299.

Hille Ris Lambers, D. (1973). *Masonaphis lambersi* (MacGillivray), a new pest of rhododendron in Europe. *Tijdschrift over Plantenziekten* **79**: 159-161.

Holman, J. (1991). Revision of the aphid genus *Acaudinum. Entomologia Generalis* **16**: 215-226.

Jacob, F. H. (1948). Note on the sexuales of *Staticobium limonii. Proceedings of the Royal Entomological Society of London* (B) **17**: 55-56.

Jacob, F.H. (1964). A new species of *Thuleaphis* H.R.L (Homoptera: Aphidoidea) from Wales, Scotland and Iceland (*Thuleaphis sedi* sp. n.). *Proceedings of the Royal Entomological Society of London* (B) **33**: 111-116.

Jousselin, E., Desdevises, Y. & Coeur d'Acier, A. (2009). Fine-scale speciation between *Brachycaudus* and *Buchneria aphidicola*: bacterial genome helps define species and evolutionary relationships in aphids. *Proceedings of the Royal Society B* **276**: 187-196.

Kim, H. & Lee, S. (2010). A molecular phylogeny of the tribe Aphidini (Insecta: Hemiptera: Aphididae) based on mitochondrial tRNA, 12S/16S, and the nuclear EF1a genes. *Systematic Entomology* **33**:711-721.

Kolesova, D.A. (1972). [The ecology of pear aphids of the genus *Anuraphis* Guercio in the Crimea.] *Vestnik Zoologii* **3**: 11-15.

Lawton, J.H. & Eastop, V.F. (1975). A bracken-feeding *Macrosiphum* new to Britain. *Entomologist's Gazette* **26**: 135-138.

Lees, A.D. (1973). Photoperiodic time measurement in the vetch aphid *Megoura viciae. Journal of Insect Physiology* **19**: 2279-2316.

Martin, J.H. (1981). A new species of *Acyrthosiphon* from *Primula* in Britain. *Systematic Entomology* **6**: 97-101.

Martin, J.H. (2000). Two new British introductions in 1999, in the context of other additions over the preceding thirty years (Sternorrhyncha: Aphidoidea). *Entomologist's Gazette* **51**: 97-105.

Massonet, B. & Weisser, W.W. (2004). Patterns of genetic differentiation between populations of *Macrosiphoniella tanacetaria. Heredity* **93**: 577-584.

Massonet, B., Leterme, N., Simon, J.-C. & Weisser, W.W. (2002). Metapopulation structure of the specialised herbivore *Macrosiphoniella tanacetaria. Molecular Ecology* **11**: 2511-2521.

Meier, W. (1954). Über *Myzus varians* Davidson und einige weitere *Myzus* Arten aus der Schweiz. *Mitteilungen der Schweizerischen entomologischen Gesellschaft* **27**: 321-409.

Meier, W. (1958). Beiträge zur Kenntnis der auf Papilionaceen lebender *Acyrthosiphon* Arten. *Mitteilungen der Schweizerischen entomologischen Gesellschaft* **31**: 291-312.

Meier, W. (1961). Beiträge zur Kenntnis der grünstreifigen Kartoffelblattlaus *Macrosiphum euphorbiae* (Thomas 1870) und verwandter Arten (Hemipt., Aphid.). *Mitteilungen Schweizerischen Entomologischen Gesellschaft* **34**: 127-186.

Miller, G.L., Stoetzel, M.B. (2005). A systematic reappraisal of the genus *Diuraphis* Aizenberg (Hemiptera: Aphididae). *Proceedings of the Entomological Society of Washington* **107**: 700-728

Minks, A.K. & Harrewijn, P. (1987). *Aphids, their Biology, Natural Enemies and Control. World Crop Pests* **2A**. Elsevier, Amsterdam, 450 pp.

Minks, A.K. & Harrewijn, P. (1988). *Aphids, their Biology, Natural Enemies and Control. World Crop Pests* **2B**. Elsevier, Amsterdam, 364 pp.

Mondor, E.B. & Roitberg, B.D. (2004). Inclusive fitness benefits of scent-marking predators. *Proceedings of the Royal Society of London* B. (Suppl.) **271**: S341-S343.

Mostafawy, M. (1967). Morphologie, Biologie und phytopathologische Bedeutung der Gattung *Appelia. Zeitschrift für Angewandte Zoologie* **54**: 373-432.

Muddathir, K. (1965). A new species of *Holcaphis* (Homoptera: Aphidoidea) together with a key to the British species. *Annals and Magazine of Natural History* (series 13) **8**: 477-485 (+ 1 pl.).

Müller, F.P. (1959). Die Männchen einiger Blattlausarten mit vorwiegend permanenter Parthenogenese. *Deutsche Entomologische Zeitschrift* (N.F.) **6**: 51-64.

Müller, F.P. (1966). Zwei weitere neue Blattlausarten (Homoptera: Aphididae) aus Mecklenburg. *Archiv der Freunde der Naturgeschichte in Mecklenburg* **12**: 149-172.

Müller, F.P. (1968). Ein Fund der Blattlaus *Dysaphis gallica* in Mitteleuropa, mit Wirtswahlversuchen und Bescreibung des oviparen Weibchens. *Entomologische Nachrichten und Berichte* **12**: 25-29.

Müller, F.P. (1969). Ein besonderes ungeflügeltes vivipares Weibchen im Adultenstadium als Überwinterungs-morphe bei *Ovatomyzus calaminthae. Entomologische Nachrichten und Berichte* **13**: 25-30.

Müller, F.P. (1973). Aphiden an Moosen. *Entomologische Abhandlungen, Staatliches Museum für Tierkunde Dresden* **39**: 205-242.

Müller, F.P. (1975a). Weitere Ergänzungen und ökologische Untersuchungen zur Blattlausfauna von Mitteleuropa. *Faunistische Abhandlungen, Staatliches Museum für Tierkunde Dresden* **5**: 265-287.

Müller, F.P. (1975b). Verbreitung und Biologie der submersen Blattlaus *Aspidaphium cuspidati*, und anderer Wasserpflanzen-Aphiden. pp. 47-53 in Verhandlungen *des Sechsten Internationalen Symposiums uber* Entomofaunistik *in Mitteleuropa* 1975. W. Junk, The Hague.

Müller, F.P. (1977). Morphen und Biologie von *Paramyzus heraclei. Reichenbachia* **16**: 233-240.

Müller, F.P. (1979). Morphologie und Biologie von *Aulacorthum speyeri* Börner vergleich mit *Aulacorthum watanabei* (Miyazaki). *Reichenbachia* **17**: 129-141.

Müller, F.P. (1980). *Ovatus crataegarius* (Walker, 1850) und *O. insitus* (Walker, 1849) als Modell für sympatrische Speziation ohne Inanspruchnahme ökologischer Nischen. *Deutsche Entomologische Zeitschrift* (N.F.) **27**: 199-217.

Müller, F.P. (1983). Untersuchungen über Blattläuse der Gruppe *Acyrthosiphon pelargonii* im Freiland-Insektarium. *Zeitschrift für Angewandte Zoologie* **70**: 351-367.

Müller, F.P. & Horatschek, A. (1979). *Brachycaudus cardui lateralis*, Erstfunde in Österreich und Generationsfulge. *Mitteilungen des Naturwissenschaftlichen Vereines für Steiermark* **109**: 309-316.

Müller, F.P. & Hubert-Dahl, M.L. (1979). Wirtswechsel, Generationenfolge und reproduktive Isolation von *Ovatus crataegaria* (Walker, 1850) und *O. insitus* (Walker, 1849) (Homoptera: Aphididae). *Deutsche Entomologische Zeitschrift* (N.F.) **26**: 241-253.

Müller, F.P. & Steiner, H. (1988). Occurrence of the aphid *Rhodobium porosum* in central Europe (Homoptera: Aphidinea: Aphididae). *Entomologia Generalis* **13**: 255-260.

Newton, C., & Dixon, A.F.G. (1988). A preliminary study of variation and inheritance of life history traits and the occurrence of hybrid vigour in *Sitobion avenae* F. (Hemiptera: Aphididae). *Bulletin of Entomological Research* **78**: 75–83.

Nieto Nafria, J. M., Mier Durante, M.P. & Remaudière, G. (1998). Les noms des taxa du group-famille chez les Aphididae (Hemiptera). *Revue française d'Entomologie* (N.S.) **19**: 77-92.

Patti, I. (1983). Nuovi reperti sulla composizione dell'afidofauna Siciliana. *Bollettino del Laboratorio di Entomologia Agraria Filippo Silvestri, Portici* **40**: 33-53.

Perrin, R.M. (1976). The population dynamics of the stinging nettle aphid *Microlophium carnosum*. *Ecological Entomology* **1**: 31-40.

Powell, W. & Parry, W.H. (1976). Effects of temperature on overwintering populations of the green spruce aphid *Elatobium abietinum*. *Annals of Applied Biology* **82**: 209-219.

Prior, R.N.B. (1971). Some notes on new or uncommon aphids recently found in Britain. *Zoological Journal of the Linnaean Society* **50**: 397-430.

Prior, R.N.B. (1976). Keys to the British species of *Metopolophium* (Aphididae) with one new species. *Systematic Entomology* **1**: 271-279.

Prior, R.N.B. & Stroyan, H.L.G. (1960). On a new collection of aphids from Iceland. *Entomologiske Meddelelser.* **29**: 266-293.

Prior, R.N.B. & Stroyan, H.L.G. (1964). A new subspecies of *Acyrthosiphon malvae* (Mosley) from *Poterium sanguisorba* L. *Proceedings of the Royal Entomological Society of London* (B) **33**: 47-49.

Rabasse, J.M., Drescher, J., Chaubet, B., Limonta, L., Turpeau, E. & Barbagallo, S. (2005). On the presence in France of two *Illinoia* aphids of North American origin (Homoptera, Aphididae). *Bollettino di Zoologia agraria e Bachicoltura* **37**: 151-168.

Remaudière, G. (1970). Identité, morphologie et biologie de *Cavariella* (sg. *Cavaraiella*) *aquatica*. *Annales de la Societe Entomologique de France* (N.S.) **6**: 153-165.

Remaudière, G. & Remaudière, M. (1997). *Catalogue des Aphididae du Monde*. INRA, Paris. 473 pp.

Remaudiere, G. Serain, M., Trouvé, C. & Demeester, S. (1992). Données nouvelles sur le genre *Trichosiphonaphis* Takahashi, 1922: cycles, hôtes, synonymies et distribution géographique [Homoptera, Aphididae]. *Revue Francaise d'Entomologie* (N.S.) **14**: 49-58.

Shaposhnikov, G. Kh. (1964). [Suborder Aphidinea – Aphids.] pp. 489-616 in Bey-Bienko, G.Y. (ed.), [*Keys to insects of European part of USSR.*] (Eng. transl. in 1967 by Israel Program for Scientific Translations Ltd., Jerusalem: Aphidinea pp. 616-799)

Shaposhnikov, G.Ch. and Sharov, A.A. (1977). [Variability in panmictic and clonal populations of *Anuraphis farfarae* Koch. (Homoptera, Aphididae) aphid.] *Entomologicheskoe Obozrenie* **56**: 601-609 (in Russian). English translation: *Entomological Review* **56**: 81-87 (1978).

Sobhani, P. (1970). Biologie, Morphologie und phytopathologische Bedeutung der *Macrosiphoniella*-Art und *Dactynotus*-Art der Schafgarbe. I and II. *Zeitschrift für Angewandte Zoologie* **57**: 145-195 and 265-301.

Sobhani, P. & Iglisch, I. (1972). Ein Beitrag zur Morphologie der Genitalien von Blattläusen (Homoptera: Aphidoidea). 2. Zur Morphologie des männlichen Geschlechtstieres von *Macrosiphoniella usquertensis* H.R.L. *Zeitschrift für Angewandte Zoologie* **59**: 447-461.

Stroyan, H.L.G. (1950). Recent additions to the British aphid fauna. Part I. *Dactynotus* to *Rhopalosiphum*. *Transactions of the Royal Entomological Society of London* **101**: 89-124.

Stroyan, H.L.G. (1953). A new account of *Aphis compositellae* Theobald. *Proceedings of the Royal Entomological Society of London* (B) **22**: 109-118.

Stroyan, H.L.G. (1955). Recent additions to the British aphid fauna. Part II. *Transactions of the Royal Entomological Society of London* **106**: 283-340.

Stroyan, H.L.G. (1957a). *The British Species of Sappaphis Matsumura*. Part 1. HMSO, London, 59 pp.

Stroyan, H.L.G. (1957b). Further additions to the British aphid fauna. *Transactions of the Royal Entomological Society of London* **109**: 311-360.

Stroyan, H.L.G. (1958). A contribution to the taxonomy of some British species of *Sappaphis* Matsumura. *Journal of the Linaean Society of London, Zoology* **43**: 644-713.

Stroyan, H.L.G. (1963). *The British Species of Dysaphis Börner (Sappaphis* auctt. nec Mats.). Part 2. HMSO, London, 119 pp.

Stroyan, H.L.G. (1964). Notes on hitherto unrecorded or overlooked British aphid species. *Transactions of the Royal Entomological Society of London* **116**: 29-72.

Stroyan, H.L.G. (1966). Notes on aphid species new to the British fauna. *Proceedings of the Royal Entomological Society of London* (B) **35**: 111-118.

Stroyan, H.L.G. (1969a). Notes on some species of *Cavariella* Del Guercio, 1911 (Homoptera: Aphidoidea). *Proceedings of the Royal Entomological Society of London* (B) **38**: 7-19.

Stroyan, H.L.G. (1969b). On a collection of aphids from Inverness-shire, with the description of a new species. *Transactions of the Royal Entomological Society of London* **18**: 227-246.

Stroyan, H.L.G. (1972). Additions and amendments to the check list of British aphids. *Transactions of the Royal Entomological Society of London* **124**: 37-79.

Stroyan, H.L.G. (1977). Homoptera Aphidoidea (Part): Chaitophoridae and Callaphididae. *Handbooks for the Identification of British Insects* **11 (4a)**: 130 pp.

Stroyan, H.L.G. (1979). Additions to the British aphid fauna. *Zoological Journal of the Linnaean Society* **65**: 1-54.

Stroyan H.L.G. (1980). The leaf curling almond aphid *Brachycaudus amygdalinus* - new record in Britain . *Plant Pathology* **29**: 146-147.

Stroyan, H.L.G. (1982). Revisionary notes on the genus *Metopolophium*, with keys to European species and descriptions of two new taxa. *Zool. J. Linn. Soc.* **75**: 91-140.

Stroyan, H.L.G. (1984). Aphids – Pterocommatinae and Aphidinae (Aphidini). *Handbooks for the Identification of British Insects* **2 (6)**: 232 pp.

Stroyan, H.L.G. (1991). Some loose ends in the British aphid fauna. *The Entomologist* **110**: 24-28.

Talhouk, A.S. (1977). Contribution to the knowledge of almond pests in East Mediterranean countries VI. The sap-sucking pests. *Zeitschrift für angewandte Entomologie* **83**: 248-257.

Theobald, F.V. (1926, 1927, 1929). *The Plant Lice or Aphididae of Great Britain.* **1**: 372 pp. (1926); **2**: 411 pp. (1927); **3**: 364 pp. (1929). Headley Bros, Ashford, Kent.

Tinguely, C. (1993). Beitrag zur Kenntnis der Blattlausfauna einiger schweizer Moore. *Bulletin de la Société Fribourgeoise des Sciences Naturelles* **82**: 64-108.

Tuatay, N. & Remaudière, G. (1965). Premiere contribution au catalogue des Aphididae de la Turquie. *Revue* de *Pathologie Vegetale et d'Entomologie Agricole de France* [1964] **43**: 243-78.

van Emden, H.F. (ed.) (1972). *Aphid Technology.* Academic Press, London, 344 pp.

van Emden, H.F. & Harrington, R. (eds) (2007). *Aphids as Crop Pests.* CAB International, 800 pp.

von Dohlen, C.D., Rowe, C.A. and Heie, O.E. (2006). A test for morphological hypotheses for tribal and subtribal relationships of Aphidinae (Insecta:Hemiptera: Aphididae) using DNA sequences. *Molecular Phylogenetics and Evolution* **38**: 316-329.

Walker, F. (1849). Notice of the hop fly. *Zoologist* 7: 2555.

Watson, G.W. (1982). *A biometric, electrophoretic and karyotypic analysis of British species of Macrosiphum (Homoptera; Aphididae).* PhD Thesis, Univ. of London, 296 pp.

Wood-Baker, C.S. (1958). The oviparous female of *Vesiculaphis theobaldi* Tak. and notes on its food-plants. *Entomologist's Monthly Magazine* **94**: 100-102.

Wood-Baker, C.S. (1970). Records of *Rhopalomyzus poae* Gillette in Britain with a note on its morphology. *Entomologist's Monthly Magazine* **106**: 79-81.

Wood-Baker, C.S. (1972). A new food plant for *Macrosiphum* (*Sitobion*) *avenae* in Britain, with biometric data (Hem, Aphididae). *Entomologist's Monthly Magazine* **107**: 185-187.

Index to names of aphid taxa

Royal Entomological Society

Founded in 1833 as the Entomological Society of London, the Royal Entomological Society plays a major national and international role in disseminating information about insects and improving communication between entomologists. The aim of the Society is 'the improvement and diffusion of entomological science'.

The aim is achieved by:
- holding meetings on all aspects of entomology;
- publishing the results of entomological research in six primary journals;
- maintaining a large entomological library;
- supporting entomological expeditions;
- generating discourse between entomologists, both amateur and professional;
- supporting activities that further the Society's aims and objectives, through the Outreach Fund.

The Society welcomes applications for membership from people who are actively involved or interested in entomology either professionally or as amateurs. Applications for Fellowship are invited from those who have made a substantial contribution to entomology, through publications, primary research or other evidence of achievement. Fellows are entitled to make use of the title 'Fellow of the Royal Entomological Society' and the suffix 'FRES' may be regarded as an academic qualification. Academic qualification is not a pre-requisite for Membership and applications are welcome from those who feel that they have a genuine interest in entomology.

For more information please contact:

Royal Entomological Society, The Mansion House, Bonehill, Chiswell Green Lane, Chiswell Green, St. Albans AL2 3NS.

Email: reg@royensoc.co.uk

Website: www.royensoc.co.uk

The Society is a Registered Charity number 213620